Advances in
MICROBIAL ECOLOGY

Volume 13

ADVANCES IN MICROBIAL ECOLOGY

A Continuation Order Plan is available for this series. A continuation order will bring delivery of each
new volume immediately upon publication. Volumes are billed only upon actual shipment. For further
information please contact the publisher.

Advances in
MICROBIAL ECOLOGY

Volume 13

Edited by

J. Gwynfryn Jones
Freshwater Biological Association
Ambleside, Cumbria, England

PLENUM PRESS • NEW YORK AND LONDON

The Library of Congress cataloged the first volume of this title as follows:

Advances in microbial ecology. v. 1–
  New York, Plenum Press c1977–
  v. ill. 24 cm.
  Key title: Advances in microbial ecology, ISSN 0147-4863
  1. Microbial ecology—Collected works.
QR100.A36   576′.15   77-649698

ISBN 0-306-44556-5

© 1993 Plenum Press, New York
A Division of Plenum Publishing Corporation
233 Spring Street, New York, N.Y. 10013

Printed in the United States of America

Contributors

Fernando Dini, Dipartimento di Scienze dell'Ambiente e del Territorio, Sez. Protistologia, Università di Pisa 56126 Pisa, Italy

Ricardo Guerrero, Departament de Microbiologia, Universitat de Barcelona, E-08028 Barcelona, Spain

Junko Hama, Water Research Institute, Nagoya University, Chikusa-ku, Nagoya 464-01, Japan

Takeo Hama, Water Research Institute, Nagoya University, Chikusa-ku, Nagoya 464-01, Japan

Nobuhiko Handa, Water Research Institute, Nagoya University, Chikusa-ku, Nagoya 464-01, Japan

David Lloyd, Microbiology Group (PABIO), University of Wales College of Cardiff, Cardiff CF1 3TL, Wales

E. Richard Moxon, Molecular Infectious Diseases Group, Institute of Molecular Medicine, Oxford University, John Radcliffe Hospital, Oxford OX3 9DU, England

Steven Y. Newell, Marine Institute, University of Georgia, Sapelo Island, Georgia, 31327

Dennis Nyberg, Department of Biological Sciences, University of Illinois at Chicago, Chicago, Illinois 60680

Carlos Pedrós-Alió, Institut de Ciències del Mar, CSIC, E-08039 Barcelona, Spain

Paul B. Rainey, Institute of Virology and Environmental Microbiology, Oxford OX1 3SR, England

Richard D. Robarts, National Hydrology Research Institute, Environment Canada, Saskatoon, Saskatchewan S7N 3H5, Canada

Val H. Smith, Station de Biologie des Laurentides, Département de Sciences Biologiques, Université de Montréal, Montréal, Québec H3C 3J7, Canada

Ian P. Thompson, Institute of Virology and Environmental Microbiology, Oxford OX1 3SR, England

Thomas Weisse, Limnological Institute of Constance, D-7750 Constance, Germany

Alan G. Williams, Hannah Research Institute, Ayr KA6 5HL, Scotland

Tamar Zohary, The Yigal Allon Kinneret Laboratory, Tiberias 14102, Israel

v

Preface

Kevin Marshall is a hard act to follow. Volume 13 of *Advances in Microbial Ecology* has been produced by a new editorial board, and we, the members of that board, are delighted to have the opportunity to pay tribute to Kevin's achievements. In his time as Series Editor, the quality of the chapters submitted and the range of subject matter covered have ensured an expanding and more stimulated readership. This represents a considerable achievement, given the growth in the number of review volumes and the increasing tendency for journals to publish review articles. The achievement was reached not only through meticulous attention to quality and detail but also by providing a forum for the expression of views, information, and results that would stimulate discussion. *Advances in Microbial Ecology* will continue to provide such a focus, although, because of the frequency of publication, it would not be practicable to introduce a "reply" or "comment" section. Although we do not deliberately aim to provide a forum for controversy, we encourage speculation based on sound scientific arguments. In addition, we would like to encourage authors to offer chapters for consideration. In the past, the volumes have largely comprised invited chapters. With the best will in the world, an editorial board of four cannot claim adequate coverage of such a vast and rapidly developing research area. We would therefore welcome submission of outline plans for chapters, which should be sent to the Editor.

As we have indicated above, the success of *Advances in Microbial Ecology* has been based, in good part, on the breadth of material covered. We trust that Volume 13 does not break this mold. Chapters range from the details of particular methodology to an examination of aspects of ecological theory, from a detailed study of one aspect of the cell cycle to a synthesis of the microbiology of a whole lake. We hope that such a variety satisfies the criteria laid down by Kevin Marshall; we thank him for all that he has done, during his period as Series Editor, to stimulate the subject of microbial ecology.

J. Gwynfryn Jones, Editor
Bernhard Schink
Warwick F. Vincent
David Ward

Contents

Chapter 3

Sex in Ciliates

Fernando Dini and Dennis Nyberg

Chapter 4

Microbial Ecology in Lake Cisó

Carlos Pedrós-Alió and Ricardo Guerrero

Chapter 5

Biological Activities of Symbiotic and Parasitic Protists in Low-Oxygen Environments

Alan G. Williams and David Lloyd

Chapter 6

Intraclonal Polymorphism in Bacteria

Paul B. Rainey, E. Richard Moxon, and Ian P. Thompson

Chapter 7

**Decomposition of Shoots of a Salt-Marsh Grass: Methodology
and Dynamics of Microbial Assemblages**

Steven Y. Newell

Chapter 8

Dynamics of Autotrophic Picoplankton in Marine and Freshwater Ecosystems

Thomas Weisse

Chapter 9

Fact or Fiction—Bacterial Growth Rates and Production as Determined by [*methyl*-³H]Thymidine?

Richard D. Robarts and Tamar Zohary

Implications of Resource-Ratio Theory for Microbial Ecology

VAL H. SMITH

1. Introduction

Microorgranisms are an essential component of the biosphere, taking part in a myriad of biogeochemical transformations, and playing a vital role in the processing of energy and in the cycling of materials. Microbes also interact strongly with plant and animal populations, both in their roles as agents of disease and as symbiotic associations. In the more than 100 years since the pioneering work of Pasteur and Koch, microbiologists have accumulated an immense body of knowledge on the structure, biochemistry, genetics, molecular biology, and physiology of microbes that is arguably second to no other group of organisms. Moreover, as has been stressed by Atlas *et al.* (1992), microbiology also is a historic and essential element of the science of ecology. Microbial ecology has become a well-established area of research, based on proven principles and tested techniques that enable changes in physical, chemical, and biological aspects of the environment to be understood as well as monitored (Atlas *et al.*, 1992).

For many years, however, the most frequently used textbooks of general ecology focused most heavily on the ecology of macroorganisms, especially in the areas of population and community ecology. Although the classic work of Gause on competition between protozoa was almost always presented, discussions of microbes were typically relegated primarily to chapters dealing with the topics of biogeochemical cycles and decomposition. Even within these chapters, however, it was most frequently microbial processes (e.g., nitrification, denitrification, mineralization) that were emphasized, and not the population or community ecology of the microbes themselves. A large gulf thus has separated

VAL H. SMITH • Station de Biologie des Laurentides, Département de Sciences Biologiques, Université de Montréal, Montréal, Québec H3C 3J7, Canada.

Advances in Microbial Ecology, Volume 13, edited by J. Gwynfryn Jones. Plenum Press, New York, 1993.

microbial ecology from animal and plant ecology (Lenski, 1992), and the need for greater cross-fertilization between macro- and microecology has been made abundantly clear by Andrews (1991) in his provocative new book.

The purpose of this review is to attempt such a cross-fertilization. Resource competition holds a central place in ecological and evolutionary theory, and a recent meta-analysis of competition in field experiments suggests that competition has a large overall effect on communities of macroorganisms (Gurevitch *et al.*, 1992). Resource competition is also thought to play an important role in the organization and function of microbial communities in a wide variety of natural environments (Campbell, 1983; Veldkamp *et al.*, 1984). Predicting the outcome of resource competition remains very difficult in either set of communities, however.

One of the more important recent contributions to macroecology has been the development by Tilman (1982) of a mechanistic resource-ratio theory of competition. Tilman's (1982) resource-ratio theory is based on well-established principles of cellular physiology and ecology. This theory recognizes (1) that organisms require resources for their growth and reproduction; (2) that different species, as well as different phenotypic strains within a given species, frequently differ significantly in their efficiency of uptake and utilization of potentially growth-limiting resources; and (3) that when such physiological differences exist, they can result in variations in competitive ability among the organisms sharing these resources. When the quantitative requirements for resources and the mortality rates are known for each species, resource-ratio theory provides a framework that can be used to predict the outcome of competitive interactions between them.

Although lively debates about the merits of resource-ratio theory have appeared in the plant ecology literature (see Grace, 1991), mounting evidence from both experimental and comparative studies suggests that resource supply ratios can shape the community structure of freshwater and marine phytoplankton (Tilman, 1982; Smith, 1983; Sommer, 1989); freshwater periphyton (Fairchild *et al.*, 1985); freshwater zooplankton (Rothhaupt, 1988); freshwater vascular plants (Barko *et al.*, 1991); marine vascular plants (Fourqurean *et al.*, 1992); and terrestrial plants (Tilman, 1982, 1988, 1990). I believe that the patterns observed in the structure and function of many natural microbial communities also will prove to be largely consistent with this body of theory.

Until recently, no explicit attempts to test the applicability of resource-ratio theory to microbial ecology have apparently been made. However, in two comparative studies of data taken from the microbial ecology literature (Smith, 1992, 1993b) I have presented evidence that the patterns observed in microbial community structure and function are consistent with resource-ratio theory, and I have further suggested (Smith, 1993a) that resource supply ratios can potentially alter the outcome of infectious disease. Thus, although many of the applications of resource-ratio theory to date have occurred in the arena of macroecology, it is my belief that it will prove to be an equally valuable theoretical framework for microbial ecology as well.

The main body of this review will be presented in four major parts below. In Section 2, I will provide a brief overview of the fundamentals of resource-ratio theory; for a more detailed and quantitative treatment, the reader should refer to Tilman (1982). I will then demonstrate the applicability of this theory to microbial ecology in Section 3 using experimental data obtained from the literature, and reanalyzing these data using graphical methods.

In Sections 4 and 5, I will explore some of the broader implications of resource-ratio theory for microbial ecology by considering two of the important interactions that occur between microbes and other organisms. In Section 4, I will consider the effects of resource supply ratios on the dynamics of infectious disease in both animals and plants. In Section 5, I will subsequently develop a series of speculations regarding the possible role of resource supply ratios in the establishment and the maintenance of host–microbial symbioses.

2. Fundamentals of Resource-Ratio Theory

2.1. Competition for a Single Resource

The Monod (1950) model of resource-limited bacterial growth is central both to the literature on microbial competition (see Fredrickson and Stephanopoulos, 1981; Veldkamp et al., 1984) and to current resource-ratio theory (Tilman, 1982). This empirical model [Eq. (1)] relates the biomass-specific microbial growth rate (μ, hr^{-1}) to the concentration of a growth-limiting resource (R, mM):

$$\mu = \mu_{max} \frac{R}{K_S + R} \qquad (1)$$

where μ_{max} is the maximum biomass-specific growth rate, and K_s is the half-saturation constant for growth on this limiting resource (Fig. 1).

The outcome of pure and simple competition (sensu Fredrickson and Stephanopoulos, 1981) between two or more species sharing a single limiting resource has been found to be predictable from a knowledge of the Monod growth kinetics and the specific mortality rates of each species (m, hr^{-1}). As has been shown for phytoplankton (Tilman, 1982) and later for zooplankton (Rothhaupt, 1988; Boraas et al., 1990), pure and simple competition between two or more bacteria for one limiting resource results in only one competitive dominant. This principle has been shown to apply to microbial competition for light (van Gemerden, 1974), as well as competition for many inorganic and organic substrates

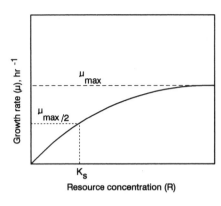

Figure 1. Generalized Monod relationship between the concentration of a growth-limiting resource (R) and the per capita growth rate (μ) of an organism (Monod, 1950). μ_{max} is the maximum per capita growth rate under conditions of resource saturation, and K_s is the resource concentration at which growth occurs at half the maximum rate.

(see Hanson and Hubbell, 1980; Kuenen and Gottschal, 1982; Tilman *et al.*, 1982).

Resource competition theory (Hsu *et al.*, 1977; Tilman, 1982; see also Lynch and Hobbie, 1988, Eq. 2.4.23) suggests that the outcome of microbial competition can be predicted from R^*, the steady-state concentration of growth-limiting resource at which the per capita growth rate μ of the bacterial population just balances its per capita mortality rate, m:

$$R^* = \frac{mK_S}{(\mu_{max} - m)} \tag{2}$$

This criterion is illustrated in Fig. 2, where two species (A and B) are competitors for the two growth-limiting resources R_1 and R_2. In this example, species A will outcompete species B when competing for resource R_1 because $R^*_{1A} < R^*_{1B}$. Species A is able to lower the concentration of this resource to levels that will result in a negative growth rate for the population of species B; the biomass of B thus will decline, and B will ultimately be excluded from the system at steady state. In contrast, because of competitive trade-offs discussed below, species B is assumed to be able to outcompete species A when both are limited by resource R_2.

The ability of the R^* criterion to predict the outcome of resource competition has been well demonstrated experimentally. For example, the dependence of competitive outcome on R^* is evident in the results of Harder and Veldkamp (1971), who examined competition for lactate between an obligate psychrophile (*Pseudomonas* sp.) and a facultative psychrophile (*Spirillum* sp.) at two dilution rates. In experiments carried out at 16°C, *Spirillum* sp. was the superior competitor at both dilution rates because of its consistently lower R^* for lactate. Similarly, the importance of the R^* criterion was demonstrated by Hanson and Hubbell (1980) in their study of competition between *Pseudomonas aeruginosa*

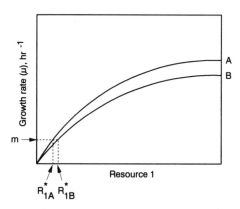

Figure 2. Graph illustrating the R^* criterion for competitive exclusion between two microbes competing for the same resource at a constant mortality rate m. In this example, species A will outcompete species B when both are competing for resource R_1 because $R^*_{1A} < R^*_{1B}$.

and *E. coli*. Numerous additional examples from experimental studies of phytoplankton are cited in Tilman *et al.* (1982).

2.2. Types of Resources

When considering the process of resource competition, it is also important to identify the nature of the limiting resources. In his development of resource-ratio theory, Tilman (1982, Table 2) defined eight different categories of resources. Of these eight categories, only three will be considered here: essential resources, interactive essential resources, and perfectly substitutable resources. Each of these three major types of resources is discussed in turn below.

2.2.1. Essential Resources

Elemental inorganic nutrients that can neither be synthesized nor destroyed by the cell (e.g., N, P, Mg, Fe, S) and important organic substrates such as vitamins (for species lacking the appropriate biosynthetic pathways) are most likely to be essential resources for microbes that have absolute growth requirements for these resources. For this class of resources, the response of bacterial growth to changes in resource concentration should follow Liebig's law of the minimum: that is, the resource that is present in least supply relative to its demands for cell growth should be growth-limiting. The transition point for the abrupt change from limitation by one essential resource (R_1) to a second essential resource (R_2) occurs when the supply ratio of two resources ($R_1:R_2$) exceeds the stoichiometric requirements of the two resources by the cell (delta, the cell's optimal nutrient ratio; see Rhee 1978). Thus, only one essential resource is limiting at any one time. A sharp transition from N- to P-limitation was observed in the green alga *Scenedesmus* by Rhee (1978), and a similarly abrupt transition was observed between vitamin- and P-limitation in the marine phytoplankton (*Monochrysis lutheri* (Droop, 1974).

This sharp transition can be shown graphically using resource-dependent growth isoclines (Tilman, 1982). Figure 3a illustrates the rectangular zero net growth isoclines (ZNGIs) of species A for two essential resources R_1 and R_2. For all combinations of R_1 and R_2 that lie on the ZNGI, the growth rate of species A will just balance its losses to mortality ($\mu = m$), and the population of species A will remain constant at its equilibrium density ($dN/dt = 0$).

For these two essential resources the abrupt transition between limitation by R_1 and R_2 occurs at the optimal ratio (the sharp corner of the isocline), which is defined by the cell's consumption vector for the two resources. As shown in Fig. 3a, this optimal ratio is defined by the values of R_2^* and R_1^*. When the $R_2^*:R_1^*$ supply ratio exceeds the optimal ratio, species A will be limited by R_1. Converse-

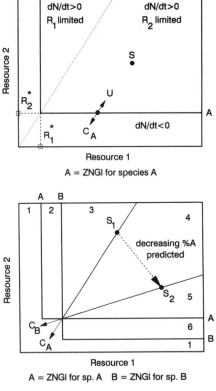

Figure 3. (a) Graph of the zero net growth isocline ZNGI, solid lines) for a hypothetical microbial population growing on the two limiting resources R_1 and R_2. The ZNGI depicts all possible combinations of these two resources in the environment that are sufficient to support a per capita growth rate (μ) by the microbial population that just equals its per capita loss rate due to cell mortality (m.) The values for R^* for both resources are indicated with open squares, and the resource consumption vector is shown as the dotted line passing diagonally from the origin through the intersection point of these two values. The solid dot on the ZNGI is the single species equilibrium point where $\mu = m$, and the resource consumption rate of the cells (C_A) just equals the rate of resource resupply (U) from the supply point S. (b) Crossing ZNGIs for two competing microbial species creates regions of coexistence and exclusion. For resource supply points located in region 1, neither species will survive because insufficient resources are available to support a positive net growth rate ($m > \mu$). For resource supply points in regions 2 and 3, species A will win by virtue of its lower R_1^*. Similarly, for resource supply points in regions 5 and 6, species B will win by virtue of its lower R_2^*. In region 4, both species coexist in varying proportions, with a linear decrease in the proportion of species A predicted along the supply ratio gradient from S_1 to S_2.

ly, when the $R_2^*:R_1^*$ supply ratio is less than the optimal ratio, species A will be limited by R_2. If the mortality rate m is increased because of cell death by predation or antibiosis, the ZNGI will move diagonally outwards away from the origin along an axis defined by the cell's optimal ratio (see Tilman, 1982, Fig. 2; see also Smith, 1993a, Fig. 7).

For all resource supply points that lie between the origin and the ZNGI, $dN/dt < 0$ and the population density of species A will decline. For all resource supply points (S) that lie outside the ZNGI, $dN/dt > 0$ and the population density of species A will increase until the available concentrations of R_1 and R_2 have been reduced to their equilibrium levels by cellular consumption. The resource consumption vector (C_A) is assumed to be parallel to the cell's optimal nutrient ratio (Tilman, 1982), and an equilibrium point (solid circle) for the population of species A will be attained when the resource consumption vector is opposite to and is equal in magnitude to the resource supply vector (U).

2.2.2. Interactive Essential Resources

Interactive essential resources are those for which the transition from limitation by one resource (R_1) to a second resource (R_2) is not abrupt, but rather is characterized by a curved region of resource interaction. Such an interaction is expected in the case of resources such as light or organic carbon compounds, which provide the metabolic energy necessary for the uptake of other inorganic and organic substrates. For example, a smooth transition was observed between zinc- and carbon-limitation in the yeast *Candida albicans* (see Lawford *et al.*, 1980, Fig. 3). Similarly, Zevenboom *et al.* (1980) and Rhee and Gotham (1981) found evidence of strong effects of light availability on nitrogen-limited phytoplankton, and Riegman (1985) has found evidence for effects of light on phosphorus-limited *Oscillatoria agardhii*. Although such data were unfortunately not collected, a smooth transition between nitrogen- and carbon-limitation might also be expected for the three soil bacteria studied by Nelson (1978). The ZNGI for two interactive essential resources is illustrated in Fig. 4a, with symbols as in Fig. 3a.

2.2.3. Perfectly Substitutable Resources

Organic or inorganic substrates that are used primarily for energy provision (e.g., lactose and maltose, or thiosulfate and acetate), or substrates which represent different chemical forms of a required inorganic nutrient (e.g., differing nitrogen sources such as ammonia, nitrate, tryptophan, and phenylalanine) would be expected to most closely approximate substitutable resources. Two resources can be said to be perfectly substitutable if all possible mixtures of the two substrates yield an identical growth rate. A theoretical example of this type of resource is shown in Fig. 5a, with symbols as in Fig. 3a. Note, however, that

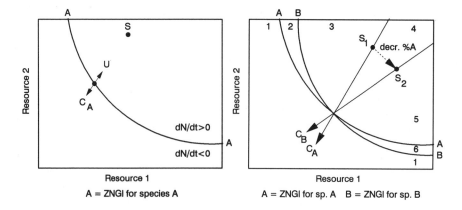

Figure 4. (a) ZNGI for interactive essential resources, illustrating the consumption vector (C_A), supply vector (U), and the equilibrium point generated by supply point S. (b) Graph of crossing ZNGI for two species competing for two interactive essential resources. As in Fig. 3b, neither species can survive for resource supply points located in region 1. For resource supply points in regions 2 and 3, species A will win by virtue of its lower R_1^*. Similarly, for resource supply points in regions 5 and 6, species B will win by virtue of its lower R_2^*. In region 4, both species coexist in varying proportions, with a linear decrease in the proportion of species A predicted along the supply ratio gradient from S_1 to S_2.

in the case of substitutable resources the slope of the resource consumption vector C_A is not constant, but may change for different points along the ZNGI because of shifts in the relative consumption rates of the two resources (Tilman, 1982).

2.3. Competition for Multiple Resources

Because different species may have distinct resource requirements, competition for multiple resources between two or more microbial species may involve competition for similar types of resources (e.g., two essential resources), or competition for differing types of resources (e.g., essential and perfectly substitutable resources). Once a particular resource pair has been identified, the outcome of competition between two or more species can be predicted graphically using resource-ratio theory if their ZNGIs, consumption vectors, and resource supply points are known.

There are two important orientations for multiple sets of ZNGIs. The ZNGIs for two or more competing species may be completely separated in the phase plane; that is, the ZNGI for one species is closer to the origin and lies wholly inside that of its competitors. Regardless of the actual resource type, the organism with the ZNGI closest to the origin would be competitively superior for all

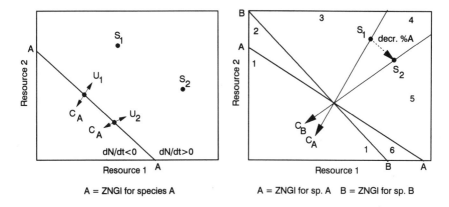

Figure 5. (a) ZNGI for perfectly substitutable resources, illustrating the consumption vector (C_A), supply vector (U), and the equilibrium point generated by supply point S. (b) Graph of crossing ZNGI for two species competing for two perfectly substitutable resources. As in Fig. 3b, neither species can survive for resource supply points located in region 1. For resource supply points in regions 2 and 3, species A will win by virtue of its lower R_1^*. Similarly, for resource supply points in regions 5 and 6, species B will win by virtue of its lower R_2^*. In region 4, both species coexist in varying proportions, with a linear decrease in the proportion of species A predicted along the supply ratio gradient from S_1 to S_2.

resource supply points lying beyond its isocline, because all its values of R^* would be lower than the corresponding values of its competitors (see Tilman, 1982, Fig. 24A,B).

Alternatively, the two sets of ZNGI may cross. Because of the presence of phenotypic trade-offs, a species that is competitively superior for one resource typically will not be competitively superior for all possible resources (see Tilman, 1982, Chapter 9). These trade-offs have been demonstrated quantitatively for phytoplankton by Tilman *et al.* (1982, Fig. 4), and such phenotypic trade-offs also are very evident among other microorganisms. For example, microbes have not been found that are simultaneously both excellent psychrophiles and excellent thermophiles; similarly, microbes that are good competitors at high substrate concentrations are poor competitors under conditions of low resource availability (Konings and Veldkamp, 1980). Examples in which even subtle phenotypic differences between organisms can lead to competitive dominance are summarized in Kuenen and Gottschal (1982), Kuenen and Harder (1982), Slater and Godwin (1980), and Smith (1993b). Such phenotypic trade-offs will cause the ZNGIs to cross, creating a two-species equilibrium point at their intersection. As long as each species consumes proportionately more of the resource that limits its own growth, this equilibrium point will be stable (Leon and Tumpson, 1975; Tilman, 1980).

As can be seen in Fig. 3b, the crossing of isoclines for two essential resources leads to a series of regions of competitive exclusion and dominance. For resource supply points located in region 1, neither species will survive because insufficient resources are available to support a positive net growth rate ($m > \mu$). For resource supply points in regions 2 and 3, both species will be limited by resource 1, and species A will win by virtue of its lower R_1^*. Similarly, for resource supply points in regions 5 and 6, both species will be limited by resource 2, and species B will win by virtue of its lower R_2^*.

In region 4, however, both species coexist because species A is limited by resource 2, and species B is limited by resource 1. However, the relative biomass of species A and B will depend on the $R_2:R_1$ supply ratio. For resource supply points placed along the resource gradient drawn across region 4, the relative biomass of species A will decline linearly with a decrease in the $R_2:R_1$ supply ratio (Fig. 3b; see also Tilman et al., 1982, Fig. 1G). Similar regions of competitive exclusion and coexistence are shown for interactive essential and for perfectly substitutable resources in Figs. 4b and 5b.

3. Effects of Resource Supply Ratios on Microbial Competition

Resource limitation of microbial growth is felt to be very widespread in the biosphere (Harder and Dijkhuizen, 1983). One of the most important predictions of resource-ratio theory is that a directional change in resource supply ratios to two or more microbial species competing for these limiting resources should result in a directional shift in competitive dominance. Movement of the resource supply point along the trajectory from S_1 to S_2 in Fig. 6a results in dramatic changes in species composition, with successive peaks of microbial dominance centered at the optimal ratios for each species in the potential assemblage (Fig. 6b).

Strong changes in microbial dominance and activity along resource gradients can be found in a wide variety of natural communities, including epilimnetic phytoplankton (Tilman, 1977), metalimnetic autotrophic bacteria (Pfennig, 1989), hypolimnetic iron bacteria (Jones, 1986), and sediment bacteria (Capone and Kiene, 1988) in lakes; aquatic and terrestrial nitrogen-fixing microorganisms (Smith, 1992); marine bacteria (Austin, 1988); bacteria in terrestrial soils (Paul and Clark, 1989); and even the intestinal microflora of vertebrates (Jones, 1980). In order to determine whether such patterns might plausibly be explained by resource supply ratio gradients, it is first necessary to demonstrate that resource-ratio theory applies to microbial communities (Smith, 1993b).

Shifts in dominance in experimental microbial communities containing prokaryotes were nicely demonstrated by Holm and Armstrong (1981) in their study of the effects of resource supply ratios on competition between the diatom *Asterionella formosa* and the cyanobacterium *Microcystis aeruginosa*. In this study,

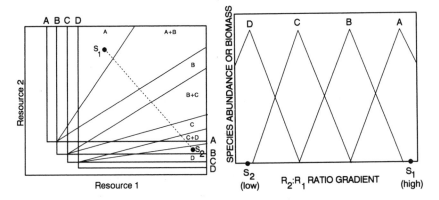

Figure 6. (a) Graph of crossing ZNGIs for four species competing for two essential resources. The regions of species dominance and coexistence are shown along a supply ratio gradient from S_1 to S_2. (b) Graph of trends in species abundance or biomass along the supply ratio gradient from S_1 to S_2. Successive peaks in the abundance of species A–D coincide with their optimal R_2/R_1 ratios.

the outcome of competition between *Microcystis* (which utilizes phosphorus as an essential resource, but which does not require silicon) and *Asterionella* (which has an absolute requirement for both phosphorus and silicon) differed under conditions of varying silicon/phosphorus supply ratios (Holm and Armstrong, 1981). The proportion of *Microcystis* decreased linearly with an increase in the Si/P supply ratio and was reduced to insignificant proportions at supply ratios exceeding the optimal Si/P ratio for *Asterionella* (see Smith, 1993b, Fig. 3). These changes in microbial species composition are consistent with resource-ratio theory (Tilman, 1982).

Further evidence for the applicability of resource-ratio theory comes from Gottschal *et al.* (1979), who studied competition between three aquatic bacteria (an obligate chemolithotroph, a heterotroph, and a facultative chemolithotroph) at a series of thiosulfate/acetate ratios. The facultative chemolithotroph *Thiobacillus* sp. strain A2 (here termed the mixotroph, M) and the heterotroph (H) *Spirillum* sp. strain G7 were grown together at five thiosulfate/acetate ratios, with a constant acetate supply rate.

Figure 7a illustrates a vertical theoretical ZNGI for the heterotroph (H), which requires the essential resource acetate, but which does not require and cannot use thiosulfate. In addition, I have drawn a diagonal theoretical ZNGI for the mixotroph (M), which as a facultative chemolithotroph is assumed to utilize both thiosulfate and acetate as substitutable resources. The consumption vector for the heterotroph is drawn parallel to the *x* axis because the heterotroph consumes only acetate. The mixotroph in contrast consumes both resources, and its consumption vector was estimated graphically (Smith, 1993b). As would be predicted by resource-ratio theory, an experimental increase in the thiosul-fate/acetate supply ratio in a direction parallel to the heterotroph's vertical ZNGI led to increasing dominance by the mixotroph (Fig. 7a).

In a separate set of competition experiments between the mixotroph (M) and the obligate chemolithotroph *Thiobacillus neapolitanus* (A), a decrease in the thiosulfate/acetate supply ratio in a direction parallel to the autotroph's hori-zontal ZNGI led to a consistent increase in dominance by the mixotroph (Fig. 7b).

In addition to these two-species competition experiments, Gottschal *et al.* (1979) also studied competition between all three bacteria along a thiosulfate–acetate gradient at a dilution rate of $0.075 \, hr^{-1}$. As would be expected from resource-ratio theory, the autotroph was dominant at the highest thiosul-fate/acetate ratios, and the heterotroph was dominant at the lowest thiosul-fate/acetate ratios (Fig. 7c). The mixotroph was numerically dominant at most, but not all, intermediate thiosulfate/acetate ratios. Gottschal and Thingstad (1982) also noted good agreement of these results with the predictions of their mathematical model of competition, and concluded that their failure to obtain complete dominance by the mixotroph at all intermediate thiosulfate/acetate ratios may have reflected a failure to wait for a true steady state to occur under these conditions (see Gottschal, 1986, Fig. 4). Resource-ratio theory also would predict complete dominance of the mixotroph in the center zone shown in Fig. 7c. However, if the intersection point between the autotroph's and the hetero-troph's ZNGIs were in very close proximity to the ZNGI of the mixotroph (as illustrated in the inset to Fig. 7c), this proximity would create a situation in which a considerable amount of time would be needed for the equilibrium outcome to occur.

Another extremely interesting set of microbial competition experiments has been performed by Veldhuis *et al.* (as cited in Veldkamp *et al.*, 1984). These investigators studied competition between two species of phototrophic bacteria, *Chlorobium phaeobacteroides* and *Thiocapsa roseopersicina*, on sulfide and ace-tate under conditions of changing light availability. In co-cultures of these two species, a stepwise decrease in light availability led to a progressive increase in the relative abundance of *Chlorobium*. Similarly, the relative abundance of the two phototrophs *Chlorobium phaeovibrioides* and *Thiocystis violacea* could be experimentally altered *in situ* by incubating mixed cultures in bottles at different depths; as might be expected from the effects of light observed in the co-culture experiments above, *Chlorobium* became progressively more dominant with depth (Veldkamp *et al.*, 1984). Such strong correlations between microbial rela-tive abundance and resource gradients are consistent with the general predictions of resource-ratio theory. Additional examples of the applicability of resource-ratio theory to microbial ecology are presented in Smith (1993b).

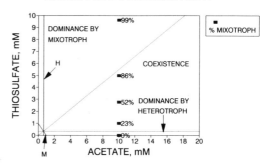

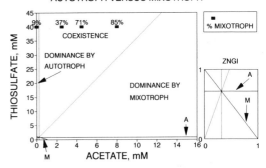

Figure 7. Effects of thiosulfate/acetate supply ratios on the outcome of competition between a heterotrophic bacterium (H: *Spirillum* sp. strain G7), a mixotrophic bacterium (M: *Thiobacillus* sp. strain A2), and an autotrophic bacterium (A: *Thiobacillus neapolitans*). Solid lines denote theoretical ZNGIs, and the dotted lines denote estimated resource consumption vectors for these species. (a) Graphical presentation of the outcome of competition between the heterotroph and mixotroph. (b) Graphical presentation of the outcome of competition between the autotroph and the mixotroph. (c) Graphical presentation of the outcome of competition between all three species along a thiosulfate/acetate supply ratio gradient. The inset illustrates a close-up of the theoretical ZNGIs for all three species. Data from Gottschal *et al.* (1979).

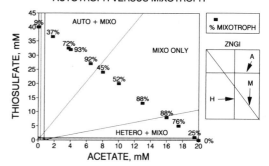

4. Resource Supply Ratios and the Outcome of Infectious Disease

4.1. Nutrients and Competition within the Vertebrate Host

Like all other organisms, invading pathogens require appropriate physical conditions, and their ability to synthesize new cells and to proliferate requires the constant provision of nutrients while inside the host (Brock *et al.*, 1984). Pathogens are unique only in the sense that their proliferation and metabolic activities alter their environment sufficiently to interfere with the host system and induce a disease state (Jones, 1980).

Many of the nutrients necessary for pathogen growth may be in critically short supply in the host system (Brock *et al.*, 1984), and the strong possibility exists that disease organisms may compete for growth-limiting resources with the tissues and indigenous microbial flora of the host (Smith, 1993a). The potential importance to the host of nutrient limitation of the pathogen is emphasized by a recent chemostat study of *Pseudomonas aeruginosa*, which was grown under conditions similar to the likely physiological status of microorganisms within the lungs of cystic fibrosis patients (Krieg *et al.*, 1988; Terry *et al.*, 1991). During prolonged chronic infection, *P. aeruginosa* undergoes alteration in the host from the classical nonmucoid form to an atypical mucoid form, and the appearance of this mucoid form is usually associated with a poor patient prognosis (Terry *et al.*, 1991). Terry *et al.* (1991) were able to demonstrate that the rate of conversion of this pathogen to the mucoid form was dependent not only on the type of nutrient limitation (e.g., phosphate versus glutamate limitation), but also on the degree of growth limitation, which was determined by nutrient availability.

Clinically important effects of nutrient limitation on pathogen growth are also evident in the yeast *Candida albicans*. *C. albicans* is a dimorphic opportunistic pathogen that can grow in either a budding yeast or a filamentous growth form (Bell and Chaffin, 1980). This transition can be induced from yeast cells only in the stationary phase, and the inducibility of these cells was studied in cultures limited by glucose, ammonium chloride, or galactose. Bell and Chaffin (1980) found that the loss of inducibility varied with the identity of the limiting nutrient, and concluded that increased access of *Candida* to nutrients may have a contributing role in the infection process.

If resource limitation is common within the vertebrate host, I hypothesize that direct competition for nutrients between the disease organism and cells in the host environment can play a pivotal role in determining the outcome of the disease process. The equilibrium outcome of resource competition takes time (Sommer, 1990). Unlike terrestrial and aquatic ecosystems, where sudden changes in environmental conditions can alter or obscure trajectories leading toward competitive exclusion, the vertebrate body is homeostatic and therefore much more likely to allow competitive cell–cell interactions to go to completion.

In addition, the internal environment of the host is not subject to quite the degree of complex interactions that characterize multitrophic-level aquatic and terrestrial communities (Carpenter, 1988; Hunter and Price, 1992).

Does competition for limiting resources actually occur in the host environment, however? Competitive interactions have in fact frequently been observed among components of a host's normal microbial flora, as well as between the host's body cells or microbial flora and an invading pathogen. Some of the best examples of dietary effects on competitive shifts in the normal gut flora have been reported in the animal literature. For example, different bacteria in the rumen of cattle have very different nutritional requirements for growth. If a ruminant is fed a high-starch diet, then starch-digesting bacteria become common where they had previously been rare; a diet rich in pasture legumes in contrast causes a shift in dominance to pectin-digesting bacteria (Brock *et al.*, 1984; see also Russell and Allen, 1984). Marked shifts in microbial community structure also can be observed in sheep provided diets of varying oxalate and nitrate contents (Allison and Reddy, 1984).

A review by Tannock (1983) suggests similar effects of diet on competition within the gut microflora of nonruminant animals. Meat-fed rats have more proteolytic bacteria and fewer saccharolytic bacteria in their feces than do rats fed pelleted food, and the presence or absence of a *Lactobacillus* layer in the mouse gut is dependent on the carbohydrate/lipid supply ratio in their diet. In primates, the intestinal flora of baboons also differs significantly in animals fed synthetic versus fruit and vegetable diets. The flora of baboons fed a synthetic diet contains significantly more clostridia, streptococci, micrococci, staphylococci, lactose-fermenting coliforms, but significantly lower numbers of lactobacilli and yeasts (Tannock, 1983). Competition between invading pathogens and an animal's gut flora also occurs. For example, invading *E. coli* populations can be controlled by a combination of indigenous clostridia and lactobacilli in gnotobiotic mice and continuous-flow cultures (Itoh and Freter, 1989). Similarly, invasions of the protozoan parasite *Cryptosporidium parvum* in experimental mouse models are resisted by the indigenous gut flora (Harp *et al.*, 1992).

In the human gut, the data are more equivocal, and the composition of the fecal flora may not be as dependent on the nature of the diet as originally thought (Freter *et al.*, 1983a; Drasar and Roberts, 1990). However, there is evidence that the competitive balance of the normal human gastrointestinal system is sensitive to certain types of change in nutrition. A high organic carbon/protein supply ratio in the diet results in protein malnutrition, and Tannock (1983) reports numerous examples of striking increases in the numbers of streptococci, coliforms, and bacteroides in the small intestine of protein-malnourished individuals relative to controls. In contrast, a long-term study of an individual fed diets of varying composition found that a high-protein diet did not affect the fecal microflora; however, a high-carbohydrate diet increased the relative numbers of the bifidobacteria, and a high-fat diet favored the bacteroides (Drasar and Roberts, 1990, citing Haenel *et al.*, 1964).

Competition for nutrients apparently is also actively involved in the suppression of pathogen infections by the colonic microflora (Borriello, 1990; Wilson and Perini, 1988), and an inverse correlation has been reported between the numbers of normal enteric coliforms and the invading *Shigella* during the course of infection in the feces of some patients suffering diarrhea (Tannock, 1983). Wilson and Perini (1988) have argued convincingly that the ability of chemostat cultures to reproduce the colonic ecosystem suggests that competition for growth-limiting substrates plays an important role in normal gut homeostasis, and it has been proposed that the population densities of individual microbial species are controlled by the concentration of their growth-limiting resource (Freter *et al.*, 1983b).

4.1.1. Resource Ratios and Infection of the Vertebrate Gut

Although a large body of experimental and clinical evidence indicates that microbial populations living on or within the host are constrained by both microbe–microbe and host–microbe interactions, the nature of this regulation is still poorly understood (Jones, 1980). Given the demonstrated applicability of chemostat theory to the gut environment (Wilson, 1988; Itoh and Freter, 1989), in the following section I will use graphical resource-ratio theory to show how the modification of resource ratios in the external nutrient supply to the host offers a potential method for successfully exploiting the competitive abilities of the host's indigenous gut microflora.

4.1.2. Principles

For simplicity, the example presented here will assume that infection is initiated by the invasion of a hypothetical microbial pathogen into the vertebrate gut, and that the subsequent dynamics of infection are influenced by competition with the resident gut flora. However, the principles are broadly general, and should apply equally well to disease-causing organisms infecting other systems of the body (Smith, 1993a).

Resource-ratio theory predicts that the successful establishment and persistence of an invading disease organism can be prevented only if (1) both the host and the pathogen are limited by the same resource and (2) the host is the superior competitor for that resource. These predictions of resource-ratio theory are illustrated below using the two limiting resources glutamine (R_1) and iron (R_2) as examples.

The choice of this resource pair is based on strong evidence that the supplies of both can strongly influence the outcome of infectious disease. Extensive data from both experimental and clinical medicine have shown that the iron supply to

Figure 8. Graphical presentation of overlapping ZNGIs for the host and pathogen, creating regions of competitive exclusion and coexistence analogous to those shown in Fig. 3b. A reduction in the iron/glutamine supply ratio along the gradient from S_1 to S_2 is predicted to move the competitive equilibrium progressively from a condition in which the host dies, to a condition of decreasing severity of persistent infection, to a condition in which the host successfully recovers from infection.

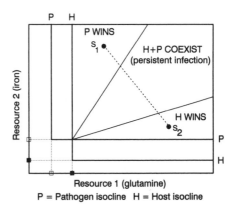

the host is an important determinant of the dynamics of many diseases: a high iron supply typically leads to very poor prognosis (Brock, 1986; Payne, 1988; Weinberg, 1966, 1978, 1988, 1989). Conversely, a high supply of glutamine has been found to be very beneficial to the host for a wide variety of traumas and infections (Souba et al., 1990).

In Fig. 8, theoretical ZNGIs are illustrated for a hypothetical pathogen competing with the host for iron and glutamine. It is assumed that competitive trade-offs exist; that is, neither the host nor the pathogen is a superior competitor for both resources. Because of the observed high iron requirements of pathogens, the host is assumed here to be the superior iron competitor. Similarly, because of the high glutamine requirements of the host, the pathogen is assumed to be the superior competitor for glutamine.

Because of these phenotypic trade-offs, these isoclines cross and create regions of competitive exclusion and dominance as shown in Fig. 8. This analysis suggests the general hypothesis that the outcome of infectious disease can potentially be modified by resource competition within the host, and that the competitive equilibrium can be deliberately managed by altering the supply of resources provided to the host (Smith, 1993a).

4.1.3. Empirical Support for the Hypothesis

In vertebrate models such as the rodent, the control that the resident gut microflora has over invading pathogens such as the bacterium *Clostridium difficile* (van der Waaij, 1989) and the protozoan parasite *Cryptosporidium parvum* (Harp et al., 1992) appears to be extremely strong. It has even proved possible to exploit this process of microbial control successfully within the vertebrate host. For example, successful treatment of human *Clostridium difficile* enterocolitis has been made by using rectal infusions of normal fecal flora (Schwan et al., 1984); by using a competing, nontoxigenic strain (Seal et al., 1987); and by providing competing strains of *Lactobacillus* (Gorbach, 1990). Similarly, inoculations both with indigenous intestinal microflora (Tannock, 1984) and with lactobacilli and pediococci (Juven *et al.*, 1991) also have been used to control intestinal colonization by human enteropathogens in live poultry. As noted by Itoh and Freter (1989), however, we do not as yet have a good knowledge of the characteristics that these competing microorganisms must have in order to successfully control the populations of unwelcome pathogens. I suggest that resource-ratio theory can help provide both the framework and the data necessary to solve this practical problem in biological control.

If the theory outlined above in Section 4.1.2 is generally applicable to the vertebrate gut, and if iron and glutamine are a reasonable resource pair for this environment, then one should see strong changes in the outcome of disease when the iron/glutamine supply ratio to the host is changed. Evidence from the biomedical research literature suggests that this may indeed be the case. For example, when stressed with an abnormally high supply of iron, even normally healthy individuals lose their ability to repel invading pathogens (Weinberg, 1978). In the case of the human gut, an elevated iron supply (and therefore a high iron/glutamine ratio) significantly lowered the LD_{50} of the intestinal pathogen *Listeria monocytogenes* (Sword, 1966; Chakraborty and Goebel, 1988). An even more dramatic effect of an excessive iron supply has been found for the intestinal pathogen *Yersinia enterocolitica*. In mouse models of infection, the LD_{50} can be lowered from $> 10^8$ to $< 10^1$ by increasing the iron supply, and in humans iron overload can lead to serious *Y. enterocolitica* infections (Bullen *et al.*, 1991). Iron availability may also be important in the establishment of intestinal infections of *Campylobacter jejuni* (Pickett *et al.*, 1992).

Support for the converse effect also can be found in the literature. Nutritional iron deficiency has been found to improve survivorship in rat models of *Salmonella typhimurium* (Baggs and Miller, 1973). The iron/glutamine supply ratio can also be lowered by increasing the supply of glutamine, and again improved host resistance to infection is observed (Alverdy, 1990; Souba *et al.*, 1990). Although the mechanisms involved may include direct effects of glutamine on the host itself, glutamine-enriched diets have been found to significantly ameliorate and even to reverse many of the adverse effects of experimentally induced enterocolitis in animal models (Rombeau, 1990). It is thus significant that Barber *et al.* (1990) suggested that glutamine supplementation may influence the composition of intestinal microflora such that noninvasive species become dominant.

The above data are very suggestive of the involvement of resource ratios in the outcome of disease in the vertebrate gut. However, I do not believe that this process is restricted to the mammalian gut alone. For example, iron also may be essential for the successful establishment of infections of the pathogen *Haemophilus influenzae* (Schryvers and Gray-Owen, 1992), which can cause serious complications in children. Weinberg (1966, 1978, 1988) has documented profound effects of iron availability on many types of bacterial, fungal, and parasitic diseases, and additional evidence for resource supply effects can be found in Smith (1993a). It is also particularly interesting that the ability to compete successfully for host iron has been identified as a potential contributing factor not only in widespread outbreaks of acute gastroenteritis in humans (Dai *et al.*, 1992), but also in devastating infections of marine fish (Austin, 1988); in both cases the infection was caused by bacteria of the genus *Vibrio*.

Two recent references from the medical literature (one on glutamine, and the other on iron) strongly suggest that manipulations of this resource pair indeed have the effects on infectious disease that I have proposed. In an experimental rat model of enterocolitis, an amendment of the rats' diet with glutamine resulted in greatly reduced morbidity and mortality relative to controls (Inoue *et al.*, 1993). Conversely, iron chelation therapy significantly increased the clearance rate of the malaria protozoan from the bloodstream of comatose children with cerebral malaria, and also increased their rate of recovery to full consciousness from deep coma (Gordeuk *et al.*, 1992). Many other important mechanisms are also involved in the disease process, however, and further experiments both with laboratory cultures and with animal models will be necessary to test the resource-ratio hypothesis of disease rigorously (Smith, 1993a). Such experiments are currently in progress using an established rat model of bacterial gut infections (Lichtman and Smith, in preparation).

4.2. Viral Infections and the Dynamics of AIDS

Resource-ratio theory also may be applicable to viral infections as well. In a recent paper on competition between zidovudine-sensitive and -resistant strains of HIV, McLean and Nowak (1992) have developed a model of the dynamics of CD4$^+$ cells in the infected host. Their model for the population dynamics of CD4$^+$ cells (X, cells per individual) can be written as follows:

$$dX/dt = \Lambda - mX - X(\beta_S L_S + \beta_R L_R) \tag{3}$$

where Λ is the rate of appearance in the host of new uninfected CD4$^+$ cells from the thymus (cells per week); m (per week) is the per capita mortality rate of the uninfected cells; L_S and L_R are the population sizes of sensitive and resistant strains of the virus (cells per individual); and β_S and β_R are the infectivity parameters of the sensitive and resistant strains of the virus (per cell per week).

Of interest to us here is the infectivity parameter β, which reflects the reproductive potential of the virus. In their model, McLean and Nowak (1992) reduced the value of β in Eq. (3) to reflect the assumption that zidovudine acts by blocking new infections via its effects on viral replication. For example, for a drug dose that causes an 80% decrease in new infections, the authors reduced the value of β to 80% of its original value in their analysis.

I wish to raise the possibility here that the value of β might also be influenced by changes in resource availability, because of competition between infected cells and uninfected cells for limiting resources within the host. Once infected by the virus, the synthesis of new virus particles should strongly alter both the uptake and the utilization of critically important resources by infected cells. I speculate that such changes in resource use may possibly create the phenotypic differences needed to create regions of competitive exclusion and dominance that are analogous to those shown in Fig. 8; only very subtle phenotypic changes are potentially required (Smith, 1993b). If such a response were indeed found to occur *in vivo*, then these phenotypic differences could provide important opportunities for the nutritional support of patients with AIDS or other viruses. It should be possible, for example, to formulate specific resource supply rates and resource supply ratios for the host that would exploit the competitive characteristics of the host's uninfected cells, and help lead to the competitive exclusion of infected cells that are actively expressing genes from the viral genome.

In order for such competitive interactions to be possible, however, the concentrations of one or more critically important resources must be reduced to limiting levels in the host. It is thus of very great interest that protein-energy malnutrition has been found to be common in many patients with AIDS (Kotler, 1992), and recent research has indicated that deficiencies of protein S (a vitamin K-dependent plasma protein) correlate very strongly with the progression of the disease (Bissuel *et al.*, 1992). Depletion of leukocyte glutathione (GSH) also occurs in HIV-infected hosts, and it has been suggested that a deficiency of this cysteine-containing tripeptide may promote viral replication and accelerate the rate of progress of the disease (Staal *et al.*, 1992).

The latter observation is particularly interesting because host levels of GSH are strongly dependent on protein intake, and can be enhanced by the provision either of *N*-acetyl cysteine (Staal *et al.*, 1992), or of glutamine in the host's nutrient supply (Robinson *et al.*, 1992). Robinson *et al.* (1992) suggest that along with the administration of antiviral agents, the provision of nutritional support supplemented with GSH precursors may prove to be a valuable treatment strategy for HIV-infected individuals. Many potential mechanisms may be involved in the benefits of such nutritional therapy (Robinson *et al.*, 1992). However, it is known that nutrients play a vital role in the modulation of the body's immune response (Cunningham-Rundles, 1992), and it would be of value to determine whether the depletion of host reserves of essential peptides (or other resources) by HIV-infected cells might place the vital population of uninfected T cells at a competitive disadvantage within the host. An experimental evaluation of the effects of diet therapy on the dynamics of HIV infection, and a critical assessment of the mechanisms involved, could potentially be made using a recent mouse model of AIDS (Fernandes *et al.*, 1992).

4.3. Nutrients, Competition, and Plant Diseases

As in the case of animal populations, disease can play an important role in the vigor and dynamics of plant populations as well (Burdon, 1987; Bierzychudek, 1988; Alexander, 1990). Walters (1985) has suggested that consideration of the physiological and biochemical aspects of the host–pathogen interaction is crucial not only for understanding the nature of plant disease, but also to more effective control measures. I suggest that an understanding of the ecological relationships between the host plant and its pathogen may be equally important.

Competition is frequently cited as a common interaction among plant-associated microbes (Bell *et al.*, 1990), and Newman (1978) has suggested that plant competition for nutrients and light can influence the interrelationships between the plant and its root-associated microflora. For example, a strong correlation between shoot weight, shoot nitrogen concentration, and rhizosphere bacterial abundance observed by Turkington *et al.* (1988) suggests that microbial activity can be strongly influenced by the host plant and its resource supply. Bainbridge (1974) noted effects of the nitrogen supply on infection of barley by powdery mildew, and interactions between nutrient limitation and light availability on plant susceptibility to pathogens also have been observed (see Mattson and Waring, 1984; Paul, 1990, and references therein).

Recent evidence suggests a similar role of resource availability in the dynamics of aquatic host–pathogen systems as well. For example, Bruning (1991a,b,c,d) and Bruning *et al.* (1992) have found pronounced effects of light and phosphorus availability on the epidemiology of infection of the freshwater diatom *Asterionella formosa* by the chytrid fungus *Rhizophydium planktonicum* Canter emend. In an experimental test of the effects of chytrid infection on natural populations of *Asterionella*, Kudoh and Takahashi (1992) found that it was possible to alter the dynamics of infection by altering light availability to the algal cells. Although these results in part may be explained by changes in the probability of encounter between the host and pathogen (Kudoh and Takahashi, 1992), I speculate that resource-ratio effects that are analogous to those shown for animal cells in Fig. 8 may also be involved.

It thus appears that resource supplies can potentially play an important role in determining the outcome of infectious diseases in plants as well as in animals. Such a conclusion is perhaps not surprising in view of recent evidence that revealed striking genetic similarities between plant and animal pathogens (Fenselau *et al.*, 1992; Gough *et al.*, 1992). I urge that direct tests be made to assess the applicability of resource-ratio theory to plant disease, using methods that are analogous to those proposed above in Sections 4.1 and 4.2. If it can indeed be shown to apply, then resource-ratio theory could provide a framework for predicting the quantitative characteristics required of any microbe that is to be used successfully in biological plant disease control (Schroth *et al.*, 1984), whether it is isolated from naturally occurring microbial communities, or created artificially via genetic engineering.

5. Resource Supply Ratios and the Formation of Stable Symbioses

Symbiotic relationships between microbes and their plant and animal hosts are common in the biosphere, and in some cases (e.g., the nitrogen-fixing bacteria associated with the root nodules of crop plants) are of very great economic importance. Although the biology and ecology of symbiotic relationships have been a focus of research for many decades (Ahmadjian and Paracer, 1986; Jennings and Lee, 1975; Smith and Douglas, 1987; Margulis, 1993), the quantitative rules involved in the establishment and maintenance of symbioses remain poorly understood.

As noted by Boucher (1985, Fig. 1), mathematical phase plane diagrams have been used by at least 29 different authors to describe the relationship between the host and symbiont. However, in each case these diagrams appear to have been based on Lotka–Volterra equations, which are phenomenological and can have restricted predictive value (see Tilman, 1982, Chapter 7). In this section, I propose that resource-ratio theory offers a superior quantitative approach to understanding the process of symbiosis, and by using the green hydra association as a model system I will show how this theory can potentially be used to predict the conditions needed for the establishment of stable symbioses.

5.1. Resource Ratios and the Green Hydra Symbiosis

Alga–invertebrate symbioses have presumably arisen from feeding relationships (Gooday and Doonan, 1980), and larvae of the brine shrimp *Artemia* can for example be used as a vector to infect aposymbiotic (non-symbiont-carrying) hydra with a variety of free-living species of algae (Rahat and Reich, 1984, 1985a). The path from algal consumption to stable symbiosis first requires avoidance by the algal cells of intracellular digestion, but beyond this initial step there must be a complex series of interactions that establish and maintain a stable algal/animal cell ratio (Gooday and Doonan, 1980).

In the case of the *Hydra viridis–Chlorella* symbiosis, a crucial feature for stable coexistence is the establishment of an endosymbiont growth rate that is harmonious with that of its host: if the algal growth rate is too rapid, the symbionts potentially can overgrow and kill the host; if too slow, the algae may be diluted out by failure to keep pace with the growth rate of the host (Muscatine *et al.*, 1975). In alga–invertebrate symbioses such as this one, the algal component typically appears to be at equilibrium at both the population and the community level (Cook, 1985). However, this equilibrium varies significantly with changes in environmental conditions (Muscatine *et al.*, 1975).

The green hydra system offers an excellent model system for the examination of the applicability of resource-ratio theory to symbiotic associations. Two important features characterize the green hydra symbiosis (Douglas, 1988): (1) stable coexistence, in which one organism does not overgrow its partner; and (2) strong nutritional interactions, in which exchanges of potentially growth-limiting nutrients take place between cells of the host and symbiont.

The intracellular environment within the digestive cells of green hydra appears to resemble a quasichemostat. As in the marine dinoflagellate–*Anemonia sulcata* symbiosis (Taylor, 1969), green hydra can regulate the number of intracellular algal symbionts by expulsion or digestion (Neckelmann and Muscatine, 1983). Such a loss mechanism would act to maintain a steady-state algal population in which the death rate of the algae just offsets their growth rate via cell division. Resource-ratio theory would predict a stable coexistence of such a continuous culture system if the respective growth rates of the host and symbiont were limited by two separate resources.

What might be the possible identities of these two growth-limiting resources? As is true of many other alga–invertebrate symbioses (Hinde, 1988), a major feature of the green hydra symbiosis is the translocation of large quantities of photosynthate from the alga to the host. In the green hydra, this translocated photosynthate is primarily in the form of the hexose sugar maltose (Cook, 1983). Starved green hydra kept in the light can obtain the majority of their energy requirements from carbohydrates translocated from the algal symbionts (Pardy and White, 1977), and this movement of fixed carbon appears to be of particular survival value when the food supply to the host is limited (Thorington and Margulis, 1981).

Furthermore, this beneficial exchange of metabolites is two-way, because the algal symbionts can be maintained in well-fed hosts even under conditions of darkness (Thorington and Margulis, 1981). In some strains of hydra, it appears that the growth rate of the resident algae may be controlled by the host (Cook, 1983). Evidence from green hydra and from other alga–invertebrate symbioses strongly suggests that the control mechanism involves restriction of the supply of nitrogen to the algal cells (Neckelmann and Muscatine, 1983; Cook and D'Elia, 1987; Rees, 1987; McAuley, 1988; Cook *et al.*, 1992).

I thus propose that an important resource pair for resource competition in alga–invertebrate symbioses such as the green hydra may be that of dissolved organic carbon (DOC) and nitrogen. In the case of the heterotrophic host, DOC and nitrogen would be expected to be interacting essential resources, with curved isoclines as discussed in Section 2.2.2. In contrast, in the presence of light, the ZNGI for the autotrophic alga would be expected to be vertical because no exogenous supply of DOC would be necessary, and its growth rate should be independent of DOC concentration.

The implications of this resource pair are illustrated in Fig. 9, which suggests that a stable coexistence between the alga and its host should occur in conditions under which the algae were N-limited, and the host cells were carbon (i.e., energy)-limited. If this were so, then the algal component of the green hydra and the zooxanthellae of similar alga–invertebrate symbioses should typically exhibit signs of nitrogen limitation. Evidence for N-limitation of zooxanthellae has in fact been observed (e.g., McAuley, 1988; Cook et al., 1992).

Douglas and Smith (1984) noted that although there was persuasive evidence that the green algal symbiosis was achieved by regulation of the growth rate of the algae, the actual mechanisms involved were not clear. Resource-ratio theory, however, makes three important predictions regarding the dynamics of

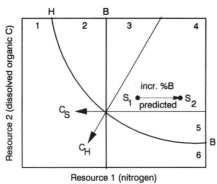

H = ZNGI for host   S = ZNGI for symbiont

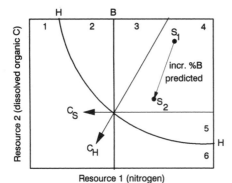

H = ZNGI for host   B = ZNGI for symbiont

Figure 9. Theoretical ZNGIs for a host *Hydra* (H) competing with its symbiotic *Chlorella* (S) for the resources nitrogen and dissolved organic carbon. In the case of the host, nitrogen and dissolved organic carbon would be expected to be interacting essential resources. In contrast, in the presence of light, the ZNGI for the autotrophic alga would be expected to be vertical because no exogenous supply of dissolved organic carbon would be necessary. The theoretical consumption vectors create regions of coexistence and exclusion analogous to those shown in Fig. 4b. (a) Enrichment of the environment with nitrogen along the gradient from S_1 to S_2 is predicted to result in a marked increase in the equilibrium density of symbiotic algae within the host cells. (b) Starvation in the light, resulting in movement of the supply point along the gradient from S_1 to S_2, is predicted to result in a marked increase in the equilibrium density of symbiotic algae within the host cells.

symbiosis based on competition for DOC and nitrogen. First, enrichment of the environment with nitrogen should move the resource supply point sharply to the right, and resource-ratio theory would predict a drastic increase in the equilibrium density of symbiotic algae within the host cells (Fig. 9a). Enrichment of the growth medium with inorganic nutrients (including N) indeed has been shown to enhance the growth rate of the algal symbiont, and at sufficiently high levels of enrichment the host is overgrown and killed by the algae (e.g., Neckelmann and Muscatine, 1983).

Second, if the resource supply point does not move in a direction parallel to the host's consumption vector during starvation of the host in the light, Fig. 9b would predict an increase in the equilibrium algal population in the host's cells. Algal density in the *Hydra viridis–Chlorella* symbiosis in fact has been observed to increase with decreasing feeding rates in the light (Douglas and Smith, 1984). An even more extreme case of this trend can be found in experimental studies of the green *Hydra magnipapillata* symbiosis: when starved in the light, the host became overgrown with algae and subsequently disintegrated (Rahat and Reich, 1985b).

Third, the green hydra symbiosis is limited only to a select few species of green algae and hydra. Resource-ratio theory would predict just such a host–symbiont specificity. Competition for a resource pair such as DOC and nitrogen should result in the steady-state coexistence of only two organisms—the hydra host and one algal symbiont. Unless the ZNGI of another potential algal symbiont lies wholly within that of the normal *Chlorella* strain, resource-ratio theory suggests that the competing alga should be outcompeted by the normal strain within the intracellular environment. Although aposymbiotic *Hydra viridis* can be infected experimentally with other algal species, ensuing interalgal competition indeed has been found to determine which species remains as the sole endosymbiont (see Rahat and Reich, 1988). A computer model of the green hydra symbiosis has been developed (Taylor *et al.*, 1989), but this model apparently does not as yet contain an explicit term quantitatively relating the nutrient supply to algal growth. Such a modification, based on Eq. 1–2, might further contribute to our understanding of the factors leading to the stable colonization of the hydra host by its symbiotic algae.

A similar exclusion of algal competitors has also been observed in other alga–invertebrate symbioses as well (Cook, 1985). Evidence for the importance of the external nutrient supply in the maintenance of stable symbiotic relationships has been found not only in the green hydra (McAuley, 1990), but also in reef corals (Muscatine *et al.*, 1989) and in the green paramecium. In *Paramecium bursaria,* the infection of aposymbiotic animals with symbiotic *Chlorella* is influenced not only by the nutritional conditions of the host (Reisser *et al.*, 1989a), but also by the nutritional state of the algae (Reisser *et al.*, 1989b). The principal N sources for these algae are apparently ammonia and glutamine (Albers *et al.*, 1982). Aposymbiotic *P. bursaria* can also be infected with cells of bacteria or yeast, but a subsequent superinfection with *Chlorella* always results in the rapid exclusion of the other symbionts (Gortz, 1982). Although the mechanisms responsible for this exclusion are not yet understood, they could involve competitive displacement due to resource competition.

Moreover, evidence from bacterial symbioses with protozoa is also suggestive of resource supply effects. For example, the marine protozoan *Parauronema acutum* contains infectious, self-reproducing symbiotic bacteria termed xenosomes (Soldo *et al.*, 1993). The frequency of infection of aposymbiotic animals with xenosomes is apparently dependent on their nutritional conditions; the threshold bacterial number required for successful infection in individuals preincubated in sea water was found to be an order of magnitude lower than for those pre-incubated in culture medium.

5.2. Relevance to Endosymbiotic Theory

Figure 9 appears to capture several of the major features of the response of the green hydra symbiosis to changes in environmental conditions, and offers a plausible potential mechanism to explain how alterations in the balance between host and symbiont can occur in natural communities. Moreover, Fig. 9 also raises interesting questions about the rules that may have been operating at the time of the original events leading to the endosymbiotic origins of today's eukaryotes (Margulis, 1993).

Based on their work on the green hydra symbiosis, Rahat and Reich (1986) concluded that the host–symbiont specificities and the interrelationships between green and brown hydra with chlorococci and chlorellae are based on nutritional and ecological factors. In presenting their test tube hypothesis, Rahat and Reich (1986, 1988) proposed that algae ingested into the vacuole of a hydra cell are subject to selection pressures similar to those occurring either in laboratory cultures or in natural communities. They argued that it is not recognition that enables algae to successfully invade the host, but a preadapted ability to survive in the intravacuolar environment.

As noted by Rahat and Reich (1986), intracellular selection for potential symbionts that are capable of coevolution toward stable coexistence would provide the mechanism by which a chance encounter between host and alga would lead to a stable symbiosis. I speculate that one essential preadaptation of a successful presymbiont should be a strong competitive ability for resource(s) that are not limiting to the host organism, as reflected in the steady-state resource requirements (R^*) of both the host and the presymbiont. A consideration of the possible resource pairs and isocline shapes that may have been involved during the acquisition of chloroplasts (dissolved organic carbon and nitrogen?), and during the acquisition of mitochondria (iron and phosphorus?), might prove to be fruitful as well as very interesting. As noted by Smith (1969), and echoed by Thorington and Margulis (1981), *Hydra* and its associated microbes should prove to be ideal testing models for the evolutionary origins of symbioses. Because the green *Hydra magnipapillata* symbiosis still appears to be at an early stage, and because its composition is so strongly dependent on environmental conditions (Rahat and Reich, 1988), this system may provide an excellent system for tests of the ideas outlined above.

6. Conclusions

In reviewing the theoretical basis of vegetation science, Austin (1986) drew a series of conclusions that I believe are equally valid for microbial ecology. Austin suggested that a good general theory should predict the life-form spectrum, the species richness, the phenological patterns, the biomass, and the spatial and temporal patterns of species composition observed in the environment. To his list I would add that a good general theory also should have the capability to predict patterns in biogeochemical processes such as photosynthesis, decomposition, and the transformations of important elements in the biosphere. A more complete understanding of ecosystems will require a knowledge not only of the biomass and species composition of the resident organisms, but also the amounts and ratios of critically important resources at each point in the food web (see Sterner *et al.,* 1992). Certainly, this is an extremely tall order, and we will be searching for such a unifying theory for many years to come. Nonetheless, I suggest that resource-ratio theory provides a framework that offers great promise for furthering our understanding of microbial ecology, and helping us move toward such an imposing goal.

I have attempted in this review to demonstrate to the reader a strong commonality in the response of microorganisms to resource gradients, and also to demonstrate that resource-ratio theory offers an insightful approach to answering questions that have attracted the attention of microbial ecologists for many decades. I believe that resource-ratio theory has profound implications for our understanding of the ecology not only of free-living microorganisms, but also of those that reside either within or in close association with eukaryotic hosts. I have shown (1) that the applicability of resource-ratio theory has been widely confirmed in communities of macroorganisms; (2) that its applicability to microbial communities until recently has not been adequately evaluated; and (3) that when I made such an evaluation, experimental data from the laboratory, from the field, and from clinical medical experience are all very consistent with the general predictions of resource-ratio theory.

The equilibrium R^*-based approach that I have presented here is nonetheless a simplification (Tilman, 1990), and in changing natural environments the actual composition of microbial communities may track the projected equilibrium state only imperfectly (see Sommer, 1990). Moreover, microbes also are capable of a very wide variety of cell–cell interactions other than pure and simple competition (Fredrickson and Stephanopoulos, 1981). It is clear from the microbial ecology literature, for example, that competition even for a single limiting resource can be complicated by the excretion of another potentially limiting resource such as vitamins (e.g., Meyer *et al.*, 1975), or by the excretion of organic growth inhibitors by one or more of the competitors (Fredrickson and Stephanopoulos, 1981; Gottschal, 1986).

Physicochemical factors such as pH and temperature, ecological factors such as predation also can have strong moderating effects. For example, the outcome of competition between the facultative chemolithotroph *Thiobacillus* sp. strain A2 and the obligate chemolithotroph *Thiobacillus neopolitans* was dependent on the culture pH (Smith and Kelly, 1979). Similarly, pH mediated the outcome of competition between the rumen bacteria *Streptococcus bovis* and *Megasphaeria elsdenii* under conditions of carbon (= energy) limitation (Russell and Allen, 1984). The presence of macro- and micropredators also may have strong effects on both the structure and the function of microbial communities (Pace and Funke, 1991; Stockner and Porter, 1988).

However, I believe that these and other apparent complications ultimately will prove to be experimentally tractable, and that these questions will provide very interesting directions for future research. The effects of environmental factors such as pH and temperature, for example, can be assessed using experimental methods similar to those used successfully by Tilman *et al.* (1981) and Tilman and Kiesling (1984). Similarly, the direct and indirect effects of predation can be approached using methods such as those of Jost *et al.* (1973), Williams (1980), and Sterner (1990).

In his review of the applicability of general ecological principles to microbial ecology, Atlas (1985) suggested that microbial ecologists faced a basic dilemma. He noted that pure culture studies were needed to determine the physiological properties of microbes, but lamented the apparent inability of these pure cultures to yield meaningful information about the ecological functioning of these organisms. Happily, however, it is just such physiological studies that are needed first to create the species-specific ZNGIs that are shown in Figs. 3–9, and then to generate *a priori* predictions of the responses of these species to resource supply gradients. Once these essential data have been obtained, explicit tests of resource-ratio theory using mixed microbial cultures can be made in continuous cultures similar to those used successfully for plankton (e.g., Tilman, 1977; Rothhaupt, 1988). The gradostat (Smith and Waltman, 1991; Wimpenny and Abdollahi, 1991) may prove to be an extremely valuable tool as well. However, subsequent field tests of resource-ratio theory will then also be necessary in both terrestrial and aquatic communities, since the success of any population-process theory such as this will ultimately be judged by its ability to predict quantitatively the patterns that we observe along natural environmental gradients (Austin, 1986).

In the final chapter of his remarkable and provocative new synthesis, Andrews (1991) concludes that microbial ecology and macroecology are mutually complementary, and I emphatically agree. I join Porter *et al.* (1988) in urging that we take advantage of microbial systems in our evaluations of general ecological theories, and also in urging that there be stronger interactions among theoreticians, experimental community ecologists, and microbial ecologists. Because of the tremendous diversity of substrates used by bacteria for growth, their very short generation times, and the wide range of metabolic responses that they exhibit, bacteria are excellent model organisms for future experimental tests of resource-based competition theory. Bacteria and other microbes have been central to the rapid development of our understanding of both biochemistry and molecular biology, and I predict that they will prove to be of similar importance in helping us better understand the fundamental principles of ecology as well.

ACKNOWLEDGMENTS. This research was supported in part by NSF grant BSR-8717638. I am indebted to David Tilman for providing the stimulus for this review, to Gwyn Jones for giving me the time and the freedom to speculate freely, to Pierre Couillard for providing valuable references on the green paramecium symbiosis, and to Marilyn Smith for providing information essential to my development of the section on AIDS.

References

Ahmadjian, V., and Paracer, S., 1986, *Symbiosis: An Introduction to Biological Associations,* University Press of New England, Hanover.

Albers, D., Reisser, W., and Weissner, W., 1982, Studies on the nitrogen supply of endosymbiotic Chlorellae in green *Paramecium bursaria, Plant Sci. Lett.* **25**:85–90.

Alexander, H. M., 1990, Dynamics of plant–pathogen interactions in natural plant communities, in: *Pests, Pathogens and Plant Communities* (J. J. Burdon and S. R. Leather, eds.), Blackwell, Oxford, pp. 31–45.

Allison, M. J., and Reddy, C. A., 1984, Adaptations of gastrointestinal bacteria in response to changes in dietary oxalate and nitrate, in: *Current Perspectives in Microbial Ecology* (M. J. Klug and C. A. Reddy, eds.), American Society for Microbiology, Washington, D.C., pp. 248–256.

Alverdy, J. C., 1990, Effects of glutamine-supplemented diets on immunology of the gut, *J. Parent. Ent. Nutr.* **14**(Suppl.):109–113.

Andrews, J. H., 1991, *Comparative Ecology of Microorganisms and Macroorganisms,* Springer-Verlag, Berlin.

Atlas, R. M., 1985, Applicability of general ecological principles to microbial ecology, in: *Bacteria in Nature,* Volume 2 (J. S. Poindexter and E. R. Leadbetter, eds.), Plenum Press, New York, pp. 339–370.

Atlas, R. M., Colwell, R. M., Pramer, D., Tiedje, J. M., Vidaver, A. K., and Wodzinski, R. J., 1992, Microbial ecology, *ASM News* **58**:4–5.

Austin, B., 1988, *Marine Microbiology,* Cambridge University Press, London.

Austin, M. P., 1986, The theoretical basis of vegetation science, *Trends Ecol. Evol.* **1:**161–164.

Baggs, R. B., and Miller, S. A., 1973, Nutritional iron deficiency as a determinant of host resistance in the rat, *J. Nutr.* **103:**1554–1560.

Bainbridge, J. J., 1974, Effect of nitrogen nutrition of the host on barley powdery mildew, *Plant Pathol.* **23:**160–161.

Barber, A. E., Jones, W. G., II, Minei, J. P., Fahey, T. J., III, Moldawer, L. L., Rayburn, J. L., Fischer, E., Keogh, C. V., Sires, G. T., and Lowry, S. F., 1990, Glutamine or fiber supplementation of a defined formula diet: Impact on bacterial translocation, tissue composition, and response to endotoxin, *J. Parent. Ent. Nutr.* **14:**335–343.

Barko, J. W., Gunnison, D., and Carpenter, S. R., 1991, Sediment interactions with submersed macrophyte growth and community dynamics, *Aquat. Bot.* **41:**41–65.

Bell, C. R., Moore, L. W., and Canfield, M. L., 1990, Growth of octopine-catabolizing *Pseudomonas* spp. under octopine limitation in chemostats and their potential to compete with *Agrobacterium tumefaciens, Appl. Environ. Microbiol.* **56:**2834–2839.

Bell, W. M., and Chaffin, W. L., 1980, Nutrient-limited yeast growth in *Candida albicans:* Effect on yeast–mycelial transition, *Can. J. Microbiol.* **26:**102–105.

Bierzychudek, P., 1988, Fungal pathogens affect plant population dynamics and evolution, *Trends Ecol. Evol.* **3:**6–7.

Bissuel, F., Berruyer, M., Causse, X., Dechavanne, M., and Trepo, C., 1992, Acquired protein S deficiency: Correlation with advanced disease in HIV-1-infected patients, *J. AIDS* **5:**484–489.

Boraas, M. E., Seale, D. B., and Horton, J. B., 1990, Resource competition between two rotifer species (*Brachionus rubens* and *B. calcyflorus*): An experimental test of a mechanistic model, *J. Plankton Res.* **12:**77–87.

Borriello, S. P., 1990, The influence of the normal gut flora on *Clostridium difficile* colonisation of the gut, *Ann. Med.* **22:**61–67.

Boucher, D. H., 1985, The idea of mutualism, past and future, in: *The Biology of Mutualism: Ecology and Evolution* (D. H. Boucher, ed.), Oxford University Press, London, pp. 1–28.

Brock, J. H., 1986, Iron and the outcome of infection, *Br. Med. J.* **293:**518–520.

Brock, T. D., Smith, D. W., and Madigan, M. T., 1984, *Biology of Microorganisms,* 4th ed., Prentice–Hall, Englewood Cliffs, N.J.

Bruning, K., 1991a, Infection of the diatom *Asterionella* by a chytrid. 1. Effects of light on reproduction and infectivity of the parasite, *J. Plankton Res.* **13:**103–117.

Bruning, K., 1991b, Infection of the diatom *Asterionella* by a chytrid. 2. Effects of light on survival and epidemic development of the parasite, *J. Plankton Res.* **13:**119–129.

Bruning, K., 1991c, Effects of phosphorus limitation on the epidemiology of a chytrid phytoplankton parasite, *Freshwater Biol.* **25:**409–417.

Bruning, K., 1991d, Effects of temperature and light on the population dynamics of the *Asterionella–Rhizophydium* association, *J. Plankton Res.* **13:**707–719.

Bruning, K., Lingeman, R., and Ringelberg, J., 1992, Estimating the impact of fungal parasites on phytoplankton populations, *Limnol. Oceanogr.* **37:**252–260.

Bullen, J. J., Ward, C. G., and Rogers, H. J., 1991, The critical role of iron in some clinical infections, *Eur. J. Clin. Microbiol. Infect. Dis.* **10:**613–617.

Burdon, J. J., 1987, *Diseases and Plant Population Biology,* Cambridge University Press, London.

Campbell, R., 1983, *Microbial Ecology,* 2nd ed., Blackwell, Oxford.

Capone, D. G., and Kiene, R. P., 1988, Comparison of microbial dynamics in marine and freshwater sediments: Contrasts in anaerobic carbon catabolism, *Limnol. Oceanogr.* **33:**725–749.

Carpenter, S. R. (ed.), 1988, *Complex Interactions in Lake Communities,* Springer-Verlag, Berlin.

Chakraborty, T., and Goebel, W., 1988, Recent developments in the study of virulence in *Listeria monocytogenes, Curr. Top. Microbiol. Immunol.* **138:**41–48.

Cook, C. B., 1983, Metabolic interchange in algae–invertebrate symbiosis, *Int. Rev. Cytol. Suppl.* **14:**177–210.

Cook, C. B., 1985, Equilibrium populations and long-term stability of mutualistic algae and invertebrate hosts, in: *The Biology of Mutualism: Ecology and Evolution* (D. H. Boucher, ed.), Oxford University Press, London, pp. 171–191.

Cook, C. B., and D'Elia, C. F., 1987, Are natural populations of zooxanthellae ever nutrient-limited? *Symbiosis* **4:**199–212.

Cook, C. B., Muller-Parker, G., and D'Elia, C. F., 1992, Ammonium enhancement of dark carbon fixation and nitrogen limitation in symbiotic zooxanthellae: Effects of feeding and starvation of the sea anemone *Aiptasia pallida, Limnol. Oceanogr.* **37:**131–139.

Cunningham-Rundles, S., 1992, *Nutrient Modulation of the Immune Response,* Dekker, New York.

Dai, J.-H., Lee, Y.-S., and Wong, H.-C., 1992, Effects of iron limitation on production of a siderophore, outer membrane proteins, and hemolysin and on hydrophobicity, cell adherence, and lethality for mice of *Vibrio parahaemolyticus, Infect. Immun.* **60:**2952–2956.

Douglas, A. E., 1988, Nutritional interactions as signals in the green hydra symbiosis, in: *Cell to Cell Signals in Plant, Animal and Microbial Symbioses* (S. Scannerini, D. Smith, P. Bonfante-Fasolo, and V. Gianinazzi-Pearson, eds.), NATO ASI Series H: Cell Biology, Volume 17, Springer-Verlag, Berlin, pp. 283–296.

Douglas, A., and Smith, D. C., 1984, The green hydra symbiosis. VIII. Mechanisms in symbiont regulation, *Proc. R. Soc. London Ser. B* **221:**291–319.

Drasar, B., and Roberts, A. K., 1990, Control of the large bowel microflora, in: *Human Microbial Ecology* (M. J. Hill and P. D. Marsh, eds.), CRC Press, Boca Raton, Fla., pp. 89–110.

Droop, M. R., 1974, The nutrient status of algal cells in continuous culture, *J. Mar. Biol. Assoc. U.K.* **54:**825–855.

Fairchild, G. W., Lowe, R. L., and Richardson, W. B., 1985, Algal periphyton growth on nutrient-diffusing substrates: An *in situ* bioassay, *Ecology* **66:**465–472.

Fenselau, S., Balbo, I., and Bonas, U., 1992, Determinants of pathogenicity in *Xanthomonas campestris* pv. *vesicatoria* are related to proteins involved in secretion in bacterial pathogens in animals, *Mol. Plant–Microbe Interact.* **5:**390–396.

Fernandes, G., Tomar, V., Venkataraman, M. N., and Venkataraman, J. T., 1992, Potential of diet therapy on murine AIDS, *J. Nutr.* **122:**716–722.

Fourqurean, J. W., Zieman, J. C., and Powell, G. V. N., 1992, Relationships between porewater nutrients and seagrasses in a subtropical carbonate environment, *Mar. Biol.* **114:**57–65.

Fredrickson, A. G., and Stephanopoulos, G., 1981, Microbial competition, *Science* **213:**972–979.

Freter, R., Brickner, H., Botney, M., Cleven, D., and Aranki, A., 1983a, Mechanisms that control bacterial populations in continuous-flow culture models of mouse large intestinal flora, *Infect. Immun.* **39:**676–685.

Freter, R., Stauffer, E., Cleven, D., Holdeman, L. V., and Moore, W. E. C., 1983b, Continuous-flow cultures as in vivo models of the ecology of large intestinal flora, *Infect. Immun.* **39:**666–675.

Gooday, G. W., and Doonan, S. A., 1980, The ecology of algal–invertebrate symbioses, in: *Contemporary Microbial Ecology* (D. C. Ellwood, J. N. Hedger, M. J. Latham, J. M. Lynch, and J. H. Slater, eds.), Academic Press, New York, pp. 377–390.

Gorbach, S. L., 1990, Lactic acid bacteria and human health, *Ann. Med.* **22:**37–41.

Gordeuk, V., Thuma, P., Brittenham, G., McLaren, C., Parry, D., Backenstose, R. N., Biemba, G., Msiska, R., Holmes, L., McKinley, E., Vargas, L., Gilkenson, R., and Poltera, A. A., 1992, Effect of iron chelation therapy on recovery from deep coma in children with cerebral malaria, *N. Engl. J. Med.* **327:**1473–1477.

Gortz, H-D., 1982, Infections of *Paramecium bursaria* with bacteria and yeasts, *J. Cell Sci.* **58:**445–453.

Gottschal, J. C., 1986, Mixed substrate utilization by mixed cultures, in: *Bacteria in Nature,* Volume 2 (J. S. Poindexter and E. R. Leadbetter, eds.), Plenum Press, New York, pp. 261–296.

Gottschal, J. C., and Thingstad, T. F., 1982, Mathematical description of competition between two and three bacterial species under dual substrate limitation in the chemostat: A comparison with experimental data, *Biotechnol. Bioeng.* **24**:1403–1418.

Gottschal, J. C., De Vries, S., and Kuenen, J. G., 1979, Competition between the facultatively chemolithotrophic *Thiobacillus* A2, an obligately chemolithotrophic *Thiobacillus* and a heterotrophic *Spirillum* for inorganic and organic substrates, *Arch. Microbiol.* **121**:241–249.

Gough, C. L., Genin, S., Zischek, C., and Boucher, C. A., 1992, hrp genes of *Pseudomonas solanacearum* are homologous to pathogenicity determinants of animal pathogenic bacteria and are conserved among plant pathogenic bacteria, *Mol. Plant–Microbe Interact.* **5**:384–389.

Grace, J. B., 1991, A clarification of the debate between Grime and Tilman, *Funct. Ecol.* **5**:583–587.

Gurevitch, J., Morrow, L. L., Wallace, A., and Walsh, J. S., 1992, A meta-analysis of competition in field experiments. *Am. Nat.* **140**:539–572.

Haenel, H., Grassman, B., Gratte, F. K., and Muller-Beuthow, W., 1964, Einflusse einer zellautosereichen Kost auf die intestinale mikrookologie beim Menschen, *Zentralbl. Bakteriol. Parasitenkd. Infektionskr. Hyg. Abt. 1 Orig.* **192**:491.

Hanson, S. R., and Hubbell, S. P., 1980, Single-nutrient microbial competition: Quantitative agreement between experimental and theoretically forecast outcomes, *Science* **207**:1491–1493.

Harder, W., and Dijkhuizen, L., 1983, Physiological responses to nutrient limitation, *Annu. Rev. Microbiol.* **37**:1–23.

Harder, W., and Veldkamp, H., 1971, Competition of marine psychrophile bacteria at low temperatures, *Antonie van Leeuwenhoek* **37**:51–63.

Harp, J. A., Chen, W., and Harmsen, A. G., 1992, Resistance of severe combined immunodeficient mice to infection with *Cryptosporidium parvum:* The importance of intestinal flora, *Infect. Immun.* **60**:3509–3512.

Hinde, R., 1988, Factors produced by symbiotic marine invertebrates which affect translocation between the symbionts, in: *Cell to Cell Signals in Plant, Animal and Microbial Symbioses* (S. Scannerini, D. Smith, P. Bonfante-Fasolo, and V. Gianinazzi-Pearson, eds.), NATO ASI Series H: Cell Biology, Volume 17, Springer-Verlag, Berlin, pp. 311–324.

Holm, N. P., and Armstrong, D. E., 1981, Role of nutrient limitation and competition in controlling the populations of *Asterionella formosa* and *Microcystis aeruginosa* in semicontinuous culture, *Limnol. Oceanogr.* **26**:622–634.

Hsu, S. B., Hubbell, S. P., and Waltman, P., 1977, A mathematical theory for single-nutrient competition in continuous cultures of microorganisms, *SIAM J. Appl. Math.* **32**:366–383.

Hunter, M. D., and Price, P. W., 1992, Playing chutes and ladders: Heterogeneity and the relative roles of bottom-up and top-down forces in natural communities, *Ecology* **73**:724–732.

Inoue, Y., Grant, J. P., and Snyder, P. J., 1993, Effect of glutamine-supplemented intravenous nutrition on survival after Escherichia coli-induced peritonitis, *J. Parent. Ent. Nutr.* **14**:335–343.

Itoh, K., and Freter, R., 1989, Control of Escherichia coli populations by a combination of indigenous clostridia and lactobacilli in gnotobiotic mice and continuous-flow cultures, *Infect. Immun.* **57**:559–565.

Jennings, D. H., and Lee, D. L., 1975, *Symbiosis,* Symposia of the Society for Experimental Biology, No. 29, Cambridge University Press, London.

Jones, G. W., 1980, Some aspects of the interaction of microbes with the human body, in: *Contemporary Microbial Ecology* (D. C. Ellwood, J. N. Hedger, M. J. Latham, J. M. Lynch, and J. H. Slater, eds.), Academic Press, New York, pp. 253–282.

Jones, J. G., 1986, Iron transformations by freshwater bacteria, *Adv. Microb. Ecol.* **9**:149–185.

Jost, J. L., Drake, J. F., Fredrickson, A. G., and Tsuchiya, H. M., 1973, Interactions of *Tetrahymena pyriformis, Escherichia coli, Azotobacter vinelandii,* and glucose in a minimal medium, *J. Bacteriol.* **113:**834–840.

Juven, B. J., Meinersmann, R. J., and Stern, N. J., 1991, Antagonistic effects of lactobacilli and pediococci to control intestinal colonization by human enteropathogens in live poultry, *J. Appl. Bacteriol.* **70:**95–103.

Konings, W. N., and Veldkamp, H., 1980, Phenotypic responses to environmental change, in: *Contemporary Microbial Ecology* (D. C. Ellwood, J. N. Hedger, M. J. Latham, J. M. Lynch, and J. H. Slater, eds.), Academic Press, New York, pp. 161–191.

Kotler, D. P., 1992, Nutritional effects and support in the patient with acquired immunodeficiency syndrome, *J. Nutr.* **122:**723–727.

Krieg, D. P., Bass, J. A., and Mattingly, S. J., 1988, Phosphorylcholine stimulates capsule formation of phosphate-limited mucoid *Pseudomonas aeruginosa, Infect. Immun.* **56:**864–873.

Kudoh, S., and Takahashi, M., 1992, An experimental test of host population size control by fungal parasitism in the planktonic diatom *Asterionella formosa* using mesocosms in a natural lake, *Arch. Hydrobiol.* **124:**293–307.

Kuenen, J. G., and Gottschal, J. C., 1982, Competition among chemolithotrophs and methylotrophs and their interactions with heterotrophic bacteria, in: *Microbial Interactions and Communities,* Volume 1 (A. T. Bull and J. H. Slater, eds.), Academic Press, New York, pp. 153–187.

Kuenen, J. G., and Harder, W., 1982, Microbial competition in continuous culture, in: *Experimental Microbial Ecology* (R. G. Burns and J. H. Slater, eds.), Blackwell, Oxford, pp. 342–367.

Lawford, H. G., Pik, J. R., Lawford, G. R., Williams, T., and Kligerman, A., 1980, Physiology of *Candida albicans* in zinc-limited chemostats, *Can. J. Microbiol.* **26:**64–70.

Lenski, R., 1992, Book review, *Ecology* **73:**377–378.

Leon, J., and Tumpson, D., 1975, Competition between two species for two complementary or substitutable resources, *J. Theor. Biol.* **50:**185–201.

Lynch, J. M., and Hobbie, J. E., 1988, *Micro-organisms in Action: Concepts and Applications in Microbial Ecology,* Blackwell, Oxford.

McAuley, P. J., 1988, Cell-to-cell interactions during the establishment of the hydra–*Chlorella* symbiosis, in: *Cell to Cell Signals in Plant, Animal and Microbial Symbioses* (S. Scannerini, D. Smith, P. Bonfante-Fasolo, and V. Gianinazzi-Pearson, eds.), NATO ASI Series H: Cell Biology, Volume 176, Springer-Verlag, Berlin, pp. 115–130.

McAuley, P. J., 1990, Uptake of ammonium by green hydra, *Proc. Roy. Soc. Lond.* B **242:**45–50.

McLean, A. R., and Nowak, M. A., 1992, Competition between zidovudine-sensitive and zidovudine-resistant strains of HIV, *AIDS* **6:**71–79.

Margulis, L., 1993, *Symbiosis in Cell Evolution: Microbial Communities in the Archean and Proterozoic Eons,* 2nd ed., Freeman, San Francisco.

Mattson, P. A., and Waring, R. H., 1984, Effects of nutrient and light limitation on mountain hemlock: Susceptibility to laminated root rot, *Ecology* **65:**1517–1524.

Meyer, J. S., Tsuchiya, H. M., and Fredrickson, A. G., 1975, Dynamics of mixed populations having complementary metabolism, *Biotechnol. Bioeng.* **17:**1065–1081.

Monod, J., 1950, La technique de culture continue: Theorie et applications, *Ann. Inst. Pasteur* **79:**390–410.

Muscatine, L., Cook, C. B., Pardy, R. L., and Pool, R. R., 1975, Uptake, recognition and maintenance of symbiotic *Chlorella* by *Hydra viridis,* in: *Symbiosis,* Symposia of the Society for Experimental Biology, No. 29 (D. H. Jennings and D. L. Lee, eds.), Cambridge University Press, London, pp. 175–203.

Muscatine, L., Falkowski, P. G., Dubinsky, Z., Cook, P. A., and McCloskey, L. R., 1989, The effect of external nutrient resources on the population dynamics of zooxanthellae in a reef coral, *Proc. Roy. Soc. Lond.* B **236:**311–324.

Neckelmann, N., and Muscatine, L., 1983, Regulatory mechanisms maintaining the *Hydra–Chlorella* symbiosis, *Proc. R. Soc. London Ser. B* **219**:193–210.

Nelson, L. M., 1978, Effect of temperature, growth rate, and nutrient limitation on the yield and composition of three bacterial isolates from an arctic soil grown in continuous culture, *Can. J. Microbiol.* **12**:1452–1459.

Newman, E. I., 1978, Root microorganisms: Their significance in the ecosystem, *Biol. Rev.* **53**:511–554.

Pace, M. L., and Funke, E., 1991, Regulation of planktonic microbial communities by nutrients and herbivores, *Ecology* **72**:904–914.

Pardy, R., and White, B., 1977, Metabolic relationships between green hydra and its symbiotic algae, *Biol. Bull.* **153**:228–236.

Paul, E. A., and Clark, F. E., 1989, *Soil Microbiology and Biochemistry,* Academic Press, New York.

Paul, N. D., 1990, Modification of the effects of plant pathogens by other components of natural ecosystems, in: *Pests, Pathogens and Plant Communities* (J. J. Burdon and S. R. Leather, eds.), Blackwell, Oxford, pp. 81–96.

Payne, S. M., 1988, Iron and virulence in the family Enterobacteriaceae, *CRC Crit. Rev. Microbiol.* **16**:81–112.

Pfennig, N., 1989, Ecology of phototrophic purple and green sulfur bacteria, in: *Autotrophic Bacteria* (H. G. Schlegel and B. Bowein, eds.), Springer-Verlag, Berlin, pp. 97–116.

Pickett, C. L., Auffenberg, T., Pesci, E. C., Sheen, V. L., and Jusuf, S. S. D., 1992, Iron acquisition and hemolysin production by *Campylobacter jejuni, Infect. Immun.* **60**:3872–3877.

Porter, K. G., Paerl, H., Hodson, R., Pace, M., Priscu, J., Riemann, B., Scavia, D., and Stockner, J., 1988, Microbial interactions in lake food webs, in: *Complex Interactions in Lake Communities* (S. R. Carpenter, ed.), Springer-Verlag, Berlin, pp. 209–227.

Rahat, M., and Reich, V., 1984, Intracellular infection of aposymbiotic *Hydra viridis* by a free-living *Chlorella* sp.: Initiation of a stable symbiosis, *J. Cell Sci.* **65**:265–277.

Rahat, M., and Reich, V., 1985a, Correlations between characteristics of some free-living *Chlorella* sp. and their ability to form stable symbioses with *Hydra viridis, J. Cell Sci.* **74**:257–266.

Rahat, M., and Reich, V., 1985b, A new alga/hydra symbiosis: *Hydra magnipapillata* of the 'nonsymbiotic' Vulgaris group hosts *Chlorococcum*-like alga, *Symbiosis* **1**:177–184.

Rahat, M., and Reich, V., 1986, Algal endosymbiosis in brown hydra: Host/symbiont specificity, *J. Cell Sci.* **86**:273–286.

Rahat, M., and Reich, V., 1988, The establishment of algal/hydra symbioses—A case of recognition or preadaptation? in: *Cell to Cell Signals in Plant, Animal and Microbial Symbioses* (S. Scannerini, D. Smith, P. Bonfante-Fasolo, and V. Gianinazzi-Pearson, eds.), NATO ASI Series H: Cell Biology, Volume 17, Springer-Verlag, Berlin, pp. 297–310.

Rees, T. A. V., 1987, The green hydra symbiosis and ammonium. I. The role of the host in ammonium assimilation and its possible regulatory significance, *Proc. R. Soc. London Ser. B* **229**:299–314.

Reisser, W., Meier, R., and Wiessner, W., 1989a, Cytological studies on the endosymbiotic unit of *Paramecium bursaria* and *Chlorella*. 1. The infection of algae-free *Paramecium bursaria* with symbiotic Chlorellae isolated from green paramecia as influenced by the nutritional conditions of the ciliate. *Arch. Protistenkd.* **123**:326–332.

Reisser, W., Meier, R., and Wiessner, W., 1989b, Cytological studies on the endosymbiotic unit of *Paramecium bursaria* and *Chlorella*. 2. The regulation of the endosymbiotic algal population as influenced by the nutritional condition of the symbiotic partners. *Arch. Protistenkd.* **123**:333–341.

Rhee, G.-Y., 1978, Effects of N:P atomic ratios and nitrate limitation on algal growth, cell composition, and nitrate uptake, *Limnol. Oceanogr.* **23**: 10–25.

Rhee, G.-Y., and Gotham, I. J., 1981, The effect of environmental factors on phytoplankton growth: Light and the interactions of light with nitrate limitation, *Limnol. Oceanogr.* **26:**649–659.

Riegman, R., 1985, Phosphate–phytoplankton interactions, Ph.D. thesis, University of Amsterdam.

Robinson, M. K., Hong, R. W., and Wilmore, D. W., 1992, Glutathione deficiency and HIV infection, *Lancet* **339**(II):1603–1604.

Rombeau, J. L., 1990, A review of the effects of glutamine-enriched diets on experimentally induced enterocolitis, *J. Parent. Ent. Nutr.* **14**(Suppl.):100–105.

Rothhaupt, K. O., 1988, Mechanistic resource competition theory applied to laboratory experiments with zooplankton, *Nature* **333:**660–662.

Russell, J. B., and Allen, M. S., 1984, Physiological basis for interactions among rumen bacteria: *Streptococcus bovis* and *Megasphaeria elsdenii* as a model, in: *Current Perspectives in Microbial Ecology* (M. J. Klug and C. A. Reddy, eds.), American Society for Microbiology, Washington, D.C., pp. 239–247.

Schroth, M. N., Loper, J. E., and Hildebrand, D. C., 1984, Bacteria as biocontrol agents of plant disease, in: *Current Perspectives in Microbial Ecology* (M. J. Klug and C. A. Reddy, eds.), American Society for Microbiology, Washington, D.C., pp. 362–372.

Schryvers, A. B., and Gray-Owen, S., 1992, Iron acquisition in *Haemophilus influenzae:* Receptors for human transferrin, *J. Infect. Dis.* **165**(Suppl. 1):S103–S104.

Schwan, A., Sjölin, S., Trottestam, U., and Aronsson, B., 1984, Relapsing *Clostridium difficile* enterocolitis cured by rectal infusion of normal feces, *Scand. J. Infect. Dis.* **16:**211–215.

Seal, D., Borriello, S. P., Barclay, F. E., Welch, A., Piper, M., and Bonnycastle, M., 1987, Treatment of a relapsing *Clostridium difficile* diarrhoea by administration of a non-toxigenic strain, *Eur. J. Clin. Microbiol.* **6:**51–53.

Slater, J. H., and Godwin, D., 1980, Microbial adaptation and selection, in: *Contemporary Microbial Ecology* (D. C. Ellwood, J. N. Hedger, M. J. Latham, J. M. Lynch, and J. H. Slater, eds.), Academic Press, New York, pp. 136–160.

Smith, A. L., and Kelly, D. P., 1979, Competition in the chemostat between an obligately and a facultatively chemolithotrophic thiobacillus, *J. Gen. Microbiol.* **115:**377–384.

Smith, D. C., 1969, From extracellular to intracellular: The establishment of a symbiosis, *Proc. R. Soc. London* Ser. B. **204:**115–130.

Smith, D. C., and Douglas, A. E., 1987, *The Biology of Symbiosis,* Arnold, London.

Smith, H. L., and Waltman, P., 1991, The gradostat: A model of competition along a nutrient gradient, *Microb. Ecol.* **22:**207–226.

Smith, V. H., 1983, Low nitrogen to phosphorus ratios favor dominance by blue-green algae in lake phytoplankton, *Science* **221:**669–671.

Smith, V. H., 1992, Effects of nitrogen and phosphorus ratios on nitrogen fixation in agricultural and pastoral ecosystems, *Biogeochemistry* **18:**19–35.

Smith, V. H., 1993a, Host nutrition, resource competition between host and pathogen, and the outcome of infectious disease, *BioScience* **43:**21–30.

Smith, V. H., 1993b, Applicability of resource-ratio theory to aquatic microbial ecology, *Limnol. Oceanogr.* **38:**239–249.

Soldo, A. T., Musil, G., and Brickson, S. A., 1993, The invasive nature of an infectious bacterial symbiont, *J. Euk. Microbiol.* **40:**33–36.

Sommer, U. (ed.), 1989, *Plankton Ecology: Succession in Plankton Communities,* Springer-Verlag, Berlin.

Sommer, U., 1990, Phytoplankton nutrient competition—from laboratory to lake, in: *Perspectives in Plant Competition* (J. B. Grace and D. Tilman, eds.), Academic Press, New York, pp. 193–213.

Souba, W. W., Hershkowitz, K., Austgen, T. R., Chen, M. K., and Salloum, R. M., 1990, Glutamine nutrition: Theoretical considerations and therapeutic impact, *J. Parent. Ent. Nutr.* **14**(Suppl.):237–243.

Staal, F. J. T., Ela, S. W., Roederer, M., Anderson, M. T., Herzenberg, L. A., and Herzenberg, L. A., 1992, Glutathione deficiency and human immunodeficiency virus infection, *Lancet* **339**(II):909–912.

Sterner, R. W., 1990, N:P resupply by herbivores: Zooplankton and the algal competitive arena, *Am. Nat.* **136**:209–229.

Sterner, R. W., Elser, J. J., and Hessen, D. O., 1992, Stoichiometric relationships among producers, consumers and nutrient cycling in pelagic ecosystems, *Biogeochemistry* **17**:49–67.

Stockner, J. G., and Porter, K. G., 1988, Microbial food webs in freshwater planktonic ecosystems, in: *Complex Interactions in Lake Communities* (S. R. Carpenter, ed.), Springer-Verlag, Berlin, pp. 69–83.

Sword, C. P., 1966, Mechanisms of pathogenesis in *Listeria monocytogenes* infection. I. Influence of iron, *J. Bacteriol.* **92**:536–542.

Tannock, G. W., 1983, Effect of dietary and environmental stress on the gastrointestinal microbiota, in: *Human Intestinal Microflora in Health and Disease* (D. J. Hentges, ed.), Academic Press, New York, pp. 517–540.

Tannock, G. W., 1984, Control of gastrointestinal pathogens by normal flora, in: *Current Perspectives in Microbial Ecology* (M. J. Klug and C. A. Reddy, eds.), American Society for Microbiology, Washington, D.C., pp. 374–382.

Taylor, C. E., Muscatine, L., and Jefferson, D. R., 1989, Maintenance and breakdown of the *Hydra-Chlorella* symbiosis: A computer model, *Proc. Roy. Soc. Lond.* B **238**:277–289.

Taylor, D. L., 1969, On the regulation and maintenance of algal numbers in zooxanthellae–coelenterate symbiosis, with a note on the nutritional relationship in *Anemonia sulcata, J. Mar. Biol. Assoc. U.K.* **49**:1057–1065.

Terry, J. M., Pina, S. E., and Mattingly, S. J., 1991, Environmental conditions which influence mucoid conversion in *Pseudomonas aeruginosa* PAO1, *Infect. Immun.* **59**:471–477.

Thorington, G., and Margulis, L., 1981, *Hydra viridis:* Transfer of metabolites between *Hydra* and symbiotic algae, *Biol. Bull.* **160**:175–188.

Tilman, D., 1977, Resource competition between planktonic algae: An experimental and theoretical approach, *Ecology* **58**:338–348.

Tilman, D., 1980, Resources: A graphical mechanistic approach to competition and predation, *Am. Nat.* **116**:362–393.

Tilman, D., 1982, *Resource Competition and Community Structure,* Princeton University Press, Princeton, N.J.

Tilman, D., 1988, *Plant Strategies and the Dynamics and Structure of Plant Communities,* Princeton University Press, Princeton, N.J.

Tilman, D., 1990, Mechanisms of plant competition for nutrients: The elements of a predictive theory of competition, in: *Perspectives in Plant Competition* (J. B. Grace and D. Tilman, eds.), Academic Press, New York, pp. 117–141.

Tilman, D., and Kiesling, R. L., 1984, Freshwater algal ecology: Taxonomic tradeoffs in the temperature dependence of nutrient competitive abilities, in: *Current Perspectives in Microbial Ecology* (M. J. Klug and C. A. Reddy, eds.), American Society for Microbiology, Washington, D.C., pp. 314–319.

Tilman, D., Mattson, M., and Langer, S., 1981, Competition and nutrient kinetics along a temperature gradient: An experimental test of a mechanistic approach to niche theory, *Limnol. Oceanogr.* **26**:1020–1033.

Tilman, D., Kilham, S. S., and Kilham, P., 1982, Phytoplankton community ecology: The role of limiting nutrients, *Annu. Rev. Ecol. Syst.* **13**:349–372.

Turkington, R., Holl, F. B., Chanway, C. P., and Thompson, J. D., 1988, The influence of microorganisms, particularly *Rhizobium,* on plant competition in grass–legume communities, in: *Plant Population Ecology* (A. J. Davy, M. J. Hutchings, and A. R. Watkinson, eds.), Blackwell, Oxford, pp. 343–366.

van der Waaij, D., 1989, The ecology of the human intestine and its consequences for overgrowth by pathogens such as *Clostridium difficile*, *Annu. Rev. Microbiol.* **43**:69–87.

van Gemerden, H., 1974, Coexistence of organisms competing for the same substrate: An example among the purple sulfur bacteria, *Microb. Ecol.* **1**:104–119.

Veldkamp, H., van Gemerden, H., Harder, W., and Laanbroek, H. J., 1984, Microbial competition, in: *Current Perspectives in Microbial Ecology* (M. J. Klug and C. A. Reddy, eds.), American Society for Microbiology, Washington, D.C., pp. 279–290.

Walters, D. R., 1985, Shoot:root interrelationships: The effect of obligately biotrophic fungal pathogens, *Biol. Rev.* **60**:47–78.

Weinberg, E. D., 1966, Roles of metallic ions in host–parasite interactions, *Bacteriol. Rev.* **30**:136–151.

Weinberg, E. D., 1978, Iron and infection, *Microbiol. Rev.* **42**:45–66.

Weinberg, E. D., 1988, Iron withholding: A defense against infection and neoplasia, *Physiol. Rev.* **64**:65–102.

Weinberg, E. D., 1989, Cellular regulation of iron assimilation, *Q. Rev. Biol.* **64**:261–290.

Williams, F. M., 1980, On understanding predator–prey interactions, in: *Contemporary Microbial Ecology* (D. C. Ellwood, J. N. Hedger, M. J. Latham, J. M. Lynch, and J. H. Slater, eds.), Academic Press, New York, pp. 349–375.

Wilson, K. H., 1988, Microbial ecology of *Clostridium difficile,* in: *Clostridium difficile: Its Role in Intestinal Disease* (R. D. Rolfe and S. M. Finegold, eds.), Academic Press, New York, pp. 183–200.

Wilson, K. H., and Perini, F. 1988, Role of competition for nutrients in suppression of *Clostridium difficile* by the colonic microflora, *Infect. Immun.* **56**:2610–2614.

Wimpenny, J. W. T., and Abdollahi, H., 1991, Growth of mixed cultures of *Paracoccus denitrificans* and *Desulfovibric desulfuricans* in homogeneous and in heterogeneous culture systems, *Microb. Ecol.* **22**:1–13.

Zevenboom, W., de Groot, G. J., and Mur, L. R., 1980, Effects of light on nitrate-limited *Oscillatoria agardhii* in chemostat cultures, *Arch. Mikrobiol.* **125**:59–65.

2

^{13}C Tracer Methodology in Microbial Ecology with Special Reference to Primary Production Processes in Aquatic Environments

TAKEO HAMA, JUNKO HAMA, and NOBUHIKO HANDA

1. Introduction

Photosynthetic production by phytoplankton supplies organic material and energy to the aquatic food web consisting of bacteria, zooplankton, fish, water bird, whale, etc., and it may well be the most important step in the biological processes in aquatic environments . The estimation of primary productivity, thus, is essential to elucidating the dynamics of the microbial community and organic material. The importance of biological processes for the transfer of CO_2 across the sea surface has recently been much discussed in relation to global changes (e.g., Berger *et al.*, 1989; Longhurst, 1991). The dynamics of primary productivity, in particular, has a significant role in the global carbon cycle. Although there have been new approaches to assessing the dynamics, such as satellite imaging and time series sediment trapping, the direct measurement of the carbon uptake rate by phytoplankton photosynthesis can be regarded as the most reliable and basic estimate.

Bottle incubation experiments have usually been used to determine the photosynthetic rate in natural aquatic environments, because the measurements of increase and/or decrease in the biomass and/or chemical elements in a non-closed system are rather difficult due to the movement of water mass and exchange with the atmosphere. Steemann Nielsen (1952) first introduced radioactive ^{14}C as a tool for measurement of the photosynthetic production rate of the natural phytoplankton population. Although some problems with the ^{14}C method have been pointed out (e.g., Gieskes *et al.*, 1979; Fitzwater *et al.*, 1982; Leftley *et al.*,

TAKEO HAMA, JUNKO HAMA, and NOBUHIKO HANDA • Institute for Hydrospheric-Atmospheric Sciences, Nagoya University, Chikusa-ku, Nagoya 464-01, Japan.
Advances in Microbial Ecology, Volume 13, edited by J. Gwynfryn Jones. Plenum Press, New York, 1993.

1983), it has been routinely applied to productivity measurement of organic carbon in natural waters because of its high sensitivity relative to the oxygen method.

In the studies on nitrogen metabolism in microbial ecology, the stable isotope ^{15}N has been applied (Dugdale and Goering, 1967), because the radioactive isotope ^{13}N is hardly available due to its rapid decay. The stable isotope of carbon, ^{13}C, on the other hand, had only very rarely been applied to measure carbon flux in the microbial ecosystem as a tracer experiment. Factors involved may be the lower sensitivity of the ^{13}C method compared with the ^{14}C method, the cost of ^{13}C tracer compounds, and the difficulty of maintenance and operation of analytical facilities.

However, the development of facilities has made it possible to determine the uptake rates of both carbon and nitrogen in the same incubation sample when the dual label (^{13}C and ^{15}N) method is used (Otsuki *et al.*, 1983; Kanda *et al.*, 1985a,b; Miyazaki *et al.*, 1985a,b). Further, the combination with gas chromatography–mass spectrometry (GC-MS) can provide significant information on the material cycling in aquatic environments (J. Hama and Handa, 1986; T. Hama *et al.*, 1987). These studies are achieved using ^{13}C rather than ^{14}C. In countries where the use of radioactive substances in natural environments has been severely restricted, such as Japan, the use of the ^{13}C method is essential to the study of carbon flux in aquatic environments.

Here, we discuss the ^{13}C tracer method which has been applied to the aquatic environment to measure the primary productivity. First, the basic principle in measuring the production rate, including the calculation equation, will be discussed in detail. Second, we will summarize briefly some applied results of the ^{13}C tracer method to lake and oceanic waters. Third, we will present a method for combining the ^{13}C tracer technique with other methods such as the ^{15}N method, GC-MS, and gel filtration; these combined methods have advantages over the ^{14}C method for analysis of the primary production processes. Finally, examples of analysis of the aquatic food web will be given, indicating the applicability of the ^{13}C method not only to primary production study but also to food web analysis.

2. Estimation of Photosynthetic Rate by ^{13}C Tracer Method

2.1. Principle

2.1.1. Calculation of Production Rate (ρc)

Slawyk *et al.* (1977, 1979) were the first to apply the ^{13}C tracer technique for the determination of photosynthetic production rate by microorganisms. Their method is based on measurements of ^{13}C atomic % of particulate matter at the end of the incubation (a_{is}), ^{13}C atomic % in the natural (nonincubated) sample (a_{ns}), the concentration of particulate organic carbon at the beginning of the incubation $(POC(0)$, μg C/liter), and ^{13}C atomic % in the dissolved inorganic carbon in the incubation bottle (a_{ic}). The balance of ^{13}C can be found as follows:

$$(POC(0) + \Delta POC(0)) \times a_{is} = POC(0) \times a_{ns} + \Delta POC(0) \times a_{ic} \quad (1)$$

where $\Delta POC(0)$ is the increase in POC concentration during the incubation (μg C/liter per incubation). The increase in particulate organic carbon can be calculated by rearrangement of Eq. (1):

$$\Delta POC(0) = \frac{(a_{is} - a_{ns})}{(a_{ic} - a_{is})} \times POC(0) \quad (2)$$

The production rate (μg C/liter per hr, usually referred to as ρc; Slawyk et al., 1977) can be obtained by division of Eq. (2) by t (hr):

$$\text{Production rate } (\rho_c(0)) = \frac{\Delta POC(0)}{t} = \frac{(a_{is} - a_{ns})}{(a_{ic} - a_{is})} \times \frac{POC(0)}{t} \quad (3)$$

T. Hama et al. (1983) proposed another way to calculate $\Delta POC(t)$ (increase in POC concentration during the incubation) by using the concentration of POC at the end of the incubation $(POC(t)$, μg C/liter). The following equation shows the balance of ^{13}C:

$$POC(t) \times a_{is} = (POC(t) - \Delta POC(t)) \times a_{ns} + \Delta POC(t) \times a_{ic} \quad (4)$$

Thus, the increase in POC and production rate per hour can be obtained by Eqs. (5) and (6), respectively:

$$\Delta POC(t) = \frac{(a_{is} - a_{ns})}{(a_{ic} - a_{ns})} \times POC(t) \quad (5)$$

$$\text{Production rate } (\rho_c(t)) = \frac{\Delta POC(t)}{t} = \frac{(a_{is} - a_{ns})}{(a_{ic} - a_{ns})} \times \frac{POC(t)}{t} \quad (6)$$

The adequacy of these two equations (3 and 6) to obtain the photosynthetic rate has been discussed repeatedly including the calculation of uptake rate of nitrogen by the ^{15}N method (Collos and Slawyk, 1985; Dugdale and Wilkerson, 1986; Slawyk et al., 1988). At the present time, Eq. (6) is preferred, because the ^{13}C atomic % and the concentration of $POC(t)$ can be measured from the same sample by mass analysis (Otsuki et al., 1983; Dugdale and Wilkerson, 1986; Slawyk et al., 1988; Sakamoto, 1989; Takahashi et al., 1990).

To use Eq. (3), $POC(0)$ must be measured from another filtered sample which is usually obtained by filtration of the water sample at the start of the incubation. This may cause a more serious experimental error compared with the case when Eq. (6) is employed. Table I summarizes the results calculated from incubation experiments carried out at a subarctic sea (45°N, 165°E). Triplicate samples were used for the measurement of the photosynthetic rate at each depth. Although the variations of a_{is} and POC(t) are rather high, the production rate showed less variability because samples with a higher ^{13}C atomic % tended to have a lower POC(t). This result indicated that the variability of a_{is} and/or POC(t) could be due to the variability of nonphytoplankton organic carbon content; a higher nonphytoplankton organic carbon content increases POC(t) and decreases a_{is}, and vice versa.

The source(s) of the variability in the content of nonphytoplankton organic carbon remain uncertain. One possibility is the heterogeneous distribution of nonphytoplankton components (zooplankton, bacteria, and/or detrital substances) among incubation bottles when the sample water is poured into the incubation bottles. Possible contamination of organic compounds during incubation and analytical steps is another.

To calculate the production rate, these effects cannot be canceled out when Eq. (3) is used, due to the decrease in a_{is}; Eq. (1), (2), and (3) do not reflect the increase in POC in the incubation sample probably due to the variation of nonphytoplankton carbon. On the other hand, the variability in a_{is} and POC(t) due to nonphytoplankton carbon can be canceled out when Eq. (6) is used. The ^{13}C content at the end of the incubation, POC(t) $\times a_{is}$ in Eq. (4), can be written as

$$POC(t) \times a_{is} = POC(t)_{pp} \times a_{pp} + POC(t)_{np} \times a_{np} \qquad (7)$$

where POC(t)$_{pp}$ is particulate organic carbon of phytoplankton at the end of incubation (μg C/liter), POC(t)$_{np}$ is particulate organic carbon of nonphytoplankton at the end of incubation (μg C/liter), a_{pp} is ^{13}C atomic % of phytoplankton carbon in the incubated sample, and a_{np} is ^{13}C atomic % of nonphytoplankton carbon in the incubated sample.

The balance of ^{13}C content can be shown as follows, with special reference to phytoplankton and nonphytoplankton carbon:

$$POC(t)_{pp} \times a_{pp} + POC(t)_{np} \times a_{np} = (POC(t)_{pp} + POC(t)_{np} - \Delta POC(t)) \times$$
$$a_{ns} + \Delta POC(t) \times a_{ic} \qquad (8)$$

Increase in organic carbon, $\Delta POC(t)$, is obtained by the following equation:

$$\Delta POC(t) = \frac{(a_{pp} - a_{ns})}{(a_{ic} - a_{ns})} \times POC(t)_{pp} + \frac{(a_{np} - a_{ns})}{(a_{ic} - a_{ns})} \times POC(t)_{np} \qquad (9)$$

Considering that the ^{13}C atomic % of nonphytoplankton organic carbon can show little increase during the incubation, and/or the contaminated organic carbon during incubation or analytical steps can have natural ¹³C abundance, $(a_{np} - a_{ns})$ in Eq. (9) should be zero. Consequently, use of Eq. (5) can cancel out the possible effect of nonphytoplankton carbon:

$$\Delta POC(t) = \frac{(a_{is} - a_{ns})}{(a_{ic} - a_{ns})} \times POC(t) = \frac{(a_{pp} - a_{ns})}{(a_{ic} - a_{ns})} \times POC(t)_{pp} \quad (10)$$

Table I compares $\Delta POC(0)$ calculated from Eq. (2) and $\Delta POC(t)$ calculated from Eq. (5). The coefficient of variation of $\Delta POC(t)$ ranged from 3.6 to 6.5%, and were smaller than the variability of $\Delta POC(0)$ ranging from 0 to 13.7%. These results could reflect the cancellation of the effect of nonphytoplankton carbon on productivity calculation using Eq. (5).

However, it is possible that a_{np} of nonphytoplankton microorganisms such as bacteria and zooplankton, increases during the incubation period, due to the incorporation of phytoplankton carbon as cellular organic constituents of such heterotrophic microorganisms; bacterial uptake of the excreted organic carbon and/or grazing of phytoplankton by zooplankton can be expected. In this case, calculated $\Delta POC(t)$ reflects not only the photosynthetic production rate but also the carbon flow from the phytoplankton to the heterotrophic microorganisms.

Collos and Slawyk (1985) also recommended Eq. (6) for calculating the production rate, from the point of view of the uptake of unlabeled compounds by phytoplankton during the experiment, such as urea. The dilution of isotopic ratio of the incubated sample due to the uptake of unlabeled compounds can be canceled out by the increase in the particulate organic carbon ($POC(t)$) by Eq. (6), whereas it cannot be canceled by Eq. (3); use of $POC(0)$ and decreased a_{is} resulted in underestimation of the production rate.

The use of Eq. (6) requires simultaneous measurements of the isotopic ratio and the carbon concentration using the same sample. For this, instrumental improvement is a prerequisite, as will be discussed presently.

2.1.2. Calculation of Specific Production Rate (Turnover Rate, Vc)

The tracer experiment using stable isotope can offer additional important information other than the production rate, i.e., the specific production rate (SPR; usually referred to as Vc by Slawyk et al., 1979). The SPR can be obtained from Eq. (3) and/or Eq. (6). Based on the POC(0), SPR(0) (μg C/μg C per hr) can be calculated as follows:

$$SPR(0) = \frac{(a_{is} - a_{ns})}{(a_{ic} - a_{is})} \times \frac{1}{t} \quad (11)$$

The SPR(t) based on the POC(t), on the other hand, is estimated by:

$$SPR(t) = \frac{(a_{is} - a_{ns})}{(a_{ic} - a_{ns})} \times \frac{1}{t} \quad (12)$$

Table I. ¹³C Atomic % (a_{ns}) and Concentration of POC(0) of Nonincubated Sample, ¹³C Atomic % (a_{is}) and Concentration of POC(t) of Incubated Sample, and the Calculated Production Rate According to Eq. (2) (Δ POC(0)) and Eq. (5) (Δ POC(t))[a]

Depth	a_{ns} (at. %)	POC(0) (μg C/liter)	a_{is} (at. %)	POC(t) (μg C/liter)	Δ POC(0)				Δ POC(t)			
					Rate	Mean (μg C/liter per day)	S.D.	%	Rate	Mean (μg C/liter per day)	S.D.	%
0 m												
Nonincubated	1.083	168										
Incubated No. 1			1.988	155	16.4				15.4			
No. 2			1.750	186	11.8	14.5	1.98	13.7	13.6	14.4	0.748	5.2
No. 3			1.938	152	15.4				14.2			
10 m												
Nonincubated	1.084	166										
Incubated No. 1			1.710	166	13.4				12.3			
No. 2			1.675	168	12.6	12.4	0.817	6.6	11.8	11.8	0.421	3.6
No. 3			1.623	176	11.4				11.3			
20 m												
Nonincubated	1.084	142										
Incubated No. 1			1.535	148	8.08				7.98			
No. 2			1.555	130	8.46	8.17	0.211	2.6	7.32	7.86	0.390	5.0
No. 3			1.529	155	7.97				8.25			

30 m										
Nonincubated	1.084	154								
Incubated No. 1	1.304	165	4.05				4.22			
No. 2	1.281	187	3.62	3.88	0.186	4.8	4.31	4.16	0.149	3.6
No. 3	1.299	158	3.96				3.96			
50 m										
Nonincubated	1.084	187								
Incubated No. 1	1.159	190	1.73				1.74			
No. 2	1.170	172	1.99	1.75	0.190	10.9	1.81	1.84	0.095	5.2
No. 3	1.150	243	1.52				1.97			
75 m										
Nonincubated	1.084	158								
Incubated No. 1	1.106	155	0.417				0.407			
No. 2	1.104	149	0.379	0.398	0.019	4.8	0.356	0.382	0.025	6.5
No. 3	—	—	—				—			
95 m										
Nonincubated	1.085	141								
Incubated No. 1	1.094	154	0.152				0.166			
No. 2	1.094	136	0.152	0.52	0	0	0.146	0.156	0.008	5.1
No. 3	1.094	145	0.152				0.157			

[a]An in situ incubation experiment was carried out at Station A' (45°N, 165°E) of the cruise (KH-91-3) of "Hakuho-maru" of the Ocean Research Institute, University of Tokyo. ^{13}C atomic % and concentration of POC were determined using ANCA MS (Europe Scientific).

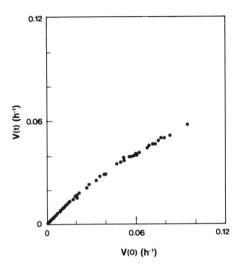

Figure 1. Relation between $V(0)$ and $V(t)$ for nitrate uptake obtained from Peru upwelling region at 15°S. (After Dugdale and Wilkerson, 1986.)

SPR(0) takes no account of the possible increase in POC during incubation, and the rate may result in an overestimation of average SPR during incubation, whereas SPR(t) leads to an underestimation, because this rate was obtained by the division by POC(t) which includes the newly taken up carbon during the incubation. Dugdale and Wilkerson (1986) compared the specific uptake rates of nitrate calculated from Eqs. (11) and (12) as shown in Fig. 1. The difference between SPR(0) and SPR(t) [these rates are shown as $V(0)$ and $V(t)$, respectively, in Fig. 1] is not significant at low rates. However, the discrepancy becomes more serious with the increasing uptake rate. Although SPR(0) may yield an overestimation of average SPR, it has usually been applied to estimate SPR (Collos and Slawyk, 1985; T. Hama *et al.*, 1988b; Sakamoto, 1989), mainly due to the fact that the carbon SPR determined by the ^{14}C method and/or chlorophyll SPR generally use the concentration of phytoplankton carbon and/or chlorophyll at the start of the incubation. Dugdale and Wilkerson (1986), on the other hand, proposed a mean value of SPR calculated from Eqs. (11) and (12) as a better estimate of SPR during incubation:

$$SPR(m) = \frac{(SPR(0) + SPR(t))}{2} \qquad (13)$$

One of the most important features of the SPR is the fact that the obtained rate is always affected by the nonphytoplankton organic carbon. Nonphytoplankton carbon is expected to have a ^{13}C abundance near the natural abundance even after the end of the incubation experiment and the measured a_{is} is consequently "diluted" by the nonphytoplankton carbon discussed before. The "dilution" effect increases in proportion to the decrease in the ratio of phytoplankton carbon to POC. The obtained SPR from the natural phytoplankton population, therefore, is not the "true" rate of phytoplankton cellular carbon. The proportion of phytoplankton carbon to POC varies in time, depth, and space, so the comparison of SPR with different season, different station, and/or different depth may not be adequate to discuss the phytoplankton activity. The effect of nonphytoplankton carbon, however, does not affect the uptake rate of carbon per sample volume as mentioned earlier.

2.2. Calculation of Atomic % Excess (Time-Zero Blank or Nonenriched Blank)

The ¹³C atomic % of a control sample (a_{ns}) must be measured to obtain the atomic % excess of an incubated sample ($a_{is} - a_{ns}$) in Eqs. (3) and (6). Fisher *et al.* (1979) pointed out that the time-zero blank is necessary due to chemical adsorption, CO_2 exchange between particulate material and dissolved inorganic carbon in the sample, and enriched particulate contamination in the isotope stock solutions. Sakamoto (1989) and Takahashi *et al.* (1990) analyzed the time-zero sample which was obtained by filtration of the incubated sample immediately after the incubation was started. T. Hama *et al.* (1983), however, used the ¹³C atomic % of a natural (nonincubated) sample instead of a time-zero sample, chiefly for two main reasons: (1) the possible adsorption of ¹³C to particulate material can be neglected by the use of a dark bottle; and (2) the measured ¹³C atomic % of nonincubated and time-zero samples did not show a significant difference. [This was equally suggested by Satoh *et al.* (1985).] Slawyk *et al.* (1977, 1979) also indicated that the use of a nonincubated sample has an insignificant effect on the productivity measurement. ¹⁵N abundance obtained from a nonincubated sample has usually also been applied in the ¹⁵N method, according to Dugdale and Wilkerson (1986); they used natural abundance of ¹⁵N ($\langle F \rangle$), to calculate the atomic % excess of ¹⁵N.

The large bottle incubation, generally used for stable isotope tracer experiments, makes it particularly difficult to obtain a reliable time-zero sample, because the filtration of a large-volume sample requires a relatively long time. Thus, the use of ¹³C atomic % of a nonincubated sample instead of a time-zero sample to calculate ¹³C atomic % excess can be practically acceptable for the calculation of the photosynthetic rate.

2.3. Correction of Dark Uptake

The correction of dark uptake has usually been applied to obtain the photosynthetic production rate (T. Hama *et al.*, 1983; Sakamoto *et al.*, 1984; Miyazaki *et al.*, 1987; Takahashi *et al.*, 1990; J. Hama and Handa, 1992d; Shiomoto and Matsumura, 1992). However, the differences between a_{ns} and a_{is} of the dark bottle are usually minimal, and sometimes it is virtually impossible to calculate the dark carbon uptake rate. In lacustrine environments, Sakamoto *et al.* (1984) reported that the dark uptake rate accounted for 1–2% of the light bottle near the surface layer and 5–9% at the deeper layer of Lake Konstanz.

Prakash *et al.* (1991) summarized the dark carbon uptake in oceanic waters which were determined by the ^{14}C tracer method and reported that the proportion of dark carbon uptake to light uptake showed a definite areal variability and it accounted for from 10 to 50% in the subtropical gyre and at high southern latitudes. A relatively high contribution of dark carbon uptake was also shown by Gomes *et al.* (1992) in the northeastern Indian Ocean by the ^{14}C method. These observations obtained by the ^{14}C method strongly suggest the necessity of measuring the dark carbon uptake rate.

To measure photosynthetic products, large incubation bottles (up to 20 liters) have been used (T. Hama *et al.*, 1987, 1990; T. Hama, 1988; J. Hama and N. Handa, 1992a,b,c) and a subsample (500 to 1000 ml) from the large bottle was used for determination of total carbon uptake rate. In these cases, dark bottles were not used and thus the rate was not corrected by dark uptake rate. Measurement of dark uptake with a small bottle (500 to 1000 ml) instead of the large one may be very practical. Further, comparison of product composition by dark fixation and photosynthesis may be valuable.

2.4. Discrimination of [13]C

It is well known that phytoplankton prefer ^{12}C to [13]C (and ^{14}C), and phytoplankton carbon is generally depleted in ^{13}C compared with the P. D. belemnite standard ranging from -20 to $-30‰$ of δ ^{13}C value (e.g., Rau *et al.*, 1982; Takahashi *et al.*, 1991). Fisher *et al.* (1979), T. Hama *et al.* (1983), and Satoh *et al.* (1985) proposed a correction for isotope discrimination. According to their suggestion, the correction can be applied to Eq. (3) or (6) by multiplying the factor of 1.02 (Fisher *et al.*, 1979) or 1.025 (T. Hama *et al.*, 1983; Satoh *et al.*, 1985). In practice, however, this correction usually has not been applied (Slawyk *et al.*, 1979; Kanda *et al.*, 1985a,b; T. Hama, 1988; Sakamoto, 1989; J. Hama and Handa, 1992a,b,c,d), because this correction has little significant effect on the uptake rate compared with the ^{14}C tracer method (factor of 1.05 or 1.06 has usually been applied). Further, because the discrimination of carbon by phytoplankton varies depending on the phytoplankton species (Falkowski, 1991) and phytoplankton growth stage (Takahashi *et al.*, 1991), the choice of a fixed factor can sometimes result in inaccuracies.

2.5. Enrichment Effect

The addition of the tracer has little effect on the total concentration of inorganic carbon in the ^{14}C method. In the case of the ^{13}C method, on the contrary, higher enrichment of substrate (5–15% in a_{ic}) than in the ^{14}C method has usually been applied (e.g., T. Hama *et al.*, 1983; Kanda *et al.*, 1985a; Miyazaki *et al.*, 19851a,b; J. Hama and Handa, 1992a,b,c,d), to achieve an adequate increase in the isotopic ratio of particulate carbon at the end of incubation (a_{is}), which means that the increase in the concentration of dissolved inorganic carbon (about 105–115% of original concentration) is not avoidable. Although the addition of ^{15}N tracer such as nitrate and ammonium to the incubation sample can perturb the nitrogen metabolism in nitrogen-limited environments (e.g., Dugdale and Goering, 1967; Dugdale and Wilkerson, 1986), the addition of ^{13}C tracer is considered to have little effect on the uptake rate, because dissolved inorganic carbon scarcely limits phytoplankton photosynthesis (Parsons *et al.*, 1984) in marine environments.

T. Hama *et al.* (1983) measured the photosynthetic rate using various concentrations of inorganic carbon (26.1 to 29.4 μg C/liter) and obtained good agreement among differential enrichment of ^{13}C tracer. Their result clearly shows that enrichment of inorganic carbon did not have any significant effect on the photosynthetic rate in oceanic environments, at least in this range. This conclusion was also ascertained by Satoh *et al.* (1985) from culture experiments of the marine diatom *Skeletonema costatum*.

Meanwhile, Miyazaki *et al.* (1985a) examined the enrichment effect of inorganic carbon in lake water, where the effect can be more serious because the concentration of inorganic carbon is generally lower in lake waters compared with oceanic waters. The production rates determined for the range from 5.25 to 6.00 mg C/liter (*in situ* concentration of dissolved inorganic carbon was 5.00 mg C/liter) were very similar. However, in surface water of a hypertrophic lake in summer, the concentration of dissolved inorganic carbon is sometimes almost exhausted. The addition of ^{13}C tracer to the sample water in this case may result in perturbation of the photosynthetic rate.

Generally speaking, enrichment of the concentration of dissolved inorganic carbon has little effect on the photosynthetic rate, unlike the case of ^{15}N tracer addition.

2.6. Instrument

A mass spectrometer has generally been used for the determination of isotopic ratio and concentration of organic carbon. Only limited studies have used infrared absorption spectrometry (Satoh *et al.*, 1985).

The first attempt to determine the photosynthetic production rate by ^{13}C tracer used a rather complicated system (Slawyk *et al.*, 1977, 1979). Further, the mass spectrometer which was used in their study can measure only the isotopic ratio of carbon. Moreover, the concentration of organic carbon of an incubated sample could not be simultaneously determined. Thus, they applied Eq. (3) to calculate the photosynthetic rate, but it might be inadequate to obtain the production rate as discussed before.

Systems combining a mass spectrometer with an automated elemental analyzer were first introduced in ^{15}N tracer studies (Barsdate and Dugdale, 1965; Preston and Owens, 1983; Barrie and Workman, 1984). On the other hand, Otsuki *et al.* (1983), Preston and Owens (1985), and Slawyk *et al.* (1988) applied the combined systems for simultaneous determination of the ^{13}C ratio and C content of incubated samples. Thus, Eq. (6) is applicable for the calculation of photosynthetic production rate.

Figure 2 is a schematic diagram of a mass spectrometer combined with an elemental analyzer (ANCA MASS, Europe Scientific). The filter sample in a tin capsule is transferred to a combustion tube, and combustion products (CO_2, N_2, NO_x, and H_2O) pass through the reduction tube where excess O_2, which is used for combustion of organic matter, is trapped, and NO_x is reduced to N_2. These gases are swept through a purification chromatographic column by helium carrier gas, and carried to the mass spectrometer. The signals from the triple collector of the mass spectrometer are integrated to calculate both the atomic % of [13]C (and ^{15}N) and further concentration of organic carbon (and nitrogen). The "bench-top" units make on-board measurements possible during a cruise (Owens, 1988).

Infrared absorption spectrometry with combustion furnace has also been applied to the measurement of primary productivity of phytoplankton (Satoh *et al.*, 1985). This kind of system was initially used for the determination of ^{13}C abundance of higher plant material and/or exhaled breath (Kokubun and Sasaki, 1979; Yanagisawa and Kumazawa, 1982). Satoh *et al.* (1985) examined the analytical error of the infrared ^{13}C analyzer (JASCO, EX-130) using the cultured

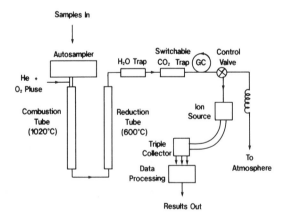

Figure 2. Schematic of a commercially available combined system of elemental analyzer and mass spectrometer (ANCA MS, Europe Scientific).

marine phytoplankton *Skeletonema costatum* and confirmed the system's accuracy. They recommended that more than 25 μg C be used to ensure reliable determination of the ¹³C ratio by the infrared analyzer. This limit is considerably higher than that recommended for mass spectrometers (10 μg C for ANCA MASS). However, considering that the operation and maintenance of an infrared analyzer is easier than for a mass spectrometer and the fact that it can measure both the ¹³C atomic % and carbon concentration, the infrared analyzer can be used effectively to measure the photosynthetic rate of phytoplankton, particularly for cultured phytoplankton and/or eutrophic areas, where a relatively large amount of phytoplankton can be collected.

2.7. Sample Volume

In the ¹⁴C method, its high sensitivity in the detection of radioactivity makes it possible to decrease the sample volume to less than 100 ml even in oligotrophic waters. With the ¹³C tracer method, however, more water sample volume is needed than with the ¹⁴C method. The sample volume used for the incubation experiment depends on the detection limit of the concentration and the isotopic ratio of carbon by the analytical instrument. Organic carbon greater than 10 μg C is necessary for a commercially available mass spectrometer with an elemental analyzer (ANCA MASS). This implies that 200 ml of sample water is adequate for measurement even in oligotrophic ocean, where we assume that the concentration of particulate organic carbon is about 50 μg C/liter. However, at present, many workers use a water sample volume of 500 to 1000 ml in oligotrophic waters to ensure reliability of the measurements.

Larger sample volume is one of the disadvantages of the ¹³C method relative to the ¹⁴C method. The former requires a 5-liter for the determination of photosynthetic production rate in oligotrophic waters using four incubation bottles (three for light and one for dark bottle) including wash of the incubation bottle. Further, the incubator must be much larger than the one used for the ¹⁴C method, and the high cost of the ¹³C tracer in order to increase the ¹³C atomic % in the incubation bottle, particularly in oceanic water, is a drawback. The use of the large bottle in the ¹³C method, on the oher hand, serves to minimize the possible bottle confinement effect during incubation.

2.8. Comparison with ¹⁴C Method

The ¹⁴C tracer technique has been routinely applied to the determination of the photosynthetic rate in aquatic environments. The compatibility of the ¹³C and ¹⁴C methods has, thus, been an issue of great interest, and the experiments have been carried out using cultured phytoplankton (Slawyk *et al.*, 1977, 1979; Satoh *et al.*, 1985) and natural phytoplankton population (T. Hama *et al.*, 1983; Sakamoto *et al.*, 1984; Slawyk *et al.*, 1984). Slawyk *et al.* (1977, 1979) first compared the two methods using batch cultures of *Fragilaria pinnata, Skele-tonema costatum,* and *Chlamydomonas* sp. They obtained the following relation-ship between ^{14}C and ^{13}C uptake rate (Slawyk *et al.,* 1979):

$$\rho^{14}C = 1.119p^{13}C + 0.162 \ (r = 0.911) \tag{14}$$

where $\rho^{14}C$ and $\rho^{13}C$ are the uptake rates determined by the ^{14}C and ^{13}C meth-ods, respectively. Although the rates determined by the ^{14}C method are rather higher than those obtained with the ^{13}C method, the difference can be admittable in the tracer study (Slawyk *et al.* 1979).

 T. Hama *et al.* (1983) determined the production rate of a natural marine phytoplankton population by both ^{13}C and ^{14}C methods. They used glass fiber filters (Whatman GF/F) of different diameters to collect the particulate matter at the end of incubation experiments (47 mm for ^{13}C method and 25 mm for ^{14}C method). To correct for the possible difference in the collection efficiency of particles, a comparison was made of the rates per unit of chlorophyll *w,* which was determined with the same filters used to collect particulate matter in the incubation bottles (Table II). These rates were also corrected using the discrimi-nation factors of ^{13}C (1.025) and ^{14}C (1.05). The results obtained showed good agreement between the ^{13}C and ^{14}C methods. However, considerable differences

Table II. Comparison of Photosynthetic Rates Determined by the ^{13}C and ^{14}C Methods[a]

Sample	Relative light intensity (%)	^{14}C (μg C/μg Chl *w* per hr)[a]	^{13}C
Sta. A13 10 m	4	2.20	2.17
	20	10.6	10.9
	100	19.6	19.2
70 m	4	3.95	3.82
	20	8.75	8.91
	100	1.30	1.56
Sta. B17 10 m	4	2.43	2.47
	20	10.2	9.75
	100	13.8	13.8
50 m	4	3.78	3.61
	20	4.90	5.59
	100	0.122	0.250

[a]Rates were determined by simulated *in situ* incubation experiments. After T. Hama *et al.* (1983).

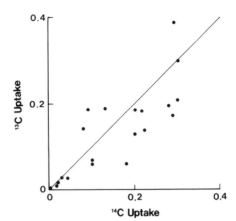

Figure 3. Comparison of carbon uptake rate by ^{13}C and ^{14}C tracer methods obtained from the Indian sector of the Antarctic Ocean. Line shows the ideal 1:1 relationship. Units in mg C/m³ per hr. (After Slawyk *et al.*, 1984.)

were noted with the lowest uptake-rate samples; the rate determined by the ^{13}C method was much higher than that by the ^{14}C method.

Slawyk *et al.* (1984) compared the photosynthetic uptake rates of inorganic carbon by oceanic phytoplankton population measured using the ^{13}C and ^{14}C methods. Figure 3 shows the portion of their results obtained for the Antarctic Ocean. Although the bottle volume used for incubation experiments was very different for the [13]C (10 liters) and [14]C (250 ml) methods, general agreement was obtained. However, there was a rather variable relation between the ^{13}C and ^{14}C values measured at equatorial Atlantic and coastal waters. The same investigators suggested that regarding the incubation volume effect, the estimation of particulate organic carbon in the ^{13}C method could affect compatibility of the ^{13}C and ^{14}C methods.

Joint studies comparing the ^{13}C and [14]C (and O_2) methods have been conducted (Sakamoto *et al.*, 1984). Table III shows the production rates at each depth of Lake Konstanz; two ^{13}C and three ^{14}C determinations were carried out for each depth. There was a significant variation among the different methods at the surface water, whereas the rates at subsurface layers were relatively compatible. It is worth noting that these results showed significant variation even in the methods which used the same tracer, rather than simply between the ^{14}C and ^{13}C methods. The variation could be traced mainly to the correction of dark uptake and discrimination of tracer, as well as the different filter pore sizes (Sakamoto *et al.*, 1984).

As summarized here, general compatibility of the ^{13}C and ^{14}C methods has been reported. However, it is to be noted that many experimental designs seem inadequate for comparing the ^{13}C and ^{14}C methods. For example, the different sizes of the incubation bottles used for two methods (up to 40-fold difference)

Table III. Chlorophyll Specific Production Rate (μg C/μg Chl w per hr or μg O$_2$/μg Chl w per hr) Determined by ^{14}C, ^{13}C, and O$_2$ Methods at Lake Konstanz[a]

Depth (m)	[14]C method (μg C/μg Chl w per hr)			[13]C method (μg C/μg Chl w per hr)		O$_2$ method (μg O$_2$/μg Chl w per hr) Tschumi	
	Tilzer	Gächter	Rai	Collos	Sakamoto	GP[b]	NP[c]
0	0.58	0.68	0.77	0.91	1.87	−1.22	−12.56
1	2.17	2.68	2.06	2.68	3.68	4.93	0.95
2	2.04	3.32	2.40	1.71	2.03	7.67	5.09
3	1.94	2.98	—	2.02	—	10.20	7.02
5	1.78	2.84	—	2.68	1.42	7.75	5.27
8	1.24	2.83	—	1.24	0.83	3.18	−0.66
10	0.68	0.79	—	—	—	0.01	−4.16
15	0.18	0.36	0.34	0.43	0.21	−5.39	−6.89

[a]Results were determined by *in situ* incubation experiments. After Sakamoto *et al.* (1984).
[b]Gross production   [c]Net production

could often result in the variation of measured production rate (Gieskes *et al.*, 1979). The results obtained by such experiments, thus, cannot specify the factor(s) which caused the possible discrepancy between the rates measured by two methods: whether the basic differences at the level of the isotopic analysis between ^{13}C and [14]C (as discussed in Collos and Slawyk, 1985) or the experimental protocol of the incubation and filtration procedures such as differences in the incubation bottle and filter. From these points of view, the results obtained by T. Hama *et al.* (1983) and Satoh *et al.* (1985) suggest the compatibility of both methods: they attempted to minimize the difference between the incubation and analytical protocols for the ^{13}C and ^{14}C methods. Further examination including bottle and filter size, of course, is desirable.

2.9. Other Methodological Problems

Other methodological problems associated with the bottle incubation technique such as bottle confinement effect, incubation bottle material, incubation length, contamination of trace metal, and sample fixation at the end of incubation are generally common to both the ^{13}C and ^{14}C methods. Due to limited space, these problems are not discussed here, but the literature dealing with the ^{14}C method offers significant information on the ^{13}C methodology (e.g., Venrick *et al.*, 1977; Gieskes *et al.*, 1979; Peterson, 1980; Fitzwater *et al.*, 1982; Leftley *et al.*, 1983).

3. Results of ¹³C Tracer Method

3.1. Background

The ¹³C tracer method has been applied both to cultured phytoplankton and to natural phytoplankton populations including oceanic and lake environments, to measure the photosynthetic rates. The literature is not as abundant as that for the ¹⁴C method, but studies using the ¹³C method have increased in number lately, particularly in Japan where the use of ¹⁴C has been very restricted under field conditions. Here we briefly summarize the literature on the use of the ¹³C method.

3.2. Application Results

3.2.1. Culture Experiments

The first examination of the ¹³C method to estimate photosynthetic rate, used cultured phytoplankton such as *Fragilaria pinnata, Skeletonema costatum,* and *Chlamydomonas* sp., and the applicability of the ¹³C method was confirmed (Slawyk *et al.,* 1977, 1979). The application of infrared absorption spectrometry was examined by Satoh *et al.* (1985), using the cultured marine diatom *Skeletonema costatum.*

3.2.2. Oceanic Waters

Slawyk (1979) applied the ¹³C method to measure the primary productivity of natural phytoplankton population along the Indian sector (66°30′E) of the Antarctic Ocean, and Collos and Slawyk (1986) reported more detailed measurements of the same area. An *in situ* incubation using the ¹³C method was carried out by T. Hama *et al.* (1983), and the vertical profiles of primary productivity were determined in three different trophic states around Japan. Subsequently, the primary productivity of various oceanic environments has been determined in the Pacific Ocean (Kanda *et al.,* 1985a), Atlantic Ocean (Slawyk *et al.,* 1984), Antarctic Ocean (Satoh and Watanabe, 1988; Satoh *et al.,* 1991), Solomon Sea (Satoh *et al.,* 1992), the regional upwelling water around the Izu Islands, Japan (Kanda *et al.,* 1985b; T. Hama, 1988, 1991), the Kuroshio warm-core ring (T. Hama, 1992), the cold water mass (Shiomoto and Matsumura, 1992), and coastal areas (T. Hama and Honjyo, 1987; J. Hama and Handa, 1992d).

3.2.3. Lake Waters

Joint field experiments for comparisons of measurements of photosynthetic production were carried out in Lake Konstanz (Sakamoto *et al.,* 1984). Other studies using the ^{13}C method have been carried out in Japanese lakes. Productivity measurements of hypertrophic lakes (Lake Kasumigaura and Lake Suwa) were conducted repeatedly (Takamura *et al.*, 1985, 1986, 1987a,b; Takamura and Yasuno, 1988; Sakamoto, 1989; Takamura and Aizaki, 1991). The ^{13}C method was also applied to eutrophic lake (Miyazaki *et al.*, 1985a,b, 1987; Miyazaki and Ichimura, 1986), oligotrophic lake (Hama *et al.*, 1988a, 1990, 1992), monomictic lake (Takahashi *et al.*, 1990), and lagoon (Satoh *et al.*, 1989a,b).

4. Combination of ^{13}C Tracer Technique with Other Methods

4.1. Combination with ^{15}N Tracer Method

4.1.1. Background

Simultaneous measurement of carbon and nitrogen uptake rate with ^{13}C and ^{15}N tracer methods is a key reason for using the ^{13}C method rather than the ^{14}C method. Slawyk *et al.* (1977, 1979) and Collos and Slawyk (1979) were the first to introduce dual stable isotope experiments for carbon and nitrogen metabolism of marine phytoplankton with favorable results. From an instrumental standpoint, however, they divided the filter sample into two portions: one for the analysis of the isotopic ratio of particulate organic carbon and another for the isotopic ratio of particulate organic nitrogen. The simultaneous measurement of the isotopic ratios of carbon and nitrogen, and the concentration of particulate organic carbon and nitrogen from the same sample was successfully introduced by Otsuki *et al.* (1983).

One of the most serious problems with the simultaneous measurement of the isotopic ratio of carbon and nitrogen is the possible imperfect combustion of organic carbon. If ^{13}CO is produced through imperfect combustion of organic carbon, the ^{15}N contents are overestimated, because the mass of ^{13}CO and $^{14}N^{15}N$ are the same. Miyazaki *et al.* (1985a) examined the possible effect of the imperfect combustion, using a ^{13}C-labeled natural phytoplankton population. The results indicated that ^{13}CO (m/z 29) was produced in the incubated sample with ^{13}C probably due to the imperfect combustion, and this caused the increase in the measured ^{15}N abundance, which was calculated using the intensity of m/z 28($^{14}N^{14}N$) and 29($^{14}N^{15}N$). The variation of ^{15}N atomic % probably due to the ^{13}CO, however, accounted for less than 1% of the nitrogen uptake rate determined using the same water sample. Thus, the imperfect combustion appeared to have a negligible effect on the measurement of nitrogen uptake rate. One must recall, however, that a detailed examination of analytical conditions such as temperature of combustion furnace and oxygen flow rate at the time of combustion is needed for simultaneous measurement of the isotopic ratios of carbon and nitrogen. The use of a tin capsule in the combustion phase can be one means of avoiding imperfect combustion.

Another problem in the simultaneous measurement of the uptake rate of carbon and nitrogen is the effect of inorganic nitrogen addition on the carbon uptake rate. The results cannot be generalized as will be discussed later, and the effect of nitrogen addition on the carbon uptake rate is a matter of controversy. Thus, care must be taken when one interprets the results of the dual tracer method.

The earlier mentioned improvements in equipment have facilitated the simultaneous measurement of the isotopic ratio of carbon and nitrogen in addition to the amount of organic carbon and nitrogen. The dual tracer technique will be able to furnish significant information on the relationship between carbon and nitrogen uptake in primary production processes (Slawyk *et al.*, 1977, 1979; Miyazaki *et al.*, 1985a,b; Kanda *et al.*, 1985a,b; Takamura *et al.*, 1987a).

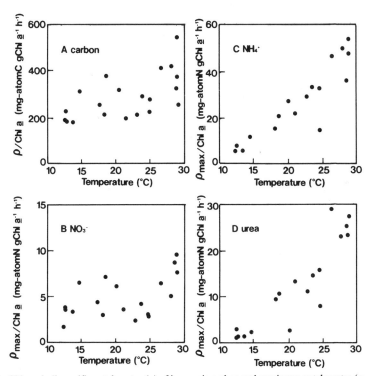

Figure 4. Chlorophyll specific uptake rates (ρ) of inorganic carbon and maximum uptake rates (ρ_{max}) of nitrate, ammonium, and urea as a function of ambient water temperature in the Pacific Ocean. (After Kanda *et al.*, 1985a.)

4.1.2. Application Results

4.1.2a. Regional Variability. Regional variability of carbon and nitrogen assimilation in the Pacific Ocean was studied by Kanda *et al.* (1985a). They applied the ^{13}C and ^{15}N dual tracer method to measure the uptake rates of carbon and nitrogenous nutrients (ammonium, nitrate, and urea) by phytoplankton from the tropical to subarctic Pacific Ocean. Figure 4 shows the relation between the ambient water temperature and the uptake rate (for C) or maximum uptake rate (for N) per unit chlorophyll *w*. The relation of water temperature and uptake or maximum uptake rates of carbon and nitrate agreed well, and the temperature dependence of these parameters was not so marked. Kanda *et al.* (1985a) suggested that the regional variability of these (maximum) uptake rates reflected light conditions in the habitat, whereas maximum uptake rates of ammonium and urea showed a distinct temperature dependence. The calculated turnover time of ammonium also depends on ambient water temperature, suggesting active regenerated production in tropical and subtropical areas.

Collos and Slawyk (1986) measured the carbon and nitrogen uptake rates along the Indian sector of the Antarctic Ocean. They found that the carbon uptake rate depended on photosynthetically available radiation (PAR) as suggested by Kanda *et al.* (1985a), while the nitrate uptake rate was inversely related to PAR. Consequently, the uptake ratio of carbon to nitrate showed a definite trend to increase with PAR both within and among stations.

4.1.2b. Vertical Variability. The vertical profiles of uptake of carbon and nitrogen (nitrate, nitrite, urea, and ammonium) by the dual tracer technique were first obtained by Slawyk (1979) in the Antarctic Ocean. Both uptake rates showed maxima at the surface or subsurface (50 or 25% of surface irradiance) and decreased with depth to the bottom of the euphotic zone. Light dependency of uptake was more pronounced for carbon, and consequently the C:N uptake ratio showed a decreasing trend with depth from 19–29 (wt/wt, calculated from atomic ratio by Slawyk, 1979) near the surface to 2.3 at 1% level of surface irradiance. Compositional C:N ratio of particulate matter, on the other hand, showed a slight vertical change from 7.1 to 7.7. Slawyk (1979) suggested that vertical movement of phytoplankton cells within the mixed layer resulted in a constant compositional ratio of particulate matter through the euphotic zone.

Miyazaki *et al.* (1985a) compared the vertical profiles of C:N ratio of particulate matter and uptake ratio in lake water. Uptake ratio varied from 3.2 to 13.1 (wt/wt) through the water column, showing a definite trend of decrease with water depth. Compositional ratios of particulate matter, however, were relatively constant through the water column (6.9 to 9.7, wt/wt), and the vertical trend was not clear. These relations between uptake and compositional C:N ratio were almost comparable in the oceanic environment (Slawyk, 1979). Such vertical changes in C:N uptake ratios can reflect the difference in the light saturation point of carbon and nitrogen. The nitrogen uptake generally saturates at lower light intensity than the carbon uptake (e.g., Kanda *et al.*, 1985a).

4.1.2c. Diel Variability. Diel variability of uptake of carbon and nitrogen was examined, in the bases of the natural phytoplankton population in lake water (Miyazaki *et al.*, 1987). Uptake of carbon and nitrogen exhibited a different diurnal variability. The carbon uptake rate showed a maximum around noon and no uptake was measured during the night. Like carbon uptake, ammonium uptake rate in the light bottle also showed a maximum at noon. In contrast to carbon uptake, ammonium uptake during nighttime was observed and it accounted for 28–47% of that in the daytime. Ammonium uptake also occurred in the dark bottle and the variability of ammonium uptake in the dark bottle was out of phase with that in the light bottle, showing maxima at dusk or early evening. Uptake of nitrate generally did not show any definite diel variability. From these results, Miyazaki *et al.* (1987) indicated that the uptake of nitrogen partly depended on the metabolism of reserved carbohydrate.

4.1.2d. Combination with Size Fractionation. Comparison of the C:N uptake ratio between natural phytoplankton populations of different sizes was examined in eutrophic Lake Suwa, Japan (Sakamoto, 1989). The uptake ratio of C:N, where only ammonium was used as the inorganic nitrogen source, was quite different between two fractions: the ratio obtained for the > 40-μm fraction, which was mainly composed of the colonial blue-green alga *Microcystis,* showed much higher values (6.5 to 135) than those for the < 40-μm fraction (2.6 to 10.1), comprising small green algae, monads, and diatoms. This reflected the difference in the specific nitrogen uptake rate between fractions of two different sizes; the specific carbon uptake rates were almost comparable. Sakamoto (1989) suggested that small phytoplankton can take up ammonium supplied from bottom sediments more efficiently than the blue-green alga, *Microcystis.* Meanwhile, Takamura *et al.* (1987a), who also examined the carbon and nitrogen uptake rates of *Microcystis* in Lake Kasumigaura, Japan, reported that the V_{max} value (maximum rate of nitrogen uptake) of *Microcystis* for ammonium was considerably higher than in other natural phytoplankton populations. Thus, active assimilation of ammonium by *Microcystis* in Lake Kasumigaura did not agree with the results obtained in Lake Suwa. Availability of other nitrogen forms such as nitrate could affect the nitrogen metabolism (Sakamoto, 1989).

The combination of the dual tracer method with size fractionation makes it possible to study not only the carbon and nitrogen metabolism but also the competition among different phytoplankton species for nutrient utilization.

4.1.2e. Effect of Nitrogen Supply on Carbon Uptake. The response of carbon uptake to a sudden nutrient increase can be an important phenomenon to assess the dynamics of primary productivity in natural environments. Collos and Slawyk (1979) studied the response of carbon uptake to the addition of

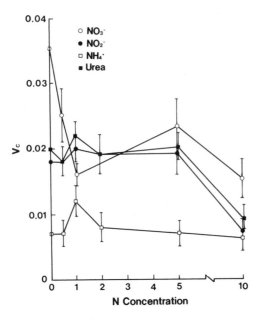

Figure 5. Carbon uptake rate by *Skeletonema costatum* in response to increasing dissolved nitrogen concentrations. Units: V_c in hr^{-1}; nitrogen concentration in μM. (After Collos and Slawyk, 1979.)

four different nitrogen compounds (nitrate, nitrite, ammonium, and urea), using nitrogen-limited culture of the marine diatom *Skeletonema costatum*. The carbon uptake rate decreased following the addition of nitrogen compounds and the most serious inhibition was observed after the addition of nitrate (Fig. 5). This decrease in carbon uptake rate generally agreed with other studies which used ^{14}C tracer (e.g., Lean *et al.*, 1982; Turpin, 1983) and indicated that energy was reallocated to uptake of limiting nutrients (nitrogen in this case) at the expense of carbon uptake. This suppression of carbon uptake, however, is considered to be a relatively short-term phenomenon.

On the contrary, Miyazaki *et al.* (1985a) and Takamura *et al.* (1987a) observed no effect of the addition of inorganic nitrogen to the natural freshwater phytoplankton population, using ^{13}C and ^{15}N tracer. Thus, the temporal effect of nutrient addition to photoassimilation of inorganic carbon is still a matter of controversy.

These studies can be important because an episodic input of nutrients to the ocean surface layer has recently been recognized as a significant phenomenon in the biogeochemical cycle in aquatic environments (Eppley and Renger, 1988; Goldman, 1988; Marra *et al.*, 1990). The dual tracer method is an excellent tool for elucidating the relation of carbon and nitrogen metabolism. Further, the use of "bench-top" mass spectrometry during a cruise makes possible the on-board study to elucidate the episodic changes in the dynamics of the microbial community and biogeochemical cycle in the ocean.

4.2. ¹³C-GC-MS Method

4.2.1. Background

The composition of photosynthetic products varies with environmental factors such as water temperature, nutrient availability, and light condition, as well as the physiological state of algae constituting the phytoplankton population. Knowledge of photosynthetic products thus makes it possible to assess the physiological state of phytoplankton population and the environmental factor(s) which limit phytoplankton growth (Morris, 1981).

Fractionation of photosynthetic products in the natural phytoplankton population was first applied by Olive and Morrison (1967). The fractionation procedure was based on extraction with solvents such as chloroform–methanol and trichloroacetic acid. Photosynthetic products could be fractionated into chloroform (lipid), methanol (low-molecular-weight metabolites), trichloroacetic acid (carbohydrate and nucleic acid), and residual (protein) fraction. The relations between composition of photosynthetic products and physiological state and/or environmental factors of phytoplankton have been elucidated (e.g., Morris, 1981; Barlow, 1982; T. Hama and Handa, 1987). Fractionation by this method, however, has some drawbacks such as incomplete separation of proteins from other organic matter (Knopka and Schnur, 1980; T. Hama and Handa, 1987) and the variation of extraction efficiency of polysaccharide with trichloroacetic acid among species (Hitchcock, 1983). Further, this method cannot offer detailed information on the composition of photosynthetic products. For example, Smith and Morris (1980a,b) demonstrated the extremely high contribution of lipid material to photosynthetic products in the Antarctic Ocean. However, they could not determine whether such high lipid production was due to the enhanced production of storage material or membrane lipids. Thus, more detailed information on photosynthetically produced material is necessary to assess the relation between photosynthetic products and environmental factors.

Gas chromatography (GC) separates organic constituents into each organic molecule and allows determination of the molecular weight of an organic molecule when the method is combined with mass spectrometry (MS). When the ¹³C (¹⁵N) tracer method is combined with GC-MS, this technique can determine the ¹³C (¹⁵N) atomic % of organic molecules. The application of GC-MS to estimate the ¹³C atomic % of organic molecules was first done in the field of biomedical science (Gordon and Frigerio, 1972; Summons et al., 1974).

The estimation of ¹³C atomic % in the carbon skeleton of each organic molecule was based on the increases in relative intensity of isotopic peaks in proportion to the ^{13}C atomic %. Van den Heuvel *et al.* (1970) introduced a method to estimate the isotope content of certain elements in molecules using the intensity of two peaks, i.e., those due to fragment ions with only a lighter isotope and ions with one heavy isotope. However, their method is only valid when the isotopes distribute randomly among molecules, and random distribution is not assured when incubation is brief. Kouchi (1982) introduced a new estimation method using a quasimolecular ion peak with no heavier isotopes and all isotopic peaks corresponding to each isotope species. This method can be used to obtain the isotopic ratio of a certain element in a molecule regardless of the pattern of isotope distribution in that molecule.

J. Hama and Handa (1986, 1992a) and T. Hama *et al.* (1987) applied the ^{13}C-GC-MS method to the primary production processes in aquatic environments. The accuracy of the estimation of ^{13}C atomic % from mass spectra was confirmed in monosaccharide (J. Hama and Handa, 1992a), amino acid (T. Hama *et al.*, 1987), and fatty acid (T. Hama, 1991), by analyzing the standards with several ^{13}C ratios.

Figure 6 shows the mass spectra of *N*-trifluoroacetyl *n*-butyl (TAB) esters of glycine with various ^{13}C atomic % produced by addition of standard (T. Hama *et al.*, 1987). The base peak for the TAB ester of glycine is the quasimolecular ion (*m/z*, 245); this *m/z* corresponds to the TAB ester of glycine (empirical formula: $C_8H_{12}O_3NF_3$) plus NH_4^+ (reagent gas for chemical ionization) with no heavy isotope. Isotopic peaks with *m/z* of 246 to 247 are observed in all of the sample and the relative intensity of these isotopic peaks to base peak increase in propor-

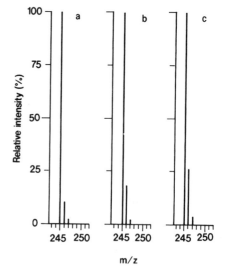

Figure 6. Mass spectra of *N*-trifluoroacetyl *n*-butyl (TAB) esters of glycine with various ^{13}C atomic % produced by addition of standards. *m/z*: mass-to-charge ratio; a: natural abundance; b: 4.89%; c: 8.10%. (After T. Hama *et al.*, 1987.)

**Table IV. Analysis of Glycine and Glutamic Acid Standards
with Various ¹³C Atomic %** [a]

| Expt. no. | Expected (at. %) | Measured | | | |
		Mean (at. %)	S.D.	%	n
		Glycine			
1	3.08	3.09	0.0047	0.15	3
2	4.89	4.96	0.0125	0.25	3
3	6.56	6.40	0.0544	0.85	3
4	8.10	8.03	0.0163	0.20	3
		Glutamic acid			
1	2.88	2.85	0.0573	2.0	3
2	4.32	4.29	0.0573	1.3	3
3	6.59	6.52	0.0464	0.7	3
4	8.21	8.23	0.0294	0.4	3

[a]After T. Hama *et al.* (1987).

tion to the increases in ¹³C atomic % of glycine. Table IV summarizes analysis of glycine and glutamic acid standards with various ¹³C atomic %. The mean value of the estimated ¹³C atomic % by GC-MS almost agrees with the expected value, which is calculated by the degree of dilution with non-¹³C-enriched standard. The low standard deviation of repeated analysis and the small deviation from the expected values strongly suggested the applicability of the ¹³C-GC-MS method to the tracer studies in an aquatic environment.

Sato *et al.* (1986) applied the ¹³C-GC-MS method to study the lipid metabolism in more detail, using cultured algae, and proposed the applicability of the ¹³C-GC-MS method to biochemical studies.

4.2.2. Application Results

4.2.2a. Photosynthetic Products. 1. *Nutrient limitation.* One of the most obvious results with the ¹³C-GC-MS method was the response of the phytoplankton population to nutrient availability (T. Hama and Honjyo, 1987; T. Hama, 1988; T. Hama *et al.*, 1988b). The compositional studies of cellular compounds and/or particulate matter found that carbohydrate increased under nitrogen limitation and this increase has been reported to be due to the accumulation of storage glucan (Myklestad and Haug, 1972; Myklestad, 1974). The compositional studies of photosynthetic products using the ¹⁴C method obtained less clear results compared with cellular composition (Morris, 1981; Priscu and Priscu, 1984).

T. Hama (1988) determined the detailed monosaccharide and amino acid composition of photosynthetic products in the regional upwelling area around the Izu Islands, Japan. He found marked differences in the composition of photosynthetic products among nonupwelling, nutrient-rich "maturing" upwelling, and nutrient-depleted "aged" upwelling. The most obvious difference in the photosynthetic products was the production rate and the contribution of glucose (Fig. 7). In the nutrient-rich "maturing" upwelling station, glucose accounted for 50% of carbohydrate production, which was calculated from the sum of the production rate of eight monosaccharides, whereas the extremely high contribution of glucose (up to 90% of total carbohydrate production) was noted at the nutrient-depleted "aged" upwelling station. These results clearly showed that nitrogen limitation in the "aged" upwelling area resulted in the accumulation of reserved carbohydrate constituted by glucan as suggested from compositional studies in cultured algae (Myklestad, 1977). Under such condition, carbohydrate constituting structural components such as cell wall was not actively produced.

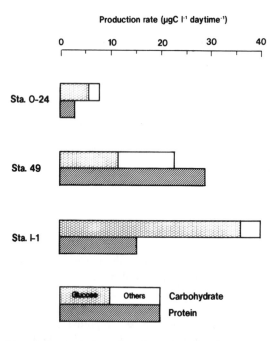

Figure 7. Composition of photosynthetic products in nonupwelling (Sta. 0-24), "maturing" upwelling (Sta. 49), and "aged" upwelling (Sta. I-1). Total carbohydrate and protein production were estimated by the sum of production rate of monosaccharides and amino acids, respectively. (Data from T. Hama, 1988.)

The absolute composition of photosynthetic products, however, can reflect the difference in the phytoplankton species composition, because the change in the environmental factors usually accompanied the change in the species composition of phytoplankton population. SPR, on the other hand, can be useful in assessing the physiological state of phytoplankton population because this value was normalized with the concentration of each organic molecule. The comparison of the spectra of SPR also showed the nutrient limitation in the "aged" upwelling area, revealing the disproportionate accumulation of glucose. The spectrum in the "maturing" upwelling area indicated the "balanced" production of organic material.

These changes in the photosynthetic products were revealed by a study using a semiclosed experimental ecosystem (T. Hama *et al.*, 1988b). The results clearly indicated that the production pattern both in composition of photosynthetic products and spectra of SPR dramatically changed with the occurrence of nitrogen limitation. The chlorophyll SPR was highest just after nitrogen exhaustion, due to the high glucose production. Although the chlorophyll SPR has usually been used for estimation of the physiological state and growth rate, the results strongly suggested that the value is not directly applicable to such parameters. More details on photosynthetic products and the like can afford significant information as has been suggested by Morris (1981).

2. *Diel variability.* The day–night cycle affects the phytoplankton metabolism and its importance in the natural environment has been pointed out. Dark loss of carbon during a day–night incubation experiment was reported by Eppley and Sharp (1975). From a ¹⁴C tracer study, Morris and Skea (1978) found evidence that night loss of carbon is mainly due to polysaccharide, whereas proteinaceous material is usually produced through the day and night.

Information on the carbon flow into monosaccharides and amino acids which constitute carbohydrate and proteinaceous material, revealed that the diel pattern of production and consumption of each molecule differs depending on whether the molecule constitutes reserved or structural material. T. Hama *et al.* (1988a) applied the ¹³C-GC-MS method to the lacustrine phytoplankton population and observed diurnal changes in the production of each monosaccharide and amino acid. Figure 8 shows the mass spectra of acetyl derivatives of mannose and glucose constituting carbohydrate. The relative intensity of isotopic peaks of mannose is higher in samples incubated throughout the day and night than those incubated only in the daytime. In the case of glucose, on the other hand, the relative intensity of isotopic peaks decreased through the nighttime. Measured monosaccharides except glucose showed the same trend as galactose in that ¹³C atomic % increased at night. These results strongly suggested the carbon flow from reserved carbohydrate mainly constituted by glucose to the structural carbohydrate during nighttime. The increases in ¹³C atomic % during the night have also been observed in amino acids constituting proteinaceous material, indicating

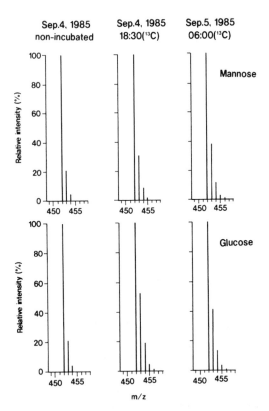

Figure 8. Mass spectra of acetyl derivatives of mannose (mannitol acetate) and glucose (glucitol acetate), of nonincubated (left), daytime-incubated (center), and day–nighttime-incubated (right) samples collected from Lake Biwa. (After T. Hama *et al.*, 1988a.)

carbon flow to proteinaceous substances. This night production of structural cellular constituents can be an important component in relation to enlargement and/or division of cells during the night.

This change, however, reflects the availability of inorganic nutrients. J. Hama and Handa (1992a,b) examined the diel changes in the composition of monosaccharide, amino acid, and fatty acid in the photosynthetic products using natural phytoplankton population from coastal water. During their incubation experiment, inorganic nitrogen was completely exhausted, resulting in little production of amino acids during nighttime.

3. *Vertical variability.* Change in photosynthetic products with depth has generally been observed in lake (Olive and Morrison, 1967; Cuhel and Lean, 1987) and oceanic (Hitchcock, 1978; Morris and Skea, 1978; Morris, 1981) phytoplankton by the ^{14}C method. These studies showed that the contri-

bution of carbohydrate to total photosynthetic rate decreased with depth. The proportion of protein and amino acids, on the contrary, tended to increase with depth. In the light of these findings, the high contribution of carbohydrate near surface water is considered primarily due to the high light intensity (Morris, 1981).

Using the ¹³C-GC-MS method, T. Hama et al. (1990) observed the same trend in Lake Biwa, and the contribution of glucose, which is considered to constitute reserved glucan, to total carbohydrate showed a marked decrease with depth. Other monosaccharides as well as proteinaceous compounds showed a lesser depth dependence than glucose. Thus, the great contribution of carbohydrate near the water surface was mainly due to the high production of reserved glucan. The results obtained by Cook (1963), who measured the concentration of protein, paramylum (storage glucan of *Euglena*), and lipid, showed that light saturation is different among organic compounds; the contribution of protein rapidly increased under low light intensity but saturated under lower light intensity than did paramylum. Further, the fact that nitrogen uptake saturates under lower light intensity than carbon uptake (e.g., Kanda et al., 1985a) also suggests that the change in photosynthetic products with depth is primarily affected by light intensity. Other environmental factors such as light quality (Wallen and Geen, 1971; Morris, 1981) and nutrient availability (Morris and Skea, 1978), however, can affect the vertical change in composition of photosynthetic products.

4. *Temperature effect.* Smith and Morris (1980a,b) observed an enhanced lipid production (up to 80–90% of total photosynthetic rate) at low water temperatures in the Antarctic Ocean by the ¹⁴C method. Such a high lipid contribution to photosynthetic products, however, has not been observed even in polar regions (Li and Platt, 1982; McConville et al., 1985). Although Smith and Morris (1980a,b) examined the reliability of the isolation of lipid material by different fractionation procedures, they did not report in detail the organic constituents of the "lipid" fraction. Thus, the enhanced production of "lipid material" at low water temperatures remains to be fully elucidated.

Because the ¹³C-GC-MS method can be used to determine the production rate of each organic molecule, the estimation of the production rate of fatty acids can be easily carried out. T. Hama et al. (1992) observed the seasonal change in the fatty acid composition of photosynthetic products and the contribution of fatty acid to total photosynthetic production (although lipids contain other molecules such as sugar of glycolipids and proteins of lipoproteins as well as fatty acids, only production rates of fatty acids were compared with total production rate in their study). The ratio generally increased with decreasing ambient water temperature, and this resulted in a high C:N ratio of photosynthetic products during the winter season (T. Hama et al., 1990).

The fatty acid composition also showed a temperature dependence and an increase in the contribution of polyunsaturated fatty acid was noted during the winter season (T. Hama *et al.*, 1992). A similar finding was reported in studies using algal culture (Holton *et al.*, 1964; Sato *et al.*, 1979). Fractionation of lipid material into lipid classes such as neutral and polar lipids (e.g., Parrish, 1987) is desirable in assessing the relation between lipid production and temperature, because it allows one to determine whether the increase in lipid contribution is caused by storage (neutral) lipid or membrane (polar) lipid.

    4.2.2b. Lipid Metabolism. The ^{13}C-GC-MS method was used to investigate in detail the mechanism of desaturation of fatty acid by Sato *et al.* (1986), who employed a monoalgal culture of *Anabaena variabilis* (Cyanophyceae). They analyzed the mechanism of desaturation of palmitic acid (16:0) to palmitoleic acid (16:1) at C-2 position of monogalactosyl diacylglycerol. After incubation with ^{13}CO$_2$ for $2^{1}/_{2}$ hr, cells were incubated for $7^{1}/_{2}$ hr in the presence of cerulenin [an inhibitor of *de novo* synthesis of fatty acids but which does not inhibit the desaturation of fatty acids (Omura, 1976)]. Monogalactosyl diacylglycerol was extracted and isolated by thin-layer chromatography (TLC). After liberating the fatty acids at the C-1 position by treatment with lipase, the resulting 2-acyl-3-galactosylglycerol was again isolated by TLC and trimethylsilylated for GC-MS analysis.

    Figure 9 shows an example of GC-MS analysis of 1-TMS-2-acyl-3-(TMS)$_4$galactosylglycerol derived from monogalactosyl diacylglycerol before and after incubation with ^{13}C and following subsequent incubation. The highest peak of m/z 385 and m/z 383 corresponds to the TMS-Gly-16:0 fragment (Fig. 9, A1) and TMS-Gly-16:1 fragment (Fig. 9, B1), which are composed of ^{12}C, ^{1}H, ^{16}O, and ^{28}Si, respectively. In the sample incubated with ^{13}C for $2^{1}/_{2}$ hr, new peaks were observed from m/z 390 to m/z 400 in TMS-Gly-16:0 Fig. 9, A2), due to the incorporation of ^{13}C into the carbon skeleton of 16:0. In TMS-Gly-16:1 (Fig. 9, B2), on the other hand, peaks greater than m/z 387 were quite small, meaning little incorporation of ^{13}C to 16:1. After subsequent incubation for $7^{1}/_{2}$ hr, although an almost comparable mass spectrum was obtained for TMS-Gly-16:0 (Fig. 9, A3), new peaks with m/z 388–398 appeared in TMS-Gly-16:1 (Fig. 9, B3). From these analyses, Sato *et al.* (1986) indicated that [^{13}C]palmitoyl-[^{13}C]glycerol and [^{12}C]palmitoyl-[^{12}C]glycerol were converted to [^{13}C]palmitoleoyl-[^{13}C]glycerol and [^{12}C]palmitoleoyl-[^{12}C]glycerol, respectively. This lipid-linked desaturation of palmitic acid to palmitoleic acid was first revealed from *in vivo* study by the ^{13}C-GC-MS method.

    This kind of study strongly suggests the applicability of the ^{13}C (or ^{15}N)-GC-MS method for the biochemical study of microbiology, because GC-MS analysis can offer information not only on organic molecular structure but also on the pathways of synthesis (and/or decomposition) when it is combined with the stable isotope tracer method.

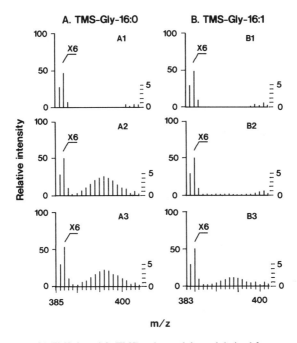

Figure 9. Mass spectra of 1-TMS-2-acyl-3-(TMS)$_4$galactosylglycerol derived from monogalactosyl diacylglycerol before and after feeding with ^{13}C and after subsequent incubation. TMS-Gly-C16 fragment ions are shown. A: TMS-Gly-16:0 fragment; B: TMS-Gly-16:1 fragment; 1: before feeding with ^{13}C; 2: after feeding with ^{13}C; 3: after feeding with ^{13}C for 2½ hr followed by incubation for 7½ hr. (After Sato *et al.*, 1986.)

4.3. Gel Filtration

4.3.1. Background

The GC-MS analysis as reviewed in the previous section requires the hydrolysis of organic constituents to monomer for separation by GC. The results obtained thus provide little information about the molecular weight distribution of cellular constituents. The solvent extraction offers some information on molecular weight; organic compounds fractionated into methanol fraction have been referred to as low-molecular-weight metabolites (e.g., Morris, 1981). However, the fractionation by solvent extraction is inadequate for inferring the dynamics of organic material in the phytoplankton cell.

Gel filtration has been widely used to fractionate organic matter depending on molecular size. In gel filtration, organic matter can be separated with high reproducibility and good recovery; large molecules move more quickly through the column of a gel than do small molecules. When the ^{13}C atomic % of fractionated organic compounds is measured by gel filtration, the molecular weight distribution of photosynthetic products can be determined.

4.3.2. Application Results

J. Hama and Handa (1992c) combined the ^{13}C-GC-MS method with gel filtration to fractionate carbohydrate of photosynthetic products of a coastal phytoplankton population and they elucidated the diel dynamics of each carbohydrate fraction.

The coastal phytoplankton population was incubated with $NaH^{13}CO_3$ from dawn to dawn on the next morning. Incubated samples were treated with boiling distilled water for 1 hr, and the obtained water-extractable organic matter was fractionated by gel filtration with a glass column packed with polyacrylamide gel. The concentration of carbohydrate in eluate was measured, and examples of molecular weight distribution of water-extractable carbohydrates are shown in Fig. 10. Definite diel variability of molecular weight distribution was observed. Large peaks of high-molecular-weight fraction (fraction A, $M_r > 6000$) and low-molecular-weight fraction (fraction C, $M_r < 1000$) were observed at the beginning of incubation. During daytime, the concentration of carbohydrate in fractions A and C showed a rapid increase. Further, fraction B (M_r 1000–6000), which was not observed at dawn, appeared during the daytime. All fractions decreased during the nighttime, and fraction B disappeared by the next dawn.

The major part of fractions A, B, and C (fractions A′, B′, and C′) to obtain the carbohydrates without contamination by other fractions were hydrolyzed to monosaccharides. The monosaccharide composition was quite different among fractions. Fraction A, the largest molecular weight fraction, consisted of glucose, xylose, galactose, fucose, mannose, rhamnose, and arabinose, while only glucose was measured as a constituent of fraction B. Low-molecular-weight fraction C comprised mainly ribose, galactose, and glucose. From the monosaccharide composition, J. Hama and Handa (1992c) suggested that fractions A and B were cell wall heteropolysaccharides and storage glucan of phytoplankton, respectively. Fraction C was considered low-molecular-weight cellular components, such as free glucose, oligosaccharides, simple glycosides, coenzyme, and/or nucleotides.

^{13}C atomic % in each monosaccharide was measured by GC-MS and results are summarized in Table V. Monosaccharide components of fractions B and C were highly labeled with ^{13}C in the daytime compared with fraction A, showing the high specific production rate. The high ^{13}C atomic % of monosaccharides in fraction C may well suggest that these low-molecular-weight carbohydrates were partly produced as precursors of polysaccharides and served as a metabolic pool with a high turnover rate. Meanwhile, the highest ^{13}C atomic % of glucose in

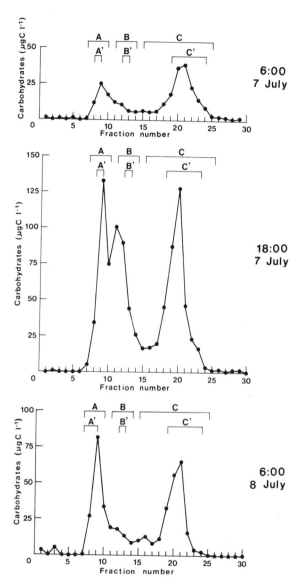

Figure 10. Diel changes in molecular weight distribution of particulate water-extractable carbohydrate with gel filtration. Data show the concentration of carbohydrate per unit natural seawater. (After J. Hama and Handa, 1992c.)

Table V. ^{13}C Incorporation into Each Monosaccharide in Fractions A′, B′, and C′[a]

	Rhamnose	Fucose	Ribose	Arabinose	Xylose	Mannose	Galactose	Glucose
Fraction A′								
7 July 1986 18:00	6.21	7.96	—	4.60	6.63	7.33	5.87	11.73
8 July 1986 06:00	7.19	9.44	—	3.69	8.09	8.57	7.15	8.14
Fraction B′								
7 July 1986 18:00	—	—	—	—	—	—	—	13.92
8 July 1986 06:00	—	—	7.19	—	—	—	—	10.33
Fraction C′								
7 July 1986 18:00	—	—	6.41	9.18	—	12.08	11.65	13.08
8 July 1986 06:00	—	—	6.91	—	—	—	11.48	11.11

[a]Data expressed as ^{13}C atomic % in each monosaccharide carbon skeleton. After J. Hama and Handa (1992c).

fraction B was consistent with the rapid production of this fraction in the daytime as shown in Fig. 10. Although ^{13}C atomic % of monosaccharides in fraction A were relatively low, indicating lower specific production than those in fractions B and C, some constituents of this fraction (rhamnose, fucose, xylose, mannose, and galactose) showed increases in ^{13}C atomic % during night. The fact that there was no photosynthetic uptake of inorganic carbon during night indicated that heteropolysaccharides which constituted cell wall material of phytoplankton were produced using organic carbon with high ^{13}C atomic % during night. Thus, J. Hama and Handa (1992c) suggested that low-molecular-weight material in fraction C and reserved glucan in fraction B acted as carbon suppliers for synthesis of cell wall components of algae in nighttime.

The combination of the ^{13}C-GC-MS method with gel filtration can infer the dynamic state of cellular carbohydrate metabolism of phytoplankton. Application to other components will yield significant information to elucidate the production, turnover, and consumption processes of phytoplankton material.

5. Application of ^{13}C Tracer Method to Aquatic Food Web

5.1. Background

Analysis of the marine and/or lake food web has recently received much attention. The importance of a currently "emerging" microbial loop has been suggested in addition to the "classical" grazing food chain.

Natural abundance of ^{13}C (and ^{15}N) has now been widely used for analysis of the food web including aquatic environments (Rau, 1978; Wada *et al.*, 1987; Fry and Sherr, 1988). On the other hand, few attempts have been made to analyze a food web using the ^{13}C tracer technique. However, the ^{13}C technique can be used to estimate the absolute carbon flux (and nitrogen flux when combined with the ^{15}N method) between different groups of organisms.

Here, we offer two examples of studies on the aquatic food web using the ^{13}C technique; the first example is the estimation of the secondary production and the second a preliminary observation of the carbon flow from phytoplankton to bacteria.

5.2. Application Results

5.2.1. Estimation of Secondary Production

A large-scale experiment was conducted on the incorporation of carbon and nitrogen into the zooplankton population via phytoplankton photosynthesis,

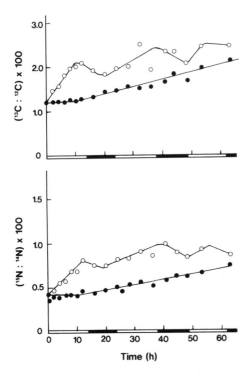

Figure 11. Changes in the $^{13}C{:}^{12}C$ and $^{15}N{:}^{14}N$ ratios of the 0.6–10 μm fraction (○) and zooplankton (●) in the enclosure. Dark bars refer to nighttime. (After Otsuki *et al.*, 1985.)

using an enclosure and bag (Otsuki *et al.*, 1985). After addition of $^{13}CO_2$ and $^{15}NO_3^-$, the isotopic ratios of carbon and nitrogen of size-fractionated particulate organic matter were monitored. The $^{13}C{:}^{12}C$ and $^{15}N{:}^{14}N$ ratios increased with time in both phytoplankton (0.6–10 μm) and zooplankton fractions (Fig. 11). The simultaneous increase in ^{13}C and ^{15}N atomic % in the phytoplankton fraction indicated that the uptake of carbon and nitrogen were strongly coupled, though the night decrease in the ratio was more obvious in ^{13}C atomic %. From 8 to 10 hr after addition of tracers to an enclosure, both isotopic ratios of carbon and nitrogen in the zooplankton fraction started to increase simultaneously, indicating the coupled transformation of inorganic carbon and nitrogen from phytoplankton to herbivorous zooplankton.

For quantitative study on the transformation of carbon and nitrogen from phytoplankton to zooplankton, Otsuki *et al.* (1987) proposed the method for measurement of the secondary production rate of herbivore. They estimated the growth rate of small, herbivorous, benthic animals, using double-labeled (^{13}C and ^{15}N) periphyton. Periphyton, which was mostly constituted by diatoms such as *Synedra tabulata*, *Navicula* spp., *Achnanthes* sp., and *Cyclotella* sp., on the blades of eelgrass, was collected by a rubber-coated rod and incubated with

$^{13}CO_2$, $^{15}NH_4^+$, and $^{15}NO_3^-$ for 24 hr. The herbivorous benthic animal *Eogammarus confervicolus* was added to the suspension of labeled periphyton, and animals were removed at 24, 48, and 72 hr. Isotopic ratios of both C and N of animals were measured.

The calculation of net growth rate by the animal (μg C or N per hr) is analogous to the calculation of primary production rate [Eq. (6)]; atomic % of labeled food is used instead of a_{ic}:

$$\text{Net growth rate} = \frac{(a_{ia} - a_{na})}{(a_{lf} - a_{na})} \times \frac{C}{t} \tag{15}$$

where C is the carbon or nitrogen content of an animal after incubation (μg C or N), a_{ia}: is the atomic % of ^{13}C or ^{15}N in the incubated animal, a_{na} is the atomic % of ^{13}C and ^{15}N in the nonincubated animal, and a_{lf} is the atomic % of ^{13}C of ^{15}N in the labeled food.

The relative growth rate (μg C or N/μg C or N per hr) can be calculated from

$$\text{Relative growth rate} = \frac{(a_{ia} - a_{na})}{(a_{lf} - a_{na})} \times \frac{1}{t} \tag{16}$$

Equation (17) is also available to obtain the relative growth rate based on carbon or nitrogen content of an animal at the start of incubation as already discussed in this chapter and by Dugdale and Wilkerson (1986):

$$\text{Relative growth rate} = \frac{(a_{ia} - a_{na})}{(a_{lf} - a_{ia})} \times \frac{1}{t} \tag{17}$$

Equation (16) or (17) means that only measurements of the isotopic ratio of carbon and nitrogen can give the relative growth rate of animals.

A significant finding from the dual label analysis was that the respective rates estimated from carbon base and nitrogen base were different; the rates from nitrogen were always lower than those from carbon. Otsuki *et al.* (1987) suggested that this discrepancy reflected the difference in the pathways between carbon and nitrogen; carbon taken up first enters the metabolic pool with a high turnover rate, and from which carbon was polymerized as constituents of structural components with a low turnover rate. Nitrogen taken up, on the other hand, was considered to be directly converted to structural components.

As Otsuki *et al.* (1987) suggested, the stable isotope tracer method can be useful in estimating the secondary production rate, and further, the combination with ^{15}N can distinguish the difference in metabolism between carbon and nitrogen at the secondary production level.

5.2.2. Carbon Flow from Phytoplankton to Bacteria

Another example of the application of the ^{13}C method is the ^{13}C incorporation into fatty acid which is specific for bacteria. The incorporation of photosynthetic products from phytoplankton to bacterial population has routinely been studied by the ^{14}C tracer technique. Some workers have suggested that excreted organic carbon during photosynthesis was rapidly taken up by the bacterial population (e.g., Berman and Gerber, 1980; Nalewajko *et al.*, 1980; Wolter, 1982). To fractionate the production rate of phytoplankton and bacteria, these studies used a differential filtration method (Derenbach and Williams, 1974); phytoplankton was collected by filter (1–3 μm in porosity), and the filtrate was again filtered with a small-pore (0.2–0.45 μm) filter to collect the bacterial population. This filtration is the critical step in estimating the bacterial production. When small phytoplankton that might pass through a filter of 1–3 μm pore size partially make up a phytoplankton population as has recently been observed (e.g., Taguchi and Laws, 1988), the radioactivity retained on the small-pore filter used for collection of the bacterial population may contain the ^{14}C photosynthetically incorporated into the phytoplankton. If the production rate of organic compounds (or molecule) for bacteria can be estimated, it is not necessary to fractionate the bacterial population from phytoplankton.

Some kinds of fatty acids such as branched 15:0, 17:0, and 18:1(*n*-7) have been considered bacteria-specific (Perry *et al.*, 1979; Joint and Morris, 1982; Wakeham and Canuel, 1988). Thus, the incorporation of tracer, which is used to measure the primary productivity, into such specific organic compounds (molecule) can yield information on the carbon flow from phytoplankton to bacteria. The ^{13}C-GC-MS method is the most suitable technique for carrying out such study.

T. Hama (1991) determined the production and turnover rates of fatty acids in marine particulate matter through phytoplankton photosynthesis by application of the ^{13}C-GC-MS method. Figure 12 shows the turnover rates of fatty acids in particulate matter at regional upwelling (Station 49) and nonupwelling (Station I-2). The turnover rates show large variability. Polyunsaturated fatty acids show the highest rate at both stations, and the secondary group comprised 14:0, 16:0, 18:1(*n*-9), 20:5, and 22:6. Fatty acids which have been reported to be bacteria-specific, such as 15:0, iso15:0, anteiso15:0, 17:0, and 18:1(*n*-7), showed a definite low turnover rate compared with other fatty acids at both stations. This indicates that organic carbon which was produced by photosynthetic production using ^{13}CO$_2$, might not be rapidly converted to bacterial organic constituents.

Several important problems in estimating the carbon flux from phytoplankton to bacteria were not examined in the above study; the time lag of

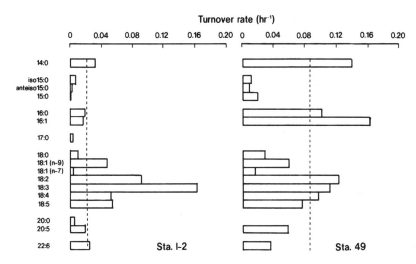

Figure 12. Turnover rates of particulate fatty acids through phytoplankton photosynthesis at 10 m at nonupwelling (Sta. I-2) and upwelling (Sta. 49) waters. Dashed line shows the weighted average at each station. Rates for 17:0 and 20:0 at Sta. 49 could not be determined, because of their low concentration. (After T. Hama, 1991.)

bacterial cell production from newly produced photosynthetic products, only bacterial fatty acids which were collected onto filter paper (Whatman GF/F; particles > 0.7 μm can be collected) were measured, and a conversion factor from measured production rate of fatty acids to total bacterial cellular organic carbon is unknown. Thus, no quantitative discussion can be given at this time. However, the preliminary results obtained by T. Hama (1991) indicated that the ¹³C (and/or ¹⁵N)-GC-MS method can yield information on the carbon (and/or nitrogen) flux through the food web in an aquatic ecosystem, if one selects suitable organic compounds (or molecule) specific to certain organisms.

6. Conclusion

Relatively few studies to date have used ¹³C as a tracer to measure the primary productivity in aquatic environments. Most have been carried out in Japan, where the use of radioactive carbon in natural environments has been highly restricted. The ¹³C tracer method has some disadvantages relative to the ¹⁴C method; among them are its low sensitivity, which requires larger volume and longer incubation periods, the difficulties in maintenance and operation of analytical instruments, and the cost of the tracer. Nevertheless, it is an outstanding tool when combined with the ¹⁵N tracer method or the GC-MS method, as summarized in this review. Further, the combination with liquid chromatography–mass spectrometry (LC-MS) or nuclear magnetic resonance (NMR) also can provide new knowledge of microbial ecology. It is noteworthy that the ^{13}C tracer constitutes no hazardous radioactive problem in environments, unlike the ^{14}C tracer. We believe that more and more studies using the ^{13}C method will be conducted not only in Japan but in other countries as well.

References

Barlow, R. G., 1982, Phytoplankton ecology in the Southern Benguela current. II. Carbon assimilation patterns, *J. Exp. Mar. Biol. Ecol.* **63**:229–237.

Barrie, A., and Workman, C. T., 1984, An automated analytical system for nutritional investigations using ^{15}N tracers, *Spectros. Int. J.* **3**:439–447.

Barsdate, R. J., and Dugdale, R. C., 1965, Rapid conversion of organic nitrogen to N_2 for mass spectrometry: An automated Dumas procedure, *Anal. Biochem.* **13**:1–5.

Berger, W. H., Smetacek, V. S., and Wefer, G., 1989, Ocean productivity and paleoproductivity—An overview, in: *Productivity of the Ocean: Present and Past* (W. H. Berger, V. S. Smetacek, and G. Wefer, eds.), Wiley, New York, pp. 1–34.

Berman, T., and Gerber, C., 1980, Differential filtration studies of carbon flux from living algae to microheterotrophs, microplankton size distribution and respiration in Lake Kinneret, *Microb. Ecol.* **6**:189–198.

Collos, Y., and Slawyk, G., 1979, ^{13}C and ^{15}N uptake by marine phytoplankton. I. Influence of nitrogen source and concentration in laboratory cultures of diatoms, *J. Phycol.* **15**:186–190.

Collos, Y., and Slawyk, G., 1985, On the compatibility of carbon uptake rates calculated from stable and radioactive isotope data: Implications for the design of experimental protocols in aquatic primary productivity, *J. Plankton Res.* **7**:595–603.

Collos, Y., and Slawyk, G., 1986, ^{13}C and ^{15}N uptake by marine phytoplankton—IV. Uptake ratios and the contribution of nitrate to the productivity of Antarctic waters (Indian Ocean sector), *Deep-Sea Res.* **33**:1039–1051.

Cook, J. R., 1963, Adaptations in growth and division in *Euglena* effected by energy supply, *J. Protozool.* **10**:436–444.

Cuhel, R. C., and Lean, P. R. S., 1987, Influence of light intensity, light quality, temperature, and daylength on uptake and assimilation of carbon dioxide and sulfate by lake plankton, *Can. J. Fish. Aquat. Sci.* **44**:2118–2132.

Derenbach, J. B., and Williams, P. L., 1974, Autotrophic and bacterial production: Fractionation of plankton populations by differential filtration of samples from the English Channel, *Mar. Biol.* **25**:263–269.

Dugdale, R. C., and Goering, J. J., 1967, Uptake of new and regenerated forms of nitrogen in primary productivity, *Limnol. Oceanogr.* **12**:196–206.

Dugdale, R. C., and Wilkerson, F. P., 1986, The use of ^{15}N to measure nitrogen uptake in eutrophic oceans; experimental considerations, *Limnol. Oceanogr.* **31**:673–689.

Eppley, R. W., and Renger, E. H., 1988, Nanomolar increase in surface layer nitrate concentration following a small wind event, *Deep-Sea Res.* **35**:1119–1125.

Eppley, R. W., and Sharp, J. H., 1975, Photosynthetic measurements in the central North Pacific: The dark loss of carbon in 24 h incubation, *Limnol. Oceanogr.* **20**:981–987.

Falkowski, P. G., 1991, Species variability in the fractionation of ^{13}C and ^{12}C by marine phytoplankton, *J. Plankton Res.* **13**(Suppl.):21–28.

Fisher, T. R., Jr., Haines, E. B., and Volk, R. J., 1979, A comment on the calculation of atom percent enrichment for stable isotopes, *Limnol. Oceanogr.* **24:**593–595.

Fitzwater, S. E., Knauer, G. A., and Martin, J. H., 1982, Metal contamination and its effect on primary production measurements, *Limnol. Oceanogr.* **27:**544–551.

Fry, B., and Sherr, E. B., 1988, δ¹³C measurement as indicators of carbon flow in marine and freshwater ecosystems, in: *Stable Isotopes in Ecological Research* (P. W. Rundel, J. R. Ehleringer, and K. A. Nagy, eds.), Springer-Verlag, Berlin, pp. 196–229.

Gieskes, W. W. C., Kraay, G. W., and Baars, M. A., 1979, Current ¹⁴C methods for measuring primary production: Gross underestimates in oceanic waters, *Neth. J. Sea Res.* **13:**58–78.

Goldman, J. C., 1988, Spatial and temporal discontinuities of biological processes in pelagic surface waters, in: *Toward a Theory on Biological–Physical Interactions in the World Ocean* (B. J. Rothschild, ed.), Kluwer, Dordrecht, pp. 273–296.

Gomes, H. D. R., Goes, J. I., and Parulekar, A. H., 1992, Size-fractionated biomass, photosynthesis and dark CO₂ fixation in a tropical oceanic environment, *J. Plankton Res.* **14:**1307–1329.

Gordon, A. E., and Frigerio, A., 1972, Mass fragmentography as an application of gas-liquid chromatography-mass spectrometry in biological research, *J. Chromatogr.* **73:**401–417.

Hama, J., and Handa, N., 1986, Analysis of the production processes of natural phytoplankton population using ¹³C–gas chromatography-mass spectrometry methods, *Res. Org. Geochem.* **5:**41–46 (in Japanese).

Hama, J., and Handa, N., 1992a, Diel photosynthetic production of cellular organic matter in natural phytoplankton populations, measured with ¹³C and gas chromatography/mass spectrometry. I. Monosaccharides, *Mar. Biol.* **112:**175–181.

Hama, J., and Handa, N., 1992b, Diel photosynthetic production of cellular organic matter in natural phytoplankton populations, measured with ¹³C and gas chromatography/mass spectrometry. II. Fatty acids and amino acids, *Mar. Biol.* **112:**183–190.

Hama, J., and Handa, N., 1992c, Diel variation of water-extractable carbohydrate composition of natural phytoplankton populations in Kinu-ura Bay, *J. Exp. Mar. Biol. Ecol.* **162:**159–176.

Hama, J., and Handa, N., 1992d, The phytoplankton bloom in the Kinu-ura Bay, Japan in the rainy season, *Proc. Conf. Pacific Ocean Environ. Probing* **2:**692–697.

Hama, T., 1988, ¹³C-GC-MS analysis of photosynthetic products of the phytoplankton population in the regional upwelling area around the Izu Islands, Japan, *Deep-Sea Res.* **35:**91–110.

Hama, T., 1991, Production and turnover rates of fatty acids in marine particulate matter through phytoplankton photosynthesis, *Mar. Chem.* **33:**213–227.

Hama, T., 1992, Primary productivity and photosynthetic products around the Kuroshio warm-core ring, *Deep-Sea Res.* **39**(Suppl. 1): S279–S293.

Hama, T., and Handa, N., 1987, Pattern of organic matter production by natural phytoplankton population in a eutrophic lake. 1. Intracellular products, *Arch. Hydrobiol.* **109:**107–120.

Hama, T., and Honjyo, T., 1987, Photosynthetic products and nutrient availability in phytoplankton population from Gokasyo Bay, Japan, *J. Exp. Mar. Biol. Ecol.* **112:**251–266.

Hama, T., Miyazaki, T., Ogawa, Y., Iwakuma, T., Takahashi, M., Otsuki, A., and Ichimura, S., 1983, Measurement of photosynthetic production of a marine phytoplankton population using a stable ¹³C isotope, *Mar. Biol.* **73:**31–36.

Hama, T., Handa, N., and Hama, J., 1987, Determination of amino acid production rate of a marine phytoplankton population with ¹³C and gas chromatography-mass spectrometry, *Limnol. Oceanogr.* **32:**1144–1153.

Hama, T., Matsunaga, K., Handa, N., and Takahashi, M., 1988a, Day–night changes in production of carbohydrate and protein by natural phytoplankton population from Lake Biwa, Japan, *J. Plankton Res.* **10:**941–955.

Hama, T., Handa, N., Takahashi, M., Whitney, F., and Wong, C. S., 1988b, Change in distribution patterns of photosynthetically incorporated C during phytoplankton bloom in controlled experimental ecosystem, *J. Exp. Mar. Biol. Ecol.* **120**:39–56.

Hama, T., Matsunaga, K., Handa, N., and Takahashi, M., 1990, Composition of photosynthetic products in Lake Biwa, Japan; vertical and seasonal changes and their relation to environmental factors, *J. Plankton Res.* **12**:133–147.

Hama, T., Matsunaga, K., Handa, N., and Takahashi, M., 1992, Fatty acid composition in photosynthetic products of natural phytoplankton population in Lake Biwa, *Japan, J. Plankton Res.* **14**:1055–1065.

Hitchcock, G. L., 1978, Labelling patterns of carbon-14 in net plankton during a winter–spring bloom, *J. Exp. Mar. Biol. Ecol.* **31**:141–153.

Hitchcock, G. L., 1983, Photosynthate partitioning in cultured marine phytoplankton. I. Dinoflagellates, *J. Exp. Mar. Biol. Ecol.* **69**:21–36.

Holton, R. W., Blecker, H. H., and Onore, M., 1964, Effect of growth temperature on the fatty acid composition of a blue-green alga, *Phytochemistry* **3**:595–602.

Joint, P. A., and Morris, R. J., 1982, The role of bacteria in the turnover of organic matter in the sea, *Oceanogr. Mar. Biol. Annu. Rev.* **20**:65–118.

Kanda, J., Saino, T., and Hattori, A., 1985a, Nitrogen uptake by natural populations of phytoplankton and primary production in the Pacific Ocean: Regional variability of uptake capacity, *Limnol. Oceanogr.* **30**:987–999.

Kanda, J., Saino, T., and Hattori, A., 1985b, Variation of carbon and nitrogen uptake capacity in a regional upwelling area around Hachijo Island, *J. Oceanogr. Soc. Japan.* **41**:373–380.

Knopka, A., and Schnur, M., 1980, Effect of light intensity on macromolecular synthesis in cyanobacteria, *Microb. Ecol.* **6**:291–301.

Kokubun, N., and Sasaki, Y., 1979, Use of stable isotope—Determination of $^{13}CO_2$ by infrared absorption spectrometry and its application to the diagnosis by breath test, *Kagaku To Seibutsu* **17**:384–389 (in Japanese).

Kouchi, H., 1982, Direct analysis of ^{13}C abundance in plant carbohydrates by gas chromatography–mass spectrometry, *J. Chromatogr.* **241**:305–323.

Lean, D. R. S., Murphy, T. P., and Pick, F. R., 1982, Photosynthetic response of lake plankton to combined nitrogen enrichment, *J. Phycol.* **18**:509–521.

Leftley, J. W., Bonin, D. J., and Maestrini, S. Y., 1983, Problems in estimating marine phytoplankton growth, productivity and metabolic activity in nature: An overview of methodology, *Oceanogr. Mar. Biol. Annu. Rev.* **21**:23–66.

Li, W. K. W., and Platt, T., 1982, Distribution of carbon among photosynthetic end-products in phytoplankton of the eastern Canadian Arctic, *J. Phycol.* **18**:466–471.

Longhurst, A. R., 1991, Role of the marine biosphere in the global carbon cycle, *Limnol. Oceanogr.* **36**:1507–1526.

McConville, M. J., Mitchell, C., and Wetherbee, R., 1985, Patterns of carbon assimilation in a microalgal community from annual sea ice, East Antarctica, *Polar Biol.* **4**:135–141.

Marra, J., Bidigare, R. R., and Dickey, T. D., 1990, Nutrients and mixing, chlorophyll and phytoplankton growth, *Deep-Sea Res.* **37**:127–143.

Miyazaki, T., and Ichimura, S., 1986, Uptake of inorganic carbon and nitrogen by phytoplankton during the winter mixing period in a freshwater lake, Lake Nakanuma, Japan, *Arch. Hydrobiol.* **105**:409–421.

Miyazaki, T., Honjo, Y., and Ichimura, S., 1985a, Applicability of the stable isotope method using ^{13}C and ^{15}N simultaneously to the estimation of carbon and nitrogen assimilation in a eutrophic, freshwater lake, Lake Nakanuma, Japan, *Arch. Hydrobiol.* **102**:355–365.

Miyazaki, T., Honjo, Y., and Ichimura, S., 1985b, Uptake of carbon and inorganic nitrogen in a eutrophic lake, Lake Nakanuma, Japan, from spring through summer, *Arch. Hydrobiol.* **102**:473–485.

Miyazaki, T., Suyama, H., and Uotani, H., 1987, Diel changes of uptake of inorganic carbon and nitrogen by phytoplankton, and the relationship between inorganic carbon and nitrogen uptake in Lake Nakanuma, Japan, *J. Plankton Res.* **9**:513–524.

Morris, I., 1981, Phyotosynthetic products, physiological state, and phytoplankton growth, *Can. Bull. Fish. Aquat. Sci.* **210**:83–102.

Morris, I., and Skea, W., 1978, Products of photosynthesis in natural populations of marine phytoplankton from the Gulf of Maine, *Mar. Biol.* **47**:303–312.

Myklestad, S., 1974, Production of carbohydrates by marine planktonic diatoms. I. Comparison of nine different species in culture, *J. Exp. Mar. Biol. Ecol.* **15**:261–274.

Myklestad, S., 1977, Production of carbohydrates by marine planktonic diatoms. II. Influence of the N/P ratio in the growth medium on the assimilation ratio, growth rate, and production of cellular and extracellular carbohydrates by *Chaetoceros affinis* var. *willei* (Gran) Hustedt and *Skeletonema costatum* (Grev.) Cleve, *J. Exp. Mar. Biol. Ecol.* **29**:161–179.

Myklestad, S., and Haug, A., 1972, Production of carbohydrates by the marine diatom *Chaetoceros affinis* var. *willei* (Gran) Hustedt. I. Effect of the concentration of nutrients in the culture medium, *J. Exp. Mar. Biol. Ecol.* **9**:125–136.

Nalewajko, C., Lee, K., and Fay, P., 1980, Significance of algal extracellular products to bacteria in lakes and in cultures, *Microb. Ecol.* **6**:199–207.

Olive, J. H., and Morrison, J. H., 1967, Variations in distribution of ¹⁴C in cell extracts of phytoplankton living under natural conditions, *Limnol. Oceanogr.* **12**:383–391.

Omura, S., 1976, The antibiotic cerulenin, a novel tool for biochemistry as an inhibitor of fatty acid synthesis, *Bacteriol. Rev.* **40**:681–697.

Otsuki, A., Ito, Y., and Fujii, T., 1983, Simultaneous measurements and determinations of stable carbon and nitrogen isotope ratios, and organic carbon and nitrogen contents in biological samples by coupling of a small quadrupole mass spectrometer and modified carbon–nitrogen elemental analyzer, *Int. J. Mass Spectrom. Ion Phys.* **48**:343–346.

Otsuki, A., Aizaki, M., Iwakuma, T., Takamura, N., Hanazato, T., Kawai, T., and Yasuno, M., 1985, Coupled transformation of inorganic stable carbon-13 and nitrogen-15 isotopes into higher trophic levels in a eutrophic shallow lake, *Limnol. Oceanogr.* **30**:820–825.

Otsuki, A., Seki, H., McAllister, C. D., and Levings, C. D., 1987, Measurement of net growth rates of herbivorous benthic animals using periphyton labeled simultaneously with ¹³C and ¹⁵N, *Limnol. Oceanogr.* **32**:499–503.

Owens, N. J. P., 1988, Rapid and total automation of shipboard ¹⁵N analysis: Examples from the North Sea, *J. Exp. Mar. Biol. Ecol.* **122**:163–171.

Parrish, C. C., 1987, Time series of particulate and dissolved lipid classes during spring phytoplankton blooms in Bedford Basin, a marine inlet, *Mar. Ecol. Prog. Ser.* **35**:129–139.

Parsons, T. R., Takahashi, M., and Hargrave, B., 1984, *Biological Oceanographic Processes*, 3rd ed., Pergamon Press, Elmsford, N.Y.

Perry, G. J., Volkman, J. K., Johns, R. B., and Bovor, H. J., Jr., 1979, Fatty acids of bacterial origin in contemporary marine sediments, *Geochim. Cosmochim. Acta* **43**:1715–1725.

Peterson, B. J., 1980, Aquatic primary productivity and the ¹⁴C-CO₂ method: A history of the productivity problem, *Annu. Rev. Ecol. Syst.* **11**:359–385.

Prakash, A., Sheldon, R. W., and Sutcliffe, W. H., Jr., 1991, Geographic variation of oceanic ¹⁴C dark uptake, *Limnol. Oceanogr.* **36**:30–39.

Preston, T., and Owens, N. J. P., 1983, Interfacing an automatic elemental analyser with an isotope ratio mass spectrometer: The potential for fully automated total nitrogen and nitrogen-15 analysis, *Analyst* **108**:971–977.

Preston, T., and Owens, N. J. P., 1985, Preliminary ¹³C measurements using a gas chromatograph interfaced to an isotope ratio mass spectrometer, *Biomed. Mass Spectrom.* **12**:510–513.

Priscu, J. C., and Priscu, L. R., 1984, Photosynthate partitioning by phytoplankton in a New Zealand coastal upwelling system, *Mar. Biol.* **81**:31–40.

Rau, G., 1978, Carbon-13 depletion in a subalpine lake: Carbon flow implications, *Science* **201**:901–902.

Rau, G. H., Sweeney, R. E., and Kaplan, I. R., 1982, Plankton ^{13}C:^{12}C ratio changes with latitude: Difference between northern and southern oceans, *Deep-Sea Res.* **29**:1035–1039.

Sakamoto, M., 1989, Inorganic carbon and ammonium uptake by phytoplankton in nitrogen depleted waters in Lake Suwa, *Jpn. J. Limnol.* **50**:45–51.

Sakamoto, M., Tilzer, M. M., Gächter, R., Rai, H., Collos, Y., Tschumi, P., Berner, P., Zbaren, D., Zbaren, J., Dokulil, M., Bossard, P., Uehlinger, U., and Nusch, E. A., 1984, Joint field experiments for comparisons of measuring methods of photosynthetic production, *J. Plankton Res.* **6**:365–383.

Sato, N., Murata, N., Miura, Y., and Ueta, N., 1979, Effect of growth temperature on lipid and fatty acid compositions in the blue-green algae *Anabaena variabilis* and *Anacystis nidulans*, *Biochim. Biophys. Acta* **572**:19–28.

Sato, N., Seyama, Y., and Murata, N., 1986, Lipid-linked desaturation of palmitic acid in mono-galactosyl diacylglycerol in the blue-green alga (Cyanobacterium) *Anabaena variabilis* studied in vivo, *Plant Cell Physiol.* **27**:819–835.

Satoh, H., and Watanabe, K., 1988, Primary productivity in the fast ice area near Syowa Station, Antarctica, during spring and summer, 1983/84, *J. Oceanogr. Soc. Japan.* **44**:287–292.

Satoh, H., Yamaguchi, Y., Kokubun, N., and Aruga, Y., 1985, Application of infrared absorption spectrometry for measuring the photosynthetic production of phytoplankton by the stable ^{13}C isotope method, *La mer* **23**:171–176.

Satoh, H., Yamaguchi, Y., Watanabe, K., and Aruga, Y., 1989a, Light conditions and photosynthetic productivity of ice algal assemblages in Lake Saroma, Hokkaido, *Jpn. J. Phycol.* **37**:274–278.

Satoh, H., Yamaguchi, Y., Watanabe, K., Tanimura, A., Fukuchi, M., and Aruga, Y., 1989b, Photosynthetic nature of ice algae and their contribution to the primary production in lagoon Saroma ko, Hokkaido, Japan, *Proc. NIPR Symp. Polar Biol.* **2**:1–8.

Satoh, H., Watanabe, K., and Hoshiai, T., 1991, Estimates of primary production by ice algae and phytoplankton in the coastal ice-covered area near Syowa Station, Antarctica, *Antarct. Rec.* **35**:30–38.

Satoh, H., Tanaka, H., and Koike, T., 1992, Light condition and photosynthetic characteristic of the subsurface chlorophyll maximum at a station in Solomon Sea, *Jpn. J. Phycol.* **40**:135–142.

Shiomoto, A., and Matsumura, S., 1992, Primary productivity in a cold water mass and the neighborhood area occurring off Enshu-Nada in the late summer of 1989, *J. Oceanogr.* **48**:105–115.

Slawyk, G., 1979, ^{13}C and ^{15}N uptake by phytoplankton in the Antarctic upwelling area: Results from the Antiprod I cruise in the Indian Ocean sector, *Aust. J. Mar. Freshwater Res.* **30**:431–448.

Slawyk, G., Collos, Y., and Auclair, J. C., 1977, The use of the ^{13}C and ^{15}N isotopes for the simultaneous measurement of carbon and nitrogen turnover rates in marine phytoplankton, *Limnol. Oceanogr.* **22**:925–932.

Slawyk, G., Collos, Y., and Auclair, J. C., 1979, Reply to comment by Fisher *et al.*, *Limnol. Oceanogr.* **24**:595–597.

Slawyk, G., Minas, M., Collos, Y., Legendre, L., and Roy, S., 1984, Comparison of radioactive and stable isotope tracer techniques for measuring photosynthesis: ^{13}C and ^{14}C uptake by marine phytoplankton, *J. Plankton Res.* **6**:249–257.

Slawyk, G., L'Helguen, S., Collos, Y., and Freije, H., 1988, Quantitative determination of particulate organic N and C in marine-phytoplankton samples using mass-spectrometer signals from isotope-ratio analyses in ^{15}N- and ^{13}C-tracer studies, *J. Exp. Mar. Biol. Ecol.* **115**:187–195.

Smith, A. E., and Morris, I., 1980a, Synthesis of lipid during photosynthesis of phytoplankton of the Southern Ocean, *Science* **207**:197–199.

Smith, A. E., and Morris, I., 1980b, Pathways of carbon assimilation in phytoplankton from the Antarctic Ocean, *Limnol. Oceanogr.* **25**:865–872.

Steemann Nielsen, E., 1952, The use of radioactive carbon (C¹⁴) for measuring organic production in the sea, *J. Cons. Int. Explor. Mer.* **18**:117–140.

Summons, R. E., Pereira, W. E., Reynolds, W. E., Rindfleisch, T. C., and Duffield, A. M., 1974, Analysis of twelve amino acids in biological fluids by mass fragmentography, *Anal. Chem.* **46**:582–587.

Taguchi, S., and Laws, E. A., 1988, On the microparticles which pass through glass fiber filter type GF/F in coastal and open waters, *J. Plankton Res.* **10**:999–1008.

Takahashi, K., Wada, E., and Sakamoto, M., 1990, Carbon isotope discrimination by phytoplankton and photosynthetic bacteria in monomictic lake Fukami-ike, *Arch. Hydrobiol.* **120**:197–210.

Takahashi, K., Wada, E., and Sakamoto, M., 1991, Relationship between carbon isotope discrimination and the specific growth rate of green alga *Chlamydomonas reinhardtii*, *Jpn. J. Limnol.* **52**:105–112.

Takamura, N., and Aizaki, M., 1991, Change in primary production in Lake Kasumigaura (1986–1989) accompanied by transition of dominant species, *Jpn J. Limnol.* **52**:173–187.

Takamura, N., and Yasuno, M., 1988, Sedimentation of phytoplankton populations dominated by *Microcystis* in a shallow lake, *J. Plankton Res.* **10**:283–299.

Takamura, N., Iwakuma, T., and Yasuno, M., 1985, Photosynthesis and primary production of *Microcystis aeruginosa Kütz.* in Lake Kasumigaura, *J. Plankton Res.* **7**:303–312.

Takamura, N., Iwakuma, T., and Yasuno, M., 1986, Photosynthesis of size-fractionated phytoplankton population in hypertrophic Lake Kasumigaura, Japan, *Arch. Hydrobiol.* **108**:235–257.

Takamura, N., Iwakuma, T., and Yasuno, M., 1987a, Uptake of ¹³C and ¹⁵N (ammonium, nitrate and urea) by *Microcystis* in Lake Kasumigaura, *J. Plankton Res.* **9**:151–165.

Takamura, N., Iwakuma, T., and Yasuno, M., 1987b, Primary production in Lake Kasumigaura, 1981–1985, *Jpn. J. Limnol.* **48**:S13–S38.

Turpin, D. H., 1983, Ammonium induced photosynthetic suppression in ammonium limited *Dunaliella tertiolecta* (Chlorophyta), *J. Phycol.* **19**:70–76.

Van den Heuvel, W. J. A., Smith, J. L., and Cohen, J. S., 1970, Gas liquid chromatography and mass spectrometry of carbon-13 enriched and deuterated amino acids as trimethylsilyl derivatives, *J. Chromatogr. Sci.* **8**:567–576.

Venrick, E. L., Beers, J. R., and Heinbokel, J. F., 1977, Possible consequences of containing microplankton for physiological rate measurements, *J. Exp. Mar. Biol. Ecol.* **26**:55–76.

Wada, E., Terazaki, M., Kabaya, Y., and Nemoto, T., 1987, ¹⁵N and ¹³C abundances in the Antarctic Ocean with emphasis on the biogeochemical structure of the food web, *Deep-Sea Res.* **34**:829–841.

Wakeham, S. G., and Canuel, E. A., 1988, Organic geochemistry of particulate matter in the eastern tropical North Pacific Ocean: Implications for particulate dynamics, *J. Mar. Res.* **46**:183–213.

Wallen, D. G., and Geen, G. H., 1971, The nature of the photosynthate in natural phytoplankton populations in relation to light quality, *Mar. Biol.* **10**:157–168.

Wolter, K., 1982, Bacterial incorporation of organic substances released by natural phytoplankton populations, *Mar. Ecol. Prog. Ser.* **7**:287–295.

Yanagisawa, K., and Kumazawa, K., 1982, Determination of ¹³C concentration by infrared absorption method using approximation formula, *J. Sci. Soil Manure Japan.* **53**:347–349 (in Japanese).

3

Sex in Ciliates

FERNANDO DINI and DENNIS NYBERG

1. Introduction

The existence of genetic variety affecting phenotype represents the presupposition for selection to operate and then for evolution to accomplish. Two means of achieving genetic variety can be basically distinguished: mutation and recombination. Both confer flexibility to the organisms enabling them to change as environmental conditions inevitably change. Understandably, variability has its hazards and its cost in terms of progeny inviability. Organisms have adopted quite different ecogenetic strategies to pursue the same aim: to manage in a balancing way the stability–variety dilemma.

The microbial world comprises prokaryotic and eukaryotic representatives which show quite different structure, organization, and life-style. Unicellular protists are certainly the first eukaryotes, hence tracing directly to prokaryotic ancestors, even if we still lack noncontroversial data on the coming-into-being of the eukaryotic cell, hence on its exact ancestry (see Corliss, 1987). The striking organismic differences do not, however, find their counterpart in the way prokaryotes and unicellular protists manage their genetic economy. Since they are haploid, bacteria have available for immediate use any mutation of recent origin. They can utilize recombinational genetic variety too throughout relatively simple "parasexual" systems. Mutational and recombinational varieties are both utilized profitably also by those unicellular protists showing the highest level of patterned integration of the elementary eukaryote and prokaryote mechanisms, certain differences in the genetic systems notwithstanding. All of this should not come as a surprise, yet it might be considered a mere corollary of the evolutionary ideas dealing with the management of the genetic information. The genetic material

FERNANDO DINI • Dipartimento di Scienze dell'Ambiente e del Territorio, Laboratorio di Protistologia, Università di Pisa, 56126 Pisa, Italy.   DENNIS NYBERG • Department of Biological Sciences, University of Illinois at Chicago, Chicago, Illinois 60680.

Advances in Microbial Ecology, Volume 13, edited by J. Gwynfryn Jones. Plenum Press, New York, 1993.

(new mutations included) is exactly duplicated at each cell cycle and equitably distributed to the progeny cells at cytokinesis. Since cell division related to cell cycle is the fundamental reproductive device in unicellular organisms, it traces directly to the same time, the same place, and the same first living being. The view that genetic exchange and recombination (fundamental processes qualifying sex) are such ancient features of life to trace their history back to the origin of life itself, gains great strength from considering the presence of sex and its characteristics in the three main evolutionary lines of living beings: the archaebacteria, the eubacteria (representing prokaryotes), and the eukaryotes (see Bernstein and Bernstein, 1991, for an authoritative review). It is well known that sexual processes occur in both eukaryotes and prokaryotes. Mating in the archaebacteria appears to be a well-established notion. Also, cyanobacteria have been recently found capable of pursuing sex. The similarities among recombination mechanisms and the sequence homologies among genes essential for recombination in prokaryotes and eukaryotes are impressive. The conclusion that sex was present in the primitive but inventive common ancestor of all three major evolutionary lineages seems to be inescapable.

Members of the phylum Ciliophora Doflein, 1901, constitute a highly differentiated assemblage characterized by a substantial degree of diversity, yet representing one of the most homogeneous groups of the kingdom Protista Haeckel, 1886 (Corliss, 1984; Small and Lynn, 1985; Sleigh, 1989; Lynn and Corliss, 1991). The possession of two kinds of nuclei (heterokaryotic condition), both the existence of an internal (subpellicular) complex system of kinetosomes closely associated with microtubules and microfibrils and a certain amount of external, patterned ciliature over the body, and the expression of sex in the typical form of temporary fusion of two partners (conjugation), briefly distinguish and characterize these predominantly heterotrophic forms. Ciliates are believed to represent one of the earliest evolutionary line of modern eukaryotes (Nanney, 1980; Nanney et al., 1989b). Nevertheless, notions which recognize ciliates as the modern-day surviving representatives of a eukaryotic evolutionary line from which multicellular organisms did arise, have received limited, if any, endorsement by evolutionists (see Corliss, 1989, for a review). What should be kept steadily in mind, however, is that ciliates, like prokaryotes, are cells but, at one and the same time, are certainly complete organisms which were successful in constraining all the integrated basic prokaryotic and eukaryotic biological functions of the multicellular organisms within the narrow boundary of the smallest living unit. In this perspective, even if ciliates represent a unique evolutionary experiment, they may be used profitably for comparative purposes as a model of a transitional evolutionary leap from the ancestral lines of prokaryotes to multicellular organisms endowed with differentiated tissues, inasmuch as we feel confident in believing that no new mechanism, but a better understanding of the system of integration of the basic processes of life, is to be sought. In the present chapter we address questions dealing with sex and sexuality and their explanations for ecological opportunities in these "eukaryotic microbes."

2. The Discovery of Sex in Ciliates

The growth of our knowledge of the microscopic organisms paralleled improvements in microscope construction. In the 17th century good magnifying lens systems became available thanks to skilled craftsmen, the most outstanding being Antonie van Leeuwenhoek. Historical grounds exist attributing to this pioneer the early discovery of protozoa and bacteria and also the first observations of pairing (for mating) in the ciliate *Paramecium,* as early as 1695. Leeuwenhoek, however, did not understand the meaning of such a pairing process. King (1693) was the first to claim the occurrence of a sexual process in ciliates. He believed that sex in ciliates was analogous to that of metazoa, and thereby erroneously interpreted *Euplotes* undergoing binary (transverse) fission as mating partners which exploited a sexual process. It remained for O. F. Müller (1786) to interpret correctly the longitudinal union between two paramecia as a sexual process (conjugation). Nevertheless, an erroneous concept of the sexual process by conjugation followed the general acceptance of its occurrence. The two partners of a pair were considered hermaphroditic (Balbiani, 1858; Stein, 1859) because the presently called macronucleus and micronucleus of each mating partner were considered the "ovary" and the "testis," respectively. According to Balbiani, the partners exchanged the "sperms" (actually the striations of the meiotic figures of the micronucleus) produced by the "testis" and a reciprocal fertilization of the produced "ova" (actually fragments of the degenerating macronucleus) occurred. According to Stein, self-fertilization versus cross-fertilization actually occurred in ciliates.

Following interpretations based on metazoan concepts, it was held that fertilized "ova" produced "embryos" which developed inside the paramecium body, and finally hatched. All of this was claimed to be supported by the occurrence of the ciliated stages within the body of members of the taxonomic group of Suctoria: flawless observation but askew interpretation. We must be greatly indebted mainly to Bütschli (1873, 1876) and Jickeli (1884) for their detailed investigations which led to recognition of the actual nature of the structures erroneously defined as "ovary" and "testis" as structures indicating a nuclear dimorphism with a large macronucleus and a small micronucleus. The fragmentation of the macronucleus and its replacement by an identical structure during the process of conjugation was correctly described. While Bütschli guessed at the occurrence of an exchange of micronuclear products between mating partners, Jickeli observed and described this important phenomenon not demonstrated earlier. Nevertheless, it remained for Maupas (1889) and Hertwig (1889) to describe independently with exactitude and detail the process of the pregamic (prezygotic) divisions of micronuclei, their reciprocal exchange between conjugating paramecia leading to concurrent fertilization of both partners. The excellent accounts of the foregoing protistologists represent the basis for the modern description of nuclear phenomena during conjugation. Since that time, many detailed observations have been produced dealing with conjugation of *Paramecium* as well as other ciliates. [Further historical information is extensively covered by Wichterman (1986).]

2.1. Conjugation

Conjugation represents the most popular type of sexual process in ciliates. Essentially, it is characterized by: (1) a cell mating; (2) nuclear phenomena with usually a two-step meiosis (prezygotic phenomena) leading to a double karyogamy (zygotic phenomena); (3) restoration of the vegetative nuclear state (postzygotic phenomena). Variation in details exists depending on the species (general review by Raikov, 1972). In specifying the full sequence of events we will refer to *Tetrahymena* (Fig. 1) in which the nuclear dimorphism, almost exclusively restricted to ciliates, has taken the simplest form of a single micronucleus [germ nucleus; of limited or replacing transcriptionally functions in the vegetative life of the organism; not indispensable for the survival of the individual, in some cases, at least for a period of time or under special circumstances, can be dispensed with entirely; serving as a repository of the unaltered germ line; diploid $(2n)$ in its genomic content; dividing mitotically during the vegetative phase and also meiotically during sexual processes] and only one macronucleus [somatic nucleus; transcriptionally active nucleus, responsible for the organism's phenotype; indispensable for the survival of the individual; much larger than the micronucleus; with a genomic content (polygenomic) resulting from a selective amplification of 10–90% of the micronuclear sequences, according to the ciliate considered; simply pinching in two at vegetative ("amitotic") fission or, as in the lower ciliates, not dividing at all being replaced by mitotic products of the micronucleus at each cell fission; disappearing during sexual phenomena to be replaced by a genetically new one of micronuclear origin at the beginning of the clonal cycle]. The conjugation process begins with two individuals which join (see Nanney, 1964, for review). There typically follow two meiotic divisions of the diploid micronucleus to produce four haploid products. Mitosis of one of the haploid products yields a "migratory" and a "stationary" pronuclei (gamete nuclei), while the remaining three meiotic products are destroyed. A mutual fertilization occurs following the simultaneous reciprocal passage of the migratory pronuclei through the contacting zone of membranes of partners to fuse with the waiting stationary pronuclei. (Because of their different behavior the migratory and stationary pronuclei are sometimes designated as "male" and "female" pro-

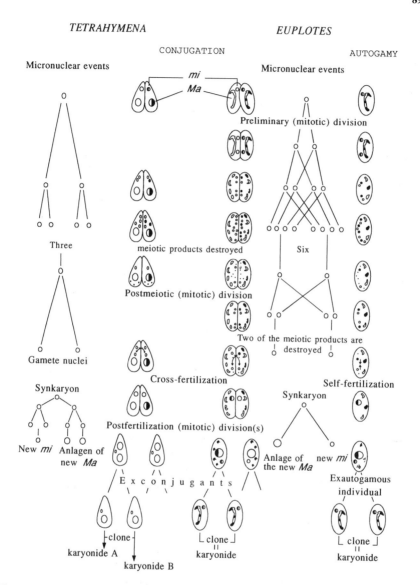

Figure 1. An outline of the nuclear events at conjugation in *Tetrahymena* and *Euplotes* and autogamy in *Euplotes*. Individuals heterozygous at the *A* locus (*A/a*) show white and black micro- and macro-nuclei; recessive homozygotes (*a/a*) have white nuclear apparatuses.

nuclei, respectively, reflecting some rather cast-off ideas widespread in the scientific community at the beginning of this century.) The nuclear fusion (karyogamy; amphimixis) yields an identical "synkaryon" or "fertilization nucleus" in each conjugating cell. Subsequently, the mating partners separate. In each "exconjugant" the synkaryon divides twice mitotically. Two out of the four mitotic products are induced to become compound constituting the "macronuclear primordia" or "anlagen," whereas the old macronucleus and one of the mitotic products are destroyed. At the first cell division after conjugation, the single remaining micronucleus divides, but the new macronuclei are assorted to the two daughter cells. Hence, each fission product of an exconjugant restores the standard nuclear equipment and achieves the vegetative state resuming asexual reproduction. It is worth noting that, because the parental nuclear framework is reestablished in the first fission products of the exconjugant, the exconjugant clone thus comprises the ancestors of two progeny lines sharing a common nuclear origin (karyonides) with exactly the same genotypes.

In other ciliate species the nuclear events appear to be more complicated because they are compound. For example, in *Euplotes* (Fig. 1) the set of nuclear events appear to be more entangled, although the restoration of the vegetative condition is simpler (reviewed by Nobili *et al.,* 1978); only one postzygotic division of the synkaryon usually occurs before the macronucleus is induced, no assortment of nuclei follows, and the exconjugant clone thus is composed of a single karyonide. *Euplotes* represents only one of the many "more complicated" examples that have been described. Variation in the number of micronuclei and macronuclei is very large among ciliates. It affects the course of nuclear events during conjugation, always leading, however, to the standard vegetative condition with renewed structures and genotypes. With reference to genotypes, one should not make categorical statements involving the genetic consequences of conjugation. Comparing, for example, the course of the nuclear reorganization during conjugation of *Tetrahymena* and *Euplotes* (see Fig. 1), it appears evident that differences may occur in the patterns of the genetic relationships among progeny of a conjugating pair. In each mate of a *Tetrahymena* pair only one randomly chosen product of meiosis divides mitotically to produce identical (sister) pronuclei (gamete nuclei). Pronuclear exchange and fertilization establish in the mates identical synkarya undergoing subsequent mitotic nuclear division. Hence, exconjugants (and karyonides) are always isogenic, that is, have alike genotypes. It is axiomatic that crossing a population heterozygous at the A locus (A/a) with a homozygous recessive one (a/a), a classical Mendelian $1(A/a):1(a/a)$ ratio is obtained, but what is worth stressing is that although different genotypes are produced in the progeny, differences do not occur among the exconjugants of the same mated pair; these last will show the same genotype, A/a-A/a or a/a-a/a. Such a behavior does not hold for *Euplotes*. As outlined in Fig. 1, in each coconjugant of each pair the micronucleus first divides mitotically (preliminary division), then the two resulting (identical) diploid nuclei pass through meiosis and give rise to eight haploid nuclei. Two of these eight meiotic products persist (six degenerating). They replicate and enter the postmeiotic (mitotic) division, generating two sets of genetically identical haploid nuclei. Two out of the four products of this division are destroyed, while the remaining two become the gamete nuclei. The possibility thus exists for the gamete nuclei to be postmeiotic-division sister nuclei (genetically identical) or postmeiotic-division nonsisters (carrying different genotypes). If a mate is heterozygous (A/a) and we assume randomness in the two sequential nuclear selection events, then the likelihood of two gamete nuclei carrying the same or different alleles at the A locus is 13(A-A) to 16(A-a) to 13(a-a) (see Dini and Luporini, 1980, following rationalization of T. M. Sonneborn and E. Beheme). Involving two populations of *Euplotes* in what is essentially a testcross, $A/a \times a/a$, the expected Mendelian segregation pattern, 1(A/a):1(a/a), will be found, but the "rule" of the iso-genicity of the two exconjugants from the same mated pair is violated. Both exconjugants should be alike at the A locus in 26/42 (13/42, A/a-A/a + 13/42, a/a-a/a) or 13/21 of the pairs, unlike in 16/42 (A/a-a/a) or 8/21, a ratio of 13:8. There is genetic evidence (reviewed by Dini, 1984) that this actually occurs, at least in some populations of *Euplotes* species. However, flexibility of the pattern of exconjugants' relationship goes further. In different populations representative of the *E. vannus-crassus-minuta* group, Lueken (1973) and Machelon (1983) reported the lack of the postmeiotic division, the two surviving products of meiosis out of the eight produced (see Fig. 1) thus becoming directly the gamete nuclei. Consequently, the pattern of the genetic relationships between exconjugants varies. Considering the same A locus, randomness of choice of two meiotic products gives the following probabilities for the persisting gamete nuclei in a mate, 6/28 A-A, 16/28 A-a, 6/28 a/a, and for the exconjugants of a mated pair to be alike, 6/28 + 6/28 = 12/28 or 3/7, or unlike, 16/28 or 4/7, a ratio of 3:4. If we assume a widespread heterozygosity even of only one mate, the gamete nuclei of this latter will in any case be virtually different because they have been derived from two different products of meiosis, and consequently the two exconjugants of a mated pair will also always be unlike in genotypes. When the cytogenetic pattern entails a postmeiotic (mitotic) division, on the other hand, the possibility persists for the gamete nuclei of each mate to be genotypically identical, and for the two exconjugants of a mated pair to carry alike genotypes, a high degree of heterozygosity of the mates notwithstanding.

Even fine modulations of the cytogenetic pattern occur in ciliates and these affect the genetic relationships of siblings. A large variety of alternatives can thus be exploited for tuning the genetic economy to the "chosen" strategy. We will return to a consideration of this matter at a later time. Here we want to stress only that the genetic consequences of conjugation in *Tetrahymena* and *Euplotes* are quite different, but not less than the habitats they colonize.

The conceptual difficulty encountered in understanding the sequence of developmental phenomena which characterize ciliate conjugation is the unconventional heritage link between parents and progeny. Each parent mating contributes all its building material to a single progeny individual and disappears from the population setting. In doing this, parents undergo a structural reorganization which entails a turnover of the nuclear apparatus as well as of portions of the cortical and endoplasmic systems to a greater or lesser extent. Finally, the structural pattern bequeathed to the offspring remains the same but organized with new manufactured parts (for review, see Ng, 1990a). This represents an extreme reproductive strategy: two parents transform directly into two progeny individuals. In some cases, the two co-conjugants fuse completely forming only one progeny individual ("total conjugation"; see also Section 3).

At least in the short term, reproduction implies an increase of at least one in the number of individuals. On the basis of this premise, conjugation in ciliates cannot be considered reproduction, because the number of individuals after the exploitation of the process remains unchanged or even reduced. To increase the number of individuals, ciliates rely on the asexual reproduction which usually takes the form of binary fission, generally transverse, more accurately, homothetogenic (see Lynn and Corliss, 1991; see also Frankel, 1989). On the other hand, if reproduction is understood as no more than the creation of an ontogenetically new individual, then the consideration of increase in number becomes peripheral. Conjugation in ciliates actually involves genetic reorganization of the entire nuclear apparatus as well as a renewal *in situ* of the maternal structures (soma) under the control of the new genomic program; an ontogenetically sharp distinction between the parent and the offspring is thus provided. In this sense, ciliates undergo true sexual reproduction, inasmuch as conjugation should be reevaluated within the framework of reproductive phenomena of multicellular organisms. We are aware that the question is anything but semantic. Its evolutionary implications are large. A discussion of the issue, however, is beyond the scope of the present review, and we refer the reader to Ng (1990b) who dealt with this topic exhaustively. Be this as it may, no doubts exist about the sexual nature of conjugation typified by meiosis and recombination following the typical eukaryotic rules.

2.2. Autogamy and Other Sexual Variations

Numerous within-species variations in the typical nuclear behavior at conjugation have been described. Several of these deserve comment because they are potentially adjuvant factors in determining the way a species manages its requirement for stability and flexibility. One variation is represented by "cytogamy." It was discovered and described by Wichterman (1939) as occurring in joined individuals of *P. caudatum*. There is no exchange of pronuclei between mates, but a fusion of migratory and stationary pronuclei from within the same mating partner. Cytogamy can be considered a process of self-fertilization occurring in paired individuals, that is, a form of inbreeding.

Another variation is "macronuclear regeneration" described by Sonneborn (1940) in stocks of different species of the *P. aurelia* complex. During conjugation of paramecia the macronucleus of each partner is fragmented and finally resorbed. Sometimes, fragments of this disintegrated, old (parental) macronucleus are not resorbed but grow, resume the size of the normal macronucleus becoming the functional macronucleus of the individual. New micronuclei and old macronuclei carrying different genotypes may thus coexist (heterokaryons). Since the phenotype is controlled by the macronucleus, macronuclear regeneration leads to purely maternal inheritance.

Both cytogamy and macronuclear regeneration are powerful tools to be used for experimental purposes, particularly because they can be induced at will. Nevertheless, laboratory evidence dealing with the occurring frequency and the peculiarity of triggering conditions render doubtful the possibility that these phenomena can play an actual role in the ecogenetic strategy of the species. On the contrary, biological and genetic observations strongly support the notion that autogamy is an important option exploited by some ciliate species to manage their genetic economies (Sonneborn, 1957; Pringle and Beale, 1960; Nyberg, 1975; Luporini and Dini, 1977; Berger and Rahemtullah, 1990; Kosaka, 1992). The basic nuclear behavior is that observed in cytogamy, except that it occurs in single unpaired cells. Hertwig (1889) observed in *P. aurelia* a reorganization process that he considered a "parthenogenetic" process. Woodruff and Erdmann (1914) studied the phenomenon at issue extensively and called it "endomixis." They claimed that neither meiosis nor karyogamy occurred during endomixis. Diller (1936) provided cytological evidence for the formation of pronuclei and their fusion in the same individual; stages overlooked by Woodruff and Erdmann. Later on, Sonneborn (1939a) produced definitive genetic evidence of autogamy. He showed the failure to maintain the heterozygous condition by exautogamous *P. aurelia;* as expected at autogamy, homozygotes arise. Moreover, he found that only homozygotes arise, concluding that autogamy in the species at issue regularly involves fusion between identical, sister, haploid gamete nuclei. [The close similarity of the postzygotic cytogenetic events with *Tetrahymena* (see Fig. 1) accounts for the genetic consequences of autogamy in *Paramecium;* refer to Beale (1954) and Preer (1986) for reviews.]

Since autogamy entails self-fertilization, it represents a form of inbreeding, that is, a genetic system leading to homozygosity. In *Paramecium,* autogamy represents the extreme form of inbreeding for its ability to produce completely homozygous offspring at the first generation. Variation in the cascade of nuclear events characterizing development of sexual process in different ciliate species exploiting autogamy may, however, affect also its genetic consequences. According to the cytogenetic pattern pursued, one or more generations may be necessary to accomplish homozygosity, if it occurs at all. In *Euplotes* the relationship between the two gamete nuclei may vary. The sequence of nuclear events in autogamy (Fig. 1) is seemingly identical to that of conjugation, except that synkaryon is formed by the union of the two gamete nuclei from a single, unpaired individual. As reported above dealing with cytogenetic events at conjugation, there is no uniformity in whether the two gamete nuclei arise from one or two different (haploid) products of meiosis. If cells are heterozygous at the *A* locus (*A*/*a*), the ratio for synkarya at autogamy, on the assumption of randomness, should be 13(*A*/*A*) to 16 (*A*/*a*) to 13(*a*/*a*). Hence, autogamy in *Euplotes* would be associated with an enforced and not immediate homozygosity as in *Paramecium;* the frequency of the heterozygous genotypic combinations would continue to decay at a regular rate in subsequent autogamous generations. This does not actually occur at least in some marine species of *Euplotes* (reviewed by Dini, 1984), but the appearance of a nonparental genotype is an extremely rare or nonexistent event in heterozygous wild stocks that have passed through many autogamies. The cytogenetic mechanism that produces the perceived end result is obscure; a speculative but testable model has been provided (Dini and Giannì, 1985).

2.3. The Life Cycle of Ciliates

Since the early 19th century the scientific community of protistologists centered a great deal of interest on the problem of whether or not a ciliate was capable of living and multiplying indefinitely provided it had adequate food and its other physiological needs were met. Ehrenberg (1838), Enriques (1907), Woodruff (1908), and Chatton and Chatton (1923) maintained that *Paramecium* and other free-living ciliates were able to divide and reproduce indefinitely, avoiding natural death. The unicellular nature of ciliates, combining into the same entity the reproductive and individual units, induced Weismann (1891) to equate these organisms to the germinal protoplasm of metazoa. As independent living units their germinal protoplasm has no opportunities to interact with somatic protoplasms; interactions occurring in metazoa and responsible for their old age and natural death. Consequently, Weismann contended that ciliates were potentially immortal like germ cells of metazoa. On the other hand, Maupas (1888), Hertwig (1892), Calkins (1904), and others, maintained that ciliates can perform an uninterrupted series of binary fissions lasting for a certain number of months, but finally a waning vitality occurs resulting in natural death. It was therefore concluded that ciliates have a finite life cycle and follow the same physiological laws of aging as metazoa. Maupas (1889), Calkins (1933), and Jennings (1939a) went beyond this point to assert the partitioning of the ciliate's life history into developmental stages, and that the occurrence of a sexual process may postpone old age characterized by the onset of cell abnormalities and a receding vitality leading to a dwindling population.

However, the thesis that ciliates would be deemed to be immortal appeared unambiguous. The literature continued to record reports indicating that in carefully controlled, long-term isolation cultures, binary fission, at least in some cultures of *Paramecium* species, could continue endlessly. Cases of clonal death were ascribed to poor techniques or inadequate culture medium. The controversy came to a critical point when Sonneborn (1954) demonstrated unequivocally in *P. primaurelia, P. biaurelia,* and *P. tetraurelia* that (1) cultures periodically reinitiate their life cycles with new fertilizations; (2) lines prevented from undergoing fertilization, by preventing their starvation, showed a typical "Maupasian life cycle" comprising the sequential stages of immaturity, maturity, and senescence which terminated in the line death within hundreds of cell fissions. Such findings were confirmed by later investigators studying either representatives of the *P. aurelia* complex of species, or other ciliate species, *P. bursaria, P. caudatum, P. multimicronucleatum, P. jenningsi, E. patella, E. crassus, E. ninuta, E. woodruffi, Oxytricha bifaria, Stylonychia mytilus, Tokophrya lemnarum, T. rostrata,* species of the *T. pyriformis* complex (general reviews by Sonneborn, 1957; Siegel, 1967; J. R. Preer, 1968; Bleyman, 1971; Grell, 1973; Nanney, 1974, 1977, 1980, 1986; Nanney and McCoy, 1976; Smith-Sonneborn, 1981; Takagi, 1988).

All of this supports the notion that fertilization is an obligatory part of the life cycle of at least some ciliates, though perhaps not all. In some species sex takes the form of conjugation (e.g., members of the *T. pyriformis* complex, most populations of the *E. vannus-crassus-minuta* group, and syngen 2 of *E. woodruffi*), in others of autogamy (e.g., *T. rostrata,* and "autogamy group" of *E. woodruffi*), and finally in others of both conjugation and autogamy (e.g., *P. aurelia* species complex, some populations comprising the *E. vannus-crassus-minuta* group, and syngens 1 and 2 of *E. woodruffi*). As far as this latter situation is concerned, species are not uniform in the timings of the two kinds of sex. The range of variation—on a contemporaneousness–succession (with a priority for conjugation) scale—is considerable, even among members of the same species group. On the other hand, each species is a separate system with its species-specific niche vicissitudes, hence with peculiar requirements of genetic stability (autogamy = self-fertilization) versus variety (conjugation = cross-fertilization) balance. Whatever kind of sexual process occurs, fertilization brings about rejuvenation and marks the onset of a new life cycle (Fig. 2). The resultant progeny then pass seriatim through the stages of immaturity, maturity, senescence, and finally death if a sexual event does not interrupt the progression and reinitiate the cycle. Death can be avoided, however, provided that fertilization occurs when the clone has not progressed too far through senescence; if this latter is the

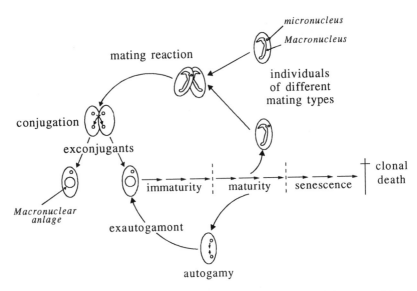

Figure 2. Diagram outlining the life cycle of the different kinds of populations comprising the *Euplotes vannus-crassus-minuta* group.

case, an inevitable decline in the capacity to survive sexual reorganization follows.

Given the large variability shown by ciliate species, it is unsafe to make generalizations dealing with the length of the various life-cycle stages or of the life span, even for a group of closely related species. (Variations occur also within species even if to a lower degree.) For example, the numbers of fissions spanning the sexual immaturity stage and the life span [two parameters believed to be roughly proportional; Smith-Sonneborn (1981)] are the following in the species listed below: 30/340 in *P. primaurelia*, 0/250 in *P. tetraurelia*, 480/2600 in *P. bursaria*, 176/1300 in *E. patella*. Interspecific variation and genetic control (specifically, as far as immaturity is concerned) of the life-cycle stages strongly suggest their adaptive significance. Results of empirical approaches argue that life cycle characteristics may have been prompted by natural selection in response to the ciliate species' requirements for a recombinational or mutational genetic variety (Nyberg, 1974, 1975). The form of sex exploited can operate synergistically with the other life cycle characteristics in accomplishing the species' genetic strategy. In *P. tetraurelia* there is no absolute immature period for autogamy (Berger and Rahemtullah, 1990). The occurrence in nature of potential mating partners appears to be a rare event (Landis, 1981, 1987). Together the observations argue for a strong commitment of this species to autogamy, rendering conjugation and cross-fertilization a trivial sexual option. On the other hand, as reported earlier, autogamy in *Paramecium* produces completely homozygous genotypes. The virtual lack of the immaturity period combined with the genetic properties of autogamy represent the most efficient genetic system to bring mutational variety to the expression in a diploid organism, as efficiently as a haploid bacterium can do. Moreover, rejuvenation brought about by fertilization should not be underrated.

Although *P. tetraurelia* has missed the stage of immaturity from its cycle, the capacity to pass through maturity and senescence to die on schedule is maintained. At variance, other ciliates lack the typical terminal stage. Some stocks of *P. multimicronucleatum* (Takagi, 1988) and strains of *P. bursaria* (for review, see Wichterman, 1986) seem capable of indefinite cell divisions without the occurrence of senescence and death. It should be worth noting that, if the maturity stage lasts for decades, it may be difficult to show the occurrence of a life span and death. Moreover, the oversight of a nuclear reorganization of sexual nature in the cultures cannot be definitively eliminated. This does not appear to be the case of the laboratory strains of *T. pyriformis* in which sex is forbidden by their amicronucleate condition. These strains have been maintained in continuous cultivation for likely over 70 years (Lwoff, 1923) without a decline in vitality (fission rate), that is, symptoms of senescence have not been observed, thereby supporting the idea of a potential "somatic" immortality of asexually reproducing ciliates. Amicronucleate strains of *T. pyriformis* are not special, however, in their capacity for indefinite somatic multiplication. Also, micronucleate strains of *T. thermophila* established directly from nature or generated from crosses in the laboratory show an indefinite maturity period following a sexual immaturity lasting about 50 fissions (for review, see Nanney, 1974). Nevertheless, notwithstanding an ability to continue growth and mating indefinitely, the capacity of these micronucleate strains to participate successfully in conjugation comes to an end: the ability to produce viable progeny in crosses drops gradually to zero over a few years of growth in mass culture. The basis for such a "genetic" death appears to be the exposure following sexual reorganization of the effects of "accidental" mutational events accumulated in the micronucleus during the vegetative reproduction. The intriguing feature of these strains is their irregularity with respect to the onset of the genetic death, in line with the accidental nature of its mutational basis. In diametric opposition is the fixed vegetative span (somatic senescence) combined with a genetic death of conspecific strains produced in the course of an inbreeding program. A possible evolutionary rationale behind this entangled state of affairs is that (1) the genome of ciliate species could likely support an indefinitely lasting vegetative vitality if this were not offset by constraints posed by evolutionary choices, and (2) the life history characteristics are not mere by-products of the individual organization, but rather a set of fine-tuned parameters prompted by natural selection to determine the genetic economy of the species.

Several ciliates have no trace of micronuclei. Nevertheless, there are no theoretical reasons to exclude that they may have had a substantial evolutionary history without such a kind of nucleus, and hence without sexual processes; the compulsiveness of the life cycle can be rejected. The foregoing survey of the micronucleate species shows large and qualitative differences in the relationships among life span–fertilization–life cycle stages. It may be worth noting, however, that the maintenance of micronuclei in the great majority of the species points to the evolutionary importance of the sexual process in ciliates. The peripheral or irrelevant role of micronuclei in the asexual reproduction strengthens such a conclusion. We have not yet learned how to mate many micronucleate ciliates, so there may be some new ideas arising about life cycle in the future, but the parallels with other eukaryotes (fertilization, immaturity, maturity, genetic senescence, and finally somatic senescence) suggest that the major ideas about the life cycle will not change very much, if at all. A teleonomic rationale can be assigned to varying characteristics of the life cycle, but thus far it largely resists a sufficient causal analysis. The biggest change in the study of sex in ciliates is toward considering evolutionary and ecological issues and away from a morphological orientation which tended to focus on labeling cell structures of developmental changes as "female" or "male."

3. The Species Concept and Sex

The existence of a staggering diversity of forms of life is one of the general features of the living world which has always elicited humbling feelings of wonder in humans. In all ages man has sought satisfying means to partition this naturally occurring variation in forms among discontinuous quanta, in other words, to operate a classification pursuing the goal to render the immense diversity of organisms manageable.

3.1. Morphospecies

Division of living beings into species on the basis of morphological discriminants is a perception which preceded any notion of evolution. In this century, the concept of species has been embodied in the theory of evolution and the key idea found on the reproductive isolation of a group of interbreeding organisms, in contrast to "essential" morphological similarities. Reproductive isolation producing discontinuous genetic and structural arrays renders the species level of classification more effective than higher-level taxonomic categories in forming "natural" groupings, insofar as discontinuities are observable realities.

The contemporary definition provided by Mayr (1970) stresses the three main biological features of the species: a reproductive community, a genetic unit, and an ecological unit. This last feature relates the species to the exploitation of a specific niche, and endorses the different species' connotation of an array of related gene combinations that occupy one of the not yet exploited adaptive peaks, in the sense proposed by Wright (1932).

By making a conservative estimate of total extant species diversity, there are about 1.4 million species of contemporary organisms (Grant, 1985). It is part of the accepted wisdom of protistologists that the distribution of ciliates is world-wide; ubiquitous and thus cosmopolitan in distribution appear more accurate connotations for these protists. Since their unicellular nature (ranges in body sizes and volumes of modern forms, viz., 10–4500 μm and 10^2–10^9 μm^3, respectively), it is conceivable to assume that ciliates perceive the environmental diversity on a smaller scale than most of the representative taxa of the Animalia, Plantae, and Fungi kingdoms. Within the larger ecosystems, they live in micro-habitats represented by small regions as tiny as a few cubic centimeters, within a body of water or moist environment of a broad variety of kinds (soil, vegetation, bodies of animals and plants, etc.). It follows that a very large number of adaptive peaks should be comparatively available for ciliates to be exploited, and then they should comprise a bulk of species. The ancient origin of ciliates (see Section 1) may be considered another important factor for their passive dispersal all over the world, thereby colonizing microhabitats of all kinds, an intrinsic low vagility notwithstanding. The ca. 7200 (Corliss, 1979) total living species known to date for the phylum Ciliophora challenge the foregoing assumptions and violate expectations. [Including also the fossil species, the total number increases to 8000 (Lynn and Corliss, 1991), but the overall picture does not essentially change.] Moreover, the assertion that a number of these species have not been described rigorously enough, is not refutable. One could argue that ciliates are special in their species-wide, genetically conditioned homeostatic mechanisms determining a remarkable tolerance or adaptability to a broad range of environmental conditions. A huge stretch of the niche breadth would follow with the possibility for individuals to overwhelm ecological forces that favor microhabitat adaptation, resulting in the mixing of locally differentiated genotypes. There are definite limits, however, to the amount of genetic variability that can be arranged in a single gene pool without producing a breaking of coadapted gene complexes resulting in high proportions of poorly fit recombinants. Selective forces may then accumulate to inhibit mating between "strangers" and the species begins to disintegrate into subunits; the basis for a species multiplication would be thus laid. By no means does this imply that species boundaries of all ciliate species are locally restricted. Certainly, a variation in the structural pattern of species exists; the genetic and developmental potentialities of a given species, and its past history determine population structure (see Sonneborn, 1957; Nyberg, 1974, 1981a; Dini, 1984). Yet, conventional ideas that ciliate species are typically cosmopolitan may require modification (see Borror, 1980).

Among the different explanations which could be conjectured to account for the relatively scanty number of ciliate species, the possibility relating the feature at issue to the young age of protistology as a branch of learning makes much more sense. In subjecting this possibility to close scrutiny, let us consider the situation in the genus *Paramecium* O. F. Müller, 1773, which is the most familiar ciliate described first by Leeuwenhoek (1674), repeatedly observed in the 18th and 19th centuries during which it was elected as the favorite object of study, and continuing to represent today one of the most useful instruments for scientific investigation. Well-defined "nominal" species which at present are recognized as valid and acceptable by most taxonomists are no more than 10–11 (see Vivier, 1974; Wichterman, 1986): *P. aurelia* O. F. Müller, 1773, *P. bursaria* (Ehrenberg, 1831) Focke, 1836, *P. caudatum* Ehrenberg, 1838, *P. trichium* Stokes, 1885 (= *P. putrinum*), *P. multimicronucleatum* Powers and Mitchell, 1910, *P. calkinsi* Woodruff, 1921, *P. polycaryum* Woodruff and Spencer, 1923, *P. woodruffi* Wenrich, 1928, *P. jenningsi* Diller and Earl, 1958, *P. wichtermani* Mohammed and Nashid, 1968, and *P. africanum* Dragesco, 1970. All these species have been based largely on established morphological criteria (see Wichterman, 1986) following the classic Linnean system. The criteria can be used effectively and easily by any systematist endowed with simple tools and few technical procedures. In connection with this, it is worth pointing out that 8 out of the 11 species were described long ago; only 3 have been added recently: *P. jenningsi* (in 1958), *P. wichtermani* (1968), and *P. africanum* (1970). Even with a distinct amplification in availability during the last four decades of sophisticated methodologies, particularly the morphometric and ultrastructural ones, the number of *Paramecium* species has not steadily increased. Hence, even if protistology was given a substantial boost not long ago, nevertheless it is a branch of learning which was born with its eyes open.

3.2. The Genetic Species Paradigm

The classification of the above-mentioned taxa at the species level is typically phenetic in nature, based on an *a posteriori* assumption from incomplete data, hence artificial to some extent. Moreover, developmental variations of morphological (cortical) characteristics of classical taxonomic relevance, and the facility with which these variations, showing a positional information transmission (Frankel, 1989), may be perpetuated, argue for the use of extreme caution in making taxonomic decisions with regard to ciliates. Indeed, two main discoveries soon posed taxonomic–nomenclatural problems dealing with *Paramecium* species. The ability to thrive and perpetuate pure lines (consisting of the strictly asexual progeny of identical genotype and phenotype descending from a single ancestor) in the laboratory and the discovery of "mating types" (Sonneborn, 1937) paved the way for an empirical study of cellular, nonmorphological characteristics. Mixing *P. aurelia* cultures of diverse sources in pairwise combinations, Sonneborn often observed cell-to-cell pairing followed by conjugation. Matings occurred under special circumstances that may be highly species specific, but, in any case, a common requirement for mating is the expression by the mixed individuals of different kinds of physiological properties determining mating affinities. If the two mixed cultures of different origin are pure lines, that is, cell populations where fission products refrain from mating, then the component individuals are representative of two distinct physiological classes, that is, of two mating types (see Section 4). These do not usually distinguish one from the other in either form or behavior, and are thus ordinarily identified by the use of living reference lines. The mating type is an inherited character (see Section 5.2).

The occurrence of mating types brings into focus the problem of sexual differentiation in ciliates. The use of the term *sexes* in referring to the mating types should be avoided because it is misleading. First, the individuals mating are usually indistinguishable, and the sexual differentiation defining sexes fails. Second, ciliate mates are diploid "gamonts" producing gamete nuclei to be involved in an act of reciprocal fertilization at conjugation, so that each mate is in a sense hermaphroditic or, as often referred to, monoecious. (The two terms of zoological and botanical origin, respectively, are not strictly equivalent, however, for monoecy refers to the plant sporophyte whereas hermaphroditism is a phenomenon related to the gamete-producing animal individual.) Third, intraspecific groupings into physiological classes of individuals often lead to the identification of two mating types (binary or bipolar systems), frequently of some (multiple or multipolar systems), seldom of many (high-multiple systems); the bipolarity commonly attributed to sexes thus has no connection with the ciliates' mating types.

Different mating types perceive a difference that is not apparent to the observer and interact for mating. Conjugation entails meiosis and fusion of separate hereditary determinants. Hence, ciliates also enjoy sex. Must we consider this a kind of sex without "sexuality," viz., sexual differentiation? Each individual ciliate exploiting sex generally produces two gamete nuclei following a meiotic process. These behave differently, one moves and the other rests undergoing fertilization. Sometimes, the gamete nuclei show a different morphology (see Raikov, 1972, for review). These behavioral and morphological differences mimic the differences between gametes, thereby warranting to some extent the connotation of "male" and "female" to the migratory and stationary pronuclei, respectively. In lower ciliates each mate of a conjugating pair produces more of both migratory and stationary pronuclei; a phenomenon considered to reflect a homology with the bisexual differentiation of gametes. In the most advanced instances of pronounced morphological differences between conjugating partners, both mates produce a single gamete and fertilization follows the complete fusion of the smaller partner (microconjugant) with the larger one (macroconjugant), a process called "total conjugation." All these considerations together lend support for the view that attributes to the differences between gamete nuclei the earmarks of sexuality. The mating-type differences may be envisaged as a phenomenon superimposed over sexuality, allowing hermaphroditic individuals to discriminate between "self" and "nonself"; an instance which has its counterpart in the self-fertilization-inhibiting systems of higher plants (Raikov, 1972; Ammermann, 1982; Dini and Luporini, 1985). Viewed from this perspective, the process of total conjugation that entails complete fusion of mates may hardly be considered "true syngamy," as it is often referred to.

The discovery of mating types provided a tool not only for controlled breeding analyses but also for gaining insights into the relationships among morphologically indistinguishable stocks (consisting of the descendants of a single individual brought in from nature) taken from various regions of the earth. It appeared that all of the mating types showing pair interaction constituted a "mating group" whose representatives were capable of mating with all other representatives of different type(s) within the group, but not with individuals belonging to other groups. Sorting all the available stocks that corresponded to the general description of the nominal species *P. aurelia* into those that could or could not breed, Sonneborn (1939b) came out with different mating groups, each comprising a set of two mating types (referred to as "Odd" and "Even"). The reproductive isolation of mating groups was complete, supported by either premating and/or postmating isolation mechanisms (Sonneborn, 1974); no introgression could be demonstrated (Levine, 1953; Haggard, 1974). Sonneborn (1947) suddenly recognized that these mating groups were good "biological species" with no gene flow between them (referred to as "full genetic species"), but refrained from according them specific binomial designations because their identification by means of tests with standard living reference stocks was burdensome, more than could reasonably be expected for routine identification. These genetic species were first named "varieties" (Sonneborn, 1939b) and later "syngens" (Sonneborn, 1957). Neither terms ever received a favorable hearing among systematists who give supporters no credit for understanding evolution [Mayr (1982); details on particular points of this disagreement can be found in Nanney (1986)]. When the *P. aurelia* syngens have been found identifiable by electrophoretic patterns of selected isozymes (Tait, 1970; Allen and Weremiuk, 1971; Allen *et al.*, 1973) without resorting to living tester stocks, then Sonneborn (1975) realized that time was ripe to Christen syngens with Latin binomials. The classical nominal species *P. aurelia* was thus split into 14 new named species. Recently, *P. sonneborni* (Aufderheide *et al.*, 1983) has been added as the 15th member to the *P. aurelia* species complex. The virtual absence of morphological differences among them qualifies these species as "sibling species" (Mayr, 1942) of the *P. aurelia* species complex. The species equation, varieties = syngens (genetic species) = formally named (latinized) sibling species, was thus completed. Nevertheless, the term *syngen* continues to be useful when the only practicable method available to discriminate between genetically isolated populations requires living tester stocks; its retention in the protistological literature is thus warranted.

3.3. Taxonomic Complexity in Marine *Euplotes*

Foundations laid by Sonneborn have been followed by investigators in analyzing other ciliate nominal species. Among these, *T. pyriformis* (Ehrenberg, 1830) Lwoff, 1947, is one of the most thoroughly studied. Interbreeding stocks of this form have been assigned to 16 sibling species, provided with Linnean names (Nanney and McCoy, 1976; Nyberg, 1981b; Simon *et al.*, 1985), after a period of being designated as "varieties" and "syngens" based on patterns of interfertility relationships (Gruchy, 1955; Nanney, 1968; Elliott, 1973).

The *T. pyriformis* species complex indicates that the characteristics described for the *P. aurelia* complex are not generalized. For example, each species of this last complex comprises two mating types (binary system), yet species of the *T. pyriformis* complex each contain three to nine different mating types (multiple system). In a system like this, conjugation follows the interaction between individuals of any two different mating types.

Euplotes crassus and *S. mytilus*—two other extensively studied nominal species—constitute a further variation on the same multiple-system theme. Their systems are highly multiple, being represented by at least 38 (Dini and Luporini, 1975) and 100 (Ammermann, 1982) different mating types, respectively. Making allowance for the laborious procedure needed for the mating-type identification, the number possible in these two forms would seem to run into the hundreds if one cared enough to invest the effort. The number of mating types comprising a species is, however, only a detail of its life history. The length of the period of immaturity following sexual processes, the total life span, the mode of mating-type determination, the presence of selfing (a shift from interclonal to intraclonal conjugation), the ability to exploit autogamy, the occurrence of resting cysts, the absence of micronucleus, and nutritional requirements are other life history features which, all together, may meaningfully contribute to determine the genetic economy, and in turn the structure of the species and its speciation pattern [see the seminal review of Sonneborn (1957)]. *E. crassus* and *S. mytilus* appear to be far less speciose than *P. aurelia* and *T. pyriformis* (Table I). Notwithstanding a certain amount of intersibling species variation within each nominal species, shifts of genetic "life-style" among these forms could render anything but fortuitous such a dissimilar evolutionary behavior.

Table I. Features of the Nominal Species Analyzed to Date for the Relationships among Conspecific Morphologically Indistinguishable Stocks

Nominal species	Mating-type[a] system	No. of sibling species	References
Aspidisca sp.	B	4	Dini et al. (1987)
Colpidium truncatum	M	1	Sonneborn (1957)
Euplotes crassus[b]	H-M	5	See text
E. eurystomus	B	5	Katashima (1959)
E. patella	M	2	Kimball (1942), Pierson (1943), Katashima (1961)
E. woodruffi	M	3	Kosaka (1982, 1990, 1992)
Glaucoma scintillans	M	5	Cho (1971)
Oxytricha bifaria	M	2[c]	Kay (1946), Siegel (1956)
Paramecium aurelia	B	15[d]	See text
P. bursaria	M	6	Jennings (1939b), Chen (1946), Bomford (1966)
P. calkinsi	B	2/4[e]	Nakata (1958), Wichterman (1951), Sonneborn (1970)
P. caudatum	B	16[f]	Gilman (1939, 1950), Hiwatashi (1949), Sonneborn (1970), Khadem and Gibson (1985)
P. jenningsi	B	1	Sonneborn (1958), Przyboz (1975)
P. multimicronucleatum	B	4/5[e]	Giese and Arkoosh (1939), Sonneborn (1958, 1970)
P. polycaryum	B	1	Hayashi and Takayanagi (1962)
P. trichium (=P. putrinum)	M	5	Jankowski (1962, 1972), Ammermann (1966), Sonneborn (1970)
P. woodruffi	B	1	Ammermann (1966)
Pseudourostyla levis	M	2	Takahashi (1973)
Stylonychia mytilus	H-M	2[d]	See text
S. pustulata	M	3	Rao (1958)
S. putrina	M	2	Downs (1959)
Tetrahymena pyriformis	M	16[d]	See text
T. vorax	M	4[d]	Vaudaux et al. (1977), Williams et al. (1984), Simon et al. (1985)
Uronychia transfuga	M	2	Reiff (1968)

[a]B, binary mating-type system (with two types); M, multiple (with more than two types but finite in number; closed system); H-M, high-multiple (with many types virtually infinite in number; open system).

[b]After the taxonomic revision of Schlegel et al. (1988) and Valbonesi et al. (1988).

[c]Unconfirmed data.

[d]Sibling species (comprising interbreeding units) accorded separate binomial species names because readily identifiable by procedures that do not require reference stocks; the unlabeled ones are referred to as "syngens" being defined only on the basis of interfertility criterion.

[e]The exact number of syngens comprising the nominal species has not been definitively established.

[f]The status of four syngens has recently been questioned (Tsukii and Hiwatashi, 1983; Khadem and Gibson, 1985).

The paradigmatic pattern of speciation shown by *P. aurelia*—based on the completely discontinuous partitioning of naturally occurring genetic variation among Mendelian populations—apparently holds true also for *S. mytilus* Ehrenberg, 1838 (Ammermann and Schlegel, 1983), whose taxonomic problems were worked out using an identical taxonomic solution: syngens were identified by routine methods without the need for living reference stocks, and thus Latin names were attached (Ammermann and Schlegel, 1983; Steinbrück and Schlegel, 1983).

The situation with *T. pyriformis* is somewhat more complex than *P. aurelia*. Together with the most frequent interbreeding stocks representative of Mendelian populations, there also exist large numbers of stocks unable to undergo any sexual process (asexual stocks); since sex is forbidden, their systematic status is beyond diagnosis with breeding tests. Still other stocks are unable to provide unequivocal evidence for membership to a breeding population because they manifest persistent selfing (intraclonal conjugation, ordinarily between individuals of the same genotype), that is, a state which does not permit a resolution of lines into distinctive mating types to be involved in interclonal crosses, and produce almost invariably unviable progeny. Finally, there may occur "defined" sibling species with substantial internal genetic barriers, warranting the species splitting into "subspecies" (Simon, 1980). All of this argues for a highly differentiated genetic strategy which defies our understanding of modes of speciation inasmuch as the definition of species by paramecium criteria is often violated.

Euplotes crassus Dujardin, 1841, presents still different problems. Whether this form deserves the nominal species status poses at once the first problem. The morphological kindred with at least two other congeneric marine forms, *E. vannus* Müller, 1786, and *E. minuta* Yocom, 1930, is so close that there is no agreement about their distinctness. Gates (1978, 1985) reported the results of quantitative analyses of multivariate morphological attributes, indicating that the morphological criteria used to describe these forms are variable enough not to constitute reliable bases for the classification of unknown specimens. By extension, he proposed to include all the populations of the foregoing three closely related *Euplotes* forms under a single nominal species name, *E. vannus*, the oldest name. It is worth mentioning the possibility of a misattribution of the analyzed stocks occurring in those laboratories that provided stocks to Gates (Valbonesi *et al.*, 1988), following a distressing exchange previously brought to effect in reviewing the morphological distinctions between *E. vannus* and *E. crassus* (see Schlegel *et al.*, 1988, and Valbonesi *et al.*, 1988). All of this could cause one to accept Gates's proposal with some reservations. Nobili *et al.* (1978) held in respect distinctions among these nominal species based on morphological criteria. Quite confidently it can be maintained, however, that in the instance at issue the degree of morphological difference may turn out to be useless as a yardstick for species status unless it is applied in conjunction with other criteria.

On the basis of isozyme and morphometric data, Machelon and Demar (1984), Machelon *et al.* (1984), and Génermont *et al.* (1985) conferred the status of nominal species to *E. crassus* (referred to as *E. vannus* by French authors, overtaking the reviewing mistake cited above) and *E. minuta,* the occurrence of bridging instances notwithstanding. This is a viewpoint supported by Schlegel *et al.* (1988) on the distribution of isozyme variation in these two *Euplotes* forms. Valbonesi *et al.* (1988) using isozyme electrophoresis, multivariate morphometrics, and mating tests (which confirmed the observations of Nobili, 1964) extended the nominal species status also to *E. vannus;* a proposition recently adopted also by the French authors (Génermont *et al.,* 1992) who, contextually, took the decision to make up for the misattribution to *E. vannus* of the *E. crassus* stocks they actually analyzed.

As noted in Section 2, in most populations of the *E. vannus-crassus-minuta* group sex takes the "biparental" form of conjugation. There exist, however, other populations, fewer in number, that associate to the biparental form of sex a "uniparental" one, that is, an autogamous "escape hatch" (see Nobili *et al.,* 1978; Frankel, 1983; and Dini, 1984, for reviews). Circumstantial evidence has been produced suggesting that autogamy, due to a recurrent dominant mutation (Nobili and Luporini, 1967a; Heckmann and Frankel, 1968; Dini and Luporini, 1980), affords opportunities for an instantaneous reproductive isolation (Nobili *et al.,* 1978; Dini, 1984) with a resulting genetic divergence (Luporini and Seyfert, 1981; Dini and Giorgi, 1982). The results of a comparative morphometric analysis of sympatric (occupying the same area) autogamous (referred to as A^+) and nonautogamous (referred to as A^-) populations of *E. vannus* (= *E. crassus*) indicate that A^+ populations may undergo a rapid drift in morphological features of intrageneric distinctive value from the "ancestral" situation of the interbreeding A^- populations (Gates, 1990). Also in *E. minuta,* A^+ and A^- populations were found to differ in outward appearance and such differences were under genetic control (Heckmann and Frankel, 1968). In the above-mentioned studies on the distinguishability among forms of the *E. vannus-crassus-minuta* group, A^+ populations have not received the consideration owed them. A source of variation contributing to determine the limits of the intraspecific variability of attributes discriminating between nominal species has been largely disregarded. The aim of taxonomy is to describe the limit of observed variation. However matters stand, the extensive intraspecific variation is a fact, and the perception of the matter is that the actual possibility exists for practical difficulties when a taxonomist endeavors to assign populations to the three nominal species at issue, particularly dealing with *E. vannus* and *E. crassus*. The main message emerging from these considerations is the particularly complex evolutionary dynamics within the *E. vannus-crassus-minuta* group. Given this state of affairs, to sort these nominal species into a single species complex designated as the *vannus* complex does appear anything but an unwarranted taxonomic oversimplification.

Even if in the future the distinction among *E. vannus, E. crassus,* and *E. minuta* were to be completely practicable, their grouping into the *E. vannus* species complex could still be justified by their close morphological similarity, according to the practice proposed by Corliss (1973) for the *Tetrahymena* nominal species (see Nanney, 1985).

By no means do the arguments reported above imply an identity between nominal and biological species. When one tries to bring the taxonomic treatment of the single nominal species, *E. vannus, E. crassus,* and *E. minuta,* into accord with their own genetic structures, the situation becomes far more entangled. Interfertility tests produced evidence indicating the existence of a naturally occurring reproductive isolation accompanied by a significant genetic divergence between the A^+ and A^- populations within both *E. minuta* (Nobili and Luporini, 1967b; Frankel, 1983) and *E. crassus* (Luporini and Dini, 1977; Luporini and Seyfert, 1981; Dini and Giorgi, 1982). In spite of severe restrictions, A^+ and A^- populations could demonstrate some interpopulation matings, at least in the laboratory, suggesting a certain degree of genetic affinity, as a result of a likely recent origin of A^+ populations from the A^- ones. This situation mimics that mentioned above in *T. pigmentosa,* which led Simon (1980) to move to a subspecific status (a status considered a synonym of "syngen") populations of this sibling species of the *T. pyriformis* complex. Génermont *et al.* (1976) and Machelon (1982) defined five autofertile and intersterile population groups within the nominal species *E. crassus* (referred to as *E. vannus*), interpreted as biological species (= syngens). Discrimination of these last based on morphometric and biochemical criteria was largely unsuccessful (Machelon and Demar, 1984; Machelon *et al.,* 1984; Génemont *et al.,* 1985). The five syngens comprised all but one A^- stock; one stock assigned to the syngen 3 represented the A^+ exception. More extensive morphometric and electrophoretic studies carried out recently by Valbonesi *et al.* (1992) corroborated the impossibility to distinguish A^- populations of *E. crassus.* Yet, these authors, on the basis of tests for affinity of sexual rather than genetic nature, challenged the existence of natural groupings corresponding to genetically isolated Mendelian populations among A^- stocks of this nominal species. It appears evident that different authors have a different perception of the crucial and stably varying characteristic of a breeding population: the sharing of a gene pool. Fruitful breeding, supported by demonstrated mobility of genes, resulting in lasting populations of offspring, is the primary criterion of a biological species. Sometimes, information concerning breeding performance is substantially less satisfactory. When prospective parental stocks can be shown refraining from conjugating under conditions promoting their conjugation in other pairwise combinations, then they can be considered to belong to presumptive different mating groups (see Section 4). Conversely, stocks which do mate are lumped into the same mating group, it does not matter if they produce unviable progeny; groups so defined could well be species complexes. Ideally, one would like to know about mating in nature as well as in the laboratory. Metazoan literature records instances suggesting that gene exchange may occur in the laboratory when it does not occur naturally (see Mayr, 1970, for a review). Dini and Luporini (1985) faced this problem in the marine *Euplotes* species at issue. They concluded that a close scrutiny mainly of premating factors that may restrict or stave off gene flow in nature, such as the readiness to pair, the grade of mating reaction, the kind of pairs (heterotypic: from pairing between individuals of the two stocks brought into the mixture, or homotypic: consisting of partners from only one of the two stocks) and their frequency in the mixture, may provide suggestive hints on the breeding performance naturally practiced by stocks. In doing this the authors followed subliminally an approach for delimiting genetic species in agreement with the "recognition concept of species" (Paterson, 1993): the field for gene recombination in nature (representing the essential genetic property of species) is delimited by the occurrence of a coadapted signal-response chain (referred to as "the specific-mate recognition system") functioning effectively only among conspecific members.

At least under the laboratory conditions, stocks of the five syngens of *E. crassus* defined by the French authors interbreed to some extent in some intersyngeneic combinations (Machelon, 1983), suggesting that the possibility of a gene "trickle" among these syngens (introgression) is not eliminated altogether. Dini (1981a) reported about commonly occurring situations in *E. crassus* [referred to as *E. vannus* following Gates (1978)], characterized by the reproductive isolation of populations from close localities only if the direct hybrid between them was concerned, yet gene exchange between these populations was possible via an intermediate population collected from a distant locality. That this situation is paradigmatic of the population structure of *E. crassus* has been observationally sustained also by Valbonesi *et al.* (1992). The scenario that emerges is that of an *E. crassus* complex of "semispecies" [in the sense of Grant (1985)] having wide, largely overlapping, geographical distributions (Dini and Giannì, 1985). In some regions the members of the complex live side by side and retain their identity, while in other regions they hybridize bridging somehow the gap between different gene pools, thereby affording opportunities for introgression. A leakage of genes from one gene pool to another could smooth out sharp differences between members of the complex. The occurrence of a reticulate introgressive hybridization between semispecies would lead to an enlargement of the variation ranges of their attributes, thus accounting for the fruitless task of disclosing morphometric and electrophoretic differences. In some regions, however, isolated diversified populations should occur, following a retreat into some exploitative adaptations in which their outcrossing specializations had become a burden. Autogamous populations could be an instance.

We do not wish to imply by the statements above that members of the *E. crassus* complex are necessarily of recent origin or species *in statu nascendi* undergoing a constant turnover, as guessed by Machelon and Demar (1984) and Génermont *et al.* (1985). Situations like that surmised in *E. crassus* are all but rare among plants, where their establishment has been found to go back many millions of years (Dobzhansky *et al.*, 1977). The parallelism between ciliates and plants could startle the reader accustomed to think about ciliates as "protozoa," that is, primitive animals, and thus as organisms in which hybridization does not appear to have a comparatively important evolutionary relevance as it has in plants. Previously, in this section we stressed another likeness between ciliates and plants dealing with mating types. The nomenclatural choice of "protozoa" evokes misleading evolutionary connections. Ciliates can hardly be qualified as ancestors of animals, worse still of plants. They belong to protists which in their adaptive radiation just following the "eukaryotic saltation" from prokaryotes experienced a range of opportunities even larger than those practiced by both of these last higher eukaryotes. Organic and evolutionary similarities can thus be explained on the basis of necessity or convergence, instead of common descent.

3.4. Ciliate Species Are Underclassified

This survey of the species problem in the *E. vannus-crassus-minuta* cluster has been in the provision of the development of an improved rationale for resolving challenges posed by the ranking of taxa as species in situations exemplified by this structurally undifferentiated group of bottom-dwelling, marine ciliates. What may be worth stressing is the heuristic value of the *E. crassus* speciation model which does not squarely cope with the uniformity of standards and precision commonly conferred to the biological species concept, elsewhere beneficial for practical as well as theoretical reasons.

Even if the extent of species crypticity in the nominal species dealt with above cannot be projected casually on the other nominal species of ciliates, we are prone to believe that many, perhaps most, nominal species are underclassified. In Table I are listed all of the nominal species, to our knowledge, that authors have surveyed for the systematic relationships of the comprising stocks available. Though these represent a small sample of the Ciliophora species known to date, the widespread occurrence of morphological species splitting into genetic species is striking. Only in 4 out of the 24 instances has a correspondence between nominal and biological species been reported. Caveats affecting the statements of such an identity must be mentioned. The scanty number of stocks analyzed (e.g., *C. truncatum*), and/or their collection from a single ditch with brackish water (*P. woodruffi*) or from sites representative of a single regional area (*P. polycaryum*) could be among the chief causes of the failure to detect syngens. Moreover, the persistent selfing in the stocks of the nominal species at issue blurs the interpretation of mating in mixtures carried out to establish their breeding relationships. Though selfing is typical also of stocks of *P. jenningsi*, a far closer scrutiny (Przybos, 1975; Allen *et al.*, 1983b) provides the stigmata of reliability to the monosyngenic structure of this nominal species. It may be relevant to note that the distribution of this freshwater form is restricted to hot regions around the world (see below). Even with the foregoing exceptions, the number of nominal species within which species-grade differences have been demonstrated is respectable. One can argue with reasonable plausibility that the identification of cryptic species has only begun. One sound reason for believing this is that the job of identifying syngens—based on breeding tests involving the unknowns and the standard mating-type stocks representative of all the established species—is very toilsome, and increases hugely as the number of genetic species increases.

The overall conclusion from these considerations is that there appears to have been a surprising amount of evolutionary differentiation in ciliates, which renders these organisms not at all less rich in species than any other comparable level taxon of living beings. The question of why there are so many species can be answered: because the terrestrial ecosystem pays a high premium in terms of adaptive peaks to be exploited for the ciliates' biological and evolutionary plasticity. In some species, the existence of numerous isolated populations endowed with a high potential for subtle genetic and developmental differentiations, combined with a certain rate of migratory flux among these populations, and the rapid propagation of mutation throughout asexual and sexual processes, afford the basis for an evolutionary dynamics that defies the biological species concept. Even more defying resolution is the problem of the phenetic constancy yet a remarkable intergenetic species divergence of some complexes. According to Mayr (1970), it is conceivable that the simpler a group of organisms is morphologically, the more difficult it is to distinguish species. Although the membership of sibling species to the category of ordinary species is recognized as unquestionable, Mayr (1970) stresses the closer genetic similarity of these evolutionary units versus that of closely related but morphologically different species. Coupling the morphological and genetic similarity, the virtual absence of morphological differences is assumed to be the consequence of a developmental homeostasis which hampers the manifestation of genetic change in the visible phenotype. Given the large extent of the ciliates' inter-sibling species genetic divergence which sometimes overcomes the level diagnostic of animal genera (Williams, 1984), an "evolutionary conservatism" appears to account more properly for the phenetic constancy. The invariance of the outward appearance of members of a species complex would be the outcome of a stringent selection of certain morphological features determining the "organismic design" so as to maintain them unchanged, or within narrow limits, since the remote time of their origin (Nanney, 1982). By no means does this imply that the preservation of these fixed features requires a perfect molecular conservation; molecular substitutions can occur, unless they do not affect the conservativeness of the organismic construct. Such an evolutionary situation parallels that of some other complex organic designs, for example, the cilium that reached "perfection" long ago and was maintained thereafter through stabilizing selection.

The widespread occurrence of grossly underclassified species demands a reconsideration of the relationship between ciliate biogeography and the species problem. It is part of the accepted wisdom that ciliate "species" are worldwide in distribution. In view of the arguments reported herein, such an axiom appears still defensible at levels not lower than the species complex (Borror, 1980). Serious consideration must be given to the possibility that among indistinguishable populations there may have been sufficient isolation to allow genetic divergence without much morphological differentiation (Finlay, 1990). There may exist a very complex spatial arrangement of genetically isolated populations in nature. How large are the boundaries of these Mendelian populations, ranging from the single local population to population groups spread over large geographical regions, depends on the genetic economy pursued, which determines the ecological and genetic potential for local differentiation (see Sonneborn, 1957; Nyberg, 1974, 1981a, 1988; Dini, 1984; Landis, 1986). In species of larger niche breadth there is little apparent pattern in the microdistribution of populations. They colonized different microhabitats spreading into different environments across wide geographic regions. Other species experienced different selective pressures for more locally restricted ecological specializations. These last also may, however, show widespread distribution. This is because these species are specialized to exploit a particular set of environmental conditions, a set which occurs widely. The distribution of *P. jenningsi* reported above seems to come close to meeting such a situation. The variety of distribution processes is very large in ciliates. It reflects the dynamism of evolution creating a great deal of nomenclatural difficulties. [A discussion of these difficulties is beyond the scope of the present review; it has been extensively covered in the reviews by Génermont (1976), Corliss and Daggett (1983), and Curds (1985).]

Because of the remarkable morphological conservatism, it is difficult to establish the taxonomic relationships between the different cryptic species within the ciliate species complexes. Breeding data remain the ideal criterion over any other for cryptic species identification, despite the fact that sometimes breeding is a difficult phenomenon to bring about, occasionally unreliable (see Section 4), and impossible with scanty material. Fruitful breeding, involving sets of standardized living cultures, is the unique criterion for the syngenic moiety of still poorly studied species complex. However, as an alternative to the laborious breeding tests and the unpractical criterion based on the gross morphology, other diagnostic criteria may be used to distinguish species after they have been validated in populations of known breeding affinities. Attention has been focused on a number of differences of molecular, morphometric, physiological, immunological, life history, ecological, and biogeographical nature. Techniques for enzyme analyses represent, at present, the most powerful and reliable tool for discriminating individual sibling species. Presumptive identification to species, within those more carefully studied complexes (see Table I), can be routinely carried out without recourse to standard living cultures, analyzing the electrophoretic patterns of selected enzyme systems of unknown stocks or new isolates. Other works along the line of a molecular approach to cryptic species taxonomy have been done by comparing the primary structure of ribosomal RNAs (Nanney *et al.*, 1989a), and extrachromosomal rDNA (Nielsen *et al.*, 1985). If on one hand these kinds of results have supported to some extent the isoenzyme analyses, on the other hand, up to now, they have not provided much help in cryptic species identification. The molecular differences have inspired a reinvestigation of morphological characters, and at least most of the sibling species of the *P. aurelia* complex are separable using multivariate analysis techniques (Gates *et al.*, 1975). Exhaustive reviews exist (Sonneborn, 1974; Nanney and McCoy, 1976; Corliss and Daggett, 1983; Nyberg, 1988) dealing with other characteristics of potential value in routine cryptic species taxonomy. Even if each of these criteria can provide useful diagnostic taxonomic information, knowing the characteristic under consideration of a stock is not generally sufficient information for unambiguous identification. Understandably, the embarrassment of ciliatologists due to this richness of species was/is large. The necessity to distinguish among virtually identical species complicates to an unacceptable extent studies of various natures. The field and experimental ecologists are those researchers for whom, much more than for others, the identification of species and the information comprising the taxonomic system are both vital (Fenchel, 1987). Notice, for example, surveys of species changes in response to pollution may not detect a change using "nominal species" definitions when, in fact, there has been a change in the "biological species." High-resolution studies need to detect the change concerned. Detecting cryptic species is thus anything but an academic exercise; it makes the difference between success and failure, effectiveness and bumbling in critical studies on ecosystems. Aware of the paramount importance of a correct identification to make meaningful later research data, Corliss and Daggett (1983) provided practical suggestions to field biologists and lab-bench experimentalists (not to mention editors, teachers, and students) for recognizing and naming species, stocks, and specimens comprising a species complex to be utilized in the area of interest.

We reported earlier in this section about an intra-nominal species heterogeneity as far as sex is concerned. Along with populations exploiting an ordinarily biparental form of sex (conjugation) where partners' recognition is founded on "nonself" mechanisms, there exist others which do not discriminate between "self" (leading to intraclonal conjugation) and "nonself" (supporting an interclonal conjugation). The involvement of the obligatory selfers in inter--crossing—the foundation of breeding tests—is impracticable or impossible.

Moreover, a number of stocks may occur which are devoid of the capacity and/or the material basis (the micronucleus) to cross (asexual stocks). Finally, whole nominal species with compulsory uniparental sex (autogamy) or, far more frequently, retreated to a vegetative, uniparental reproduction—the lack of sexual processes in these "species" should be considered likely—represent the largest fraction of the Ciliophora species. In all these cases, the gene pool concept of species cannot be applied, simply for the impossibility of recognizing a common gene pool using interbreeding as the methodological approach. Such a situation unfortunately results in considerable uncertainty as to proper identification of species, whose representatives have, however, found their way into research laboratories. Once again, the following confusion causes difficulty in comparing research results and in correlating observations.

In the nominal species consisting of a series of distinct Mendelian populations upon which are superimposed a mass of obligatory selfer and/or sexless populations, these last are likely derivatives from the former and represent exceptions to the "rule" that each population belongs to a particular biological species. These exceptions, however, are not hard to understand, and a system that accommodates them can be constructed. Comparative studies of the distribution of enzyme variations in Mendelian and "exceptional" populations permit assessment of affinity sets within which the molecular diversity between any two stocks is smaller than any two representatives of different sets. Were this the case, then well-defined discontinuities among populations would become established. Following this procedure, sexless stocks of *T. pyriformis* could be assigned to different "asexual assemblages" with a molecular diversity mimicking that of genetic species. Even if these assemblages do not constitute Mendelian populations, they are biological entities and thus have been assigned Latin binomials; a topic comprehensively covered by the review of Meyer and Nanney (1987). Proceeding along this line of reasoning, a compelling link is established between asexual assemblages and evolutionary units, that is, entities produced by natural selection. The uniqueness of the speciation process mechanisms, whatever the kind of breeding, sexual or asexual, pursued by the ciliate, emerges as a corollary of such an idea. The principles of classification into species which are equally applicable to sexual and asexual groups thus become a matter dealing with the task of finding some useful biological correlates of sharp discontinuities occurring among populations.

One of the most refractory issues is the significance of vegetative (asexual) ciliate groups in ecological and evolutionary diversification. According to the conventional belief, supported mainly by theoretical reasons, these groups are reputed to be devoid of evolutionary flexibility and ecological plasticity, suitable for short-term exploitation of stable environmental niches. Ciliates' phenotype is controlled by the macronucleus (see Section 2). It is a highly compound nucleus which, however, does not follow the conservative rules of mitotic processes in maintaining its genic balance [see Preer and Preer (1979) for a discussion of the alternative theories of the underlying genomic regulation mechanisms]. Information dealing with the macronuclear behavior shows a genetic plasticity of vegetative individuals far larger than that previously suspected (see Bruns, 1986, as a review). Heterozygotes may expose recessive components of the genome during their vegetative clonal life (see Section 5.3), and empirical evidence has been provided for an induction and selection of mutants in vegetative lines (Orias and Bruns, 1976). Hence, we cannot doubt that within such lines selection forces could identify and perpetuate in nature useful genetic changes. This possibility in connection with the potential capability of the ciliate genome to support an indefinite vegetative life (see Section 2) provides the basis for a long-term evolutionary persistence.

4. Breeding Systems and the Species Problem

Ideas about the amount and types of evidence necessary to define a species have changed considerably in the last 200 years, primarily in response to what information is accessible. The microscope opened our eyes to the complex morphology of ciliates. Continued developments of stains and electron microscopy have kept ciliates among the most interesting cells. While studies of ultrastructure have continued to serve those with an interest in development and above-the-species-level taxonomy, they have not had much impact at the species level. The paradigm that has dominated research for the last 50 years is that of reproductive isolation evaluated by mating reactions between pairs of stocks (Poljansky, 1992). The biological species concept arose from evolutionary theory and helped put taxonomic problems into an evolutionary mainstream. Sonneborn's (1939b) discovery that *P. aurelia* stocks could be separated into noninterbreeding groups was, along with the sibling species of *Drosophila,* the most widely known example where the new species concept best revealed limitations of morphological taxonomy. The inability of the biological species concept to include asexual organisms within its purview has always been known (see Section 3). Recently a variety of results in sexual species have raised uncertainties in its application to some sexual groups. These problems and the utility of DNA sequencing at many taxonomic levels make it likely that the last years of this century are likely to emphasize DNA sequencing or banding patterns because they can be applied to all stocks regardless of whether or not they have sex.

Problems with the Ciliate Paradigm

The ciliate paradigm which emerged (Sonneborn, 1957) was that each morphological species could be subdivided into groups called syngens such that within the group all stocks, except those assigned to the same mating type, could mate and exchange genes, and that between groups no gene exchange was possible, even if mating reactions did occur. This paradigm describes one specific pattern of mating behavior for a collection of stocks and is illustrated in Table IIA. Nine stocks of a morphospecies have been mixed pairwise under conditions appropriate for mating. If a "−" appears in the matrix, no pairs

Table II. Idealized and Exceptional Mating Patterns

A. Idealized mating pattern: two species, one with two mating types and the other with four

| Stock | Stock | | | | | | | | |
	A	B	C	D	E	G	H	I	J
A	−a								
B	−	−							
C	+b	+	−						
D	+	+	−	−					
E	+	+	−	−	−				
G	−	−	−	−	−	−			
H	−	−	−	−	−	+	−		
I	−	−	−	−	−	+	+	−	
J	−	−	−	−	−	+	+	+	−

B. Mating deficiency or restricted mating rules

| Stock | Stock | | | | |
	A	B	C	D	E
A	−				
B	−	−			
C	+	+	−		
D	+	−	−	−	
E	+	+	−	−	−

C. Mating excess or relaxed mating rules

| Stock | Stock | | | | |
	A	B	C	D	E
A	−				
B	−	−			
C	+	+	−		
D	+	+	+	−	
E	+	+	−	−	−

a"−" indicates pairs were not seen.
b"+" indicates pairs were seen during the assay period. See text for elaboration.

formed in the mixture represented by that row and column. A "+" indicates that pairs formed. The stocks by themselves are all "−", indicating there is no selfing (intraclonal conjugation) among these nine stocks. In Table IIA stocks A and B do not mate with each other, nor do C, D, and E mate with each other, but all combinations between the two groups are positive. Thus, we call stocks A and B mating type I (MT I) and stocks C, D, and E, MT II of a presumptive biological species. (The convention of using roman numerals for mating types has caused many mix-ups because of the ease of misreading III, IV, and VI and other combinations of these symbols; it would be wise to abandon that convention.) We say "presumptive" because to be recognized as a biological species, the matings would have to produce viable progeny, and those progeny would have to produce viable progeny among themselves or in back-crosses to the parents. None of these five stocks, A, B, C, D, or E, have positive reactions with any of the four stocks G, H, I, or J. Those four could be im-mature or they could be members of another species. In this example, stocks G, H, I, and J do mate among themselves so they are not immature. They repre-sent a second biological species. In fact, in this case every mixture among these four stocks produces pairs so these stocks define four mating types in that species.

Much more diverse mating behaviors are conceivable, especially when the number of stocks being tested becomes large. Two simple types of exceptions are illustrated in Table IIB and IIC, where we are only mixing stocks of the same species. The first exception involves no mating where some is expected. An example of this exceptional pattern is illustrated in Table IIB, where stocks B and D fail to mate even though on the basis of their reactions to the other stocks they should mate. Because we expect stocks B and D to mate, they could be called a restricted pair. The second exception is at the other end of the spectrum. Some pair of stocks might mate, even though they would not be expected to on the basis of their reactions to other stocks. In the example illustrated in Table IIC, stock E does not mate with D or C and that suggests all three have the same mating type. Stocks C and D do mate, so they are not the same mating type, but neither mates with E so they cannot be different. We might choose to call stocks C and D members of MT II but add that as a pair they have a "relaxed" mating relationship. If many pairs of stocks have these stock specific mating behaviors, the number of possibilities becomes bewildering when as few as ten stocks are mixed together. Other types of imaginable exceptions could occur between syn-gens, if, for example, one discovered a stock that could produce viable progeny with both of two previously apparently isolated syngens. This has happened. These exceptional behaviors greatly complicate the taxonomic interpretation of breeding behavior observations. None of these exceptional behaviors has ever been described in stocks of the *P. aurelia* complex extensively studied by Son-neborn, but they have been in other ciliates. Exceptional mating behavior descriptions go back to the earliest reports of mating types (Jennings, 1944a) and continue through many reports dealing with wild stocks (e.g., Gilman, 1941; Orias, 1959; Nakata, 1969; Magagnini and Santangelo, 1977). The report of Jennings (1944a) of stocks that temporarily fail to mate with two different mating types while mating with at least one other was eventually rationalized as adolescence (Siegel, 1963), but many other reports remained as puzzling exceptions to the paradigm whose significance was unknown. Recently, considerable progress in interpreting exceptional mating behaviors has been made on two fronts. Tsukii and Hiwatashi (1983) have used intersyngenic crosses in *P. caudatum* to reveal that mating type specificity is controlled by three loci. Their crosses have produced stocks that mate readily with both parental syngens and others in which no mating type is expressed (Tsukii, 1988). On the other front, Mancini and Valbonesi (1991) have developed an algorithm for making groups out of the bewildering patterns that arose when they assayed the mating patterns of many stocks (Valbonesi *et al.*, 1992). Using this program and other evidence, Valbonesi *et al.* (1992) concluded that the morphospecies *E. crassus* is a single biological species, although there are groups of stocks that will not mate with each other in the laboratory. Others may feel that a few stocks that could be a bridge between groups are not sufficient to override the typical result. Regardless of one's opinions on the criteria appropriate to delimit species, it is clear that mating reactions do not always follow the simple ideal pattern and, therefore, that there is no simple way to assign a stock to an evolutionary species.

Another complication is the possible environmental conditionality of mating type tests. This is most clearly illustrated in *T. pigmentosa.* Originally reported as two syngens, Orias (1959) found conditions under which intersyngeneic pairs would form. Simon (1980) later studied these crosses and demonstrated that they were true crosses not just intersyngeneic pairing that did not lead to syngamy and viable progeny (parenthetically, *Tetrahymena* does not seem to exhibit pairing without fertilization as is often observed in the *P. aurelia* complex; this may arise from the fact that pairs do not emerge from a large mass of agglutinated cells as they do in *Paramecium;* see Section 7). In screening large collections of wild *Tetrahymena,* Nyberg (1981b), however, found it necessary to use testers of both syngens 6 and 8 of *T. pigmentosa* and never observed intersyngenic mating though stocks of both syngens 6 and 8 were found. Some species of *Tetrahymena* are very difficult to mate in the laboratory, i.e., *T. borealis* and *T. canadensis,* and their molecular similarity (Nanney *et al.,* 1989a) suggests that a link between them might be found in the future. We stressed in Section 3 that mating reactions or lack thereof observed in the laboratory may not show a complete correspondence with what happens in nature. The realization of this means that attaching a species label even to micronucleate stocks will be influenced by other information, such as tolerances, behaviors, or DNA sequences, rather than depending solely on the genetic behavior.

5. How Breeding Systems Affect the Practice of Genetics in Ciliates

Euplotes, Paramecium, and *Tetrahymena* all have the following elements of conjugation in common: (1) only two cells are involved—called a pair; (2) meiosis is initiated and completed in both cells of the pair; (3) in each cell the old macronucleus degenerates; (4) there is a reciprocal exchange of haploid nuclei. They also all show clonal aging in which the micronucleus eventually can no longer successfully complete meiosis, fertilization, and the development of a new macronucleus (see Section 2 and Fig. 2). Despite these similarities there are many differences in the practice of genetics and stock maintenance brought about largely by differences in the breeding systems.

5.1. Wild Stocks and Their Culture

Wild stocks of species in which autogamy results in complete homozygosity, i.e, the *P. aurelia* complex, are, of course, completely homozygous (see Section 2). If the cell collected in nature was heterozygous at any loci, the laboratory wild stock will not have the same genotype as the originally collected cell. The collection and maintenance of mutants is relatively easy in species with autogamy because one does not have to do anything special to avoid the aging problem. Both mutant and wild stocks with autogamy get the rejuvenating effect of sex while remaining genotypically identical from year to year. Consequently, they can be indefinitely maintained in a "ready-for-genetics" condition by just keeping them fed. Wild stocks of species without autogamy and without selfing are clonal descendants of a cell from nature. While such stocks can continue to grow indefinitely they do become "genetically dead," that is, unable to produce viable progeny, after some years of cultivation (e.g., Nanney, 1957). If a stock can self (formation of pairs within a clone), it is difficult to definitively know about the genetic identity of samples taken at two different times. Selfing may be necessary to keep a stock genetically vigorous. During normal maintenance of stocks it is not normally known whether or not selfing has taken place, if selfing is a possibility. The discovery of techniques for storage in liquid nitrogen has been very important to the progress of genetics in outbreeding species which otherwise would require a regular breeding program to avoid clonal aging.

Species that do not have autogamy are generally considered to be outbreeding. In these species almost all crosses result in an immaturity period, which can be as long as months. Both the immaturity period and clonal senescence are typically given in fissions postfertilization rather than days, because the number of fissions is more constant than days (e.g., Takagi, 1988). An advantage of an immaturity period is that it can be used as evidence of cross-fertilization. [Ciliate pairs occasionally fail to execute the normal pattern; exceptions include cytogamy (the meiotic products within one or both exconjugants fuse with another from the same cell) and macronuclear regeneration (the fertilization nucleus aborts and fragments of the old macronucleus do not degenerate but continue as macronuclei)]. An obvious disadvantage to a long immaturity is that the intervals between sexual generations are not less than they are in *Drosophila,* and may be longer. The outbreeding species that have a developed genetics (i.e., the segregation at, at least, one locus has been studied and published) include syngens of *Euplotes, Tetrahymena, P. bursaria,* and *P. caudatum.*

Another difference among ciliate species that is important to genetics is the number of mating types and the mode of mating-type determination. All of the slipper-shaped *Paramecium* species have only two mating types. All cells of unlike mating type can mate, and many species have multiple mating types. *P. bursaria* syngens have four or eight mating types (Bomford, 1966). Species of *Tetrahymena* have three to nine mating types, always an odd number in the more thoroughly studied species. The *Euplotes* syngens always seem to have more than nine mating types and in many cases the number seems not to be bounded (Nobili *et al.,* 1978). Another hypotrich *Aspidisca* has only two mating types per syngen (Dini *et al.,* 1987). Sonneborn (1957) argued that more mating types would increase the probability that two cells drawn at random are compatible. The mode of mating-type determination influences whether or not descendants of the two exconjugants of a single pair can mate. This has obvious practical implications for a breeding program and may also be important in nature.

5.2. Mating-Type Determination

Mating types are categories of mating behavior, that is, rules about who mates with whom. Ideally a large collection of stocks can be put into categories (called mating types) such that no mating is possible within the category and all pairings between categories result in pairing. Earlier (Section 4) we discussed the fact that many species behave in this manner, but that numerous exceptions exist. Because mating type determines which lines can pair, the manner in which mating type is inherited and determined is critical in understanding the breeding system. Much information is available on mating-type determination because the information emerges in the process of performing crosses between the stocks and using those progeny for breeding. Thus, the study of the pattern of mating-type determination is almost always the first character studied at the beginning of genetic studies of ciliates. Three major patterns of mating-type determination, "genic," "karyonidal," and "cytoplasmic," have been described. At the practical level, i.e., how one manipulates exconjugants and their first fission products, the three patterns are quite different. The karyonidal pattern is the only one that requires some explanation. In many ciliates two new macronuclei develop from the early fission products of the fertilization nucleus. The two macronuclei go to different daughters of the first cell division without dividing (see Fig. 1). In karyonidal inheritance of mating type, the mating types eventually manifested by various sublines derived from a pair are traceable to the two new macronuclei. The new macronuclei differentiate irreversibly very early in development. In species in which there is only a single karyonide, karyonidal inheritance could be inferred if the mating types of progeny could not be explained with a genic model.

With the discovery that the cytoplasmic pattern is not really a cytoplasmic system and the realization that the genic pattern can arise from a karyonidal system, if the differentiations from a multistate potential could be transmitted from generation to generation, then all patterns have the common element of nuclear differentiation of a system of genes maintaining multiple potentials (Sonneborn, 1977). The genotype(s) at a *mat* locus (loci) determine a unique mating type in the genic pattern. Thus, when the two exconjugants are genetically identical (see Section 2), their descendants have the same mating type. Karyonidal mating-type differentiations have long been known to be sensitive to temperature and probably are sensitive to other environmental parameters as well. The exconjugant clones of a pair may have the same mating type with karyonidal determination but probably do not. In *Tetrahymena* a common pattern of mating-type determination involves alleles with different potentials and a karyonidal choice of the one mating type expressed (Nanney, 1980). In the cytoplasmic pattern of mating-type determination, the exconjugant clones retain the same mating type as their cytoplasmic parent. Thus, the descendants of the two exconjugant clones can always mate again. Almost all mating-type determination systems are "sloppy" with exceptions to the general pattern comprising 1 to 5% of all observations.

5.3. Genetics and Breeding Biology Specific to Species Groups

Both marine and freshwater species of the genus *Euplotes* have a developed genetics. Some species in this genus can form homotypic pairs as well as heterotypic pairs. Feeding one stock bacteria and the other algae enables one to distinguish heterotypic from homotypic pairs. One of the technical devices that has assisted genetic studies is the ability of certain stocks of *E. minuta* to induce selfing in *E. crassus* (Dini et al., 1990). In this genus the events of meiosis and fertilization do not invariably result in genotypically identical exconjugants though that is a possible outcome (see Section 2). Autogamy does occur in some stocks of *Euplotes* but no nominal species has all stocks capable of autogamy. Unlike autogamy in *Paramecium,* instead of producing homozygosity in *Euplotes* it retards its development. That is, a cell undergoing autogamy is more likely to remain heterozygous than if that cell mated (Dini, 1984). In *E. crassus* exceptional stocks whose progeny do not have an immaturity period are known

(Dini *et al.*, 1990). Unlike the other species being considered, the new macronucleus is clearly visible using the dissecting microscope in *Euplotes*. This feature makes it easy to separate cells which have successfully completed fertilization and development from those in which something went wrong along the way. All species have a large number of mating types and it is likely that there is no limit to the number of mating types in many syngens. Endosymbionts are known in some species (Heckmann, 1983).

P. caudatum syngens include the largest ciliates with a developed genetics. As large ciliates they are especially suitable for microinjection. The two exconjugants are genotypically identical. Many even mating-type stocks are persistent selfers. There are only two mating types in each syngen. A group of behavioral mutants particularly suitable for genetic studies are available (Takahashi, 1988). There are many endocytobionts (Görtz, 1988). These endocytobionts have relevance to the species issue because at least one of them inhabits the micronuclei. If a stock with micronuclear endocytobionts crosses with a normal cell of its species all the progeny die, creating an impression of genetic incompatibility when there is none.

P. bursaria syngens all have four or eight mating types. In syngen 1 the mating types are genically determined. There are two alleles at each of two or presumptively three loci in the four-type or eight-type syngens, respectively (Siegel, 1963; Bomford, 1966). Pairs are all heterotypic and both exconjugants have the same genotype. Long immaturity periods are characteristic of these species. Endocytobiontic algae are present in all syngens.

Tetrahymena is smaller than the above genera. Species of the *T. pyriformis* complex that have been genetically studied (meaning that at least the mode of mating-type inheritance is known) include *T. americanis, T. borealis, T. canadensis, T. hegewischi, T. hyperangularis, T. malaccensis, T. nanneyi, T. nipissingi, T. pigmentosa, T. thermophila,* and *T. sonneborni* (Nanney *et al.*, 1989a). Four species have karyonidal mating-type determination (*T. borealis, T. canadensis, T. malaccensis, T. thermophila*) and are grouped with "Riboset A"; the others all have "peck order" dominance at a single locus for mating-type determination and are members of "Riboset C" (Nanney *et al.*, 1989a). Heterotypic pairing is the rule, even if exceptional (< 0.1%) homotypic pairs may occur in some mixtures (Ron, 1974). The meiosis and fertilization sequence results in genotypically identical exconjugant clones (see Section 2 and Fig. 1). There are no endocytobionts known in *Tetrahymena*. The most thoroughly studied is *T. thermophila*, which has seven mating types. Each studied mating-type allele has the potential to express five or six of the seven mating types. Only one of the potentially expressed types is expressed after differentiation which occurs shortly after fertilization. The differentiations are not known to be reversible, but they occur when there are multiple copies of the alleles in the developing macronucleus and it is not unusual to observe a selfing clone (see Section 6.2) which is believed to result from different differentiations in different copies and the subsequent "sorting out" of the alternative specificities. Heterozygotes at all loci "assort" during macronuclear division and by 200 fissions almost all cells are pure (homozygous) for one of the two alleles (Nanney, 1980). Selfing of wild stocks is generally rare and is presumed not to occur in stocks maintained axenically in peptone.

T. thermophila is the only species with inbred lines and in which special stocks and techniques which greatly facilitate genetic analysis have been developed (Orias and Bruns, 1976). A variety of special stocks (Allen, 1967) or manipulations (Orias *et al.,* 1979) have been developed to generate the homozygotes that are desired when screening for mutations. These techniques include the discovery of "star" or "*" strains which have a defective micronucleus. After a second round of mating, completely homozygous lines are produced. Another major development was techniques for producing "heterokaryons" and the selection of useful mutants (Bleyman and Bruns, 1977). As normally employed the micronucleus is homozygous for an allele conferring resistance to cycloheximide while the macronucleus gives a sensitive phenotype (usually as a result of "sorting out" of an originally heterozygous genotype). After a mass mating, clones which resulted from fertilization can be separated from clones which never mated or aborted along the way by using a cycloheximide screen. Another important result of heterokaryons was the development of nullisomic strains. In these strains the micronucleus is missing one chromosome of one or more of the five pairs (Bruns and Brussard, 1981). Using these strains allows one to rapidly assign a new mutation to a particular chromosome.

As for *Tetrahymena* (see Section 2), species of the *P. aurelia* complex destroy all but one meiotic product which then divides so that the reciprocal exchange of nuclei results in genotypically identical exconjugant lines. In *P. aurelia* species all pairs are heterotypic. The formation of pairs within a clone, selfing, is present in all species, typically at a greatly increased frequency at advanced ages. Over 180 mutants have been characterized (Sonneborn, 1974). Despite the relative ease of collecting mutants, only ten groups of linked loci are known in *P. tetraurelia* (Aufderheide and Nyberg, 1990) because of the large number of chromosomes. Many endocytobionts are known from these species. The disadvantages of the *P. aurelia* complex include the large number of chromosomes, and the relative (to *Tetrahymena*) difficulty of growth in axenic media (but see Schonefeld *et al.,* 1986) and a low percent recovery from storage in liquid nitrogen.

6. The Timing of Sex in Ciliates

When events potentially could occur, but are not always occurring, one typically is interested in what "controls" the time at which events occur. Generally, the further away the event is from the known point at which timing is set, the more mysterious and interesting the control of the timing seems.

The experimental genetics of ciliates had difficulty in getting off at the beginning of the century. The underlying deterrent was the impossibility of controlling mating. As reported in Section 1, conjugation has long been known, and was also rightly interpreted as a developmental sexual process. Yet, the time and mating partners could not be arranged at will. Knowledge of both of the partners to be brought together (the discovery of mating types) and the various circumstances under which mating occurs at least in some ciliates, made possible a scientific analysis of their sexual processes. These circumstances do not appear meaningless, but regulated in order to turn the benefits of mating to advantage of the genetic economy of the species. Species arrange sex to occur in coordination with two kinds of variables superimposed on any common mechanism of intimate cell–cell union characterizing conjugation: environmental and internal cues.

6.1. Environmental Cues

Almost universally in ciliates, sex (conjugation or autogamy) is associated with a decline in the resources available for growth. If abundant nutrients for reproduction (i.e., cell division) are available, meiosis cannot be induced. In fact, the transfer of recently formed pairs of some species to fresh food can result in a reversal of the course of conjugation and a resumption of growth. Under laboratory conditions, 60 hr must elapse from pairing for conjugation of representatives of the *E. vannus-crassus-minuta* group to the restart of asexual reproduction by exconjugants. During this interval, a nonmating cell provided with food undergoes five–eight binary fissions, producing 32–256 cells versus only one produced by each co-conjugant. Hence, the selective advantage to restrict mating to conditions limiting population growth should be apparent (Nanney, 1980).

The depletion of the food supply is a necessary but not sufficient condition for mating. Circadian controls may limit mating within the interval of time of nutritional depletion. In stocks representative of species of *Paramecium* (Jennings, 1939a; Ehret, 1953; Barnett, 1965; Karakashian, 1965; for reviews, see Wichterman, 1986, and Nyberg, 1988) and of the *E. vannus-crassus-minuta* group (Miyake and Nobili, 1974; Gates and Ramphal, 1991), there exists a diurnal periodicity in the mating behavior dealing with either the mating reactivity [*P. bursaria, P. triaurelia,* and *E. crassus* (a synonym of *E. vannus,* see Section 3)] or the expression of the mating type itself (*P. multimicronucleatum*). The rhythm of mating may persist in the absence of environmental cues at least for some time, indicating it can be maintained through cell replication. Examples of a preference for night mating (*P. triaurelia*), day mating (*P. bursaria* and *E.*

crassus), and both night and day matings (*P. multimicronucleatum*) are known. From an evolutionary perspective, given the interclonal variation of the mating activation time in the diurnal cycle (e.g., *P. bursaria*) and the occurrence of selfing—i.e., a change of the breeding strategy—in clones shifting mating type twice a day (e.g., *P. multimicronucleatum*), we do not have a consistent hypothesis for the adaptive significance of entrained rhythm in the mating behavior, even if its contribution to the survival strategy of the species cannot be doubted.

We currently do not know much of seasonal controls, but there is a lot of circumstantial evidence (see Section 8.2) to suggest they exist, and fewer and fewer laboratories are exposed to the environmental signals that would trigger change, so our lack of positive knowledge should not be interpreted as meaning seasonal control does not exist.

Finally, there is evidence for regulation of mating capacity in some species by temperature, pH, light, salt concentration of the medium (Bruns and Brussard, 1974), oxygenation of water (Luporini and Teti, 1979), etc. It is difficult to summarize meaningfully these regulatory systems, mainly because of their likely restricted spreading.

6.2. Internal Cues

Cells differ in how they respond to environmental cues according to how old they are. As reported in Section 2, some ciliates have a complete life cycle whose first stage corresponds to an interval of sexual immaturity. Shortly after mating, the clone is unable to respond to competent cells of another mating type under appropriate environmental conditions, i.e., under the conditions when those competent cells will respond to other competent cells. As time goes by, the members of the clone do become able to respond. The mechanisms for the changes responsible for the shift from an immature to a mature state are not completely understood. A substance has been isolated from immature cells of *P. caudatum* (Haga and Hiwatashi, 1981) which when injected into mature cells results in the loss of mating capacity. This substance is naturally present in immature cells and it disappears from mature ones. The acquisition of maturity, the ability to mate with a different mating type in an appropriate environment, is progressive and not necessarily irreversible, at least at the cellular level (Dini and Nyberg, 1991). However, once the cells are "fully mature" they never lose the capacity to mate. Individuals in this transitional stage are said to be "adolescent." Adolescence can be manifested as the ability of a clone to mate with only certain but not all mating types, comprising a multiple mating system, to which it will eventually become compatible (Jennings, 1939b; Siegel, 1967; Nyberg and Bishop, 1981; Rogers and Karrer, 1985; Kuhlmann and Heckmann, 1989; Dini and Nyberg, 1992), or as the inability to complete the sequential developmental steps leading to the regional fusion of cell membranes of mating partners (Takagi, 1971), prerequisite for successful conjugation following the reciprocal exchange of genetic information between mates. These two characterizations of adolescence have different bases: a sequential gene activation the first (Siegel and Cohen, 1963; Kuhlmann and Heckmann, 1989), and presumably a gradual increasing of the amount of mating substances the second (Nanney, 1977). Studies of variation within and among species have demonstrated the importance of genes in the control of the timing of maturity (Siegel, 1967; Bleyman, 1971; Nanney, 1974), a certain degree of intraclonal variation (Nyberg and Bishop, 1981; Dini and Nyberg, 1992) and sensitivity to the environment (Nyberg and Bishop, 1981) notwithstanding. The regulation by genetic factors brings into focus the adaptive significance of the length of the immaturity interval. The timing of this interval is of considerable interest from both developmental and ecogenetic points of view, inasmuch as it represents a device for regulating "who mates with whom, when, and where" (Sonneborn, 1957). The control of the genetic relationships of mating partners establishes the breeding strategy, outbreeding or inbreeding, in response to the ciliate's requirements for recombinational and mutational variety, respectively.

As a clone progresses throughout the life cycle, it ages—with age most appropriately measured in fissions since fertilization—and eventually reaches senescence if not allowed to engage in some kind of sexual process (see Section 2). In some species committed to an outbreeding economy, senescent individuals which failed to find an appropriate mating partner, acquire the capacity to mate within the clone (selfing); a taboo considering the laws governing their outbreeding life-style. In *E. crassus,* it has been demonstrated that senescent clones, heterozygous at the *mat* (mating type) locus, manifest a programmed expression of the recessive mating-type alleles (Heckmann, 1967) in some of their members. The cultures thus become heterogeneous and selfing occurs, producing rejuvenated progeny. [This kind of selfing is referred to as "senile," and must be distinguished from both the "juvenile selfing" occurring transiently early in the clonal life cycle (e.g., in *T. thermophila*) and the "ordinary selfing" characterizing all or some clones comprising some species.] Even if we do not have a mechanistic explanation of such a temporal programming, the adaptive significance of the regulatory system at issue for colonizing species which show a finite life cycle is apparent.

A circumstance of general occurrence in regulating mating capacity is represented by the cell cycle coordination. There is a point of commitment within the cell cycle where the potential partners can initiate mating. This point is represented by the G_1 phase of the metabolism-controlling macronucleus (Wolfe, 1973; Luporini and Dini, 1975; Doerder and DeBault, 1976; Chadha *et al.,* 1978); the very early macronuclear S phase is also permissive (Luporini and Dini, 1975). We have stressed in Section 6.1 that nutrient starvation is a condition necessary for mating. Decline in nutritional reserves does not further support metabolic demands, and cells then do not synthesize DNA and are arrested in the G_1 phase. Evidence is available pointing against a starvation-conditioned synchronization of potential partners in G_1. Yet, the occurrence of pair members in equivalent cell cycle states is achieved by preparatory cellular interactions (Wolfe, 1976; Dini and Luporini, 1979), despite the diversity of mechanisms employed to achieve mating competency (see Section 7). Conjugation entails highly coordinated events to assure a reciprocal exchange of separate hereditary determinants between mating partners. The arrest of the cell cycle can thus be rationalized as a necessity to tune the temporal programs of mating cells.

A further auxiliary regulatory system of the mating capacity deals with the interaction between eukaryotic and prokaryotic genetic systems. The presence of endosymbionts [= endocytobionts (Görtz, 1988)] in the cytoplasm (Sonneborn, 1959; Beale *et al.*, 1969; Preer *et al.*, 1974; Soldo *et al.*, 1974; Rosati *et al.*, 1976; Heckmann, 1983) and/or in the nuclear apparatus (L. B. Preer, 1968; Ossipov *et al.*, 1974; Rosati and Verni, 1976; Görtz, 1983, 1988) is the "rule" in ciliates. Sexually reactive individuals of the *P. caudatum* species complex infected with the macronucleus-specific bacterium *Holospora obtusa* lose the ability to mate (Ossipov *et al.*, 1974). Cells spontaneously get rid of endonuclear symbionts throughout a certain number of cell fissions, and regain the capacity to mate, maintaining the same mating type as before. Using other stocks of the same species complex, Görtz (1983) did not observe a loss of the mating ability following infection with *H. obtusa*, but only a remarkable fall of the mating reactivity. Interstock or/and intersyngenic differences in the sensitivity to the infection or differential virulence of the bacterium strains could explain the observed contradictory mating behavior of *Holospora*-bearing paramecia. Naturally occurring infection of individuals with nucleus-specific symbionts preventing the expression of the *mat* genes causes an extension of the interval of their life span characterized by the inability to mate. The spatial dispersal of individuals from their point of origin would thus be far enlarged, and the encounters between siblings discouraged. In view of this rationalization, the regular versus exceptional occurrence of endonuclear symbionts in outbreeder (e.g., *P. caudatum*) and inbreeder (*P. aurelia*) species complexes, respectively, is not surprising (Görtz, 1983). The mechanistic basis of this differential host–endonuclear symbiont relationship is the capability of the autogamic process (characterizing an inbreeding strategy) to produce a catharsis of *P. aurelia* individuals from symbionts (L. B. Preer, 1968).

7. Communication between Cells for Sexual Purposes

As long as optimal environmental conditions persist, vegetative ciliates will continue to grow and reproduce. When a shift occurs in these conditions, individuals can be diverted into sexual activities. With respect to autogamy, conjugation requires another factor for it to be triggered, that is, the presence of potential mating partners usually of different mating type(s). If this circumstance is not met, then individuals do not become committed to the pathway that leads to conjugation. They get assurance of the presence of potential mates after either intercepting long-range signals ["mating pheromones" (Luporini and Miceli, 1986), synonyms of "gamones" (Miyake, 1974), representing the specific mating-type substances] released into the aqueous medium (e.g., species of *Blepharisma, Dileptus, Oxytricha, Tokophrya,* and some freshwater and marine species of *Euplotes*), or coming into direct contact as signals are bound to the cell surface (e.g., species of *Aspidisca, Paramecium, Tetrahymena, Uronychia,* and some species of marine *Euplotes*). Whichever alternative is exploited, two interacting individuals must each be equipped with a system comprising an inducer (a signal of cellular origin) and a receptor for the inducer of the other potential mate. The foregoing groupings of signal-excreter and -nonexcreter species do not reflect any phylogenetic relationship. Species comprising the same genus, or even the same species complex (Kosaka, 1973, 1991b), exploit different mechanisms of cell–cell communication. Relatively minor biochemical differences may be assumed to underlie such a differential behavior. Opportunism, rather than conservatism, would seem to be at the root of the alternative choice performed by a species, according to demands of the exploited environmental niche.

The exchange of mating availability messages prepares potential mates to come together into physical association. In some cases, chemoattractant signals come into operation to bring partners within mating distance. The same mating pheromones serve as specific chemoattractants in *B. japonicum* (see Miyake, 1981). *T. infusionum* (Sonneborn, 1978), and in syngen 3 of *E. woodruffi* (Kosaka, 1991b). The final goal of this exercise is to elicit mating-type-specific cell unions for exchanging different hereditary determinants to be fused (fertilization). For this to be accomplished, cells must be able to recognize each other as compatible; the specific mating-type substances achieve this task. A control of the mating specificities by mating-type products permits a control of the genetic relationships of the mating cells. One would expect natural selection to put a premium on the existence of devices increasing the rate of genetic variability in response to requirements of recombinational variety. It is not surprising that those species of ciliates pursuing different genetic strategies abandoned conjugation entirely or returned to a random cell union system, where only interspecific conjugation is forbidden.

Proceeding through the cascade of events characterizing cell–cell interaction for mating, the mating-type-specific cell recognition induces the production of a pair-forming factor(s), distinctly different from mating-type substances, that transforms the cell surface so that partners can cement together in conjugant pairs. The surface-related events are followed by a complex sequence of changes concerning the cortex and the nuclear apparatus (see Section 2), which are required for meiosis, reciprocal fertilization of conjugating partners, and replacement of somatic nuclear and cortical structures; conjugation *sensu strictu* is thus accomplished.

Analytical studies on cell–cell communication and recognition have been reviewed extensively from various angles and in individual ciliates—e.g., Metz (1954), Miyake (1974, 1981), Nanney (1977, 1980), Sonneborn (1978), Ricci (1981), Hiwatashi and Kitamura (1985), Luporini and Miceli (1986), Nobili *et al.* (1987), Dini *et al.* (1987), Luporini (1988), Beale (1990), Rosati and Verni (1991).

When cells of different mating types come together, they enter a period of activation ending in cell pairing. This period may be visibly asymptomatic (e.g., *Tetrahymena*) or may be manifested in ciliary adhesion throughout its entire duration (e.g., *Paramecium*), or may appear asymptomatic in its first part ("waiting period") followed by a stereotyped and ritualistic behavior of potential mates until they unite in pairs ("mating reaction"; e.g., *Aspidisca, Euplotes, Oxytricha, Stylonychia, Uronychia,* and *Urostyla*). The partners of the resulting pairs show a species-specific orientation with respect to each other. [The subject has been extensively reviewed by Raikov (1972) and Lynn and Corliss (1991).] Pairing paramecia stick throughout their ventral surfaces bringing together oral surface-to-oral surface. Tetrahymenas pair opposing only their anterior–ventral regions. Both of these ciliates have rounded bodies with the cell surfaces uniformly covered by cilia. Yet, hypotrich forms are dorsoventrally flattened with relatively few, single, resilient cilia (bristles) on the dorsal surface, whereas cilia of the ventral surface are compounded into unit-functioning organelles, membranelles and cirri, the latter being mainly used by the individual to crawl on the substrate. In *Aspidisca,* the right ventral side of one mate overlaps the left dorsal side of the other maintaining the partners in the correct (homopolar) anterior–posterior orientation; both partners' ventral surfaces face the substrate. Similarly, one of the two partners of *Oxytricha* involved in the mating reaction rotates sideways on the other; when pairing is accomplished, mates lie side by side so that both can creep on the substrate. Conversely, in *Euplotes* the two mating partners unite side-by-side by their left ventral surface, maintaining a homopolar anterior–posterior orientation; the resulting "vis-à-vis" position renders possible the creeping on the substrate of only one mate at a time.

A comparative analysis of the species-specific variants in the mating pattern has been based on an "ethological" approach (Ricci, 1990, 1992). Convincing evidence has been produced for considering the interspecific morphological and related behavioral differences as adaptive answers the single species opportunistically provided to the demands posed by the colonized habitat. For example, the mating reaction and pair morphology of *Oxytricha* and *Euplotes* appear arranged to exploit a two-dimensional, flat substrate (e.g., sunken leaves), and a three-dimensional, articulated one (e.g., the narrow channels among the granules of a sandy substrate), respectively.

Models for the Molecular Control Mechanism of Mating

The mating-type-specific cell–cell interaction and recognition assume that mating-type substances bind to specific receptors on the cell surface. There is fundamental disagreement about these receptors.

Developing from the idea that is now classic in molecular biology, Miyake (1974, 1981) pursued the isolation and characterization of two "gamones" (= mating pheromones) from *B. japonicum,* providing eventually their molecular structures. Miyake's idea—developed for a binary mating-type system, but applied also to multiple mating-type systems like those of *E. patella* and *E. octocarinatus* (Heckmann and Kuhlmann, 1986)—hypothesizes that a cell homozygous at the *mat* (mating-type) locus produces a single gamone and carries all kinds of receptors for the whole series of gamones excreted within the species, except the receptor specific for the gamone produced by itself.

In opposition to this "gamone-receptor" hypothesis, there exists the alternative "self-recognition" hypothesis developed in *E. raikovi* (see Luporini and Miceli, 1986), a species with a multiple mating-type system. It assumes that each "mating pheromone" produced by a cell and controlled by one allele at the *mat* locus, may bind to both receptors carried by cells producing the same pheromone ("homologous binding") and receptors on cells unable to produce that pheromone ("heterologous binding"). Homologous binding inhibits mating, whereas heterologous binding inhibits self-recognition and promotes cell activation for mating. This occurs when receptor–non-self-pheromone complexes are formed up to a threshold value, in competition with the receptor–self-pheromone complexes. There is evidence suggesting that single genes are responsible for the specificity of pheromones and that of receptors (Miceli *et al.,* 1992).

Assuming that the receptor and the pheromone share the molecular part giving the specificity, the "self-recognition" hypothesis does not require the simultaneous appearance of the gamone and its own receptor that is apparently required in the simplest form of the "gamone-receptor" hypothesis. This latter looks at regulation as positive, while the "self-recognition" hypothesis views the primary regulation as negative. Since the same behavior could result from either positive or negative regulation depending on how the other parts interact, it is difficult to devise experiments that differentiate between the two hypotheses. In fact, while they are philosophical opposites, the diverse and complex interactions of regulatory molecules mean that both ideas could be operating in a single species.

8. Breeding System Theory and Ecological Associations

Most, but not all, organisms are sexual. What are the advantages or disadvantages of being sexual? Bell (1988) argues that the primary role of sex is an escape from the increasing load of deleterious mutations inevitable in asexual organisms. Our main interest is not, however, to explain the gulf between no sex and sex but to understand differences among breeding systems within the sexual group.

8.1. Ideas about Sex and Breeding Systems

As the load of mutations should be heavier in species with less redundancy, the deleterious mutation theory predicts greater intervals between sex should be associated with greater redundancy. We reject Bell's argument as an important answer explaining differences in breeding systems, primarily because species with smaller genomes such as *Tetrahymena* often have longer life spans than those with larger genomes like *Paramecium*. Another major idea about the evolutionary advantage of sex is that sexual progeny are more variable than asexual progeny. This idea would seem to suggest that more frequent sex will lead to more total variation, and thus, apparently, would explain shorter intervals between meioses as advantageous in situations in which variation was advantageous. The other major idea about sex is that it allows the production of hybrids and heterozygotes, which frequently seem more vigorous than progeny from selfing. But after a single generation of random mating the genotypes reach the Hardy–Weinberg equilibrium which is not changed by further rounds of mating. The frequency of sexual events is not obviously related to the amount of heterozygosity expected in the average individual. As we will see, the breeding system ideas have included a lot of other aspects and ideas about evolution, such as "being among strangers" which may or may not be true, but are clearly not part of current population genetics theory.

Within sexual organisms there are tremendous variations in choice of mates and the frequency of mating. The biggest gap in choice of mates is between uniparental sex and biparental sex (see Section 2). Among those with biparental sex, one frequently finds suites of characters that are interpreted as discouraging mating between siblings or with oneself (genic determination of mating type being the most obvious in ciliates). The frequency of mating is also highly variable. Some organisms become mature at a very young age while others may be over 20 years old before they become mature (see Section 2). Among the ciliates there are very large variations in characteristics that affect the choice of mates and the frequency of sex. Sonneborn (1957) reviewed the characteristics of ciliates and organized and rationalized these characters as contributing to an inbreeding–outbreeding continuum. On the extreme outbreeding end the ideal species had many mating types, the longest immaturity interval, genic determination of mating type, and no selfing or autogamy after the long period of maturity. This was associated with a "generalist" ecology and worldwide geographical distribution. The extreme inbreeding species had only two mating types, no period of immaturity, and a short period of maturity before uniparental (autogamy) sexual processes began. Such species were asserted to be ecological specialists and evidence of more localized geographical distributions was presented. The local specialization was encouraged by a "haploid economy" which exploited mutational variation, in contrast to an "outbreeding economy" relying on recombination for variety (see also Nanney, 1980). Most species fall between these two extremes. They were presumably compromising mutational variety and phenotypic stability. Sonneborn (1957) proposed that the length of the immaturity period was the single most important variable of the breeding system and proposed it as a quantitative measure of breeding systems by which species could be ranked on an inbreeding–outbreeding scale. The ability to place every species on a measurable scale is very useful to being able to correlate the ecology and natural history of species with their breeding system.

Two rather important elements were left out of this proposal. First, there is variation within species. Did these ideas apply to a stock (Sonneborn, having worked primarily with the *P. aurelia* stocks, seemed to favor this) or the syngen as a whole? In other words, can only species balance variety and stability or can each stock? Second, Sonneborn never explicitly dealt with the alternative ways of measuring the immaturity period, namely days or fissions. [There is usually less variation in the number of fissions to maturity than in the number of days to maturity when the cells are grown under different conditions (Takagi, 1988).] This question is crucial because small species may reach maturity in fewer days than a large species but undergo many more fissions during that interval. This question is still not resolved and attempts to do so reveal other nebulous aspects of the breeding system idea.

Sonneborn (1957) stated that longer intervals between two consecutive fertilizations would lead to greater average distances of birth places of the partners. The greater distance and time were argued to lead to more generalization and less specialization to local conditions. Given this idea, it seems the immaturity interval should be measured in days rather than fissions, because dispersal distance is presumably determined by real time. That is, longer intervals between consecutive meioses mean encountering more environmental variation between sexual events. But when we recall that the only way these cells reproduce is by cell division, then it seems that the environmental variability encountered by the descendants of a cell will primarily depend on their average rate of dispersal, i.e., in meters per day, not in meters per sexual generation. That is, if the dispersal of cells is at the same rate (meters per day), why should it make any difference if a descendant cell has not had a sexual event in its line of descent compared with another cell that had had four or five meioses in the line of descent but ends up in the same place? A plausible scenario could propose a gradient of some stress with each sexual event increasing tolerance a little, but this is a recombination model, the type that is supposed to be associated with outbreeding. In the laboratory, mutational adaptation is associated with huge changes in numbers of individuals. The best way to exploit a "haploid economy" would seem to be to increase population size. Another way that the theory is weak is the association of shorter interval between sex with more local adaptation. Because every biparental sexual event has the potential to mix genomes with different histories, one could argue that more frequent mating leads to less microgeographic variation rather than more. Thus, the expectation that inbreeders would be more "specialized" and that inbreeders would have a more limited geographical distribution no longer seems obvious. The ideas need to be developed much more explicitly in terms of rates of mutation and population size regulation and variation before we can know how useful these ideas are.

Another of Sonneborn's arguments proposed that more mating types increased one's chance of being compatible with "strangers." It goes as follows: If there are two equally frequent mating types, then the chance encounter between two "strangers" has only a $1/2$ chance of permitting mating, while if there are eight equally frequent types the chance of compatibility is $7/8$. "If a species 'wants' to increase the chance of mating with a stranger, it can do so by increasing the number of mating types" (Nanney, 1980, p. 90). In this way more mating types was viewed as an outbreeding adaptation. But if we think of two populations, we can create a somewhat differ "model." Consider two populations, in each population there being an equal frequency of N mating types. We wish to compare the compatibility within populations with that between populations. If there are two mating types the probability of compatibility within either population is $1/2$ and the probability of compatibility with one cell from each population is also $1/2$. If there are eight mating types the within-population compatibility is $7/8$ and so is the between-population compatibility. Thus, increasing the number of mating types increases the likelihood of mating with siblings (within a population) and with strangers (between populations). If one regards mating within populations as more likely than that between populations, the primary effect of increasing the number of mating types may be to increase the chances of mating within a population. Increased mating within a population could be considered an inbreeding adaptation. But this way of thinking is not very populational, for as long as there are reasonable number of individuals in each population, they are likely to encounter compatible individuals during their lifetime, if not on the first try.

Our final exploration of breeding system theory will look at its connections with population genetics theory. Heterozygosity is the premier population parameter of population genetics. The decrease of heterozygosity compared with that expected under random mating is the quantitative measure of inbreeding, $F = (H_{expected} - H_{observed})/H_{expected}$. One can measure F_{IS} within local populations and F_{ST} between local populations. How do we expect the elements of the breeding system to effect F? Do more mating types increase the expected heterozygosity? By analogy to the behavior of monoecious populations (see Section 3) compared with those with separate sexes this effect is slight. After a single round of random mating the expected genotype frequencies at a two-allele locus will be in Hardy–Weinberg proportions in each mating type. As with separate sexes the only increase in expected heterozygosity will arise from a finite population size or sampling effect. Because the actual frequencies in the different mating types will not be identical there will be a slight excess of heterozygotes (actually it is more accurately thought of as a deficiency of homozygotes) compared with the randomly mating population. For example, consider a two-allele system, A and a, where "p" is the frequency of A and "q" that of a, with subscripts denoting the mating types (MT). If p = 0.51 in MT O (odd) and 0.49 in MT E (even), then the expected heterozygosity = $p_O q_E + p_E q_O$ = 0.2601 + 0.2401 = 0.5002, compared to the 0.5000 expected with random mating. Given the other forces impinging on protozoan populations this effect seems rather insignificant.

How might the length of immaturity affect inbreeding within populations, F_{IS}, and differentiation between populations, F_{ST}? The length of the immaturity period would seem to have a much smaller effect on F_{ST} than the rate of migration. While the mean "birth" distance between conjugants should increase with longer immaturity intervals on a per generation basis, distances traveled on a per unit time basis should not be affected by breeding system. If differences between populations or departures from allelic equilibrium within a population accumulate uniformly with time, longer immaturity periods would allow more genetic differences generated by selection to accumulate (both within and between populations) during the interval between sexual generations. For example, the longer interval might allow the population to become entirely heterozygous due to selection, a state which could not be reached if random mating had occurred recently. When the long immaturity population does finally mate, the homozygotes would appear in equal proportions. One disadvantage of long immaturity periods and genic mating-type determination is that selection can reduce the genetic variability so much that mating within the population is no longer possible because all of the cells are the same mating type. Such a population must wait for migrants from other populations and this will reduce F_{ST}.

Thus, the consideration of population genetic behavior within and between local populations has led us to the conclusion that much of the breeding system ideas do not have as much effect as suggested by their originators. Specifically, heterozygosity, the standard measure of inbreeding, is greatly affected by uniparental versus biparental sex, but breeding system variants within the biparental sex category seem insignificant. This does not mean that the breeding system ideas need to be rejected. One must remember that population genetics has not been very successful in offering a rationale of sex. Maybe some of the breeding system ideas, despite the fact that many are not now explicit, will be useful not only in understanding breeding system differences but also sex itself.

8.2. Natural History of Sex and Breeding Systems

Siegel (1961) reviewed the literature and presented new results demonstrating that ciliates conjugate in nature. Pringle and Beale (1960) studied a natural population for 6 years during which time they found 38 heterozygotes at the *G* locus whereas the gene frequencies lead one to expect 84.8 if mating were random. Thus, we can estimate *F* as 0.56 for that population of *P. novaurelia*. The excess of homozygotes they found presumably reflects a mixture of the two sexual alternatives, conjugation and autogamy. Recently a trap for ciliates in nature was devised (Kosaka, 1991b). One of the baits of the trap was mature cells of *E. woodruffi* syngen 3. These mature cells attracted mature cells of the same species, further supporting mating in nature as a regular phenomenon. Genetic studies have found many heterozygotes in *E. crassus* (Luporini and Dini, 1977), an outbreeder. In contrast to the above, Landis (1988) proposes that *P. tetraurelia* rarely if ever conjugates in nature and that the lack of conjugation is an adaptation to the maintenance of the killer trait. His argument is based on the polymorphism at the *K* locus involved with the loss or maintenance of the killer particles. By inbreeding cells with the endosymbiontic killer bacteria suffer no losses due to segregation at the *K* locus.

There is very little information on the seasonality or periodicity of mating. One could imagine that, in nature, the environmental cues leading to mating occur frequently and that most cells are mature and waiting for the cue that will get almost 100% of the population to participate in mating at these rare times. At the other extreme mating could be occurring all the time. As a cell became mature it would find a mate and return to immaturity. In this case most of the cells in nature would be immature. The only detailed study pertinent to these kinds of questions is that of Kosaka (1991a) who studied populations of *P. bursaria* in Japan. Densities throughout the year varied widely, ranging from 0 to 104 per ml. The proportion of mature and adolescent cells never exceeded 50%. The proportion immature during the entire year was 74%. Based of changes in the proportion immature, Kosaka (1991a) concluded that sexual reproduction probably occurred near the peak of population density which was in April, May, or June in the streams he studied. Coleman (1981) described how the introduction of specific stocks of exotic syngens could be used to determine the frequency and importance of sex in flagellates. The same methods would apply to many ciliates.

While we know little about sex in ciliates in nature we do know that in the laboratory viability of exconjugants after biparental sex is often low and typically declines with inbreeding. Jennings (1944b) described this decline in *P. bursaria*. Nanney (1957) described the loss of viability and cellular anomalies brought about by inbreeding in *T. thermophila*, though he was eventually able to overcome these problems by selection. Both the marine (e.g., Luporini and Dini 1977) and freshwater (e.g., Kosaka, 1990) *Euplotes* typically show low viability upon inbreeding and backcrossing. Crosses involving *P. caudatum* also frequently have viabilities around 50% (Tsukii and Hiwatashi, 1983). In contrast, crosses between stocks of *P. tetraurelia* have an F_1 viability of > 90%, though the viability may be very low in the F_2-by-autogamy generation (Sonneborn, 1957).

8.3. Ecological Attributes Associated with Breeding System Differences

In an attempt to measure the qualities of specialization versus generalization, Nyberg (1974) did a comparative study of the tolerance to environmental stress of species with very different breeding systems. He measured the median tolerance limit (MTL) of the ciliates to seven stresses he regarded as environmentally significant. The correlations of tolerance to breeding system were impressive, ranging from +0.45 to +0.89. The higher average tolerance of more outbreeding species was taken as evidence of their being "generalists" and evidence of "specialization" was found in the large variability in tolerance to copper in two of the inbreeding species, *P. primaurelia* and *P. tetraurelia*, and in tolerance to high temperature in *P. primaurelia*. The pattern of higher tolerance in outbreeding stocks was supported when Dini (1981b) compared autogamous and nonautogamous stocks of *E. crassus*. This higher tolerance is not due to heterosis *per se*. Dini (1981b) found that both F_1 and F_2 generations had slightly lower tolerance than the parents. Nyberg and Bogar (1986) found no general enhancement of heavy metal tolerance of between stock hybrids in *P. primaurelia*. Nyberg (1974) found that the tolerance of the 18th generation of inbreeding stocks was indistinguishable from that of wild *T. thermophila*. The higher tolerance of the outbreeding species was speculated (Nyberg, 1974) to have arisen from their presumed greater dispersal and mixing of genomes and/or from the presumption that they had to survive more environmental change between meioses than species with more frequent sex. The inbreeding species were presumed to be able to track environmental change mutationally. This part of the hypothesis has been studied.

Genetic studies of the large *P. tetraurelia* between stock copper tolerance differences discovered a single copper locus, consistent with the "mutational haploid economy" idea (Nyberg, 1975). Fresh collections were analyzed (Nyberg and Bishop, 1983) and large differences were found among stocks of *P. primaurelia* and *P. triaurelia* in tolerance to heavy metals. Though the bulk of the *Tetrahymena* tolerance data were never published, the only case of a between-stocks-within-species difference found was in nickel tolerance in *T. sonneborni* (Nyberg and Bishop, 1979). The different species of *Tetrahymena* did show a considerable range of temperature tolerance (Nyberg, 1981b) and there is great overlap between the *T. pyriformis* complex and the *P. aurelia* complex even though all stocks of the latter group have the capability of autogamy. In general the tolerance to ion stresses is higher in *Tetrahymena* than in those *Paramecium* species belonging to the "aurelia" group (see Wichterman, 1986), but the role of the breeding systems in influencing those differences seems less clear than it did earlier. Outbreeding *P. caudatum* and *P. multimicronucleatum* have copper tolerances more like the "aurelia" group than like *Tetrahymena* (Howard, unpublished M.S. thesis from Nyberg's lab).

Landis (1982) found that *P. bursaria* [syngen(s) not identified] had a more uniform distribution in space than did *P. tetraurelia*. He develops the idea (see Landis, 1988) that the difference between these species reflects differences in their breeding system. The nearly random distribution of *P. bursaria* reflects its "generalist" strategy, while the contagious distribution of *P. tetraurelia* reflects its "high rate of reproduction under a comparatively narrow range of conditions" (Landis, 1988). This interesting idea has not been pursued, so the generality of Landis's observations is not known. One would also wish to investigate other species with respect to this association. The symbiotic *Chlorella* are likely to play a large role in the spatial distribution of *P. bursaria,* and the appropriate control would be an inbreeder with photosynthetic endosymbionts.

8.4. Heterozygosity and Genetic Geography of Breeding Systems

Are the stocks of outbreeding species frequently heterozygous but showing little geographical differentiation, while stocks of inbreeding species exhibit considerable geographic differentiation? The answer from isozymes seems to be "no." Allen and Weremiuk (1971) reported intrasyngeneic variation in esterases and phosphatases among the syngens of *Tetrahymena*. Subsequent investigations have generally found some intrasyngeneic variations in isozyme banding patterns but not at a level which prevents using zymograms to identify species (e.g., Nanney *et al.,* 1980; Simon *et al.,* 1985). A finding which apparently does not support breeding system theory is that the species with genic mating-type determination have less polymorphism than those species with karyonidal mating-type determination (Meyer and Nanney, 1987).

The species of the *P. aurelia* complex show an exceptionally low amount of intrasyngenic variation in esterases and acid phosphatases, though *P. biaurelia* is exceptional in having a hypervariable esterase (Allen *et al.,* 1982, 1983a). The lack of geographic differentiation within any of the "aurelia" group species was in contrast to some differentiation in *P. multimicronucleatum* syngen 2. Additionally, all syngens of *P. multimicronucleatum* which would be considered outbreeding, had a higher frequency of variant stocks than the "aurelia" group (Allen *et al.,* 1983b). What seems unusual in these results is the lack of differences among stocks of the "aurelia" group. We have previously mentioned the low F_2-by-autogamy viability of interstock crosses. Nyberg and Bishop (1983) found high levels of variability in heavy metal and temperature tolerance in *P. primaurelia* and *P. triaurelia*. Thus, the isozymes and the conventional characters do not reinforce each other.

Nyberg (1988) previously reviewed the information about the distribution of *Paramecium* species. In contrast to the expectations generated by Sonneborn (1957), the geographic distribution of most species of the "aurelia" group has spread around the world and only one new species has been discovered (Aufderheide *et al.*, 1983). There were supposed to be a few widespread species in outbreeders like *Tetrahymena;* since 1957 the breadth of the known distribution has increased but the number of *Tetrahymena* species has mushroomed (Simon *et al.*, 1985; Preparata *et al.*, 1989). It would be difficult to argue that there is any association between geographical distribution and the breeding system in 1993.

8.5. Concluding Remarks

There is great diversity among the breeding systems of ciliates. Stories explaining how the breeding system variations can be related to ecological, geographical, and other environmental phenomena have been an attractive part of ciliate lore. Most of these comparisons are based on pairs of species or species groups. When a broader set of species is included and/or more concrete characters are used for comparison, the stories are found to have many exceptions. Ciliates can be parasites and can be parasitized, they live in marine and moderately extreme freshwater environments, some apparently have very local distributions while others are largely distributed, they come in very different sizes, and some can become carnivores. None of these characters are simply related to ciliates lacking sex entirely or to being an inbreeder or an outbreeder given that there is sex. Within more circumscribed groups there are patterns and at this point we just do not know whether the other differences between the groups obscure the patterns due to sex or if those patterns are much more neutral than has previously been thought.

9. Laboratory Investigations of Sexual Alternatives

An alternative to correlating or associating differences among breeding systems of species with their ecology, natural history, and biogeography is to measure the properties of stocks in the laboratory and associate them with the breeding system.

9.1. Growth Rates and Hybridity

One of the first experiments along the foregoing line was by Kimball *et al.* (1957) who studied a laboratory population of *P. primaurelia* and showed that it remained heterozygous at an immobilization antigen locus for over a year. They observed only a small deficiency of heterozygotes and concluded that 90% of the sex in their tubes was biparental. Siegel (1958) studied the growth rate of wild stocks and their hybrids, also in *P. primaurelia*. He found that the F_1 hybrids grew faster than both parents or as fast as the faster parent. He also found that some of the F_2-by-autogamy progeny grew faster than both parental stocks. Siegel interpreted this as supporting the dominance theory of heterosis rather than the overdominance idea [see Zouros and Foltz (1988, pp. 2–3) for the relationship between these two phenomena].

Nyberg (1982) sought experimental evidence that recombination generated variance in fitness. He used four freshly collected wild stocks of *P. primaurelia* and the classical stock (P or 16) restricted to expressing the odd mating type. He found that the F_1 lines had uniformly high fitness (fitness was measured as the expected number of descendant cells per original cell per 10 days; highly correlated to the mean fissions per day, but not identical to that measure), while the parental stocks had large differences among themselves. One of the parental stocks had a higher fitness than any of the F_1 hybrids. Among these stocks the benefit to outcrossing was strongly conditional on the fitness status of the parents. Low-fitness stocks gained a lot by outcrossing, while high-fitness stocks gained little or even lost a little by outcrossing. These observations are consistent with the dominance theory of heterosis. Even more importantly, the observations suggest that the benefits (and losses) of outcrossing are conditional or stock specific. There is no general incremental advantage to outcrossing even though one can, of course, calculate an average advantage. The increase in the variance in fitness of the F_2 was solely due to the production of low-fitness genotypes. None of the recombinant genotypes were higher than their F_1 parent.

Nyberg (1982) measured the fitness of parents, F_1, and F_2 clones grown alone. Since one of the five wild stocks had the highest average fitness, his results suggested that the ultimate winner of a contest in which the stocks were all pooled together would be the autogamous descendants of that highest fitness stock. He did not mix the stocks to confirm this assumption. If a single wild stock (equivalent to a genome) has the highest fitness and autogamous reproduction preserves that genome, why does conjugation persist in nature? This paradox was answered by speculating that there were other environmental conditions in which conjugation was generally or always beneficial. Finally, one should realize that the projection that emerges from knowing the properties of stocks grown alone does not always predict their behavior when they are actually grown together. Actually working with synthetic populations in the laboratory and having the cells tell us which breeding systems are winners seems to have a lot of potential.

9.2. Dynamics of Mating-Type Alleles in Laboratory Populations

Orias and Rohlf (1964) developed a theory showing there was a stable equilibrium at which all three mating types of *T. pigmentosa* should be equally frequent. Mating type is determined by three alleles with "peck-order" dominance in that species. Only seven cells had been collected from nature and since all three types were included in the sample of seven, the sample was compatible with the expectation. Iwasa and Sasaki (1987) developed different models of mating-type dynamics. Under certain assumptions there was a tendency to collapse to only two mating types. A student in Nyberg's laboratory (Bowbal, 1988) decided to study the dynamics of mating-type alleles in the laboratory. She chose to study *T. hyperangularis,* a species with "peck-order" dominance at its mating-type locus. Three stocks, each with a different mating type and involving a total of four different mating-type alleles, were mixed in various eccentric ratios (0.78:0.18:0.04 or 0.80:0.20) for a total of 12 combinations each with two replicates. The cells mixed in the initial cultures were mature. The cultures were fed 5 days a week for total of 11.6 fissions per week (assuming the cell density remained constant). Immature cells appeared in the sample about 2 weeks after mixing. At this point the only mature cells sampled had the majority mating types, indicating that all cells with minority mating types had found a mate. The proportion of immature cells increased steadily and eventually reached 100% of all samples. This suggests that immature clones generally have higher fitness than mature ones. The caveat "suggests" has been used because in the majority of replicates when mature cells began reappearing in the culture, they were all of the same mating type. Thus, the favoring of a particular genotype, rather than any immature line, is a viable possibility. Only 3 of the 12 populations remained polymorphic for mating type at 248 days. The average immaturity period in these populations was estimated as 102 fissions, a bit longer than is typical for this species in single cell transfer estimates. Thus, Bowbal's (1988) results did not support the equality of mating types expected from theory. They also suggest that fitness differences among clones can result in the loss of mating-type polymorphism and therefore loss in the ability of the population to continue to mate.

9.3. Investigating Breeding Systems in Laboratory Populations

Why have there not been more direct tests of the evolutionary ideas using synthetic populations? There are a number of possible reasons that population experiments have not been more widely done in the laboratory. The ideas arose primarily as a way to compare species and there are many differences between species which force extensive "qualifications" of an experiment using two different species. That is, the species differ in properties other than just the breeding system differences. Within a species we have already discussed a few examples of laboratory population dynamics. They tend to be labor-intensive, because it is generally not possible to identify the sexual origin of an individual without testing the sampled cell for its genetic constitution. This is usually a lot of work per "bit" of information. Finally, evolutionists are often weak in thinking in population terms. The dynamics within and between populations is not the most simple way to relate to laboratory cultures. But, if one thinks it is an advantage to have biparental reproduction over uniparental reproduction, why not test it directly? What sort of experiments seem to be possible in the laboratory that will test some of the ideas about the advantages and disadvantages of breeding system alternatives in a species?

The dynamics of mating types is one experiment that has already been mentioned. If conjugation is generally advantageous, rare mating types will generally increase in frequency until they reach equality. Another nice feature of ciliates is the fact that the increase in the population size is only through cell division. Sexual events have no effect on the population size. By mixing stocks of different origins but of the same mating type, one can separate the effects of variety from those of sex *per se*. Finally, one can see under what environmental circumstances sex is more advantageous. That is, if biparental conjugation and uniparental autogamy seem about equal in pure cultures, then they can be compared when the variable species is under competition pressure with say *P. caudatum* or predation pressure from *Dileptus*. Let us look at some of these ideas in more detail. The dynamics of mating-type alleles in species with genic determination of mating type allows one to test whether or not rare mating-type alleles can regularly invade segregating populations? Will fitness differences generated by recombination regularly result in the loss of mating-type polymorphism? If so, what are the dynamics of loss? Additionally, one can ask which environments, if any, seem more favorable to maintaining mating-type polymorphism. Whether or not the ability to mate is an advantage in competition could be evaluated by setting up the following populations: A,B,1; A,B,2; A,1,2; where A and B are different mating types of Species X, and 1 and 2 are different mating types of species Y. If mating enhances competitive ability, then species X should win in the first two mixtures and species Y in the latter two.

Species with cytoplasmic inheritance of mating type have a number of advantages for evaluating the population dynamics of sexual alternatives. If there are no fitness differences, the initial ratio of the two mating types should stay the same indefinitely. Measuring the departures from the initial ratio as the population grows (evolves), allows one to estimate the fitnesses of the mating types and, if known, the genotypes. *P. tetraurelia* has another particular advantage. All wild stocks have the genetic potential to be either Odd or Even. In many cases we have stocks with identical genotypes but opposite mating types. If one is willing to search through enough cultures, one can get both mating types for every genotype. By manipulating the initial ratio of the mating types, one can control the amount of biparental sex (conjugation) versus the amount of uniparental sex (autogamy). Not only can the amount of conjugation versus autogamy be controlled but one can independently regulate the amount of genetic variety in the initial population. For example, one can mix diverse stocks of the same mating type for variety without sex and one can mix genotypically identical stocks of different mating type for sex without variety. The four basic combinations (biparental sex—yes or no; genetic variety—yes or no) are illustrated in Table IIIA. Which of these mixtures achieves a higher rate of population growth? Which reaches a higher population density? Which mixture does better in competition with another species of *Paramecium?* All of these questions are answerable in the laboratory.

Not only can these simple extreme alternatives be compared but one can adjust both the amount of genetic variety and the proportion of biparental sex continuously and almost independently. Four possible combinations are illustrated in Table IIIB. The first row has a small amount of variety and no biparental sex. The difference between zero and a small amount is crucial to many theoret-

Table III. Simple Designs Separating the Effects of Sex from Variety Percentages in Initial Populations

A. The simple extremes

	Stocks			Amount of	
	MT^a–genotype^b				
Odd–*AABB*	Odd–*aabb*	Even–*AABB*	Even–*aabb*	Variety	Sex
100				MIN	MIN
50	50			MAX	MIN
50		50		MIN	MAX
50			50	MAX	MAX

B. Some more complex initial conditions

	Stocks			Initial percent	
	MT^a–genotype^b				
Odd–*AABB*	Odd–*aabb*	Even–*AABB*	Even–*aabb*	Variety	Sex
80	20			20%	0%
50		25	25	25%	100%
50	40	10		40%	20%
25	25	25	25	50%	100%

^{a}Mating type (Odd or Even) of the stock.
^{b}The genotype at two loci (each with two alleles) is shown as illustration.
For these stocks mating type is independent of genotype. Differences in genotypes increase variety. Equality of mating types maximizes the amount of mating. The initial percent variety is the proportion of the culture that has the minority genotype. It ranges from 0 to 50%. The initial percentage mating is the proportion of the culture expected to conjugate. It is twice the initial proportion of the minority mating type and ranges from 0 to 100%.

ical treatments. The amount of variety can be reduced to any arbitrarily small value in this system. Row two has a maximum amount of biparental sex but only a small amount of variety. Row three has fairly high variety and a small amount of biparental sex. Row four has a maximum of both variety and sex (given only two genotypes). Using other stocks with different genotypes allows one to increase the level of genetic variety considerably. In fact, the genotype of the stocks was illustrated with two loci because there is a situation with the two trichocyst loci in *P. tetraurelia* in which the double heterozygote, equivalent to *AaBb* in Table III symbolism, is distinguishable from the homozygotes (Nyberg, 1978).

Finally, one could exploit polymorphisms among stocks in the immaturity interval to evaluate under which, if any, circumstances longer immaturity intervals are favored. Will more frequent changes of the environment favor more sex and shorter immaturities as predicted by the theory? To us it seems that the talk about the evolutionary and ecological effects of sex must move from the glib to the lab. Only then will we really understand the evolutionary meanings of breeding systems and sexual alternatives in ciliates.

References

Allen, S. L., 1967, Genomic exclusion: A rapid means for inducing homozygous diploid lines in *Tetrahymena pyriformis,* syngen 1, *Science* **155:**575–577.

Allen, S. L., and Weremiuk, S. L., 1971, Intersyngenic variations in the esterases and acid phosphatases of *Tetrahymena pyriformis, Biochem. Genet.* **5:**119–133.

Allen, S. L., Farrow, S. W., and Golembiewski, P. A., 1973, Esterase variations between the 14 syngens of *Paramecium aurelia, Genetics* **73:**561–573.

Allen, S. L., Lau, E. T., Nerad, T. A., and Rushford, C. L., 1982, Esterase variants in four species of the *Paramecium aurelia* complex, *J. Protozool.* **29:**604–611.

Allen, S. L., Nerad, T. A., and Rushford, C. L., 1983a, Intraspecific variability in the esterases and acid phosphatases of four species of the *Paramecium aurelia* complex, *J. Protozool.* **30:**131–143.

Allen, S. L., Rushford, C. L., Nerad, T. A., and Lau, E. T., 1983b, Intraspecific variability in the esterases and acid phosphatases of *Paramecium jenningsi* and *Paramecium multimicronucleatum:* Assignment of unidentified paramecia; comparison with the *P. aurelia* complex, *J. Protozool.* **30:**155–163.

Ammermann, D., 1966, Das Paarungssystem der Ciliaten *Paramecium woodruffi* und *Paramecium trichium. Arch. Protistenkd.* **109:**139–146.

Ammermann, D., 1982, Mating types in *Stylonychia mytilus* Ehrbg., *Arch. Protistenkd.* **126:**373–381.

Ammermann, D., and Schlegel, M., 1983, Characterization of two sibling species of the genus *Stylonychia* (Ciliata, Hypotrichida): *S. mytilus* Ehrenberg, 1838 and *S. lemnae* n. sp. I. Morphology and reproductive behavior, *J. Protozool.* **30:**290–294.

Aufderheide, K. J., and Nyberg, D., 1990, *Paramecium tetraurelia,* in: *Genetic Maps* (S. J. O'Brien, ed.), Cold Spring Harbor Laboratory Press, Cold Spring Harbor, N.Y., pp. 2130–2131.

Aufderheide, K. J., Daggett, P. M., and Nerad, T. A., 1983, *Paramecium sonneborni* n. sp., a new member of the *Paramecium aurelia* species-complex, *J. Protozool.* **30:**128–131.

Balbiani, E. G., 1858, Note relative a l'existence d'une génération sexuelle chez les infusoires, *Compt. Rend.* **46:**628–632.

Barnett, A., 1965, A circadian rhythm of mating type reversals in *Paramecium multimicronucleatum*, in: *Circadian Clocks* (J. Aschoff, ed.), North-Holland, Amsterdam, pp. 305–308.

Beale, G. H., 1954, *The Genetics of Paramecium aurelia*, Cambridge University Press, London.

Beale, G. H., 1990, Self and nonself recognition in the ciliate protozoan *Euplotes*, *Trends in Genetics* **6:**137–139.

Beale, G. H., Jurand, A., and Preer, J. R., Jr., 1969, The classes of endosymbionts in *Paramecium aurelia*, *J. Cell Sci.* **5:**69–91.

Bell, G., 1988, *Sex and Death in Protozoa: The History of an Obsession*, Cambridge University Press, London.

Berger, J. D., and Rahemtullah, S., 1990, Commitment to autogamy in *Paramecium* blocks mating reactivity: Implications of regulation of the sexual pathway and the breeding system, *Exp. Cell Res.* **187:**126–133.

Bernstein, C., and Bernstein, H., 1991, *Aging, Sex, and DNA Repair*, Academic Press, New York.

Bleyman, L. K., 1971, Temporal pattern in the ciliated protozoa, in: *Developmental Aspects of the Cell Cycle* (I. L. Cameron, G. M. Padilla, and M. Zimmerman, eds.), Academic Press, New York, pp. 67–91.

Bleyman, L. K., and Bruns, P. J., 1977, Genetics of cycloheximide resistance in *Tetrahymena*, *Genetics* **87:**275–284.

Bomford, R., 1966, The syngens of *Paramecium bursaria:* New mating types and intersyngenic mating reactions, *J. Protozool.* **13:**497–501.

Borror, A. C., 1980, Spatial distribution of marine ciliates: Micro-ecologic and biogeographic aspects of protozoan ecology, *J. Protozool.* **27:**10–13.

Bowbal, D. A., 1988, Studies in population genetics, D. A. thesis, University of Illinois at Chicago.

Bruns, P. J., 1986, Genetic organization of *Tetrahymena*, in: *The Molecular Biology of Ciliated Protozoa* (J. G. Gall, ed.), Academic Press, New York, pp. 27–44.

Bruns, P. J., and Brussard, T. B., 1974, Pair formation in *Tetrahymena pyriformis:* An inducible developmental system, *J. Exp. Zool.* **188:**337–344.

Bruns, P. J., and Brussard, T. B., 1981, Nullisomic *Tetrahymena:* Eliminating germinal chromosomes, *Science* **213:**549–551.

Bütschli, O., 1873, Vorlaufige Mittheilung einiger Resultate von Studien uber die Conjugation der Infusorien und die Zelltheilung, *Z. Wiss. Zool.* **25:**426–441.

Bütschli, O., 1876, Studien über die ersten Entwicklungsvorgänge der Eizelle, die Zellteilung und der Conjugation der Infusorien, *Abh. Senckenb. Naturforsch. Ges.* **10:**1–250.

Calkins, G. N., 1904, Studies on the life history of Protozoa: IV. Death of the A series, *J. Exp. Zool.* **1:**423–461.

Calkins, G. N., 1933, *The Biology of the Protozoa*, Lea & Febiger, Philadelphia.

Chadha, R., Sapra, G. R., and Dass, C.M.S., 1978, Cell cycle stages and their relationship with conjugation in *Stylonychia mytilus* Ehrenberg, *Indian J. Exp. Biol.* **16:**5–9.

Chatton, E., and Chatton, M., 1923, L'influence des facteurs bactériens sur la nutrition, la multiplication et la sexualitè des Infusoires, *C. R. Acad. Sci.* **176:**1262–1265.

Chen, T. T., 1946, Varieties and mating types in *Paramecium bursaria*. I. New variety and types from England, Ireland, and Czechoslovakia, *Proc. Natl. Acad. Sci. USA* **32:**173–181.

Cho, P. L., 1971, The genetics of mating types in a syngen of *Glaucoma*, *Genetics* **67:**377–390.

Coleman, A. W., 1981, The use of natural genetic markers to study colonization and sexuality in nature, *Am. Nat.* **188:**761–769.

Corliss, J. O., 1973, History, taxonomy, ecology, and evolution of species of *Tetrahymena*, in: *Biology of Tetrahymena* (A. M. Elliott, ed.), Dowden, Hutchinson & Ross, Stroudsburg, Pa., pp. 1–55.

Corliss, J. O., 1979, *The Ciliated Protozoa: Characterization, Classification, Guide to the Literature*, 2nd ed., Pergamon Press, Elmsford, N.Y.

Corliss, J. O., 1984, The kingdom Protista and its 45 phyla, *BioSystems* **17**:87–126.

Corliss, J. O., 1987, Protistan phylogeny and eukaryogenesis, *Int. Rev. Cytol.* **100**:319–370.

Corliss, J. O., 1989, Protistan diversity and origins of multicellular/multitissued organisms, *Boll. Zool.* **56**:227–234.

Corliss, J. O., and Daggett, P.-M., 1983, *Paramecium aurelia* and *Tetrahymena pyriformis:* Current status of the taxonomy and nomenclature of these popularly known and widely used ciliates, *Protistologica* **19**:307–322.

Curds, C. R., 1985, The species problem in ciliates—A taxonomist's view, *Atti Soc. Toscana Sci. Nat. Pisa Mem. P. V. Ser. B* **92**:29–41.

Diller, W. F., 1936, Nuclear reorganization processes in *Paramecium aurelia*, with descriptions of autogamy and "hemixis," *J. Morphol.* **59**:11–67.

Dini, F., 1981a, An example of related semispecies in *Euplotes crassus*, *Proc. VI Int. Congr. Protozool.* **1981**:79.

Dini, F., 1981b, Relationship between breeding systems and resistance to mercury in *Euplotes crassus* (Ciliophora: Hypotrichida), *Mar. Ecol. Prog. Ser.* **4**:195–202.

Dini, F., 1984, On the evolutionary significance of autogamy in the marine *Euplotes* (Ciliophora:Hypotrichida), *Am. Nat.* **123**:15–162.

Dini, F., and Giannì, A., 1985, Breeding systems in the *Euplotes vannus-crassus-minuta* group, *Atti Soc. Toscana Sci. Nat. Pisa Mem. P. V. Ser. B* **92**:75–93.

Dini, F., and Giorgi, F., 1982, Electrophoretic analysis of *Euplotes crassus* stocks from populations differing in their breeding systems, *Can. J. Zool.* **60**:929–932.

Dini, F., and Luporini, P., 1975, The multiple mating type system of the marine ciliate *Euplotes crassus*, (Dujardin), *Arch. Protistenkd.* **121**:238–245.

Dini, F., and Luporini, P., 1979, Preconjugant cell interaction and cell cycle in the ciliate *Euplotes crassus*. *Dev. Biol.* **69**:506–516.

Dini, F., and Luporini, P., 1980, Genetic determination of the autogamy trait in the hypotrich ciliate *Euplotes crassus*, *Genet. Res.* **35**:107–119.

Dini, F., and Luporini, P., 1985, Mating-type polymorphic variation in *Euplotes minuta* (Ciliophora: Hypotrichida), *J. Protozool.* **32**:111–117.

Dini, F., and Nyberg, D., 1991, The transition from immaturity to maturity in *Euplotes minuta*, *J. Protozool.* **38**(Suppl.):32.

Dini, F., and Nyberg, D., 1992, Development of sexual maturity in the ciliate *Euplotes crassus:* Sources of variation in the timing of maturity, *Dev. Genet.* **13**:41–46.

Dini, F., Bracchi, P., and Giannì, A., 1987, Mating types in *Aspidisca* sp. (Ciliophora, Hypotrichida): A cluster of cryptic species, *J. Protozool.* **34**:236–243.

Dini, F., Bleyman, L. K., and Giubbilini, P., 1990, Non-Mendelian inheritance of early maturity in *Euplotes crassus*, *J. Protozool.* **37**:475–478.

Dobzhansky, T., Ayala, F. J., Stebbins, G. L., and Valentine, J. W., 1977, *Evolution*, Freeman, San Francisco.

Doerder, F. P., and DeBault, L. E., 1976, Cytofluorometric analysis of nuclear DNA during meiosis, fertilization and macronuclear development in the ciliate *Tetrahymena pyriformis*, syngen 1, *J. Cell Sci.* **17**:471–493.

Downs, L. E., 1959, Mating types and their determination in *Stylonychia putrina*, *J. Protozool.* **6**:285–292.

Ehrenberg, C. G., 1838, *Die Infusionsthierchen als Vollkommene Organismen*, Leipzig.

Ehret, C. F., 1953, An analysis of the role of electromagnetic radiations in the mating reaction of *Paramecium bursaria, Physiol. Zool.* **26**:274–300.

Elliott, A. M., 1973, Life cycle and distribution of *Tetrahymena,* in: *Biology of Tetrahymena* (A. M. Elliott, ed.), Dowden, Hutchinson & Ross, Stroudsburg, Pa., pp. 259–286.

Enriques, P., 1907, La coniugazione e il differenziamento sessuale negli Infusori, *Arch. Protistenkd.* **9**:195–296.

Fenchel, T., 1987, *Ecology of Protozoa,* Springer-Verlag, Berlin.

Finlay, B. J., 1990, Physiological ecology of free-living protozoa, in: *Advances in Microbial Ecology,* Volume 2 (K. C. Marshall, ed.), Plenum Press, New York, pp. 1–35.

Frankel, J., 1983, Developmental underpinnings of evolutionary changes in protozoa, in: *Development and Evolution* (B. C. Goodwin, N. Holder, and C. G. Wylie, eds.), Cambridge University Press, London, pp. 279–314.

Frankel, J., 1989, *Pattern Formation: Ciliate Studies and Models,* Oxford University Press, London.

Gates, M. A., 1978, Morphometric variation in the hypotrich ciliate genus *Euplotes, J. Protozool.* **25**:338–350.

Gates, M. A., 1985, Suggestion for revision of the ciliate genus *Euplotes, Atti Soc. Toscana Sci. Nat. Pisa Mem. P. V. Ser. B* **92**:43–52.

Gates, M. A., 1990, Morphological drift accompanying nascent population differentiation in the ciliate *Euplotes vannus, J. Protozool.* **37**:78–86.

Gates, M. A., and Ramphal, C., 1991, Daily rhythm of mating in the ciliated protist *Euplotes vannus, Trans. Am. Microsc. Soc.* **110**:128–143.

Gates, M. A., Powelson, E. E., and Berger, J., 1975, Syngenic ascertainment in *Paramecium aurelia, Syst. Zool.* **23**: 482–489.

Génermont, J., 1976, Le probleme de l'espèce chez les protozoaires, in: *Les Problèmes de l'Espece dans le Règne Animal,* Volume 1 (C. Bocquet, J. Génermont, and M. Lamotte, eds.), Société Zoologique de France (Mém. No. 38), Paris, pp. 375–407.

Génermont, J., Machelon, V., and Tuffrau, M., 1976, Données expérimentales relatives au problème de l'espèce dans le genre *Euplotes* (Ciliés Hypotriches), *Protistologica* **12**:239–248.

Génermont, J., Machelon, V., and Demar, C., 1985, The "*vannus*" group of genus *Euplotes.* Sibling species and related forms; evolutionary significance and taxonomical implication, *Atti Soc. Toscana Sci. Nat. Pisa Mem. P. V. Ser. B* **92**:53–65.

Génermont, J., Demar, C., Fry-Versavel, G., Tuffrau, H., and Tuffrau, M., 1992, Polygenic control of an all-or-none morphological trait in *Euplotes* (Ciliata, Hypotrichea). Evolutionary significance of naturally occurring morphological variation in ciliates, *Genet. Sel. Evol.* **24**: 89–105.

Giese, A. C., and Arkoosh, M. A., 1939, Tests for sexual differentiation in *Paramecium multimicronucleatum* and *Paramecium caudatum, Physiol. Zool.* **12**:70–75.

Gilman, L. C., 1939, Mating types in *Paramecium caudatum, Am. Nat.* **73**:445–450.

Gilman, L. C., 1941, Mating types in diverse races of *Paramecium caudatum, Biol. Bull.* **80**:384–402.

Gilman, L. C., 1950, The position of Japanese varieties of *Paramecium caudatum* with respect to American varieties, *Biol. Bull.* **99**:348–349.

Görtz, H.-D., 1983, Endonuclear symbionts in ciliates, *Int. Rev. Cytol.* (Suppl.) **14**:145–176.

Görtz, H.-D., 1988, Endocytobiosis, in: *Paramecium* (H.-D. Görtz, ed.), Springer-Verlag, Berlin, pp. 393–405.

Grant, V., 1985, *The Evolutionary Process: A Critical Review of Evolutionary Theory,* Columbia University Press, New York.

Greel, K. G., 1973, *Protozoology,* Springer-Verlag, Berlin.

Gruchy, D. G., 1955, The breeding system and distribution of *Tetrahymena pyriformis, J. Protozool.* **2**:178–185.

Haga, N., and Hiwatashi, K., 1981, A protein called immaturin controlling sexual immaturity in *Paramecium, Nature* **289**:177–179.

Haggard, B., 1974, Interspecies crosses in *Paramecium aurelia* (syngen 4 by syngen 8), *J. Protozool.* **21**:152–159.

Hayashi, S., and Takayanagi, T., 1962, Cytological and cytogenetical studies on *Paramecium polycaryum*. IV. Determination of the mating system based on some experimental and cytological observations, *Jpn. J. Zool.* **13**:357–364.

Heckmann, K., 1967, Age-dependent intraclonal conjugation in *Euplotes crassus, J. Exp. Zool.* **165**:269–278.

Heckmann, K., 1983, Endosymbionts of *Euplotes, Int. Rev. Cytol.* (Suppl.) **14**:111–144.

Heckmann, K., and Frankel, J., 1968, Genic control of cortical pattern in *Euplotes, J. Exp. Zool.* **168**:11–38.

Heckmann, K., and Kuhlmann, H. W., 1986, Mating types and mating inducing substances in *Euplotes octocarinatus, J. Exp. Zool.* **237**:87–96.

Hertwig, R., 1889, Ueber die Konjugation der Infusorien, *Abh. Bayer. Akad. Wiss.* **17**:150–233.

Hertwig, R., 1892, Ueber Befruchtung und Konjugation, *Verh. Dtsch. Zool. Ges.* **2**:95–112.

Hiwatashi, K., 1949, Studies on the conjugation of *Paramecium caudatum*. I. Mating types and groups in the races obtained in Japan, *Sci. Rep. Tohoku Imp. Univ.* **18**:137–140.

Hiwatashi, K., and Kitamura, A., 1985, Fertilization in *Paramecium*, in: *Biology of Fertilization,* Volume 1 (C. B. Metz and A. Monroy, eds.), Academic Press, New York, pp. 57–85.

Iwasa, Y., and Sasaki, A., 1987, Evolution of the number of sexes, *Evolution* **41**:49–65.

Jankowski, A. W., 1962, Conjugation processes in *Paramecium putrinum* Clap. et Lachm. III. The multiple mating type system in *Paramecium putrinum, Zh. Obshch. Biol.* **23**:276–282 (in Russian).

Jankowski, A. W., 1972, Cytogenetics of *Paramecium putrinum* C. and L., 1858, *Acta Protozool.* **10**:285–394.

Jennings, H. S., 1939a, Genetics of *Paramecium bursaria*. I. Mating types and groups, their interrelations and distribution; mating behavior and self sterility, *Genetics* **24**:202–233.

Jennings, H. S., 1939b, *Paramecium bursaria:* Mating types and groups, mating behavior, self-sterility; their development and inheritance, *Am. Nat.* **73**:414–431.

Jennings, H. S., 1944a, *Paramecium bursaria:* Life history. I. Immaturity, maturity and age, *Biol. Bull.* **86**:131–145.

Jennings, H. S., 1944b, *Paramecium bursaria:* Life history. IV. Relation of inbreeding to mortality of ex-conjugant clones, *J. Exp. Zool.* **97**:165–197.

Jickeli, C. F., 1884, Ueber die Kernverhaltnisse der Infusorien, *Zool. Anz.* **7**:468–473.

Karakashian, M. W., 1965, The circadian rhythm of sexual reactivity in *Paramecium aurelia*, in: *Circadian Clocks* (J. Aschoff, ed.), North-Holland, Amsterdam, pp. 305–308.

Katashima, R., 1959, Mating types in *Euplotes eurystomus, J. Protozool.* **6**:75–83.

Katashima, R., 1961, Breeding systems of *Euplotes patella* in Japan, *Jpn. J. Zool.* **13**:39–61.

Kay, M. V., 1946, Studies on *Oxytricha bifaria*. III. Conjugation. *Trans. Am. Microsc. Soc.* **65**:131–137.

Khadem, N., and Gibson, I., 1985, Enzyme variation in *Paramecium caudatum, J. Protozool.* **32**:622–626.

Kimball, R. F., 1942, The nature and inheritance of mating types in *Euplotes patella, Genetics* **27**:269–285.

Kimball, R. F., Gaither, N., and Wilson, S., 1957, Genetic studies of a laboratory population of *Paramecium aurelia,* Variety 1, *Evolution* **11**:461–465.

King, E., 1693, Several observations and experiments on the Animalcula, in pepper-water, *Philos. Trans. R. Soc.* **17**:861–865.

Kosaka, T., 1973, Mating types of marine stocks of *Euplotes woodruffi* (Ciliata) in Japan, *J. Sci. Hiroshima Univ. Ser. B Div. 1* **24**:135–144.

Kosaka, T., 1982, Predominance of autogamy over conjugation in a new syngen in fresh-water *Euplotes woodruffi* (Ciliophora), *J. Sci. Hiroshima Univ. Ser. B Div. 1* **30**:111–122.

Kosaka, T., 1990, Methods for inducing selfing, selfing and its role in the life cycle of *Euplotes woodruffi* syngen 3 (Ciliophora), *J. Protozool.* **37**:33–39.

Kosaka, T., 1991a, Life cycle of *Paramecium bursaria* syngen 1 in nature, *J. Protozool.* **38**:140–148.

Kosaka, T., 1991b, Mature cells attracting cells of the complementary mating type in *Euplotes woodruffi* syngen 3 (Ciliophora, Hypotrichida), *Zool. Sci.* **8**:681–692.

Kosaka, T., 1992, Autogamy and autogamy inheritance in *Euplotes woodruffi* syngen 1 (Ciliophora), *Zool. Sci.* **9**:101–111.

Kuhlmann, H.-W., and Heckmann, K., 1989, Adolescence in *Euplotes octocarinatus*, *J. Exp. Zool.* **251**:316–328.

Landis, W. G., 1981, The ecology, role of the killer trait, and interactions of five species of the *Paramecium aurelia* complex inhabiting the littoral zone, *Can. J. Zool.* **59**:1734–1743.

Landis, W. G., 1982, The spatial and temporal distribution of *Paramecium bursaria* in the littoral zone, *J. Protozool.* **29**:159–161.

Landis, W. G., 1986, The interplay among ecology, breeding systems, and genetics in the *Paramecium aurelia* and *Paramecium bursaria* complexes, in: *Progress in Protistology*, Volume 1 (J. O. Corliss and D. J. Patterson, eds.), Biopress, Bristol, pp. 287–307.

Landis, W. G., 1987, Factors determining the frequency of the killer trait within populations of the *Paramecium aurelia* complex, *Genetics* **115**:197–205.

Landis, W. G., 1988, Ecology, in: *Paramecium* (H.-D. Görtz, ed.), Springer-Verlag, Berlin, pp. 131–140.

Leeuwenhoek, A. van, 1674, More observations from Mr. Leeuwenhook, in a letter of 7 September 1674, sent to the publisher, *Philos. Trans. R. Soc.* **9**:178–182.

Levine, M., 1953, The interaction of nucleus and cytoplasm in the isolation and evolution of species of *Paramecium*, *Evolution* **7**:366–385.

Leuken, W. W., 1973, A marine *Euplotes* (Ciliophora, Hypotrichida) with reduced number of prezygotic micronuclear divisions, *J. Protozool.* **20**:143–145.

Luporini, P., 1988, Cellular interactions in conjugation of ciliated protozoa, in: *Cell Interactions and Differentiation* (G. Ghiara, ed.), University of Naples, Naples, pp. 11–26.

Luporini, P., and Dini, F., 1975, Relationships between cell cycle and conjugation in 3 hypotrichs, *J. Protozool.* **22**:541–544.

Luporini, P., and Dini, F., 1977, The breeding system and the genetic relationship between autogamous and non-autogamous sympatric populations of *Euplotes crassus* Dujardin from the Somalian coast, *Monit. Zool. Ital. N.S.* **11**:119–154.

Luporini, P., and Miceli, C., 1986, Mating pheromones, in: *The Molecular Biology of Ciliated Protozoa* (J. G. Gall, ed.), Academic Press, New York, pp. 263–299.

Luporini, P., and Seyfert, H.-M., 1981, Variation in the total protein patterns of *Euplotes* species with a single-type dargyrome, *Proc. VI Int. Congr. Protozool.* **1981**:225.

Luporini, P., and Teti, C. M., 1979, Oxygen concentration of the cultural fluid and variations in the mating reactivity of the marine ciliate *Euplotes crassus*, *Experientia* **35**:50–51.

Lwoff, A., 1923, Sur la nutrition des Infusoires, *C. R. Acad. Sci.* **176**:928–930.

Lynn, D. H., and Corliss, J. O., 1991, Ciliophora, in: *Microscopic Anatomy of Invertebrates*, Volume 1 (F. W. Harrison and J. O. Corliss, eds.), Wiley, New York, pp. 333–467.

Machelon, V., 1982, Données sur le complexe *Euriplotes vannus:* L'existence d'une cinquième espèce, analyse des mécanismes d'isolement reproductif, *Protistologica* **18**:345–354.

Machelon, V., 1983, Etude du Complexe *Euplotes vannus* (Ciliés Hipotriches), Tèse de Doctorat, Université de Paris-Sud, Orsay Cédex.

Machelon, V., and Demar, C., 1984, Electrophoretic variations among the genus *Euplotes* (Ciliata, Hypotrichida): Comparative data for the sibling species complex *Euplotes vannus* and survey of infrageneric variability, *J. Protozool.* **31**:74–82.

Machelon, V., Génermont, J., and Dattée, Y., 1984, A biometrical analysis of morphological variation within a section of genus *Euplotes* (Ciliata, Hypotrichida), with special reference to the *E. vannus* complex of sibling species, *Origins Life* **13**:249–267.

Magagnini, P., and Santangelo, G., 1977, Temporal distribution of mating type in a natural population of *Euplotes crassus, Monit. Zool. Ital. N.S.* **11**:223–230.

Mancini, G., and Valbonesi, A., 1991, MCS/SEL/BAS program—An overlapping clustering method with examples from mating type interactions of ciliated protozoa, *Comput. Appl. Biosci.* **7**:365–371.

Maupas, E., 1888, Recherches expérimentales sur la multiplication des Infusoires ciliés, *Arch. Zool. Exp. Gen.* **6**:165–277.

Maupas, E., 1889, Le rajeunissement karyogamique chez les Ciliés, *Arch. Zool. Exp. Gen.* **7**:149–517.

Mayr, E., 1942, *Systematics and the Origin of Species,* Columbia University Press, New York.

Mayr, E., 1970, *Population, Species, and Evolution,* Harvard University Press, Cambridge, Mass.

Mayr, E., 1982, *The Growth of Biological Thought: Diversity, Evolution and Inheritance,* Harvard University Press, Cambridge, Mass.

Metz, C. B., 1954, Mating substances and the physiology of fertilization in ciliates, in: *Sex in Microorganisms* (D. H. Wenrich, ed.), American Association for the Advancement of Science, Washington, D.C., pp. 284–334.

Meyer, E. B., and Nanney, D. L., 1987, Isozymes in the ciliated protozoan *Tetrahymena,* in: *Isozymes: Current Topics in Biological and Medical Research,* Volume 13 (M. C. Rattazzi, J. G. Scandalios, and G. S. Whitt, eds.), Liss, New York, pp. 61–102.

Miceli, C., LaTerza, A., Bradshaw, R. A., and Luporini, P., 1992, Identification and structural characterization of a cDNA clone encoding a membrane-bound form of the polypeptide pheromone Er-1 in the ciliate protozoan *Euplotes raikovi, Proc. Natl. Acad. Sci. USA* **89**:1988–1992.

Miyake, A., 1974, Cell interaction in conjugation of ciliates, *Curr. Top. Microbiol. Immunol.* **64**:49–77.

Miyake, A., 1981, Physiology and biochemistry of conjugation in ciliates, in: *Biochemistry and Physiology of Protozoa,* Volume 4 (M. Levandowsky and S. H. Hutner, eds.), Academic Press, New York, pp. 95–129.

Miyake, A., and Nobili, R., 1974, Mating reaction and its daily rhythm in *Euplotes crassus, J. Protozool.* **21**:584–587.

Müller, O. F., 1786, *Animalcula Infusoria Fluviatilia et Marina,* Hauniae, Copenhagen.

Nakata, A., 1958, Mating types, *Paramecium calkinsi, Zool. Mag. (Tokyo)* **67**:210–213.

Nakata, A., 1969, Mating types in *Glaucoma scintillans, J. Protozool.* **16**:689–692.

Nanney, D. L., 1957, Inbreeding degeneration in *Tetrahymena, Genetics* **42**:137–146.

Nanney, D. L., 1964, Macronuclear differentiation and subnuclear assortment in ciliates, in: *The Role of Chromosomes in Development* (M. Locke, ed.), Academic Press, New York, pp. 253–273.

Nanney, D. L., 1968, Ciliate genetics: Pattern and programs of gene actions, *Annu. Rev. Genet.* **2**:121–140.

Nanney, D. L., 1974, Aging and long-term temporal regulation in ciliated protozoa: A critical review, *Mech. Ageing Dev.* **3**:81–105.

Nanney, D. L., 1977, Cell–cell interactions in ciliates: Evolutionary and genetic constraints, in: *Microbial Interactions,* Ser. B, Volume 3 (J. L. Reissig, ed.), Chapman & Hall, London, pp. 353–390.

Nanney, D. L., 1980, *Experimental Ciliatology: An Introduction to Genetic and Developmental Analysis in Ciliates,* Wiley, New York.

Nanney, D. L., 1982, Genes and phenes in *Tetrahymena, BioScience* **32**:783–788.

Nanney, D. L., 1985, The entangled tempos underlying *Tetrahymena* taxonomy, *Atti Soc. Toscana Sci. Nat. Pisa Mem. P. V. Ser. B* **92**:1–13.

Nanney, D. L., 1986, Introduction, in: *The Molecular Biology of Ciliated Protozoa* (J. G. Gall, ed.), Academic Press, New York, pp. 1–26.

Nanney, D. L., and McCoy, J. W., 1976, Characterization of the species of the complex *Tetrahymena pyriformis* complex, *Trans. Am. Microsc. Soc.* **95**:664–682.

Nanney, D. L., Cooper, L. E., Simon, E. M., and Whitt, G. S., 1980, Isozymic characterization of three mating groups of the *Tetrahymena pyriformis* complex, *J. Protozool.* **27**:451–459.

Nanney, D. L., Meyer, E. B., Simon, E. M., and Preparata, R. M., 1989a, Comparison of ribosomal and isozymic phylogenies of tetrahymenine ciliates, *J. Protozool.* **36**:1–8.

Nanney, D. L., Preparata, R. M., Preparata, F. P., Meyer, E. B., and Simon, E. M., 1989b, Shifting ditypic site analysis: Heuristics for expanding the phylogenetic range of nucleotide sequences in Sankoff analyses, *J. Mol. Evol.* **28**:451–459.

Ng, S. F., 1990a, Developmental heterochrony in ciliated protozoa: Overlap of asexual and sexual cycles during conjugation, *Biol. Rev.* **65**:19–101.

Ng, S. F., 1990b, Embryological perspective of sexual somatic development in ciliated protozoa: Implication on immortality, sexual reproduction and inheritance of acquired characters, *Philos. Trans. R. Soc. London Ser. B* **329**:287–305.

Nielsen, H., Simon, E. M., and Engberg, J., 1985, Updating rDNA restriction enzyme maps of *Tetrahymena* reveals four new intron-containing species, *J. Protozool.* **32**:480–485.

Nobili, R., 1964, Coniugazione ibrida tra specie di *Euplotes* (Ciliata, Hypotrichida), *Boll. Zool.* **31**:1338–1348.

Nobili, R., and Luporini, P., 1967a, Maintenance of heterozygosity at the *mt* locus after autogamy in *Euplotes minuta* (Ciliata, Hypotrichida), *Genet. Res.* **10**:35–43.

Nobili, R., and Luporini, P., 1967b, New mating types and the problem of one or more syngens in *Euplotes minuta* Yocom (Ciliata, Hypotrichida), *Atti Assoc. Genet. Ital.* **12**:345–360.

Nobili, R., Luporini, P., and Dini, F., 1978, Breeding systems, species relationships and evolutionary trends in some marine species of Euplotidae (Hypotrichida Ciliata), in: *Marine Organisms: Genetics, Ecology, and Evolution* (B. Battaglia and J. A. Beardmore, eds.), Plenum Press, New York, pp. 591–616.

Nobili, R., Esposito, F., and Luporini, P., 1987, Compatibility systems in ciliates, in: *Invertebrate Models: Cell Receptors and Cell Communication* (A. H. Greenberg, ed.), Karger, Basel, pp. 6–28.

Nyberg, D., 1974, Breeding systems and resistance to environmental stress in ciliates, *Evolution* **28**:367–380.

Nyberg, D., 1975, Genetic analysis of copper resistance in *Paramecium aurelia* syngen 4, *Genetics* **80**:463–473.

Nyberg, D., 1978, Genetic analysis of trichocyst discharge of the wild stocks of *Paramecium tetraurelia, J. Protozool.* **25**:107–112.

Nyberg, D., 1981a, Fertility is not a function of geographic distance in *Tetrahymena, J. Hered.* **72**:94–96.

Nyberg, D., 1981b, Three new "biological" species of *Tetrahymena* (*T. hegewischi* n. sp., *T. sonneborni* n. sp., *T. nipissingi* n. sp.) and temperature tolerance of members of the "*pyriformis*" complex, *J. Protozool.* **28**:65–69.

Nyberg, D., 1982, Sex, recombination, and reproductive fitness: An experimental approach using *Paramecium, Am. Nat.* **120**:198–217.

Nyberg, D., 1988, The species concept and breeding systems, in: *Paramecium* (H.-D. Görtz, ed.), Springer-Verlag, Berlin, pp. 41–58.

Nyberg, D., and Bishop, P., 1979, Nickel tolerance inheritance in *Tetrahymena sonneborni, Genetics* **91**(Suppl.):89.

Nyberg, D., and Bishop, P., 1981, The immaturity interval in *Tetrahymena:* Genetic and environmental sources of variation, *Dev. Genet.* **2**:159–170.

Nyberg, D., and Bishop, P., 1983, High levels of phenotypic variability of metal and temperature tolerance in *Paramecium, Evolution* **37**:341–357.

Nyberg, D., and Bogar, A. E., 1986, Genotypic and subgenotypic variation in heavy metal tolerance in *Paramecium, Am. Nat.* **127**:615–628.

Orias, O., 1959, Mating interaction between varieties 6 and 8, *Tetrahymena pyriformis, J. Protozool.* **6**(Suppl.):19.

Orias, O., and Bruns, P. J., 1976, Induction and isolation of mutants in *Tetrahymena,* in: *Methods in Cell Biology,* Volume 13 (D. M. Prescott, ed.), Academic Press, New York, pp. 247–282.

Orias, O., and Rohlf, F. J., 1964, Population genetics of the mating type locus in *Tetrahymena pyriformis,* variety 8, *Evolution* **18**:620–629.

Orias, O., Hamilton, E. P., and Flacks, M., 1979, Osmotic shock prevents nuclear exchange and produces whole-genome homozygotes in conjugating *Tetrahymena, Science* **203**:660–663.

Ossipov, D. V., Rautian, M. S., and Skoblo, I. I., 1974, The loss of the ability for sexual process in cells of *Paramecium caudatum* infected with endonuclear symbiotic bacteria, *Genetika* **10**:62–70.

Paterson, H.E.H., 1993, *Evolution and the Recognition Concept of Species,* Johns Hopkins University Press, Baltimore.

Pierson, B. F., 1943, A comparative morphological study of several species of *Euplotes* closely related to *Euplotes patella, J. Morphol.* **72**:125–165.

Poljansky, G. I., 1992, Protozoology and the problem of species, *J. Protozool.* **39**: 177–180.

Preer, J. R., Jr., 1968, Genetics of protozoa, in: *Research in Protozoology,* Volume 3 (T. T. Chen, ed.), Pergamon Press, Elmsford, N.Y., pp. 130–278.

Preer, J. R., Jr., 1986, Surface antigens of *Paramecium,* in: *The Molecular Biology of Ciliated Protozoa* (J. G. Gall, ed.), Academic Press, New York, pp. 301–339.

Preer, J. R., Jr., and Preer, L. B., 1979, The size of the macronuclear DNA and its relationship to models for maintaining genic balance, *J. Protozool.* **26**:18–28.

Preer, J. R., Jr., Preer, L. B., and Jurand, A., 1974, Kappa and other endosymbionts in *Paramecium aurelia, Bacteriol. Rev.* **38**:113–163.

Preer, L. B., 1968, "Alfa" an infectious macronuclear symbiont in *Paramecium aurelia, J. Protozool.* **16**:570–578.

Preparata, R. M., Meyer, E. B., Preparata, F. P., Simon, E. M., Vossbrinck, C. R., and Nanney, D. L., 1989, Ciliate evolution: The ribosomal phylogenesis of the tetrahymenine ciliates, *J. Mol. Evol.* **28**:427–441.

Pringle, C. R., and Beale, G. H., 1960, Antigenic polymorphism in a wild population of *Paramecium aurelia, Genet. Res.* **1**:62–68.

Przybos, E., 1975, Genetic studies of *Paramecium jenningsi* strains (Diller and Earl, 1958), *Folia Biol. (Krakow)* **23**:425–471.

Raikov, I. B., 1972, Nuclear phenomena during conjugation and autogamy in ciliates, in: *Research in Protozoology,* Volume 4 (T. T. Chen, ed.), Pergamon Press, Elmsford, N.Y., pp. 148–289.

Rao, M.V.N., 1958, Mating types in *Stylonychia pustulata, Curr. Sci.* **27**:395.

Reiff, I., 1968, Die genetische Determination multipler Paarungstypen bei dem Ciliaten *Uronychia transfuga* (Hypotrichida, Euplotidae), *Arch. Protistenkd.* **110**:372–397.

Ricci, N., 1981, Preconjugant cell interaction in *Oxytricha bifaria* (Ciliata, Hypotrichida): A two-step recognition process leading to cell fusion and the induction of meiosis, in: *Sexual Interactions in Eukaryotic Microbes* (D. H. O'Day and P. A. Horgen, eds.), Academic Press, New York, pp. 319–350.

Ricci, N., 1990, The behaviour of ciliated protozoa, *Anim. Behav.* **40**:1048–1069.

Ricci, N., 1992, Etho-ecology of ciliates: A reappraisal of their adaptive biology, an insight in their environment constrains, *Acta Protozool.* **31**:19–32.

Rogers, M. B., and Karrer, K. M., 1985, Adolescence in *Tetrahymena thermophila, Proc. Natl. Acad. Sci. USA* **82**:436–439.

Ron, A., 1974, Autoconjugates in *Tetrahymena, Experentia* **30**:1001–1002.

Rosati, G., and Verni, F., 1991, Sexual recognition in protozoa: Chemical signals and transduction mechanisms, *Zool. Sci.* **8**:415–429.

Rosati, G., and Verni, F., 1976, Macronuclear symbionts in *Euplotes crassus* (Ciliata Hypotrichida), *Boll. Zool.* **42**:231–232.

Rosati, G., Verni, F., and Luporini, P., 1976, Cytoplasmic bacteria-like endosymbionts in *Euplotes crassus* (Dujardin) (Ciliata Hypotrichida), *Monit. Zool. Ital. N.S.* **10**:449–460.

Schlegel, M., Kramer, M., and Hahn, K., 1988, Taxonomy and phylogenetic relationship of eight species of the genus *Euplotes* (Hypotrichida, Ciliophora) as revealed by enzyme electrophoresis, *Eur. J. Protistol.* **24**:22–29.

Schonefeld, U., Alfermann, A. W., and Schultz, J. E., 1986, Economic mass cultivation of *Paramecium tetraurelia* on a 200-liter scale, *J. Protozool.* **33**:222–225.

Siegel, R. W., 1956, Mating types in *Oxytricha* and the significance of mating type systems in ciliates, *Biol. Bull.* **110**:352–357.

Siegel, R. W., 1958, Hybrid vigor, heterosis and evolution in *Paramecium aurelia, Evolution* **12**:402–416.

Siegel, R. W., 1961, Direct and indirect evidence that free-living ciliates conjugate in nature, *J. Protozool.* **8**:27–29.

Siegel, R. W., 1963, New results on the genetics of mating types in *Paramecium bursaria, Genet. Res.* **4**:132–142.

Siegel, R. W., 1967, Genetics of ageing and the life cycle in ciliates, *Symp. Soc. Exp. Biol.* **21**:127–148.

Siegel, R. W., and Cohen, L. W., 1963, A temporal sequence for genic expression: Cell differentiation in *Paramecium, Am. Zool.* **3**:127–134.

Simon, E. M., 1980, Mating-type inheritance and maturity times in crosses between subspecies of *Tetrahymena pigmentosa, Genetics* **94**:93–113.

Simon, E. M., Meyer, E. B., and Preparata, R. M., 1985, New wild *Tetrahymena* from southeast Asia, China, and North America, including *T. malaccensis, T. asiatica, T. nanneyi, T. caudata,* and *T. silvana* n. spp., *J. Protozool.* **32**:183–189.

Sleigh, M. A., 1989, *Protozoa and Other Protists,* 2nd ed., Arnold, London.

Small, E. B., and Lynn, D. H., 1985, Phylum Ciliophora Doflein, 1901, in: *An Illustrated Guide to the Protozoa* (J. J. Hutner and E. C. Bovee, eds.), Society of Protozoologists, Lawrence, Kans., pp. 393–575.

Smith-Sonneborn, J., 1981, Genetics and aging in protozoa, *Int. Rev. Cytol.* **73**:319–354.

Soldo, A. T., Godoi, G. A., and Brikson, S., 1974, Infectious particles in a marine ciliate, *Nature* **249**:284–286.

Sonneborn, T. M., 1937, Sex, sex inheritance and sex determination in *Paramecium aurelia, Proc. Natl. Acad. Sci. USA* **23**:378–395.

Sonneborn, T. M., 1939a, Genetic evidence of autogamy in *Paramecium aurelia, Anat. Rec.* **75**:85.

Sonneborn, T. M., 1939b, Mating types and groups, lethal interactions; determination and inheritance, *Am. Nat.* **73**:390–413.

Sonneborn, T. M., 1940, The relation of macronuclear regeneration in *Paramecium aurelia* to macronuclear structure, amitosis and genetic determination, *Anat. Rec.* **78**:53–54.

Sonneborn, T. M., 1947, Recent advances in the genetics of *Paramecium* and *Euplotes, Adv. Genet.* **1**:264–358.

Sonneborn, T. M., 1954, The relation of autogamy to senescence and rejuvenescence in *Paramecium aurelia, J. Protozool.* **1:**38–53.

Sonneborn, T. M., 1957, Breeding systems, reproductive methods, and species problems in protozoa, in: *The Species Problem* (E. Mayr, ed.), AAAS Publication, Washington, D.C., pp. 155–324.

Sonneborn, T. M., 1958, Classification of syngens of the *Paramecium aurelia-multimicronucleatum* complex, *J. Protozool.* **5**(Suppl.):21.

Sonneborn, T. M., 1959, Kappa and related particles in *Paramecium, Adv. Virus Res.* **6:**229–365.

Sonneborn, T. M., 1970, Methods in *Paramecium* research, in: *Methods in Cell Physiology,* Volume 4 (D. M. Prescott, ed.), Academic Press, New York, pp. 241–339.

Sonneborn, T. M., 1974, *Paramecium aurelia,* in: *Handbook of Genetics: Plants, Plant Viruses and Protists,* Volume 2 (R. C. King, ed.), Plenum Press, New York, pp. 469–594.

Sonneborn, T. M., 1975, The *Paramecium aurelia* complex of fourteen sibling species, *Trans. Am. Microsc. Soc.* **94:**155–178.

Sonneborn, T. M., 1977, Genetics of cellular differentiation: Stable nuclear differentiation in eukaryotic unicells, *Annu. Rev. Genet.* **11:**349–367.

Sonneborn, T. M., 1978, Genetics of cell–cell interactions in ciliates, in: *Molecular Basis of Cell–Cell Interaction,* Birth Defects: Original Article Series, Volume 14 (R. A. Lerner and D. Bergsma, eds.), Liss, New York, pp. 417–427.

Stein, F., 1859, *Der Organismus der Infusionsthiere nach eigenen Forschungen in Systematischer Reihenfolge bearbeitet,* Leipzig.

Steinbrück, G., and Schlegel, M., 1983, Characterization of two sibling species of the genus *Stylonychia* (Ciliata, Hypotrichida): *S. mytilus* Ehrenberg, 1838 and *S. lemnae* n. sp. II. Biochemical characterization, *J. Protozool.* **30:**294–300.

Tait, A., 1970, Enzyme variation between syngens in *Paramecium aurelia, Biochem. Genet.* **4:**461–470.

Takagi, Y., 1971, Sequential expression of sex-traits in the clonal development of *Paramecium multimicronucleatum, Jpn. J. Genet.* **46:**83–91.

Takagi, Y., 1988, Aging, in: *Paramecium* (H.-D. Görtz, ed.), Springer-Verlag, Berlin, pp. 131–138.

Takahashi, M., 1988, Behavioral genetics in *P. caudatum,* in: *Paramecium* (H.-D. Görtz, ed.), Springer-Verlag, Berlin, pp. 271–281.

Takahashi, T., 1973, Mating types and two conjugation types of *Pseudourostyla levis* sp. n. (Ciliata), *J. Sci. Hiroshima Univ. Ser. B Div. 1* **24:**145–163.

Tsukii, Y., 1988, Mating-type inheritance, in: *Paramecium* (H.-D Görtz, ed.), Springer-Verlag, Berlin, pp. 59–69.

Tsukii, Y., and Hiwatashi, K., 1983, Genes controlling mating-type specificity in *Paramecium caudatum:* Three loci revealed by intersyngenic crosses, *Genetics* **104:**41–62.

Valbonesi, A., Ortenzi, C., and Luporini, P., 1988, An integrated study of the species problem in the *Euplotes crassus-minuta-vannus* group, *J. Protozool.* **35:**38–45.

Valbonesi, A., Ortenzi, C., and Luporini, P., 1992, The species problem in a ciliate with a high multiple mating type system, *Euplotes crassus, J. Protozool.* **39:**45–54.

Vaudaux, P. E., Williams, N. E., Frankel, J., and Vaudaux, C., 1977, Inter-strain variability of structural proteins in *Tetrahymena, J. Protozool.* **24:**453–458.

Vivier, E., 1974, Morphology, taxonomy and general biology of the genus *Paramecium,* in: *Paramecium: A Current Survey* (W. J. van Wagtendonk, ed.), Elsevier, Amsterdam, pp. 1–89.

Weismann, A., 1891, *Essays upon Heredity and Kindred Biological Problems,* 2nd ed., Oxford University Press (Clarendon), London.

Wichterman, R., 1939, Cytogamy: A new sexual process in joined pairs of *Paramecium caudatum, Nature* **144:**123–124.

Wichterman, R., 1951, The biology of *Paramecium calkinsi* with special reference to ecology, cultivation, structural characteristics and mating type phenomena, *Proc. Am. Soc. Protozool.* **1951**:11–12.

Wichterman, R., 1986, *The Biology of Paramecium,* 2nd ed., Plenum Press, New York.

Williams, N. E., 1984, An apparent disjunction between the evolution of form and substance in the genus *Tetrahymena, Evolution* **38**:25–33.

Williams, N. E., Buhse, H. E., and Smith, M. G., 1984, Protein similarities in the genus *Tetrahymena* and a description of *Tetrahymena leucophrys* n. sp., *J. Protozool.* **31**:313–321.

Wolfe, J., 1973, Conjugation in *Tetrahymena:* The relationship between the division cycle and cell pairing, *Dev. Biol.* **35**:221–231.

Wolfe, J., 1976, G_1 arrest and the division/conjugation decision in *Tetrahymena, Dev. Biol.* **54**:116–126.

Woodruff, L. L., 1908, The life-cycle of *Paramecium* when subjected to a varied environment, *Am. Nat.* **42**:520–526.

Woodruff, L. L., and Erdmann, R., 1914, A normal periodic reorganization process without cell fusion in *Paramecium, J. Exp. Zool.* **17**:425–518.

Wright, S., 1932, The roles of mutation, inbreeding, crossbreeding, and selection in evolution, *Proc. VI Int. Congr. Genet.* **1932**:356–366.

Zouros, E., and Foltz, D. W., 1988, The use of allelic isozyme variation for the study of heterosis, in: *Isozymes: Current Topics in Biological and Medical Research,* Volume 13 (M. C. Rattazzi, J. G. Scandalios, and G. S. Whitt, eds.), Liss, New York, pp. 1–59.

4

Microbial Ecology in Lake Cisó

CARLOS PEDRÓS-ALIÓ and
RICARDO GUERRERO

1. Introduction

1.1. Why Study Microbial Ecology in Lake Cisó?

The principles of ecology have been developed from the study of animals and plants. The contribution of microorganisms to ecological theory has been extremely limited. Their role in ecosystems is usually considered to be only as mineralizers of organic matter and intermediates in some cycles of nutrients, despite the fact that different guilds of the bacterioplankton carry out a large variety of functions in aquatic environments (Jones, 1987; Pedrós-Alió, 1989). Experimentally, they have been used only to test some models of predation and competition. If ecology is to be universally valid, however, its principles should be applicable to microorganisms. Further, by limiting the objects of study to animals and plants, most of the history of life on Earth (and thus most of its ecological history) is ignored. It seems that one of the main purposes of microbial ecology, therefore, should be to test whether general ecological principles are applicable to microorganisms, trying to integrate microorganisms in the current ecological paradigms. There seem to be two alternatives for this purpose. In the first one, some easily measurable macroscopic parameter of microbial communities can be measured in a significant number of systems so that generalizations can be derived (Peters, 1986). In the second one, a given system can be used as a model ecosystem, and its components studied in a degree of detail impossible with the first approach (Brock, 1978; Ward et al.,

CARLOS PEDRÓS-ALIÓ • Institut de Ciències del Mar, CSIC, E-08039 Barcelona, Spain. RICARDO GUERRERO • Departament de Microbiologia, Universitat de Barcelona, E-08028, Barcelona, Spain.
Advances in Microbial Ecology, Volume 13, edited by J. Gwynfryn Jones. Plenum Press, New York, 1993.

1987). We took this second alternative when initiating the study of Lake Cisó 16 years ago.

But, why in Lake Cisó? One of the most important decisions confronting an ecologist is choosing the right system for study. For example, microbial ecology was put on a solid footing thanks to the simple nature of the hot springs in Yellowstone National Park chosen by T. D. Brock and co-workers (Brock, 1978). The ongoing introduction of molecular methods in microbial ecology has been extremely successful in simple ecosystems such as Octopus Spring (Stahl *et al.*, 1985) or deep-sea vents (Distel *et al.*, 1988). Results from the more complex oligotrophic ocean, however promising, have been modest (Giovannoni *et al.*, 1990; Schmidt *et al.*, 1991). Thus, we were careful to pick a system offering many advantages for our purposes.

Lake Cisó has some of the simplicity of the extreme environments studied by others (Brock, 1978; Ward *et al.*, 1987), but it is not an extreme environment. There are many lakes in the world with very similar summer communities (Takahashi and Ichimura, 1968; Lindholm, 1987; Vicente *et al.*, 1991; Finlay *et al.*, 1991; Gervais, 1991; Miracle *et al.*, 1992; Hurley and Garrison, 1992). Thus, we were studying a "normal" yet accessible ecosystem.

Lake Cisó is very small and, thus, very easy to work with. In fact, some visitors refuse to call it a lake! Of course, the size of the lake is large enough for microorganisms. Water could be pumped from any depth at the center of the lake, and sampling carried out on shore by just adding a few meters of tubing. The small size, together with the thick bushes and trees surrounding the lake, protected it from the wind. In this way sampling could be carried out with a precision of a few centimeters consistently. The spatial resolution adequate to detect the events relevant to the microorganisms was easily achieved, unlike in microbial mats, where sophisticated electronic gear is needed just to obtain vertical profiles of compounds, or large water bodies, where waves preclude this precision.

A field laboratory, generously maintained by the City Hall of Banyoles, was available nearby, facilitating field studies, especially during diel cycles. Altogether, this combination of circumstances made it cheap to study, which is a fundamental question in a chronically underfunded scientific environment.

Because of the presence of sulfide only a few species were present, but in enormous amounts. Thus, study of the whole system could be carried out and simultaneous dissection of guilds and *in situ* physiological studies of the main populations were possible. There were no fishes, which resulted in a substantial economy of methods.

The community was dominated by microorganisms. There was an alternation between anaerobic and aerobic situations that resulted in an absolute dominance by prokaryotes during the winter and a more diverse microbial community in summer. Finally, the holomixis situation, with an essentially anaerobic prokaryotic community, could bring some insight into the structure and functioning of Archean ecosystems.

We must admit there were also some problems with the choice of Lake Cisó. The area is karstic and so dynamic that several new sinkholes have appeared since 1977. The "Estanyol Nou" ("New pond"), for example, suddenly appeared on November 16, 1978, only 200 m away from Lake Cisó. It is not only the uneasiness caused by working in such a dangerous place that gave us headaches. We have been embarrassed to report different depths for the lake in different papers, from 11 m (Guerrero *et al.*, 1980) to 9 m (Guerrero *et al.*, 1986) and to 7.5 m (Guerrero *et al.*, 1987a). Two different landslides have occurred in the lake since 1977, one in February 1980 and another in February 1986, causing severe changes in its morphology (García-Gil *et al.*, 1985). The system has also proven to be more complicated than we originally thought, as can be gathered from a quick look at the food web in Fig. 10.

1.2. Taxonomy, Size, and Trophic Role

One of the main goals of ecologists is to understand the structure of natural systems and its changes with time. For this purpose, the way in which the total biomass is distributed among different groups of organisms has to be assessed. The total biomass of an ecosystem is divided into discrete heterogeneous packages. The classification of these living packages or particles can be approached from different perspectives (Fig. 1). In one approach, a taxonomic name is given to each package, and then the distribution of numbers of packages per taxon can be analyzed. This comprises the study of diversity (May, 1986; Magurran, 1988). A different approach considers the size of the packages as the main property to classify them, and then proceeds to group them into size classes. In this approach one studies the size spectrum or size distribution of organisms in a community (Sheldon *et al.*, 1972; Platt, 1985). Yet a third approach assigns a trophic role to each package and packages with the same trophic role are included in common trophic groups. In this case, the trophic dynamics, or the guild structure of the system, are analyzed (Lindeman, 1942; Cousins, 1980). These alternative classification systems provide different views of ecosystem structure and function.

Most classification schemes were developed before sufficient knowledge of microorganisms was available. Too often, microorganisms do not fit within such schemes. The diversity of microorganisms can be used to show the inconsistencies in current classification systems. Their inclusion may bring a change in perspective in our way of looking at the living world. Our biases will become more obvious and, thus, steps will be taken to correct them. The three approaches have been used in Lake Cisó (Gasol *et al.*, 1991b, 1992a, 1993; Pedrós-Alió *et al.*, 1986), and a summary will be presented here.

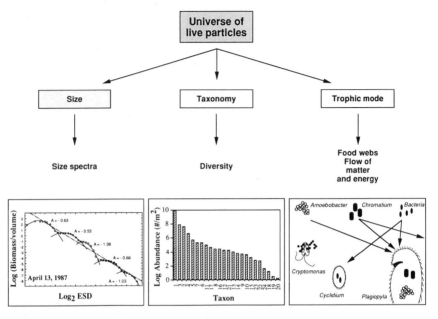

Figure 1. Three different ways to examine the structure of communities depend on the kind of property chosen to classify living particles. If size is chosen, the size spectrum of a community can be examined. In the figure, the size spectrum for Lake Cisó during stratification is shown. If genetics or taxonomy is picked, one studies diversity of communities. In the figure, the main taxa in the Lake Cisó stratification community are ranked according to their abundance. Finally, if trophic mode is chosen, the food web structure and fluxes through the community are the subject of study. The anaerobic microbial food web of Lake Cisó is shown in the figure.

1.3. A Brief Description of the Lake

Lake Cisó is a small lake (599 m² and 8 m maximum depth) in the karstic area of Banyoles (northeast Spain, 48°08′N, 2°45′E). The lake has been described in detail elsewhere (Guerrero *et al.*, 1985; Pedrós-Alió *et al.*, 1986; Gasol *et al.*, 1990). Water enters the lake via surface runoff, rainfall and, mostly, seepage. There is only one small surface outlet, which dries up in summer. Underground water percolates through gypsum-rich layers before entering the lake and this causes high sulfate (near 10 mM) concentration and, as a consequence of bacterial reduction, high sulfide concentrations in the water. Lake Cisó is holomictic, with one mixing season lasting from mid-October to mid-March. At the beginning of April, stratification separates a shallow epilimnion from the hypolimnion. Summer epilimnetic temperatures are close to 24°C, and the hypolimnion is always at <14°C. The epilimnion is not very transparent (the extinction coefficient is $3-4m^{-1}$) and the water is deeply colored by dissolved organic matter. Around 1% of surface light reaches $1-1.5$ m deep. Alkalinity is high (8.7 meq/liter) especially in the hypolimnion. The pH oscillates around 7.5 in the whole lake while nitrate and nitrite appear in high concentrations (up to 5 μM for both ions) only in the epilimnion, but they can be found at all depths when the lake has just mixed. Ammonium is present all over the lake, with hypolimnetic concentrations up to 1 mM, and $10-50$ μM in the epilimnion. For most of the year, soluble reactive phosphorus was below detection limits, but appeared at given times during the studied period, usually below 10 μg PO_4-P/liter.

1.4. A Note about Sampling

Lake Cisó is sharply stratified and the lower layers are always anaerobic and rich in reduced compounds such as sulfide. Thus, considerable care has to be given both to exact positioning of the sampling devices and to protect anoxic water samples from oxidation (Pedrós-Alió et al., 1986; Miracle et al., 1992). Several probes are lowered to determine vertical profiles of oxygen, temperature, conductivity, and light penetration. The depths to be explored in more detail are determined on the basis of the profiles found.

Two different systems have been used for close-interval sampling (e.g., 5 cm). The first is a version of the fine-layer sampler described by Jørgensen et al. (1979). This system consists of a conical inlet device, connected to a surface pump, which smoothly sucks the organisms toward the tubing, minimizing turbulence and escape responses of rotifers and crustacean nauplii and juveniles. Larger members of the zooplankton, such as cladocerans and adult copepods, are not properly sampled by this system. The double cone allows pumping large volumes of water from a given depth, with minimal disturbance of the stratification.

The second sampling system is a modification of the syringe systems devised by Baker et al. (1985) and Mitchell and Fuhrman (1989) and is described in Miracle et al. (1992). The syringes are filled simultaneously at the desired depth by the action of a vacuum pump connected to the device. A detailed instantaneous image of the vertical distribution of the organisms can be obtained quickly, avoiding problems created by surface waves. The model used in Lake Cisó had 33 syringes in a 1-m copper column.

The systems are lowered to the desired depth with utmost care not to disturb the fine stratification of organisms. In order to determine the exact depth of the peaks of phototrophic organisms, samples are taken at 5-cm intervals and filtered immediately through glass fiber filters. The color of the filters shows which is the dominant organism at each depth, and where the layers of algae and phototrophic bacteria are present. Samples are then collected at the appropriate depths taking into account that accumulations of zooplankton are usually found a few centime-

ters above the layers of algae and bacteria. Details about the sampling procedures, fixation and analysis of samples can be found in Pedrós-Alió and Mas
(1993), Pedró-Alió *et al.* (1986, 1993), and Miracle *et al.* (1992).

2. Taxonomy

2.1. General Assignment of Biomass to Taxa

The taxa present in Lake Cisó have been summarized in Pedrós-Alió *et al.*
(1986) and Gasol *et al.* (1990, 1992a). Different groups of organisms have
received special attention from a taxonomic point of view: phototrophic bacteria
(Guerrero *et al.*, 1985, 1987a), algae (Gasol and Pedrós-Alió, 1991), ciliates
(Dyer *et al.*, 1986; Gasol *et al.*, 1991a, 1992a), rotifers and crustaceans (Alfonso
and Miracle, 1987). The relative contribution of these organisms to total biomass
is presented in Fig. 2 for the period 1985–1987. The organisms have been
separated into phototrophic (Fig. 2A) and chemotrophic (Fig. 2B). This assignment was relatively straightforward based on the presence or absence of autofluorescence, indicative of chlorophylls. The contribution of phototrophic and
chemotrophic biomass to the total is shown in Fig. 2C. It is quite obvious from
these panels that a few organisms are dominant in the community and constitute
large percentages of the biomass. Among phototrophs, for example, 90% of the
biomass is formed by three species: the purple phototrophic bacteria *Chromatium
minus* and *Amoebobacter purpureus* and the flagellate *Cryptomonas phaseolus*
(Fig. 2A). Diatoms, dinoflagellates, and chlorophytes are present only in small
amounts and at certain times of the year. Finally, a variable amount of phototrophic biomass is formed by green sulfur bacteria. Some of these organisms are
illustrated in Fig. 3. Their sizes and contribution to summer biomass are summarized in Table I.

Most of the chemotrophic biomass is formed by bacteria, almost 100%
during holomixis and around 50% during stratification. Among the eukaryotes,
rotifers are the most important, followed by ciliates and copepods. There are no
fishes in the lake. Nothing can yet be said about the identity of the chemotrohpic
bacteria, but the other groups of chemotrophs are also dominated by one or a few
species. Thus, rotifers are mostly represented by *Anuraeopsis fissa,* ciliates by
Coleps hirtus and *Prorodon* sp., and crustaceans by *Thermocyclops dybowskii.*

This extreme dominance by a few species provides a unique situation. In
effect, measurements of general processes such as CO_2 fixation can be ascribed
to one or a few species. In this way, it is possible to determine primary production for the whole system and, at the same time, the growth rates of the main
organisms in the community. Finally, the analysis of the community becomes
extremely simplified and, therefore, feasible.

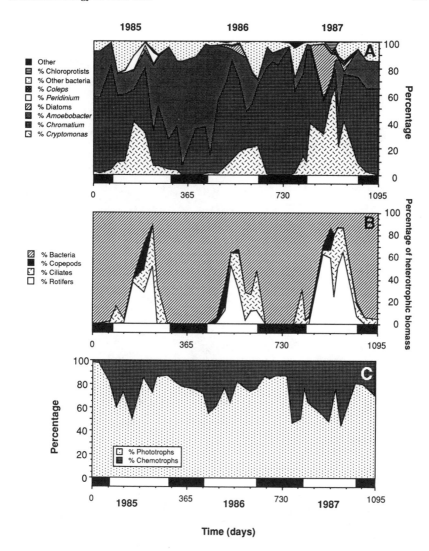

Figure 2. Distribution of biomass among different taxa in Lake Cisó, from 1985 to 1987. (A) Distribution of phototrophic taxa as percentage of total phototrophic biomass. (B) Distribution of chemotrophic taxa as percentage of total chemotrophic biomass. (C) Partition of biomass between phototrophic and chemotrophic taxa. From Gasol *et al.* (1992a).

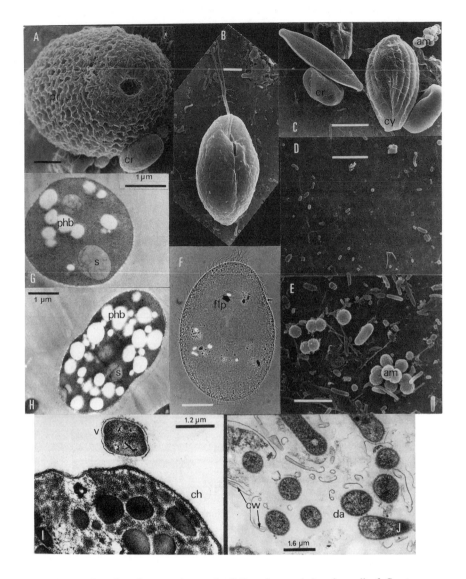

Figure 3. (A) Scanning electron micrograph of *Prorodon* sp. (pr) and a cell of *Cryptomonas phaseolus* (cr). Bar = 5 μm. (B) SEM micrograph of *C. phaseolus*. Bar = 2.5 μm. (C) SEM micrograph of *C. phaseolus* (cr), *Cyclidium* sp. (cy), a diatom, and an aggregate of *Amoebobacter purpureus* (am). Bar = 10 μm. (D) SEM micrograph of epilimnetic bacterial assemblage. Bar = 5 μm. Note small size and relatively low morphological diversity. (E) SEM micrograph of metalimnetic bacterial assemblage, including cells and an aggregate of *A. purpureus* (am). Bar = 5 μm. Note large size and morphological diversity of bacteria. (F) Phase-contrast and epifluorescence micrograph

Table I. Trophic Roles of the Main Planktonic Organisms in Lake Cisó

Organism	Size (μm)	Percent of summer biomass	Trophic mode	Water layer[a]
Phototrophs				
Amoebobacter purpureus	2 × 2[b]	10–50	Photoautotroph	M, H
Chromatium minus	5.6 × 3.3	20–60	Photoautotroph	M, H
Cryptomonas phaseolus	20 × 12	20–60	Photoautotroph	M
Diatoms	58 × 2.5	0–40	Photoautotroph	E, M
Other small algae		0–10	Photoautotroph	E, M
Osmotrophs[c]				
Colorless bacteria			Chemoautotrophs	M
	0.7 × 0.4	15–35	Chemoheterotrophs	E
	1.1 × 0.4		Chemoheterotrophs	M
	1.3 × 0.5		Chemoheterotrophs	H
Phagotrophs				
Flagellates	4.5		Bacterivore	E
Coleps hirtus	50 × 27	20–40	Algivore[d]	M
Prorodon sp.	61 × 42		Algivore[d]	M
Strombidium	28 × 24		Algivore	E, M
Paramecium spp.	105 × 46	0–10	Bacterivore	E, M
Vorticella	45 × 45		Bacterivore	E, M
Cyclidium	33 × 19		Bacterivore	M
Plagiopyla ovata	100 × 45	0–5	Bacterivore	H
Metopus es	168 × 72	0–1	Bacterivore	H
Anuraeopsis fissa	81 × 35	10–40	Bacterivore	M
Mytilina compressa	137 × 35		Bacterivore	H
Keratella quadrata	90 × 60	0–10	Algivore	E
Polyarthra sp.	108 × 75	0–10	Algivore	E
Thermocyclops dybowskii	340 × 70	5–10	Raptorial feeder	E
Nauplii	90 × 80		Bacterivore	E, M

[a]E, epilimnion; M, metalimnion; H, hypolimnion.
[b]Size of individual cells. Cells usually form aggregates.
[c]Autotrophs cannot be differentiated from heterotrophs. Percent of summer biomass is given for the whole assemblage.
[d]Besides eating algae, these ciliates carry intracellular *Chlorella* cells (Esteve *et al.*, 1988) which perform oxygenic photosynthesis.

Figure 3 (cont.) of *Plagiopyla* sp. with fluorescently labeled *Chromatium* cells (flp). Arrow points to an flp in the mouth area of the ciliate. Bar = 20 μm. (G) Transmission electron micrograph of *Chromatium minus* cells from the top layer, with abundant sulfur globules (s) and a few inclusions of PHB (phb). (H) TEM micrograph of *C. minus* cells from the bottom layer, with many PHB inclusions (phb) and degraded sulfur globules (s). (I) TEM micrograph of *C. minus* cells (ch) attacked by *Vampirococcus* (v). (J) TEM micrograph of *C. minus* cells attacked by *Daptobacter* (da). Note remaining pieces of cell walls (cw). SEM images taken by J. I. Calderon and J. M. Fortuño (Institut de Ciències del Mar, Barcelona). TEM images taken by I. Esteve (Universitat Autònoma de Barcelona) and D. Chase. F taken by C. Stumm (University of Nijmegen, The Netherlands). Panels G and H reproduced with permission from Esteve *et al.* (1990) and J from Guerrero *et al.* (1987b).

2.2. Seasonal Distribution of Organisms

Some impression of seasonal succession can be obtained from Fig. 2. Detailed seasonal distributions of organisms in Lake Cisó can be seen in Gasol *et al.* (1992a). The distributions of *Cryptomonas phaseolus* and *Coleps hirtus* are shown in Fig. 4 as examples. By comparing Figs. 2A and 4A it is obvious that

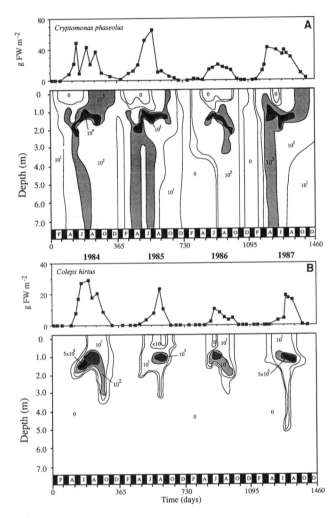

Figure 4. (A) Biomass, in g fresh weight/m² (upper panel), and vertical distribution in individuals/ml (lower panel) of *Cryptomonas phaseolus* in Lake Cisó from 1984 to 1987. (B) Biomass, in g fresh weight/m² (upper panel), and vertical distribution in individuals/ml (lower panel) of *Coleps hirtus* in Lake Cisó from 1984 to 1987. From Gasol *et al.* (1992a).

phototrophic biomass is dominated by the purple sulfur bacteria during mixing. During stratification *C. phaseolus* becomes very abundant, but the purple bacteria remain as important components of the plankton. Comparing Figs. 2B and 4B it can be seen that bacteria are the only chemotrophs during mixing. Several eukaryotic organisms appear during stratification, among which *C. hirtus* is a typical example.

Gasol *et al.* (1992a) have detailed the seasonal succession of organisms in the lake and have compared it with the PEG model of seasonal succession in temperate zone lakes (Sommer *et al.*, 1986). The community in Lake Cisó was shown to follow the first stages of the PEG model during spring and early summer. During most of the summer, however, most of the biomass became concentrated in the metalimnion and the community departed from the general model. Just a few species, in very large abundance and with very slow growth rates, remained throughout the stratification period.

Of particular interest was the appearance of metalimnetic blooms of several algae. Gasol and Pedrós-Alió (1991) showed that most of these maxima were the consequence of growth throughout the epi- and metalimnion, followed by faster disappearance from the epi- than from the metalimnion. On the other hand, the bloom of *C. phaseolus* was caused by *in situ* growth at the metalimnion (Fig. 4A). This maximum has received considerable attention (Pedrós-Alió *et al.*, 1987; Gasol *et al.*, 1991a, 1992a,b, 1993) since it is responsible for most of the eukaryotic phototrophic biomass (Fig. 2A) and most of the oxygenic photosynthesis in the lake. The population ecology of this organism will be summarized later (Section 5.1).

Associated with the metalimnetic peak of *C. phaseolus*, several chemotrophic or mixotrophic organisms formed extraordinarily abundant populations: *C. hirtus* reached 10^4 cells/ml (Fig. 4B), *Prorodon* sp. 10^3 cells/ml, and *A. fissa* 4×10^2 individuals/ml.

2.3. Vertical Distribution

The vertical distribution of the most important organisms on a particular date can be seen in Fig. 5. It appears that three different assemblages of organisms can be differentiated: (1) the epilimnion with low abundance of a few diatoms and chlorophytes, around 10^3 flagellates/ml and 10^6 bacterial cells/ml, and a few ciliates; (2) the metalimnion with extremely large abundance of *C. phaseolus*, ciliates such as *C. hirtus* and *Prorodon, Strombidium, Vorticella,* and *Cyclidium,* the rotifer *A. fissa,* purple sulfur bacteria, almost no flagellates, and 10^7 bacterial cells/ml; (3) finally, the hypolimnion has large amounts of chemotrophic (10^7 cells/ml) and phototrophic (10^6 cells/ml) bacteria, a few ciliates of the genera *Metopus* and *Plagiopyla,* and the rotifer *Mytilina compressa.* The hypolimnetic assemblage occupied the whole lake during mixing (see also Table I).

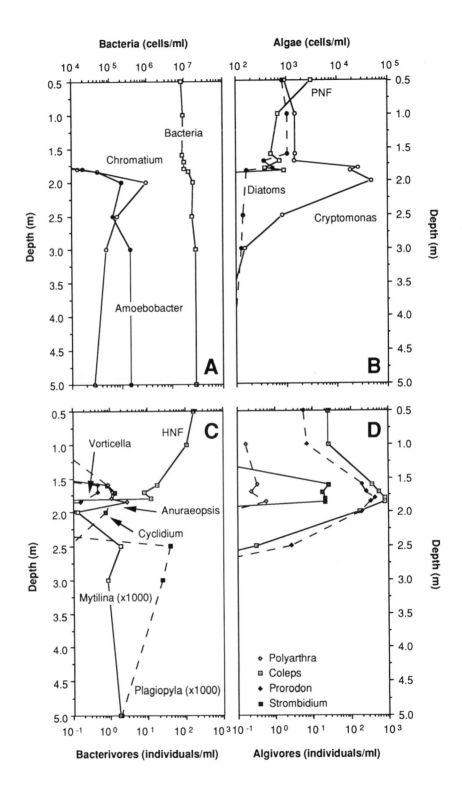

In order to quantify this subjective ordination of the planktonic community, multivariate analyses were carried out (Gasol *et al.*, in preparation). A cluster analysis separated the summer planktonic community into two groups: the epilimnetic assemblage on the one hand, and the meta- and hypolimnetic assemblage on the other. This result was contrary to our intuitive separation of meta- and hypolimnetic assemblages and may result from the smooth overlap among the vertical distributions of meta- and hypolimnetic organisms (Fig. 5). This ordination into two communities is consistent with the simultaneous appearance of the same meta- and hypolimnetic assemblages in many karstic stratified lakes, where the same organisms are found in the meta- and hypolimnion despite completely different epilimnetic assemblages, e.g., in lakes Cisó and Estanya (Huesca, Spain). In effect, the combination of *A. fissa, C. hirtus* and/or *Prorodon, C. phaseolus,* and purple bacteria has been found in lakes Cisó, Vilar, Estanya, Arcas-2 (Finlay *et al.*, 1991), Suigetsu (Takahashi and Ichimura, 1968), and Schlachtensee (Gervais, 1991) among others. The clustering of meta- and hypolimnetic assemblages is probably a consequence of the presence of sulfide, a toxic substance with which members of this assemblages have to cope.

Another type of multivariate analysis is principal components analysis (PCA). The PCA suggested a community organized along the vertical gradient determined by a combination of light, oxygen, and sulfide gradients among others (Gasol *et al.*, in preparation). There was a continuous distribution of phototrophic organisms along this axis represented by the first component. Aerobic species (*Peridinium, Ankistrodesmus*) had the highest loadings on the first principal component. Metalimnetic species, such as *C. phaseolus,* had low positive or negative loadings. Finally, the anaerobic phototrophs, the purple bacteria, had high negative loadings. Therefore, the whole community was organized vertically through the differential distribution of the phototrophs. This is quite similar to the vertical stratification of organisms in a forest or the substitution of species along environmental gradients of height or latitude (Whittaker, 1978). Thus, a microbial community was seen to have a very definite structure in space and time. The fact that microbial communities generally appear unorganized to us, seems to be just a matter of analysis at the improper scale.

2.4. Microdistribution through the Diel Cycle

Precisely because the time and space scales adequate for microorganisms are substantially smaller than the usual ones, analysis of the distribution of organisms in Lake Cisó was carried out at the centimeter scale in space and at the

---

Figure 5. Vertical distribution of the main taxa in the plankton of Lake Cisó for September 20, 1991. (A) Bacteria; (B) algae; (C) bacterivores; and (D) algivores. HNF and PNF stand for heterotrophic and phototrophic nanoflagellates, respectively. "Bacteria" includes all bacteria different from purple sulfur bacteria. Data from R. Massana (unpublished).

scale of a few hours in time through diel cycles (Gasol *et al.*, 1991a; Pedrós-Alió and Sala, 1990). The fine syringe sampler described above was used for this purpose. Thirty-three simultaneous samples were obtained in a 1-m vertical column for every profile and these were repeated through day and night.

Several members of the assemblage were observed to perform diel vertical migrations spanning about 20 cm. *C. phaseolus* carried out the widest excursions migrating about 40 cm (Fig 6B; Gasol *et al.*, 1991a, 1992b, 1993). These distances may seem negligible, but they were found to have a dramatic impact on

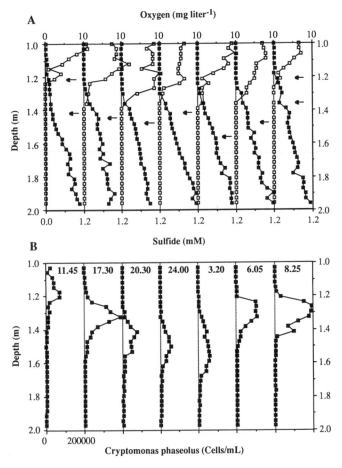

Figure 6. Vertical distribution of oxygen (□) and sulfide (■) (A), and of *Cryptomonas phaseolus* (B) in Lake Cisó, at different times through a diel cycle, August 1989. Arrows in A indicate depths of the *Chromatium* peaks. A, from Pedrós-Alió and Sala (1990); B, data of R. Massana (unpublished).

the survival of the different populations (see below). Without the use of the fine sampling device, vertical migration would not have been discovered. In fact, vertical movements were not detected in a previous diel study with the cone-shaped sampler (Guerrero *et al.*, 1985; van Gemerden *et al.*, 1985).

One of the purple bacteria, the flagellated *Chromatium*, was found to migrate vertically, while no migration could be detected for the other species, the gas-vacuolate *Amoebobacter* (Pedrós-Alió and Sala, 1990). In conjunction with these movements the oxic/anoxic interface also moved up and down. During the day, oxygenic photosynthesis produced oxygen, while anoxygenic photosynthesis consumed sulfide, and the interface was displaced slowly downwards (Fig. 6A, panels from 11:45 to 20:30). During the night, photosynthesis was inactive, while aerobic respiration and sulfide reduction both contributed to displace the interface upwards (Fig. 6A, panels from 20:30 to 8:25). A surprising finding was the fact that *C. phaseolus* was observed in the aerobic side of the interface during the day, but in the anaerobic side at night, in the presence of sulfide (Fig. 6A,B). The importance of these migrations will become clear when we review the population ecology of *C. phaseolus* and the purple bacteria in Section 5.

3. Size

3.1. Size Structure of Communities

Size is one of the most important properties of living particles. Most biological processes have a clear dependence on size (Peters, 1983). Size is also one of the easiest things to measure. This is particularly true for microorganisms, where species determination is problematic and controversial, and where the establishment of clear-cut trophic groups is many times impossible. Thus, it seems that the second approach to the ecology of living particles exposed in the Introduction should be explored in ecosystems dominated by microorganisms. This approach consists of determining the size of individual living particles and assigning them to arbitrarily defined size classes. Convention dictates $\log_2$ size classes (Platt and Denman, 1978; Platt, 1985). The number of particles in each size class is then plotted against size and the result is the size spectrum of the community. There exists an abundant literature of both the theory and applications of such size spectra (Platt and Denman, 1978; Sprules *et al.*, 1983; Dickie *et al.*, 1987; Rodríguez *et al.*, 1990). Here, we will only point out the main findings of Gasol *et al.* (1991b), who used this approach with the planktonic community of Lake Cisó.

3.2. The Size Structure of Lake Cisó

Data taken at 34 sampling dates from 1985 to 1987 were used to calculate an "average" size spectrum for the planktonic community of Lake Cisó (Fig. 7;

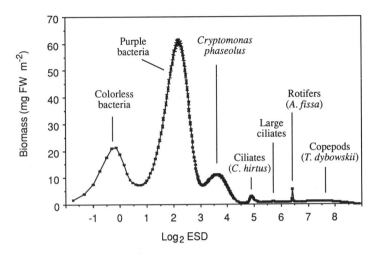

Figure 7. Average biomass size spectrum for Lake Cisó calculated with data from 1985 to 1987. The main peaks correspond to colorless bacteria (0.5–0.7 μm), purple bacteria (4 μm), *C. phaseolus* (15 μm), small cilates (32 μm), large ciliates (64 μm), rotifers (85 μm), and copepods (200 μm). Sizes are given in equivalent spherical diameters (ESD). Modified from Gasol *et al.* (1991b).

Gasol *et al.*, 1991b). This spectrum shows the general characteristics of the community. Peaks appeared at 0.5–0.7 μm, 4–6 μm, 15 μm, 32 μm, 64, 85, and 200 μm equivalent spherical diameter (ESD). These peaks corresponded to sizes of the most abundant organisms in the lake, respectively: colorless bacteria, purple phototrophic bacteria, *Cryptomonas phaseolus*, ciliates including *Coleps hirtus*, large ciliates, rotifers, and copepods. Maximal biomass appeared in the second smallest peak at 4–6 μm ESD corresponding to purple phototrophic bacteria. Peaks were displaced toward smaller sizes than those typical of lakes (Sprules *et al.*, 1983). This was interpreted as an effect of the "stress" represented by sulfide.

Winter mixing spectra showed only the prokaryotic peaks, as all eukaryotic life essentially disappeared from the lake at this time of the year. When stratification began, usually in March, peaks in larger size classes started to appear. First, the peak of phototrophic bacteria and *C. phaseolus* increased in biomass. Toward the middle of the summer these peaks decreased while peaks for larger size classes appeared. This pattern repeated itself during the 3 years of study, showing it to be a robust feature of the community size spectrum.

Examples of summer and winter normalized spectra can be seen in Fig. 8. Gasol *et al.* (1991b) carried out the usual linear fit to these spectra (dot and dash lines in Fig. 8) and polynomial fits (discontinuous line in Fig. 8B). While the two fits were indistinguishable in summer, the two differed considerably during win-

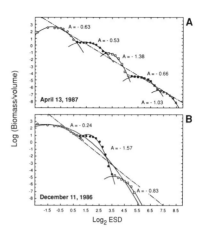

Figure 8. Secondary scaling of the normalized spectrum for one summer (A) and one winter (B) date. The value of the second-order coefficient of the polynomial fit is shown near each curve. The overall linear fit in A is $y = 1.679 - 1.104x$, $R^2 = 0.967$. The overall linear fit in B is $y = 1.745 - 1.43x$, $R^2 = 0.866$; and the polynomial fit in B is $y = 2.082 - 0.64x - 0.23x^2$, $R^2 = 0.964$. From Gasol et al. (1991b).

ter. In effect, the second-order coefficient of the polynomial fit proved to be a good indicator of the degree of dominance by microorganisms. When the lake was mixed and completely anaerobic, most large size classes disappeared, the spectrum became truncated, and this coefficient became larger (Fig. 8B). When the lake stratified, large organisms (the eukaryotes) appeared again, the spectrum recovered the large size classes, and the second-order coefficient became close to zero and, thus, the polynomial became a straight line indistinguishable from the linear fit (Fig. 8A).

Normalized size spectra usually have a wavy appearance, suggesting they are the sum of different subgroups within the community (see Fig. 8). Dickie et al. (1987) proposed that communities are allometrically scaled at two different levels: the primary physiological level corresponds to the global size spectrum and has a slightly negative slope. When this spectrum is broken into subgroups, a secondary or ecological scaling appears where each group has its own characteristic slope. Gasol et al. (1991b) broke the Lake Cisó spectrum into groups (see different types of points in Fig. 8) and showed that each of the subgroups was actually better described by a polynomial than by a linear function. In Fig. 8 the second-order coefficients of the polynomial fits to these subgroups are indicated by the letter A. During summer, five different groups could be detected and the overall appearance of the spectrum was linear. During winter, on the other hand, only the three smallest subgroups were present and the overall spectrum was better fit by a polynomial.

The spectra could be broken up into five subgroups (Fig. 8A): group 1 (from 0.2 to 1.4 μm diameter), 2 (1.4–8.0 μm), 3 (8–22 μm), 4 (22–128 μm), and 5 (128–512 μm). The limits of the groups were stable throughout the year, and seemed a general feature of the community. Group 1 was composed of nonphototrophic bacteria, some phototrophic bacteria (*Chlorobium*), and some small phototrophic protists (like *Selenastrum* and *Hyaloraphidium*). Large phototrophic bacteria (*Chromatium* and *Amoebobacter*) as well as protists (*Crucigenia, Scenedesmus*) formed group 2. Group 3 was mainly composed of *Cryptomonas*, diatoms, *Coleps*, and small ciliates (*Cyclidium*). Group 4 was composed of ciliates, nauplii, and small rotifers (*Anuraeopsis*), wihle group 5 was made up of rotifers and crustaceans. Only groups 2 (phototrophic), 4 and 5 (heterotrophic) could be assigned to one trophic mode. Group 3 had both autotrophs and heterotrophs, and group 1 included heterotrophs, photoautotrophs, and chemoautotrophs.

From the analysis of the primary and secondary scaling in an oligotrophic mountain lake, Rodríguez *et al.* (1990) concluded that the size structure and the dynamics of the planktonic community of that particular system were controlled by the secondary or ecological scaling. They interpreted this observation as an effect of the simplicity of the system, where some subgroups were almost entirely composed of one or two species (Echevarría *et al.*, 1990). Gasol *et al.* (1991b) also argued that secondary scaling controlled the structure of the planktonic community in Lake Cisó. This observation was based on the fact that the overall plankton spectrum was better described by a polynomial fit. This was especially marked in winter, and less clear in summer. Both lakes La Caldera and Cisó are small, fishless, and subject to different forms of stress (anoxia in Lake Cisó and only 3½ ice-free months in Lake La Caldera), and both have simple zooplankton communities. The biology of both lakes is dominated by small organisms.

The seasonal changes in both unlinearized spectra and the coefficient of the polynomial fit showed a very consistent pattern from year to year. There was an alternation of conditions between a completely anaerobic system during mixing and a more complex system during stratification. This alternation favored anaerobic prokaryotes excluding eukaryotes on the one hand, while allowing the presence of the latter through compartmentalization of the system on the other. From a trophic-dynamic point of view, both situations are similar. There are primary producers and several levels of consumers in both, but all these organisms are smaller and anaerobic during mixing. Therefore, our analysis of size structure in Lake Cisó could characterize the seasonal changes and degree of dominance by prokaryotes in the community, avoiding the difficulties of the taxonomy and trophic levels as approaches to community structure. The special traits of Lake Cisó should be useful in comparisons with other systems, so that truly general properties of size spectra can be discerned and used in the study of plankton ecology.

4. Trophic Roles

Once the particles in Lake Cisó had been classified into taxa, it was possible to assign a trophic role to each taxon. Knowing the trophic roles of the organisms in the community would allow an analysis of biomass allocation to different trophic modes, of the structural properties of the food web, and provide a map for the quantitative analysis of energy and carbon flow through the community.

4.1. Assigning Trophic Roles to Organisms

García-Cantizano *et al.* (in preparation) concentrated their study on the organisms forming most of the summer biomass (Table I). The organisms considered would account for more than 95% of the biomass in the lake at any particular date. Autoradiography with [14C]bicarbonate and chlorophyll autofluorescence were used to identify autotrophic microorganisms (Fig. 9). By carrying out incubations in the light and in the dark, photoautotrophic organisms could be differentiated from chemoautotrophic organisms. DCMU was used to discriminate between oxygenic and anoxygenic photosynthesis. Light microscopy was used to identify phagotrophic heterotrophs. A combination of phase-contrast and epifluorescence microscopy allowed detection of algae inside of algivorous phagotrophs. Epifluorescence microscopy with fluorescently labeled bacteria was used to detect bacterivorous phagotrophs (according to the methods in Sherr *et al.*, 1987). Additional experiments were carried out with fluorescent latex beads and microautoradiography with [3H]thymidine ([3H]-TdR). The conclusions from these experiments are summarized in Table I and Fig. 9.

4.2. Biomass Allocation to Trophic Groups

The relative amount of biomass allocated to phototrophic and chemotrophic organisms during the seasons has been shown in Fig. 2C. Very few aquatic systems have been studied in a way that a comparable data set for all of the components of the system is available. General works (such as those of Nauwerck, 1963; Brock, 1985; Likens, 1985; and others), although very useful otherwise, offer incomplete data bases. An alternative approach to the lack of comparable data is to combine the different empirical relations that have been derived with the intention to predict the values of all of the components of the system from a few meaningful parameters (del Giorgio and Gasol, in press).

One of the most remarkable results presented in Fig. 2 is that, regardless of the seasonal and annual changes in the presence of eukaryotes, phytoplankton, and zooplankton, the relative amount of phototrophic and chemotrophic biomass is quite constant: the phototrophs oscillate between 65 and 85% of the total biomass. These values mean a Ch/Ph ratio (chemotrophic biomass/phototrophic biomass) of 0.2–0.5. There is always more phototrophic than chemotrophic biomass. Is this a general pattern for eutrophic lakes?

del Giorgio and Gasol (in press) have collected data from some of the available studies and, although very different methods have been used, and some of the components of the systems have been ignored in most cases, a general trend appears very clearly: oligotrophic lakes have high Ch/Ph values (between

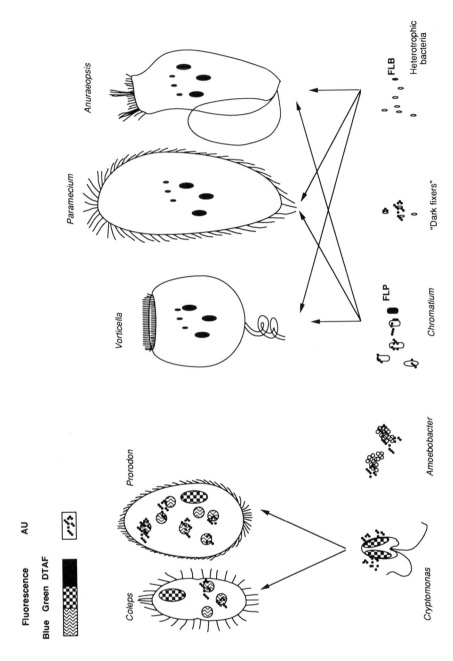

1.4 and 6.5), while eutrophic lakes have values lower than 1 (between 0.2 and 0.9). Thus, there is more chemotrophic than phototrophic biomass in oligotrophic lakes, while the reverse is true for eutrophic lakes. The extreme would be an ultraoligotrophic lake, where bacteria and zooplankton were present but algae were almost absent.

Ch/Ph values for Lake Cisó are close to those expected for eutrophic lakes, although part of the phototrophic biomass is due to phototrophic bacteria instead of algae. The reason for this particular pattern is that instead of a shift in algal structure with eutrophic conditions, phototrophic bacteria—the main autotrophs—are poorly exploited by heterotrophs because of the absence of oxygen at the depths where they live. The few ciliates living inside the anaerobic part of the lake cannot build up a whole web of trophic interactions in part because of their low growth efficiency (Fenchel and Finlay, 1990). Fenchel and Finlay (1990) postulated that there is an energetic limitation to the amount of phagotrophic organisms that can live in an anaerobic environment, thus limiting the food chain to a few steps. This would also explain why almost all of the biomass is prokaryotic during winter (Fig. 8B), when sulfide is present. The appearance of an oxic epilimnion allows the growth of eukaryotes that slowly increase up to 50–80% of the biomass. Right after mixing, when the sulfide concentration is low, some eukaryotes still remain, but as soon as the sulfide concentration increases, they disappear almost totally from the lake.

4.3. Structure of the Food Web

Once the list of the species present in a community has been prepared, and the trophic relationships among them have been determined, the community food web can be built. The food web is a "diagram depicting which species interact" agonistically (Lawton, 1989). The food web is a qualitative, easy-to-comprehend representation of the carbon and energy flow through the community. The food web of Lake Cisó during stratification is shown in Fig. 10 and the food web during holomixis is shown in Fig. 11.

A data base of over 100 food webs has been assembled from the ecological literature (Cohen *et al.,* 1990). Patterns in the structure of such food webs have been found, and models to explain the observed distributions have been developed. Several of these patterns or laws have been summarized by Pimm (1982), Cohen (1988), and Lawton (1989). A recent review can be found in Pimm *et al.*

←────────────────────────────────────

Figure 9. Schematic drawing of the techniques and results of the qualitative analysis of the aerobic food web in Lake Cisó. Three types of fluorescence were used: autofluorescence with a blue excitation filter (detection of chlorophyll a, wavy pattern) and with a green excitation filter (detection of phycobilins, checkered pattern), and fluorescence conferred by DTAF to FLB and FLP (black pattern). Autoradiography was used to detect organisms fixing CO_2 (black circles).

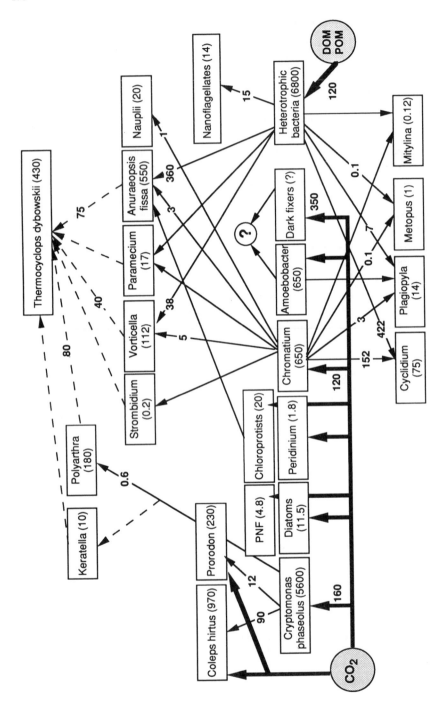

(1991). Although this approach has been criticized (Paine, 1988; Peters, 1988), the patterns seem to be fairly universal and robust in front of any manipulations of the food web. It turns out that such patterns are fairly invariant with variable degrees of pooling of species, thus being to a certain degree independent of taxonomic accuracy.

The microbial food web of Lake Cisó does not seem to contradict significantly any of the relevant patterns exposed (Fig. 10; Pedrós-Alió et al., in preparation). In the winter food web, this is true only if the osmotrophic relationships between the bacteria guilds are considered (Fig. 11). If one assumes exchange of organic matter among the bacterial guilds, the fit to general patterns is almost perfect. There seems to be a high proportion of omnivores, but this would diminish if viruses were added. On the other hand, the fit to the remaining patterns would not be affected by this addition. A further analysis of several other microbial food webs is in preparation (Pedrós-Alió et al., in preparation) and the conclusion seems to be that they generally fit the expectations if osmotrophic relationships are included.

4.4. Quantitative Analysis of Carbon Flux through the Food Web

Having built the food web of the system, it can be used as a map to trace carbon flow. Thus, we tried to estimate the sizes of each node and the magnitude of the main fluxes between nodes. Fluxes will be divided into three categories for convenience: autotrophic miroorganisms, osmotrophic heterotrophs, and phagotrophic heterotrophs (see Table I).

4.4.1. Autotrophic Microorganisms

Total CO_2 fixation was estimated in incubations carried out in situ. This total fixation was fractionated through the use of DCMU into oxygenic and anoxygenic photosynthesis. The use of dark incubations allowed estimates of dark fixation. The latter process was actually the most important, accounting for 58% of total fixation. Oxygenic and anoxygenic photosynthesis accounted for 25 and 19% during stratification and for 4 and 35% during mixing, respectively (García-Cantizano et al., 1987; García-Cantizano, 1992). Oxygenic photosynthesis could be assigned essentially to C. phaseolus. Most of it took place at the metalimnion where this organism formed more than 95% of the phototrophic

---

Figure 10. Preliminary food web of Lake Cisó. Discontinuous arrows indicate assumed relationships. Continuous arrows indicate demonstrated relationships. Numbers within boxes indicate a typical number for summer carbon biomass (mg C/m²). Numbers next to arrows indicate estimates of carbon flux (mg C/m² per day) for a typical stratification date. The heavy arrows indicate autotrophic incorporation of CO_2. The question mark indicates the lack of data concerning the fate of these two compartments.

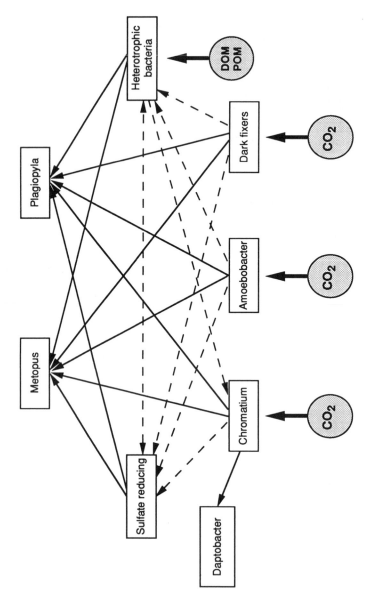

Figure 11. Holomixis food web for Lake Cisó. Discontinuous arrows indicate probable osmotrophic relationships.

biomass. Therefore, production and growth rates could be calculated for *C. phaseolus* (see Section 5.1). Anoxygenic photosynthesis could also be assigned to the two main purple bacteria, and production and growth rates estimated for these organisms (see Section 5.2). Dark fixation, however, could not be assigned to a single, recognizable taxon. Some was carried out by purple bacteria, some by unidentified bacteria. In Figs. 10 and 11, all dark fixation has been assigned to a box labeled "dark fixers," whose biomass and fate are unknown.

4.4.2. Osmotrophic Heterotrophs

Colorless bacteria are the most difficult group to characterize trophically. Surely, many different metabolisms are involved in this group of organisms. The only possibility was to estimate global production and growth rate with the conventional techniques. Thymidine uptake and frequency of dividing cells (FDC) were used. The first technique has been more widely used, but it gives unreliable results in anaerobic environments (Pedrós-Alió *et al.*, 1993). For this reason, FDC was also used in the lake. Production estimates were between 2 and 133 mg C/m^3 per day and doubling times varied between 0.5 and 3 days in the epilimnion and between 5 and 15 days in the hypolimnion (García-Cantizano *et al.*, submitted; Calderon *et al.*, 1993). An average value for biomass and production of this black box has been incorporated in Fig. 10.

4.4.3. Phagotrophic Heterotrophs

The same techniques used to identify phagotrophic organisms were used to determine their feeding rates *in situ*. Both fluorescently labeled phototrophic and heterotrophic bacteria were used as tracers for bacterivory. Feeding rates and abundance of the bacterivorous ciliates *Paramecium, Vorticella, Cyclidium, Plagiopyla* (Fig. 3), and *Metopus,* of heterotrophic nanoflagellates, and of copepod nauplii were determined at different times of the year (Massana and Pedrós-Alió, submitted).

Algivory could only be quantified for the ciliates *Coleps* and *Prorodon* feeding on *Cryptomonas* (Pedrós-Alió *et al.*, in preparation). This was done both with radioactively labeled algal cells and through the appearance of cells inside the ciliates in time course experiments. For the remaining algivores—the ciliate *Strombidium* and the rotifers *Polyarthra* and *Keratella*—rates from the literature were used.

In order to calculate the flux between prey and predator, an algorithm was developed which took into account not only the feeding rates and the abundance of prey and predator, but also their respective vertical distributions (Massana and Pedrós-Alió, in press). This was very important, since the distributions of both organisms overlapped only partially on most occasions. Differences were partic-

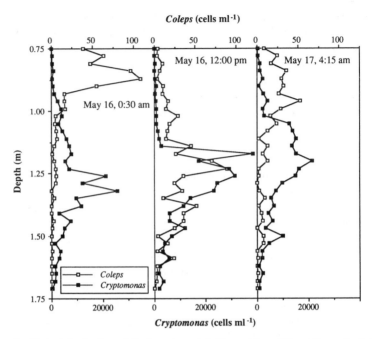

Figure 12. Vertical distributions of *C. phaseolus* and *C. hirtus* at three different times of a diel cycle in Lake Cisó, showing different degrees of overlap. From Massana and Pedrós-Alió (1994).

ularly spectacular through the diel cycle in the case of *Coleps* and *Cryptomonas* (Fig. 12), where the vertical migration of the alga reduced the impact of predation to 30% of the potential (Pedrós-Alió *et al.*, in preparation, see Section 5.1.3c).

With all of these calculations, numbers could be added to the food web in Fig. 10. The analysis of the food web, however, is still preliminary. In the future, comparisons with webs formed by animals and plants should be carried out.

5. Population Ecology of the Main Primary Producers

Purple bacteria and *C. phaseolus* form about 90% of the phototrophic biomass (Fig. 2A). In addition, phototrophic biomass represents on average 80% of total biomass (Fig. 2C). Thus, three species form most of the biomass in the planktonic community of Lake Cisó. It was apparent that these species deserved some special attention and, therefore, their population ecology was studied in detail.

5.1. Population Ecology of *Cryptomonas phaseolus*

5.1.1. Statics and Kinetics

A typical vertical distribution of *C. phaseolus* at daytime can be seen in Fig. 5B. The kinetics of this metalimnetic peak with the seasons appear in Fig. 4A and with the diel cycle in Figs. 6B and 12. The metalimnetic peak of *C. phaseolus* is a very repeatable feature of the seasonal succession: it has been observed every year since 1983. The population is dispersed through the lake during mixing in very low numbers, sometimes even disappearing from the lake (Fig. 4A, winters of 1985–86 and 1986–87). As soon as stratification begins in March, the population starts to grow *in situ* (Gasol and Pedrós-Alió, 1991; Gasol *et al.*, 1992b), and reaches its maximal abundance toward the middle of June. The depth of the peak follows the depth of oxygen and sulfide coexistence through the stratification period. The depth where sulfide appears is, therefore, the lower limit for the distribution of *C. phaseolus* (Gasol *et al.*, 1992b). The factors determining the upper limit of the distribution will be discussed in the next two sections. When the lake mixes in October, the population is distributed throughout the lake and disappears as the winter advances.

Both holomixis-to-stratification and stratification-to-holomixis transitions are slow and proceed through a series of weeks (sometimes months) of diurnal shallow stratification and nocturnal mixing. The population of *C. phaseolus* is able to concentrate at the interface as it forms in the morning and is mixed again through the water column as the interface dissipates at night. This is possible because *C. phaseolus* not only can survive in the presence of sulfide, but can also carry out some metabolism (see Section 5.1.2). Thus, when the lake finally establishes its permanent stratification in late March, the population of *C. phaseolus* has already grown to substantial numbers and has a head start with respect to any other algae. Likewise, its ability to metabolize in the presence of sulfide allows the population to persist for longer periods than any other alga until holomixis is permanently established in November.

During permanent stratification, *C. phaseolus* performs vertical migrations spanning about 40 cm in depth (Gasol *et al.*, 1991a, 1992b). An example of this movement is shown in Fig. 6B. The population spends the morning slightly above the oxic/anoxic boundary (see panels for 11:45 in Fig. 6A,B) where it creates a deep oxygen maximum through oxygenic photosynthesis (panels for 17:30). Through the afternoon, the population starts descending, as the oxic/anoxic boundary is displaced downwards (panels for 17:30 and 20:30). After sunset the population disperses through a 75-cm region of low sulfide concentrations (around 0.6 mM) just below the oxic/anoxic boundary (panels for 24:00 and 3:20). In early morning, before sunrise, the population moves upwards again reaching the oxic side of the oxic/anoxic boundary slightly before sunrise (panel for 6:05). The cells of *C. phaseolus* increase their polyglucose content during the morning and afternoon, indicating that CO_2 fixation proceeds faster than the synthesis of new cell material. During the night, when the cells are immersed in sulfide, the polyglucose content decreases (Gasol *et al.*, 1993) suggesting it is being used as carbon and energy source for biosynthesis (probably through fermentation). The implications of this vertical migration for the growth efficiency and the ecology of the population will be discussed later.

5.1.2. Physiological Ecology

The trophic role of the *C. phaseolus* population in Lake Cisó was discussed in Section 4.1. It was shown that this organism is autotrophic, carrying out oxygenic photosynthesis during the day. It was also shown that it did not incorporate any of the tracer particles offered (latex beads, fluorescently labeled heterotrophic and purple bacteria). Since the organism lives away from the lake surface and uses light, it was of interest to explore the characteristics of its photosynthesis and the nature of the factors limiting growth. This was also important to explain the persistence of the metalimnetic peak. Several hypotheses have been postulated to explain such peaks, but very few experimental studies have been carried out (Fee, 1976; Konopka, 1980; Pick *et al.*, 1984). Therefore, the study of the Lake Cisó population could bring some insight into metalimnetic peaks in general (Gasol and Pedrós-Alió, 1991; Gasol *et al.*, 1993).

An example of a photosynthesis versus irradiance curve can be seen in Fig. 13A, together with the vertical distribution of light, temperature, and *C. phaseolus* cells for the same date (Fig. 13B). The striped region of the pie chart indicates the percent of the biomass represented by *C. phaseolus* at the depth where the sample for the experiment was taken. In general, the population was photoinhibited at irradiances above 200 μE/m² per sec, and it was limited at irradiances below 100 μE/m² per sec (Gasol *et al.*, 1993). Since the light arriving at the metalimnetic population in Lake Cisó generally varied between 10 and 400 μE/m² per sec at noon, it seemed that *C. phaseolus* was reasonably well adapted to the metalimnetic light regime. From these data, photoinhibition could be expected at the surface on the days with highest irradiances. This would explain the presence of *C. phaseolus* at depth on sunny days. On days with the lowest irradiances, however, the population would have been light-limited in the metalimnion. On these days, moving to the surface would have been advantageous. Yet *C. phaseolus* remained at the metalimnion (Gasol *et al.*, 1993).

Other factors which could influence the distribution of the populations were oxygen and sulfide. Gasol *et al.* (1993) studied the influence of these two gases on CO_2 fixation by natural samples of *C. phaseolus*. Photosynthesis was clearly inhibited by sulfide in this organism, while an increase in oxygen concentration from that at the metalimnion to saturation did not affect the organism signifi-

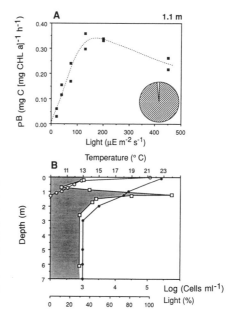

Figure 13. (A) Influence of light intensity on specific photosynthetic rate (■) and percent of total phototrophic biovolume constituted by *C. phaseolus* (striped sector of the pie chart). The line was fitted with the model of Platt *et al.* (1980). (B) Depth distribution of light (○), temperature (●), and *C. phaseolus* (□) on July 17, 1985 corresponding to the experiment shown in A. From Gasol *et al.* (1993).

cantly (Fig. 14A). Thus, *C. phaseolus* in Lake Cisó could only perform oxygenic photosynthesis (not anoxygenic photosynthesis) and only in the absence of sulfide. This would explain the presence of the organisms in the aerobic side of the oxic/anoxic interface during the day, but discarded oxygen toxicity as the reason for remaining at the metalimnion on cloudy days.

Nutrients were another potentially important factor regulating the depth distribution of the population. In effect, a series of biochemical indicators suggested that the population was nutrient-limited more often than light-limited (Gasol *et al.*, 1993). Because of the large amounts of nitrate and ammonia in the lake, the most likely limiting nutrient was phosphorus. Figure 14B shows the nutrients remaining in solution after artificial additions to natural samples for a particular date. The exponential disappearance of phosphorus together with the linear disappearances of nitrate and ammonia are strong indications of phosphorus limitation (Zevenboom, 1988). The same experiments, however, did not indicate nutrient limitation at other dates. Moreover, phosphorus was not more abundant in the meta- or hypolimnion than in the epilimnion. Therefore, nutrients were not the cause of the vertical distribution of *C. phaseolus* either (Gasol *et al.*, 1993).

In summary, the *C. phaseolus* population in Lake Cisó seems to have an adequate light regime most of the time at the metalimnion. It is frequently nutrient-limited and on several occasions the limiting nutrient is phosphorus. It

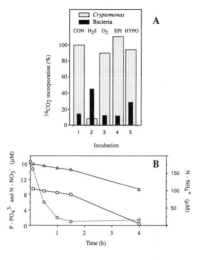

Figure 14. (A) Influence of oxygen and sulfide on $^{14}CO_2$ fixation by *C. phaseolus* (stippled histograms) and by phototrophic bacteria (black bars) from a 1.2-m sample taken in Lake Cisó on September 5, 1985. (1) Control without additions; (2) sulfide addition (0.6 mM final concentration); (3) water stirred until at equilibrium with air; (4) epilimnetic water added (1:1 in volume with metalimnetic water, results corrected for dilution); and (5) hypolimnetic water added (1:1 in volume, corrected for dilution). (B) Time course of nutrient disappearance after nutrient additions to metalimnetic subsamples taken at 1.3 m on July 15, 1986 in Lake Cisó. Symbols correspond to phosphate (○), nitrate (□), and ammonia (△). From Gasol *et al.* (1993).

carries out oxygenic photosynthesis, which is sensitive to sulfide, during the day slightly above the oxic/anoxic interface, accumulating polyglucose reserves. During the night it migrates into the sulfide-rich side of the oxic/anoxic interface and consumes the polyglucose reserves in anaerobiosis. None of the physiological questions examined seems to determine the upper limit for the distribution of the organism, while the lower limit during the day is clearly determined by the sulfide sensitivity of photosynthesis.

5.1.3. Population Dynamics: Growth and Losses

The actual biomass of any population is the result of the balance between growth and losses. This can be expressed by the equation:

$$\frac{dN}{dt} = (\mu - k_p - k_d - k_W - k_S)N \qquad (1)$$

where N is the population abundance, t is time, μ is the gross growth rate, and k_p, k_d, k_w, and k_s are the exponential loss rates corresponding to predation, decomposition, washout, and sedimentation, respectively. Ideally, all of these processes should be determined simultaneously. In practice, however, this is not usually possible. In the case of *C. phaseolus* in Lake Cisó the components of the equation were determined in different studies. Thus, net growth rate *(dN/dt)*, and losses corresponding to decomposition, washout, and sedimentation (k_d, k_w, and k_s) were determined through 2-year cycles by Pedrós-Alió *et al.* (1987). Gross growth rate (μ) was determined by García-Cantizano *et al.* (1987) and García-Cantizano (1992) by estimating CO_2 incorporation on several dates. Finally, losses through predation (k_p) were estimated separately by Pedrós-Alió *et al.* (preparation) and Massana and Pedrós-Alió (submitted).

5.1.3a. Instantaneous Estimates of Gross Growth Rate. Determinations of CO_2 fixation through oxygenic photosynthesis gave very low values, between 3 and 120 μg C/liter per hr (average = 39). This low productivity is comparable to that of the oligotrophic Mediterranean Sea (Estrada *et al.*, 1993) and is in accordance with the dystrophic status of Lake Cisó. It must be kept in mind, however, that addition of anoxygenic photosynthesis and dark fixation would bring primary production up to 100 μg C/liter per hr on average. When integrated for the whole day, oxygenic photosynthesis amounted to 160 mg C/m² per day during stratification. Some fixation took place during transitions between holomixis and stratification, amounting to about 24 mg C/m per day. Oxygenic photosynthesis represented 38% of annual CO_2 fixation in the lake and was carried out essentially by *C. phaseolus*. Thus, instantaneous gross growth rates (μ, days⁻¹) and doubling times (t_d, days) for this organism could be calculated from the CO_2 fixation data and biomass determinations (Fig. 15B). Doubling

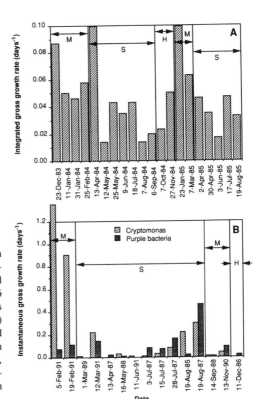

Figure 15. (A) Integrated gross growth rates of *C. phaseolus* in Lake Cisó calculated from net growth rates and losses. Drawn with data of Pedrós-Alió *et al.* (1987). (B) Instantaneous gross growth rates of *C. phaseolus* (striped) and purple bacteria (shaded) calculated from CO_2 fixation rates, drawn with data of García-Cantizano (1992). S, stratification; H, holomixis; M, transition periods with daily stratification and mixing.

times varied between 0.5 and 192 days (average 39 days). The shortest doubling times were found during the holomixis-to-stratification transition, from February to March (average 20 days). During holomixis almost no growth was detected. Finally, during stratification both fast and slow growth rates could be measured at different sampling dates (García-Cantizano, 1992), depending on the particular light conditions, depth of the thermocline, and other factors (Fig. 15B).

   5.1.3b. Integrated Estimates of Gross Growth Rates.   If net growth rate and loss constants are measured simultaneously, gross growth rate can be calculated from Eq. (1). Pedrós-Alió et al. (1987) carried out a 2-year study where these variables were measured. The only loss factor which was not taken into account was predation. This loss factor was considered in a separate study (see below). Since one of the loss factors was not considered, estimates of gross growth rates should be underestimates. Decomposition was the most important loss factor for *C. phaseolus,* especially during stratification. Sedimentation was only important for a short period in spring, while outwash was nonexistent during the summer and secondarily important during mixing (Pedrós-Alió et al., 1987).

   The calculated doubling times varied between 7 and 50 days (average 21 days; Fig. 15A). Longest doubling times were found during holomixis (October–November 1984). During the holomixis-to-stratification transition (December 1983–February 1984, January–March 1985) the shortest doubling times were found. After stratification, doubling times tended to increase through the summer, but high and low values could be found sporadically (Fig. 15A). The average doubling time, the range of values, and the seasonal trends were very similar to those obtained from instantaneous determinations (see Section 5.1.3a). The similarity of patterns obtained with these two very different methods, and in different years, indicated that estimates were reasonable and that seasonal patterns were very robust. In addition, the fact that both estimates were similar suggested that predation could not be a very important loss factor. However, predation had to be determined directly in order to make firm conclusions about its importance.

   5.1.3c. Estimates of Predation Losses.   As shown in Fig. 10, the predators of *C. phaseolus* were the rotifers *Polyarthra* and *Keratella,* and the ciliates *C. hirtus* and *Prorodon.* The two rotifers appeared throughout the epilimnion in May and June, and disappeared afterwards. Thus, their preferred food was probably a collection of small epilimnetic algae which disappeared shortly before the rotifers. The ciliates, on the other hand, were always found in enormous concentrations at the metalimnion (Fig. 4B). This suggested that they depended on *C. phaseolus* for subsistence. The relationship between these latter organisms and *C. phaseolus,* therefore, was studied in detail.

   Feeding experiments were carried out *in situ* and in the laboratory to determine the feeding rates of the ciliates on *C. phaseolus* (Pedrós-Alió et al., in preparation). Feeding rates (in *Cryptomonas* cells ingested/ciliate per hr) were between 0.12 and 0.55 for *Coleps* and between 0.17 and 1.25 for *Prorodon*. These rates could then be used, together with the abundance of predators and prey, to estimate the predatory losses of *C. phaseolus*. Since both populations were vertically stratified (Fig. 12) and they did not always overlap, an algorithm had to be developed to estimate predation taking this factor into account (Massana and Pedrós-Alió, 1994). This algorithm also solved another problem: when the predator and prey populations do not completely overlap and are vertically stratified, the predator finds different concentrations of algae at every depth. Since feeding rates are dependent on prey concentration (the functional response), the feeding rates are probably different at each depth. Thus, the algorithm also included the functional response in its calculations (Massana and Pedrós-Alió, 1994).

There was a further element to consider, however. As we have seen in Section 5.1.1, *C. phaseolus* performed diel vertical migrations. The ciliates also performed vertical migrations although of a lesser amplitude (Gasol *et al.,* 1991a). Thus, the overlap of prey and predator populations changed during the day. Three examples have been represented in Fig. 12 taken from a diel cycle in May 1988. The overlap was almost perfect at noon, extremely low at midnight, and intermediate at 4 am. Thus, the predation algorithm was applied to each of several profiles through diel cycles (Pedrós-Alió *et al.,* in preparation) and total daily predation integrated. It was found that, because of vertical migration, *C. phaseolus* could reduce predatory losses to 30% of the value without vertical migration. This showed why the organism was not found in the epilimnion, where it would have been quickly eaten by rotifers and ciliates. Moreover, this explained why *C. phaseolus* spent the night in the sulfide-rich part of the metalimnion. Predators could not follow it into this zone and, thus, predation was reduced. The lesser growth efficiency from anaerobic metabolism was apparently compensated by the reduced predation losses.

Predatory losses were always around 5% of the biomass, and usually around 50% of the production. Thus, predatory losses were not very important except on a few dates when 150% of the production could be cropped by the predators. This is consistent with the findings from the previous two sections: a small role for predation except on particular dates.

From all of these studies a model of the population dynamics through the year could be pieced together, which stresses the relative importance of each one of the processes involved (Fig. 16). During mixing the population survives longer than any other alga. Some winters, the population survives through the mixing period in the water column, while other winters it disappears from the plankton. It appears that winter survival is more likely when sulfide concentrations are low (1984–85) than when they are high (1985–86 and 1986–87). During the holomixis-to-stratification transition, the population is able to grow

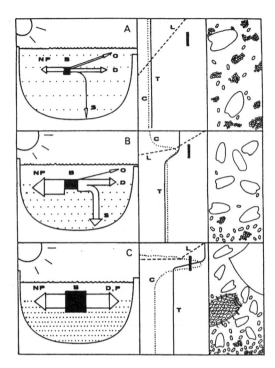

Figure 16. Schematic model of the population ecology of *C. phaseolus* in Lake Cisó. See text for explanation. From Pedrós-Alió *et al.* (1987).

by migrating every morning to the daily thermocline. Since this is very shallow, and there is no self-shading, increasing temperatures and sunlight provide for the fastest growth rates. As permanent stratification is established, the population remains at the metalimnion, where it finds protection from predation by micro-aerophilic ciliates by migrating daily toward the sulfide-rich lower metalimnion. During the early stratification, sedimentation becomes an important loss factor, but decomposition increases in importance as the summer advances. During stratification, a large biomass maintains itself in a dynamic equilibrium with slow growth rates, thanks to reduced losses. The population seems well adapted to the light regime and is often limited by nutrients, especially phosphorus. During the day, it carries out oxygenic photosynthesis (which is sensitive to sulfide) and accumulates polyglucose. During the night it consumes the poly-glucose in anaerobiosis and is surrounded by sulfide. During this time, the feeding activities of the microaerophilic ciliates may crop around 5% of the biomass and around 50 to 80% of the production daily. While this does not affect the population very much, it is enough to maintain large populations of *C. hirtus* and *Prorodon* sp. During the stratification-to-holomixis transition, the population is able to remain active by migrating every morning to the daily thermocline, and being mixed through the lake at night. Finally, photosynthesis cannot be carried out during holomixis and the population slowly declines.

5.2. Population Ecology of Sulfur Phototrophic Bacteria

5.2.1. Statics and Kinetics

Typical vertical distributions of the two purple bacteria can be seen in Fig. 5. During stratification, *C. minus* forms a metalimnetic maximum slightly below that of *C. phaseolus* and overlapping with it. *A. purpureus* presents a more uniform distribution with depth. The kinetics of both bacteria through the seasons appear in Fig. 17. *C. minus* has been the most permanent member of the community, having always been found since studies were initiated in Lake Cisó in 1977 (Guerrero and Abellà, 1978). Numbers of *C. minus* tend to decrease during holomixis and increase in a very distinct metalimnetic maximum during stratification. The other purple bacterium appeared in the lake in 1982, after one of the shore landslides and increased water flux through the lake (Mas, 1982; Guerrero *et al.*, 1985) and has been present ever since. Sulfide concentrations in the lake have been much lower after this event (0.4–2 mM) than before it (0.5–9 mM). This has been accompanied by a reduction of green sulfur bacteria and the appearance of *A. purpureus*. *A. purpureus* tends to be more abundant during holomixis, while its numbers decrease during stratification (Fig. 17B), probably because of shading by *Chromatium minus* and *Cryptomonas phaseolus*. The upper limit of the distribution of both purple bacteria is obviously the presence of oxygen above the metalimnion. The lower limit for the *C. minus* peak is probably determined by the limited amount of light reaching the hypolimnion.

The diel kinetics of *C. minus* are represented by the arrows in Fig. 6A. Vertical migration spanning 20 cm was detected by Pedrós-Alió and Sala (1990) for a subpopulation of this bacterium. Thus, two peaks of abundance could be detected at 11:45 am (the two arrows in Fig. 6A). The upper peak had migrated down, joining the lower peak, at 17:30. The center of gravity of this composite peak was at the lowest depth at 3:20 am. The two peaks appeared again at 8:25 am, next morning. No vertical migration could be demonstrated for *A. purpureus*. The physiology of purple bacteria experiences dramatic changes through the diel cycle, and these will be reviewed in the next section.

5.2.2. Physiological Ecology

It was shown in Section 4 that purple bacteria were anoxygenic photoautotrophs. Although they are able to photoassimilate thymidine, the role of organic matter in their growth is probably small (Guerrero *et al.*, 1985; Montesinos, 1987). As in the case of *C. phaseolus* the characteristics of the photosynthesis by these organisms and their limiting factors were explored both in the

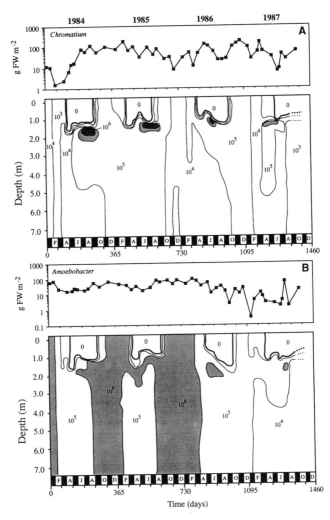

Figure 17. (A) Biomass, in g fresh weight/m² (upper panel), and vertical distribution in cells/ml (lower panel) of *Chromatium minus* in Lake Cisó from 1984 to 1987. (B) Biomass, in g fresh weight/m² (upper panel), and vertical distribution in cells/ml (lower panel) of *Amoebobacter purpureus* in Lake Cisó from 1984 to 1987. From Gasol *et al.* (1992a).

field and in the laboratory (Pedrós-Alió *et al.*, 1984; Guerrero *et al.*, 1985; van Gemerden *et al.*, 1985; Montesinos, 1987). Since both populations extended from the lower metalimnion, with crepuscular illumination, to the absolutely dark depths of the hypolimnion, the physiological status of cells at different depths was studied (Montesinos and Esteve, 1984; Guerrero *et al.*, 1985; van

Gemerden *et al.*, 1985; Montesinos, 1987; Esteve *et al.*, 1990). Finally, the physiology of the organisms through the diel cycle was also analyzed (van Gemerden *et al.*, 1985; Gasol *et al.*, 1991a; Pedrós-Alió and Sala, 1990; García-Cantizano, 1992).

In a study of a metalimnetic maximum of *Oscillatoria*, Konopka (1980) had divided the population into top, peak, and bottom layers, based on their different contents of some intracellular compounds. Usually, most of the biomass is at the peak, while the highest specific activities are found at the top. The bottom is formed by inactive and even dead cells. This division in layers was used with the Lake Cisó assemblage of purple bacteria in order to determine whether differences existed among cells located at different depths (Fig. 18).

van Gemerden *et al.* (1985) determined the viability of the different layers by assaying for the ability of the cells to form intracellular sulfur from sulfide and to oxidize sulfur to sulfate. They could show that essentially all of the cells were active at the top and peak layers, but only around 20% of the cells were active at the bottom layer. The specific content of both bacteriochlorophyll *a* and the reserve polymers glycogen, sulfur, and PHB decreased with depth (Guerrero *et*

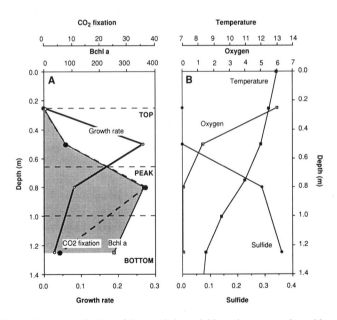

Figure 18. (A) Vertical subdivision of the purple bacterial layer into top, peak, and bottom layers. Biomass and total CO_2 fixation are higher at the peak, but specific activity and, thus, growth rate are maximal at the top. Only around 20% of the bottom cells are viable. Bacteriochlorophyll is shown as the shaded area. (B) Temperature, oxygen, and sulfide for the same date as A (March 12, 1991; from García-Cantizano, 1992).

al., 1985; Montesinos, 1987). The specific activity, as measured by CO_2 fixation and sulfide oxidation, also decreased with depth (Guerrero *et al.*, 1985; García-Cantizano, 1992).

The influence of different factors on light-dependent sulfide oxidation was studied at the top and peak layers (Guerrero *et al.*, 1985). Phosphate and acetate did not have any influence on sulfide oxidation. The effects of sulfide and light, however, were quite clear. Samples from the peak (receiving 24.3 $\mu E/m^2$ per sec) and from the top (receiving 330 $\mu E/m^2$ per sec) experienced 48% and 9% increases in sulfide oxidation rates when incubated at a depth of 1 m (receiving 798 $\mu E/m^2$ per sec). In different experiments of photosynthesis versus light intensity, purple bacteria showed I_k values between 40 and 115 $\mu E/m^2$ per sec (Montesinos, 1987; Gasol and Pedrós-Alió, unpublished). In the lake, bacteria were active at light intensities between about 1 and 60 $\mu E/m^2$ per sec.

Sulfide had an inhibitory effect on the peak layer (when added to a final concentration of 0.8 mM). Samples from the top had a comparatively low concentration of sulfide (0.01 mM). Thus, sulfide oxidation could only be determined experimentally after additions of 0.6 mM sulfide. Therefore, while the peak layer was clearly light-limited, the top layer seemed to be mostly sulfide-limited (Guerrero *et al.*, 1985). The latter point is reinforced by the results shown in Fig. 14, where additions of sulfide to the top layer stimulated CO_2 fixation by purple bacteria (Gasol *et al.*, 1993).

These measurements were confirmed by thin sections of bacteria from the different layers examined by transmission electron microscopy (Esteve *et al.*, 1990). At the bottom, the intracytoplasmic membrane system was disrupted and appeared to be nonfunctional. Bottom and peak cells had a larger amount of PHB granules than top cells (Esteve *et al.*, 1990). The significance of this latter finding will be discussed next in connection with the diel cycle.

Purple bacteria carried out anoxygenic photosynthesis during the day. This photosynthesis resulted in the accumulation of glycogen as a carbon reserve polymer (Fig. 19). Sulfide was used as an electron source for this process, but it was only oxidized to sulfur (instead of sulfate), which accumulated intracellularly during the light hours (van Gemerden *et al.*, 1985). The oxidation to sulfur produces only one-fourth of the electrons produced by the complete oxidation of sulfide to sulfate. The fact that the cells did not need to completely oxidize sulfide while accumulating glycogen, confirmed that sulfide was not limiting photosynthesis. During the night, glycogen and sulfur disappeared from the cells, while PHB accumulated simultaneously (van Gemerden *et al.*, 1985). This corresponded to the dark metabolism of *Chromatium* in culture (Fig. 19). It had been shown that glycogen could be converted to PHB in an anaerobic respiration process, where electrons were accepted by sulfur, which was then converted to sulfide (van Gemerden, 1968). Thus, this anaerobic respiration was

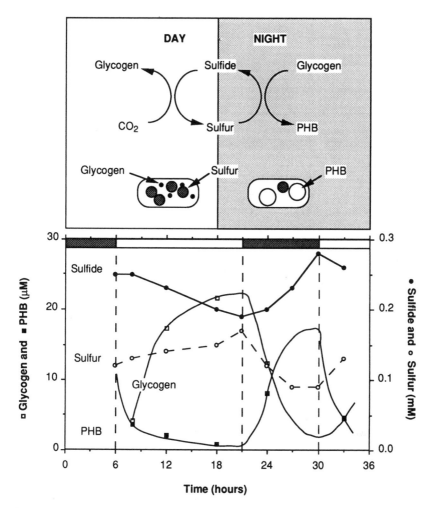

Figure 19. Changes in the physiology of purple phototrophic bacteria through a day–night cycle (July 1982). The lower panel shows changes in concentrations of sulfide, sulfur, glycogen, and PHB. The upper panel shows the different metabolisms carried out by the bacteria during the day and night and a schematic drawing of their appearance under the electron microscope. Prepared with data of van Gemerden *et al.* (1985) and electron micrographs in Fig. 3G,H.

shown to take place in nature during the night. During the day, PHB decreased and glycogen and sulfur increased again (Fig. 19).

If some cells were unable to swim up to the illuminated zone of the metalimnion in the morning, they would be trapped in the dark. For a while they would be able to respire their glycogen reserves to PHB. But, after these reserves were depleted, the cells would be unable to remain viable. This is consistent with the higher PHB content and the lack of viability of most bottom cells (see above and Fig. 3G,H).

5.2.3. Population Dynamics: Growth and Losses

The approach discussed in Section 5.1.3 for *C. phaseolus* was also used with the purple bacteria in Lake Cisó. Thus, net growth rate (dN/dt), and losses from decomposition, washout, and sedimentation (k_d, k_w, and k_s) were determined through 2-year cycles by Mas *et al.* (1990). Instantaneous gross growth rates (μ) were determined by Montesinos and Esteve (1984), Guerrero *et al.* (1985), Montesinos (1987), García-Cantizano *et al.* (1987), and García-Cantizano (1992) by estimating CO_2 incorporation on several dates. Finally, losses through predation (k_p) were estimated separately by Massana and Pedrós-Alió (in preparation). Bacterial predators specific for purple sulfur bacteria were discovered and studied (Esteve *et al.*, 1983, 1992; Guerrero *et al.*, 1986, 1987b), although their impact could not be clearly established (Gaju *et al.*, 1992).

 5.2.3a. Instantaneous Estimates of Gross Growth Rate. Determinations of CO_2 fixation through anoxygenic photosynthesis gave very low values, between 2 and 116 µg C/liter per hr (average = 25). These values are on the same order of magnitude as those for oxygenic photosynthesis. Average values during holomixis (65 µg C/liter per hr) were twice those measured during stratification (25 to 38 µg C/liter per hr). Since the whole lake is anaerobic during holomixis, the purple bacteria can be found next to the surface and, thus, they have more light available than during stratification, when they are confined to the metalimnion and shaded by the layer of *C. phaseolus*.

 Integrated daily values of production were 900 mg C/m² per day during holomixis and 630 mg C/m² per day during stratification. Anoxygenic photosynthesis represented 25% of total annual carbon fixation and was carried out almost exclusively by *C. minus* and *A. purpureus* (some was carried out by green sulfur bacteria). Doubling times for purple bacteria could be calculated by pooling the biomass of both populations and using daily carbon fixation rates (Fig. 15B). Global doubling times varied between 1.5 and 240 days (average 50 days). Fastest growth was found during the holomixis-to-stratification transition (average 26 days) and lowest growth during stratification (average 60 days), although very high values could be found at particular dates (Fig. 15B).

 We saw in Section 5.2.2 that the bottom layer of the purple bacterial populations was essentially formed by nonviable cells. Thus, doubling times were also calculated assigning all of the production to the top and peak layers only. Doubling times calculated in this way varied between 4 and 300 hr, but were generally much shorter: between 4 and 27 hr during mixing (average 11), and between 3 and 324 hr during stratification (average 50). The global average was 36 hr.

Doubling times of around 4 hr have been recently found in continuous cultures of *C. vinosum* (J. Mas, personal communication). Thus, bacteria in nature are able to grow as fast as those in culture at some particular dates.

In summary, the purple bacterial assemblage was composed of an active part in the peak and top layers and an inactive, and mostly nonviable, part in the bottom layer. Growth was faster during holomixis and the transition to stratification, when the cells were closer to the surface and, thus, exposed to higher light intensities than during stratification. Growth rates were generally very low, although they could reach the maximal growth rates measured in pure cultures at the top layer, or during holomixis, on some occasions (Montesinos, 1987; García-Cantizano *et al.*, 1987; García-Cantizano, 1992).

    5.2.3b. Integrated Estimates of Gross Growth Rates. In a way analogous to that used with *C. phaseolus,* gross growth rates were calculated for purple bacteria from losses and net growth rates (Mas *et al.*, 1990). Net growth rates were calculated from actual biomass changes assuming exponential growth (Fig. 20A). Exponential loss rates through decomposition, sedimentation, and washout were determined independently (Fig. 20B). Washout was of significance only during the winter months, coinciding with holomixis and after the rainy fall season (Fig. 20B). Decomposition was very important for *Chromatium,* especially when temperature increased during the summer. *A. purpureus,* on the other

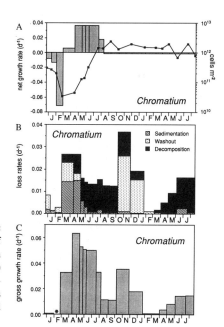

Figure 20. Population dynamics of *Chromatium minus* in Lake Cisó during 1984 and part of 1985. (A) Biomass changes (■) and net growth rates calculated from such changes (bars). (B) Loss rates from sedimentation, washout, and decomposition through the same period. (C) Gross growth rates calculated by adding rates in A and B. From Mas *et al.* (1990).

hand, could not be seen to decompose in the water column. Probably, the thick mucus layers surrounding aggregates of this organism prevent ready attack by heterotrophic bacteria or their enzymes. Interestingly, pure cultures of *A. purpureus* only form aggregates or mucus during the stationary phase, but not during exponential growth (M. Martínez Alonso, personal communication). This is consistent with the finding that most of the *A. purpureus* biomass in the lake is in the dark and inactive, at least during stratification. Finally, sedimentation was important only during the spring, right after the establishment of stratification, and especially for *C. minus* (Pedrós-Alió *et al.*, 1989; Mas *et al.*, 1990).

Gross growth rates were calculated by adding net growth plus losses (Fig. 20C). Maximal values were 0.063 per day for *Chromatium* and 0.037 per day for *Amoebobacter*. In terms of doubling times this meant between 10 and 19 days for *C. minus* and between 16 and 31 days for *A. purpureus*. These numbers are in agreement with the instantaneous rates calculated in the previous section (Fig. 15B). Of course, the growth rates at the top layer, as was discussed, were much faster and sometimes close to the maximal growth rates obtained in the laboratory. The *C. minus* growth rates were shown to be correlated with the amount of light available per unit of growing biomass (Mas *et al.*, 1990). This confirmed that growth of phototrophic bacteria in Lake Cisó was limited by light. Again, the situation during holomixis was more dynamic than during stratification. Because of increased rainfall, water flux through the lake also increased and losses from washout were significant. The disappearance of algae made more light available for bacteria and fastest growth rates were found during the holomixis-to-stratification transition.

5.2.3c. Estimates of Predation Losses. Since dense layers of phototrophic bacteria are found slightly below rotifer and ciliate accumulations, it is tempting to assume a trophic relationship. Moreover, purple sulfur bacteria have been observed in the interior of several ciliates (Finlay *et al.*, 1991) and cladocerans (Sorokin, 1970), and several of the rotifers found in Lake Cisó were known to be at least partially bacterivorous (Table I). Massana and Pedrós-Alió (in preparation) carried out experiments with fluorescently labeled purple sulfur bacteria in Lake Cisó to quantify this potential relationship. It could be shown that both ciliates and rotifers were able to feed on the bacteria in experimental bottles. In the lake, however, the populations of predators and prey were slightly separated in space and, thus, the impact of predation was very small for the phototrophic bacteria. For example, the most important bacerivore in terms of biomass was the rotifer *A. fissa* (Fig. 2B), but its impact on purple bacteria only accounted for less than 10% of the prey biomass daily (Massana and Pedrós-Alió, 1994).

The last possible source of predatory losses is the existence of predatory bacteria and viruses. Viruses have not been studied in this context, but the existence of several predatory bacteria has been shown in lakes Estanya (Esteve *et al.*, 1983, 1992; Guerrero *et al.*, 1986), Arcas-2 (Vicente *et al.*, 1991), Cisó

(Guerrero *et al.*, 1986; Esteve *et al.*, 1992; Gaju *et al.*, 1992), and Vilar (Gaju *et al.*, 1992) always attacking purple sulfur bacteria (Fig. 3I,J). These predatory bacteria tend to be more abundant where the purple bacteria are less active, that is, in the deeper parts of the bacterial layer, suggesting that their role is that of opportunistic scavengers. Their actual impact, however, remains to be assessed.

5.2.4. Competition among Sulfur Phototrophic Bacteria

Ecologists are still arguing about whether competition does or does not exist in nature (Schoener, 1982). The few experimental studies carried out have involved animals or plants. Bacteria, however, offer more advantages for these types of experiments; their kinetic parameters can be determined very easily and their small size, as well as that of their habitat, makes manipulation relatively easy. Their fast growth rates make it possible to follow many generations in one "grant funding period," something totally impossible with large organisms. Bacteria are not without problems, however. The first is that it is not always possible to isolate in pure culture the dominant microorganisms to study their physiology, and the second disadvantage is that removal experiments, in which one population is removed from the environment, cannot be performed with bacteria.

Competition and coexistence have been shown to occur among bacteria in the laboratory (van Gemerden, 1974; van Gemerden and Beeftink, 1983; Veldkamp *et al.*, 1984). But does competition among bacteria take place in nature, and does it have an influence on guild structure? The studies of phototrophic bacteria in Lake Cisó show not only that competition exists in nature, but also that it has a clear influence on the species composition of the guild. This example illustrates the importance of long-term studies (relative to the doubling times of the organisms) by showing that environmental fluctuations, both predictable and unpredictable, occur frequently enough to maintain communities away from equilibrium for a substantial portion of the year.

According to Arthur (1987, p. 116) two conditions are necessary and sufficient to demonstrate the existence of competition: niche overlap and resource limitation. The existence of niche overlap among phototrophic bacteria is obvious from the definition of the guild itself: they use light as the source of energy, sulfide as the source of electrons, and CO_2 as the carbon source, in addition to the same inorganic nutrients. Since the Earth's atmosphere became aerobic about 2 billion years ago, light and sulfide are found together only in certain habitats, such as the metalimnion of lakes or shallow water sediments, where light diminishes from top to bottom and sulfide increases from the bottom up. Thus, where both light and sulfide coexist, they are usually found in very low amounts and tend to be the most common limiting factors for phototrophic bacteria (Montesinos and van Gemerden, 1986; Pfennig and Trüper, 1989).

There is some degree of resource partitioning, but overlap is extensive. For sulfide this is easily determined by measuring growth at different sulfide concetrations (Fig. 21A). The case of light is slightly more complicated. Plots of growth versus light show the characteristic saturation curves (Fig. 21B). But another factor, light quality, has to be considered. This is best seen by comparing the *in vivo* absorption spectra of the organisms (Fig. 21C). The spectrum of an organism depends on the properties of its pigments. The peaks indicate the wavelengths that can be used, while the troughs indicate wavelengths that cannot be used. Obviously there is wide overlap, although some degree of partitioning exists.

Resource limitation can be shown in two different ways: by comparison of the growth kinetics described above with the light intensities and sulfide concentrations found in Lake Cisó, and by resource addition experiments.

Seasonal distribution (Fig. 22) shows that biomass of purple bacteria increases with light intensity in the spring and decreases in the fall. Light intensity explains 89% of the variability in the biomass of Chromatiaceae (Pedrós-Alió *et al.*, 1983). All of this is suggestive of light limitation, but resource addition experiments provide the final proof. These were discussed in Section 5.2.2.

All of the evidence, thus, points to a light limitation of the phototrophic bacteria in Lake Cisó. Since both niche overlap and resource limitation exist, competition should take place. Evidence for competition also comes from two lines of evidence: observational data of abundance through the seasons and resource manipulation experiments.

Each of the phototrophic bacteria found in the lake presents a set of characteristics which separates it from the others. The purple bacteria differ from the green bacteria in being larger (about 50 μm^3) instead of small (1 μm^3), motile instead of nonmotile, accumulating sulfur intracellularly instead of depositing it outside the cells, and being more tolerant of microaerophilic conditions. The green bacteria are more tolerant of high sulfide concentrations and are able to use lower light intensities (van Gemerden and Beeftink, 1983; Pfennig and Trüper, 1989). Thus, the purple bacteria are able to position themselves farther up in the water column than the green bacteria and the latter, in turn, are better adapted to the deeper zones of the lake.

In 1977 and 1978 there was a single species of dominant purple sulfur bacteria, *Chromatum minus,* and two of green bacteria, *Chlorobium limicola* and *C. phaeobacteroides* (Guerrero and Abellà, 1978; Abellà *et al.*, 1980; Guerrero *et al.*, 1980). The relative abundance of these organisms changed depending on physicochemical conditions in the lake (Fig. 22A). High solar radiation and high water flux through the lake favored *Chromatium minus.* This bacterium was more abundant in early summer (12 mg wet weight/m^2) than during the winter (1 mg wet weight/m^2). The purple bacterium positioned itself in the upper part of the thermocline during stratification, shading the nonmotile green bacteria underneath. Thus, the latter were more abundant in winter and fall (5 mg wet

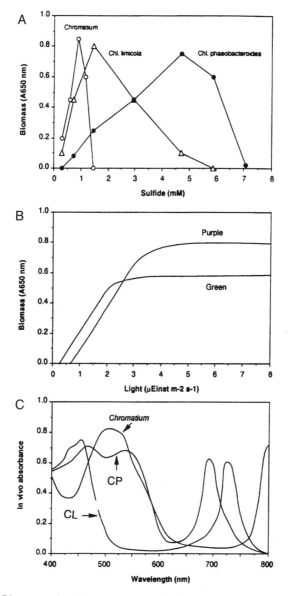

Figure 21. (A) Biomass attained by pure cultures of sulfur bacteria isolated from Lake Cisó at different sulfide concentrations. (B) Biomass attained by purple and green bacteria at different light intensities. (C) *In vivo* absorption spectra of the three sulfur bacteria shown in A. CL, *Chlorobium limicola;* CP, *Chlorobium phaeobacteroides.* Prepared with data from E. Montesinos.

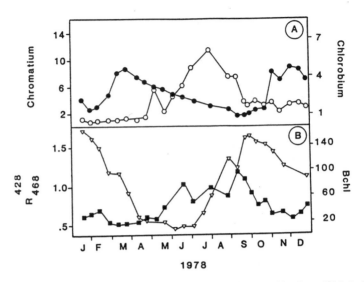

Figure 22. (A) Seasonal changes in biomass of *Chromatium* (○) and *Chlorobium* (●) in Lake Cisó during 1978. (B) Seasonal changes for the 428/468 ratio (▽) and bacteriochlorophyll specific content of the Chlorobiaceae (■). From Pedrós-Alió (1989) with data of Montesinos *et al.* (1983).

weight/m²) than during the summer (1 mg wet weight/m²). The green bacteria responded to the shading of *Chromatium minus* by increasing the concentration of their pigments. The amounts of both bacteriochlorophyll and carotenoids were five times larger during stratification than during mixing despite the lower biomass (Abellà *et al.*, 1980; Pedrós-Alió *et al.*, 1983; Fig. 22B), but this was not sufficient to trap enough light, and the population declined.

During mixing periods, motility was of no use to *C. minus*, as it could not maintain its position above the population of green bacteria. Therefore, the better adaptation of the latter to low light intensities and its higher affinities for sulfide (van Gemerden and Beeftink, 1983; Kuenen *et al.*, 1985; Montesinos and van Gemerden, 1986) allowed these bacteria to dominate the phototrophic guild (Fig. 22A). In this case, the outcome of competition between the green and purple bacteria changed throughout the year (and thus produced a seasonal species succession), and was seen to depend on a set of environmental factors which favored one or the other at different times of the year. This caused an alternation in the pattern of dominance of the guild by the two types of phototrophic bacteria.

The impact of *C. minus* shading on the green bacteria was in fact more dramatic. Through resource manipulation experiments, Montesinos *et al.* (1983) were able to show that the outcome of competition between the two green bacteria in the lake depended on the presence or absence of shading by *C. minus*.

Figure 21C shows the absorption spectra of the three bacteria. The dense layer of *C. minus* was in effect a filter selectively absorbing wavelengths between 490 and 590 nm and around 830 nm. The water itself strongly absorbs in the infrared region and, therefore, there are two windows around 450 and 650 nm where light actually reaches the layer of green bacteria. The green bacteria do not absorb in the 650 nm region (Fig. 21C) and *Chlorobium phaeobacteroides* (a brown bacterium) cannot absorb at 450 nm either. However, *Chlorobium limicola* (a green bacterium) has a peak of absorption at 445 nm. Thus, Montesinos *et al.* (1983) predicted that the green species would be present under layers of *Chromatium* and the brown species could only exist when the layers of *Chromatium* were absent. This was actually shown to occur in the lake (Fig. 22B) by following the ratio of absorbances at 428 and 468 nm. The two species of *Chlorobium* cannot be differentiated morphologically, but the absorbance ratio will increase when the green species is more abundant (428 is one of the absorption peaks of its bacteriochlorophyll) and decrease when the brown species is more abundant (468 is one of the absorption peaks of its bacteriochlorophyll). In Fig. 22B, the ratio can be seen to increase when the Chromatiaceae were more abundant (June to September) and to decrease when they were absent (October to April) as predicted.

Montesinos *et al.* (1983) also performed laboratory experiments to demonstrate that changes in light quality caused by the presence or absence of *Chromatium* were indeed the cause of the shift in species composition. They grew a mixture of the two *Chlorobium* species in cultures with and without filters mimicking the absorbance of *Chromatium* plus water. The results were, again, those predicted from the absorption spectra of the bacteria. When the filter was present, the ratio of absorbances increased indicating the dominance by the green species. Without the filter, the ratio remained at its initial values. The dominance of the brown species in the lake when *Chromatium* was absent was probably the result of its adaptation to lower light intensities and higher sulfide concentrations, but this point was not studied further.

Superimposed on these annual fluctuations, there are longer period oscillations related to changes in weather and morphology of the lake basin. As explained before, Lake Cisó is located in an area that is geologically very active. As a result of the reduction in sulfide concentration after one of the landslides, the bacterial phototrophic guild has shifted its species composition. In addition to the 10^6 cells/ml of *C. minus*, 10^6 cells/ml of *A. purpureus* could be found after 1981. The lower sulfide concentrations have presumably allowed more purple bacteria to develop. Doubling the biomass of such bacteria has diminished tremendously the biomass of green bacteria through more intense shading. Thus, while the function of the guild (as estimated by the amount of bacteriochlorophyll and CO_2 fixation) has remained more or less constant, the composition of the guild has shifted as the environmental conditions changed.

Of course, the two purple bacteria also compete. Again, a combination of adaptive traits and physicochemical changes in the environment result in coexistence of the two species. *A. purpureus* is a purple phototrophic bacterium forming colonies of small, nonmotile, coccoid cells surrounded by a thick slime layer and packed with gas vesicles. Within the Chromatiaceae, *A. purpureus* presents a set of characteristics (nonmotile, colonial, gas vesicles, slime layer) as different as possible from *C. minus*. As in the case of *C. minus* versus Chlorobia, the case of *C. minus* versus *A. purpureus* illustrates the high pressure toward maximal possible differentiation among the members of a guild in order to avoid mutual exclusion.

This case illustrates several important points. First, competition among the species forming at least one bacterial guild does exist in nature. Second, competition is responsible, at least partially, for the species composition of the guild. Third, the guild composition is rarely at equilibrium. Usually it is changing from that at one set of environmental conditions (e.g., winter holomixis) to another (e.g., stratification and increased spring light intensities). For bacteria with generation times between 10 and 15 days, there are regular seasonal changes, responses to irregular drastic perturbations, and slow changes taking place over 5- to 10-year periods. It is then no surprise that little agreement exists about the importance of competition in experiments with plants and animals with doubling times of years to decades!

6. Conclusions

The study of the microbial community of Lake Cisó has shown that principles from general ecology are in some cases applicable to bacteria. However, they will have to be modified in other cases. Among the first class, competition was shown to occur among bacteria in the field and to be responsible for two features of the guild: the species composition and the tendency for coexisting species to be as different as possible among themselves (Pedrós-Alió, 1989). Both of these features are known to apply in the case of animals and plants. Their importance in at least one bacterial guild (sulfur phototrophic bacteria) suggests that it is probably present in other bacterial guilds as well.

Other aspects added new perspectives to current models. Thus, the community in Lake Cisó was shown to depart from the PEG model of seasonal succession. The case of Lake Cisó in this respect is probably exportable to all aquatic systems with deep-living populations of algae (Gasol *et al.*, 1992a).

The community was shown to maintain large biomass with slow growth, which is also opposed to the current thinking about most pelagic microbial communities, where limited biomass is maintained by active predation on very fast growing populations of algae and bacteria. It was shown that when a refuge from predation is available, large biomass can be attained and growth can proceed slowly. This feature is probably one of the main causes for the existence of many metalimnetic maxima of algae and bacteria (Pedrós-Alió *et al.*, in preparation), and also seems to apply to communities living in marine snow (Azam *et al.*, 1993) and freshwater sediments (Gasol, 1993).

The hypolimnetic and winter food web from Lake Cisó has been the first anaerobic food web studied quantitatively. It was shown that the food web structure conformed to the general paradigm (Pimm *et al.*, 1991) if osmotrophic relationships and viruses were taken into account. These relationships are very different from the usual phagotrophic relationships considered in models of animals and plants. Yet, the resultant community structure is quite similar in both types of environments.

One completely different aspect in microbial communities is the size structure. Since relationships are not dependent on phagotrophic predation, size is not an important factor to obtain "food." Thus, the size spectrum appears truncated and nonlinear, despite the same trophic structure as in communities of larger organisms (Gasol *et al.*, 1991b). Again, this feature is probably general for all ecosystems dominated by microorganisms.

Finally, the question of diversity of microbial, and especially bacterial, assemblages remains open. The introduction of molecular techniques based on the analysis of RNA (Pace *et al.*, 1986), however, promises to allow comparisons of microbial diversity to that of animal and plant assemblages (Pedrós-Alió, 1993).

We hope the results of the work carried out in Lake Cisó will provide food for thought for microbial ecologists and remind them that their discipline is certainly a part of ecology, but with a grist.

ACKNOWLEDGMENTS. Many people have participated in studies in Lake Cisó through the years. We are indebted to all of them: Carles A. Abellà, Isabel Esteve, and Emilio Montesinos were responsible for starting the project. Hans van Gemerden provided fresh insight at a stage when it was most needed. Jordi Mas Gordi and Josep M. Gasol have carried it forward significantly. The work of Núria Gaju has been instrumental at different stages. The 1986 class has been extremely productive and includes Josefina García-Cantizano, Maira Martínez Alonso, Jordi Mas Castellà, and Joan Mir. The last wave of students has taken the project far beyond its modest beginning: Joan Isidre Calderon, Ramon Massana, and Emilio Ortega. The following individuals have worked in the lake during short periods of time: Mònica Algueró, Teresa Babià, David Brugada, Rosa Debón, Ferran Garcia Pichel, Pere Guillén, Mikel Latasa, James G. Mitchell, Miguel A. Molina, Vicki Pavón, Francesc Peters, Lluis Pérez Ginesta, Jordi Romero, Ma. Montserrat Sala, and Santiago Sánchez. Juan Manuel Cuartero and Carmen Chica have provided extremely able technical and administrative support. Finally, we thank J. M. Gasol for many helpful suggestions during the preparation of this review.

Studies in Lake Cisó have been financed by several grants from the Spanish Ministry of Education and Science (CICYT and DGICYT), from the CIRIT of the Catalan Government, and from the European Community.

References

Abellà, C. A., Montesinos, E., and Guerrero, R., 1980, Field studies on the competition between purple and green sulfur bacteria for available light. (Lake Sisó, Spain), *Dev. Hydrobiol.* **3:**173–181.

Alfonso, M. T., and Miracle, M. R., 1987, Variación temporal de las poblaciones zooplanctónicas de la laguna anóxica del Cisó (Girona), *Limnetica* **3:**167–177.

Arthur, W., 1987, *The Niche in Competition and Evolution*, Wiley, New York.

Azam, F., Smith, D. C., and Martínez, J., 1993, Bacteria–organic matter coupling on marine aggregates, Proceedings of the Sixth International Symposium on Microbial Ecology, Barcelona (in press).

Baker, A. L., Baker, K. K., and Tyler, P. A., 1985, A family of pneumatically-operated thin layer samplers for replicate sampling of heterogeneous water columns, *Hydrobiologia* **122:**207–211.

Brock, T. D., 1978, *Thermophilic Microorganisms and Life at High Temperatures*, Springer-Verlag, Berlin.

Brock. T. D., 1985, *A Eutrophic Lake: Lake Mendota, Wisconsin*, Springer-Verlag, Berlin.

Calderon, J. I., García-Cantizano, J., and Pedrós-Alió, C., 1993, Thymidine incorporation in warm water bodies of different trophic status, *Verh. Int. Verein. Limnol.* **25:** (in press).

Cohen, J. E., 1988, Food webs and community structure, in: *Perspectives in Ecological Theory* (J. Roughgarden, R. M. May, and S. A. Levin, eds.), Princeton University Press, Princeton, N.J., pp. 181–202.

Cohen, J. E., Briand, F., and Newman, C. M., 1990, *Community Food Webs: Data and Theory,* Springer-Verlag, Berlin.

Cousins, S. H., 1980, A trophic continuum derived from plant structure, animal size, and a detritus cascade, *J. Theor. Biol.* **82:**607–618.

del Giorgio, P., and Gasol, J. M., 1993. Biomass allocation in freshwater plankton communities *Am. Nat.* (in press).

Dickie, L. M., Kerr, S. R., and Boudreau, P. R., 1987, Size-dependent processes underlying regularities in ecosystem structure, *Ecol. Monogr.* **57:**233-250.

Distel, D. L., Lane, D. J., Olsen, G. J., Giovannoni, S. J., Pace, B., Pace, N. R., Stahl, D. A., and Felbeck, H., 1988, Sulfur-oxidizing bacterial endosymbionts: Analysis of phylogeny and specificity by 16S rRNA sequences, *J. Bacteriol.* **170:**2506–2510.

Dyer, B. B., Gaju, N., Pedrós-Alió, C., Esteve, I., and Guerrero, R., 1986, Ciliates from a fresh water sulfuretum, *BioSystems* **19:**127–135.

Echevarría, F., Carrillo, P., Jiménez, F., Sánchez-Castillo, P., Cruz-Pizarro, L., and Rodríguez, J., 1990, The size-abundance distribution and taxonomic composition of plankton in an oligotrophic, high mountain lake (La Caldera, Sierra Nevada, Spain), *J. Plankton Res.* **12:**415–422.

Esteve, I., Guerrero, R., Montesinos, E., and Abellà, C. A., 1983, Electron microscope study of the interaction of epibiontic bacteria with *Chromatium minus* in natural habitats, *Microb. Ecol.* **9:**57–64.

Esteve, I., Mir, J., McKhann, H. I., and Margulis, L., 1988, Green endosymbiont of *Coleps* from Lake Cisó identified as *Chlorella vulgaris*, *Symbiosis* **6:**197–200.

Esteve, I., Montesinos, E., Mitchell, J. G., and Guerrero, R., 1990, A quantitative ultrastructural study of *Chromatium minus* in the bacterial layer of Lake Cisó (Spain), *Arch. Microbiol.* **153:**316–323.

Esteve, I., Gaju, N., Mir, J., and Guerrero, R., 1992, Comparison of techniques to determine the abundance of predatory bacteria attacking Chromatiaceae, *FEMS Microbiol. Ecol.* **86**:205-211.

Estrada, M., Marrasé, C., Latasa, M., Berdalet, E., Delgado, M., and Riera, T., 1993, Variability of deep chlorophyll maximum characteristics in the northwestern Mediterranean, *Mar. Ecol. Prog. Ser.* **92**:289-300.

Fee, E. J., 1976, The vertical and seasonal distribution of chlorophyll in lakes of the Experimental Lakes Area, northwestern Ontario: Implications for primary production, *Limnol. Oceanogr.* **21**:767-783.

Fenchel, T., and Finlay, B. J., 1990, Anaerobic free-living protozoa: Growth efficiencies and the structure of anaerobic communities, *FEMS Microbiol. Ecol.* **74**:269-276.

Finlay, B. J., Clarke, K. J., Vicente, E., and Miracle, M. R., 1991, Anaerobic ciliates from a sulphide-rich solution lake in Spain, *Eur. J. Protistol.* **27**:148-159.

Gaju, N., Esteve, I., Mir, J., and Guerrero, R., 1992, Predatory bacteria attacking Chromatiaceae in a sulfureous lake, *Microb. Ecol.* **24**:171-179.

García-Cantizano, J., 1992, Análisis funcional de la comunidad microbiana en ecosistemas planctónicos, Ph.D. thesis, Universitat Autònoma de Barcelona.

García-Cantizano, J., Gasol., J. M., and Pedrós-Alió, C., 1987, Producción primaria por fototrofía y por quimiolitotrofía en la laguna de Cisó, *Actas del IV Congreso español de Limnología* pp. 75-84.

García-Cantizano, J., Calderon, J. I., and Pedrós-Alió, C., 1993, Thymidine uptake in Lake Cisó: Problems in estimating bacterial secondary production across oxic-anoxic interfaces (submitted for publication).

García-Gil, J., Brunet, R. C., Montesinos, E., and Abellà, C. A., 1985, Estudi comparatiu de l'evolució de la morfometria dels estanyols de la Riera Castellana (Banyoles): Estanyol Nou, Sisó i brollador, *Sci. Gerundensis* **11**:81-90.

Gasol, J. M., 1993, Benthic flagellates and ciliates in fine freshwater sediments: Calibration of a live counting procedure and estimation of their abundances, *Microb. Ecol.* **25**:247-262.

Gasol, J. M., and Pedrós-Alió, C., 1991, On the origin of deep algal maxima: The case of Lake Cisó, *Verh. Int. Verein. Limnol.* **24**:1024-1028.

Gasol, J. M., Mas, J., Pedrós-Alió, C., and Guerrero, R., 1990, Ecología microbiana y limnología en la laguna Cisó: 1976-1989, *Sci. gerundensis* **16**:155-178.

Gasol, J. M., García-Cantizano, J., Massana, R., Peters, F., Guerrero, R., and Pedrós-Alió, C., 1991a, Diel changes in the microstratification of the metalimnetic community of Lake Cisó, *Hydrobiologia* **211**:227-240.

Gasol, J. M., Guerrero, R., and Pedrós-Alió, C., 1991b, Seasonal variations in size structure and procaryotic dominance in sulfurous Lake Cisó, *Limnol. Oceanogr.* **36**:860-872.

Gasol, J. M., Peters, F., Guerrero, R., and Pedrós-Alió, C., 1992a, Community structure in Lake Cisó: Biomass allocation to trophic groups and differing patterns of seasonal succession in the meta- and epilimnion, *Arch. Hydrobiol.* **123**:275-303.

Gasol, J. M., Guerrero, R., and Pedrós-Alió, C., 1992b, Spatial and temporal dynamics of a metalimnetic *Cryptomonas* peak, *J. Plankton Res.* **14**:(11):1565-1579.

Gasol, J. M., García-Cantizano, J., Massana, R., Guerrero, R., and Pedrós-Alió, C., 1993, Physiological ecology of a metalimnetic *Cryptomonas* population: Relationships to light, sulfide and nutrients, *J. Plankton Res.* **15**:255-271.

Gervais, F., 1991, Which factors controlled seasonal and spatial distribution of phytoplankton species in Schlachtensee (Berlin, F.R.G.) 1987? *Arch. Hydrobiol.* **121**:43-65.

Giovannoni, S. J., Britschgi, T. B., Moyer, C. L., and Field, K. G., 1990, Genetic diversity in Sargasso Sea bacterioplankton, *Nature* **345**:60-63.

Guerrero, R., and Abellà, C. A., 1978, Dinámica espacio-temporal de las poblaciones bacterianas fotosintéticas en una laguna anaeróbica de aguas sulfurosas, *Oecol. Aqua.* **3**:193-205.

Guerrero, R., Montesinos, E., Esteve, I., and Abellà, C. A., 1980, Physiological adaptation and growth of purple and green sulfur bacteria in a meromictic lake (Vilà) as compared to a holomictic lake (Sisó), *Dev. Hydrobiol.* **3**:161–171.

Guerrero, R., Montesinos, E., Pedrós-Alió, C., Esteve, I., Mas, J., and van Gemerden, H., 1985, Phototrophic sulfur bacteria in two Spanish lakes: Vertical distribution and limiting factors, *Limnol. Oceanogr.* **30**:919–931.

Guerrero, R., Pedrós-Alió, C., Esteve, I., Mas, J., Chase, D., and Margulis, L., 1986, Predatory prokaryotes: Predation and primary consumption evolved in bacteria, *Proc. Natl. Acad. Sci. USA* **83**:2138–2142.

Guerrero, R., Pedrós-Alió, C., Esteve, I., and Mas, J., 1987a, Communities of phototrophic sulfur bacteria in lakes of the Spanish Mediterranean region, *Acta Acad. Abo.* **47**:125–151.

Guerrero, R., Esteve, I., Pedrós-Alió, C., and Gaju, N., 1987b, Predatory bacteria in prokaryotic communities. The earliest trophic relationships, *Ann. N.Y. Acad. Sci.* **503**:238–250.

Hurley, J. P., and Garrison, P. J., 1992, Identification of deep plankton in lakes by HPLC pigment analyses, Abstracts ASLO 92, Aquatic Sciences Meeting, Santa Fe, N.M.

Jones, J. G., 1987, Diversity of freshwater microbiology, in: *Ecology of Microbial Communities* (M. Fletcher, T. R. G. Gray, and G. J. Jones, eds.), Soc. Gen. Microbiol. Spec. Symp. 41, Cambridge University Press, London, pp. 235–259.

Jørgensen, B. B., Kuenen, J. G., and Cohen, Y., 1979, Microbial transformations of sulfur compounds in a stratified lake (Solar Lake, Sinai), *Limnol. Oceanogr.* **28**:1075–1093.

Konopka, A., 1980, Physiological changes within a metalimnetic layer of *Oscillatoria rubescens*, *Appl. Environ. Microbiol.* **40**:681-684.

Kuenen, J. G., Robertson, L. A., and van Gemerden, H., 1985, Microbial interactions among aerobic and anaerobic sulfur-oxidizing bacteria, *Adv. Microb. Ecol.* **8**:1–59.

Lawton, J. H., 1989, Food webs, in: Ecological Concepts. The Contribution of Ecology to an Understanding of the Natural World. (J. M. Cherrett, ed.), 29th Symp. British Ecological Society, Blackwell, Oxford, pp. 43–78.

Likens, G. E. (ed.), 1985, *An Ecosystem Approach to Aquatic Ecology,* Springer-Verlag, Berlin.

Lindeman, R. L., 1942, The trophic-dynamic aspect of ecology, *Ecology* **23**:399–417.

Lindholm, T. (ed), 1987, Ecology of photosynthetic prokaryotes with special reference to meromictic lakes and coastal lagoons, *Acta Acad. Abo. Ser. B* 47(2).

Magurran, A. E., 1988, *Ecological Diversity and Its Measurement,* Princeton University Press, Princeton, N.J.

Mas, J., 1982, Sucesión de bacterias planctónicas en su sistema anaeróbico de baja diversidad, M.S. thesis, Universitat Autònoma de Barcelona, Bellaterra, Barcelona.

Mas, J., Pedrós-Alió, C., and Guerrero, R., 1990, *In situ* specific loss and growth rates of purple sulfur bacteria in Lake Cisó, *FEMS Microbiol. Ecol.* **73**:271–281.

Massana, R., and Pedrós-Alió, C., 1994, A method to determine integrated predation in stratified waters, *Limnol. Oceanog.* **39**: (in press).

Massana, R., and Pedrós-Alió, C., 1993, The role of anaerobic ciliates in planktonic food webs, (submitted).

May, R. M., 1986, The search for patterns in the balance of nature: Advances and retreats, *Ecology* **67**:1115–1126.

Miracle, R. M., Vicente, E., and Pedrós-Alió, C., 1992, Biological studies in Spanish meromictic and stratified karstic lakes, *Limnetica* **8**:59–77.

Mitchell, J. G., and Fuhrman, J. A., 1989, Centimeter scale vertical heterogeneity in bacteria and chlorophyll a, *Mar. Ecol. Prog. Ser.* **54**:141–148.

Montesinos, E., 1987, Change in size of *Chromatium minus* cells in relation to growth rate, sulfur content, and photosynthetic activity: A comparison of pure cultures and field populations, *Appl. Environ. Microbiol.* **53**:864–871.

Montesinos, E., and Esteve, I., 1984, Effect of algal shading on the net growth and production of phototrophic sulfur bacteria in lakes of the Banyoles karstic area, *Verh. Int. Verein. Limnol.* **22:**1102–1105.

Montesinos, E., and van Gemerden, H., 1986, The distribution and metabolism of planktonic phototrophic bacteria, in: *Perspectives in Microbial Ecology* (F. Megusar and M. Gantar, eds.), Slovenian Society for Microbiology, Ljubljana, pp. 349–359.

Montesinos, E., Guerrero, R., Abellà, C. A., and Esteve, I., 1983, Ecology and physiology of the competition between *Chlorobium limicola* and *Chlorobium phaeobacteroides, Appl. Environ. Microbiol.* **46:**1007–1016.

Nauwerck, A., 1963, Die Beziehungen zwischen Zooplankton und Phytoplankton im See Erken, *Symbolae Bot. Uppsaliensis* **8:**5–162.

Pace, N. R., Stahl, D. A., Lane, D. J., and Olsen, G. J., 1986, The analysis of natural microbial populations by ribosomal RNA sequences, *Adv. Microb. Ecol.* **9:**1–55.

Paine, R. T., 1988, Food webs: Road maps of interactions or grist for theoretical development, *Ecology* **69:**1648–1654.

Pedrós-Alió, C., 1989, Towards an autecology of bacterioplankton, in: *Plankton Ecology: Succession in Plankton Communities* (U. Sommer ed.), Springer-Verlag, Berlin, pp. 297–336.

Pedrós-Alió, C., 1993, Diversity of bacterioplankton, *Trends Ecol. Evol.* **8:**86–90.

Pedrós-Alió, C., and Sala, M. M., 1990, Microdistribution and diel vertical migration of flagellated vs. gas-vacuolate purple sulfur bacteria in a stratified water body, *Limnol. Oceanogr.* **35:**1637–1644.

Pedrós-Alió, C., and Mas, J., 1993, Bacterial sinking losses, in: *Current Methods in Aquatic Microbial Ecology* (P. F. Kemp, B. F. Sherr, E. B. Sherr, and J. J. Cole, eds.), Lewis Publishers, Chelsea, Mich., pp. 677–684.

Pedrós-Alió, C., Montesinos, E., and Guerrero, R., 1983, Factors determining annual changes in bacterial photosynthetic pigments in holomictic Lake Cisó, Spain, *Appl. Environ. Microbiol.* **46:**999–1006.

Pedrós-Alió, C., Abellà, C. A., and Guerrero, R., 1984, Influence of solar radiation, water flux and competition on biomass of phototrophic bacteria in Lake Cisó, Spain, *Verh. Int. Verein. Limnol.* **22:**1097–1101.

Pedrós-Alió, C., Gasol, J. M., and Guerrero, R., 1986, Microbial ecology of sulfurous Lake Cisó, in: *Perspectives in Microbial Ecology* (F. Megusar and M. Gantar, eds.), Slovenian Society for Microbiology, Ljubljana, pp. 638–643.

Pedrós-Alió, C., Gasol, J. M., and Guerrero, R., 1987, On the ecology of a *Cryptomonas phaseolus* population forming a metalimnetic bloom in Lake Cisó, Spain: Annual distribution and loss factors, *Limnol. Oceanogr.* **32:**285–298.

Pedrós-Alió, C., Mas, J., Gasol, J. M., and Guerrero, R., 1989, Sinking speeds of free-living phototrophic bacteria determined with covered and uncovered traps, *J. Plankton Res.* **11:**887–905.

Pedrós-Alió, C., García-Cantizano, J., and Calderon, J. I., 1993, Bacterial production in anaerobic water columns, in: *Current Methods in Aquatic Microbial Ecology* (P. F. Kemp, B. F. Sherr, E. B. Sherr, and J. J. Cole, eds.), Lewis Publishers, Chelsea, Mich., pp. 519–530.

Peters, R. H., 1983, *The Ecological Implications of Body Size,* Cambridge University Press, London.

Peters, R. H., 1986, The role of prediction in limnology, *Limnol. Oceanogr.* **31:**1143–1159.

Peters, R. H., 1988, Some general problems for ecology illustrated by food web theory, *Ecology* **69:**1673–1676.

Pfennig, N., and Trüper, H. G., 1989, Anoxygenic phototrophic bacteria, in: *Bergey's Manual of Systematic Bacteriology,* Volume 3 (J. T. Staley, M. P. Bryant, N. Pfennig, and J. G. Holt, eds.), Williams & Wilkins, Baltimore, pp. 1635–1709.

Pick, F. R., Nalewajko, C., and Lean, D. R. S., 1984, The origin of a metalimnetic chrysophyte peak, *Limnol. Oceanogr.* **29:**125–134.

Pimm, S. L., 1982, *Food Webs,* Chapman & Hall, London.

Pimm, S. L., Lawton, J. H., and Cohen, J. E., 1991, Food web patterns and their consequences, *Nature* **350:**669–674.

Platt, T., 1985, Structure of the marine ecosystem: Its allometric basis, in: *Ecosystem Theory for Biological Oceanography* (R. E. Ulanowicz and T. Platt, eds.), Can. Bull. Fish. Aquat. Sci. 213.

Platt, T., and Denman, K., 1978, The structure of pelagic marine ecosystem, *Rapp. P.-V. Reun. Cons. Int. Explor. Mer.* **173:**60–65.

Platt, T., Gallegos, C. L., and Harrison, W. G., 1980, Photoinhibition of photosynthesis in natural assemblages of marine phytoplankton, *J. Mar. Res.* **38:**697–701.

Rodríguez, J., Echevarría, F., and Jiménez-Gómez, F., 1990, Physiological scaling of body size in an oligotrophic, high mountain lake (La Caldera, Sierra Nevada, Spain), *J. Plankton Res.* **12:**593–599.

Schmidt, T. M., DeLong, E. F., and Pace, N. R., 1991, Analysis of marine picoplankton community by 16S rRNA gene cloning and sequencing, *J. Bacteriol.* **173:**4371–4378.

Schoener, T. W., 1982, The controversy over interspecific competition, *Am. Sci.* **70:**586–595.

Sheldon, R. W., Prackash, A., and Suttcliffe, W. H., 1972, The size distribution of pelagic particles in the ocean, *Limnol. Oceanogr.* **17:**327–340.

Sherr, B. F., Sherr, E. B., and Fallon, R. D., 1987, Use of monodispersed, fluorescently labeled bacteria to estimate in situ protozoan bacterivory, *Appl. Environ. Microbiol.* **53:**958–965.

Sommer, U., Gliwicz, Z. M., Lampert, W., and Duncan, A., 1986, The PEG-model of seasonal distribution of planktonic events in freshwaters, *Arch. Hydrobiol.* **106:**433–471.

Sorokin, Y. I., 1970, Interrelations between sulphur and carbon turnover in meromictic lakes, *Arch. Hydrobiol.* **66:**391–446.

Sprules, W. G., Casellman, J. M., and Shuter, B. J., 1983, Size distribution of pelagic particles in lakes, *Can. J. Fish. Aquat. Sci.* **40:**1761–1769.

Stahl, D. A., Lane, D. J., Olsen, G. J., and Pace, N. R., 1985, Characterization of a Yellowstone hot spring microbial community by 5S ribosomal RNA sequences, *Appl. Environ. Microbiol.* **45:**1379–1384.

Takahashi, M., and Ichimura, S., 1968, Vertical distribution and organic matter production of phototrophic sulfur bacteria in Japanese lakes, *Limnol. Oceanogr.* **13:**644–655.

van Gemerden, H., 1968, On the ATP generation by *Chromatium* in darkness, *Arch. Microbiol.* **64:**118–124.

van Gemerden, H., 1974, Coexistence of organisms competing for the same substrate: An example among the purple sulfur bacteria, *Microb. Ecol.* **1:**104–119.

van Gemerden, H., and Beeftink, H. H., 1983, Ecology of phototrophic bacteria, in: *The Photo- trophic Bacteria: Anaerobic Life in the Light* (J. G. Ormerod, ed.), Blackwell, Oxford, pp. 146– 185.

van Gemerden, H., Montesinos, E., Mas, J., and Guerrero, R., 1985, Diel cycle of metabolism of phototrophic purple sulfur bacteria in Lake Cisó (Spain), *Limnol. Oceanogr.* **30:**932– 943.

Veldkamp, H., van Gemerden, H., Harder, W., and Laanbroek, H. J., 1984, Competition among bacteria: An overview, in: *Current Perspectives in Microbial Ecology* (M. J. Klug and C. A. Reddy, eds.), American Society for Microbiology, Washington, D.C., pp. 279–290.

Vicente, E., Rodrigo, M. A., Camacho, A., and Miracle, M. R., 1991, Phototrophic prokaryotes in a karstic sulphate lake, *Verh. Int. Verein. Limnol.* **24:**998–1004.

Ward, D. M., Tayne, T. A., Anderson, K. L., and Bateson, M. M., 1987, Community structure and interactions among community members in hot spring cyanobacterial mats, in: *Ecology of*

Microbial Communities (M. Fletcher, T. R. G. Gray, and G. J. Jones, eds.), Soc. Gen. Microbiol. Spec. Symp. 41, Cambridge University Press, London, pp. 180–210.

Whittaker, R. H., 1978, Direct gradient analysis, in: *Ordination of Plant Communities* (R. H. Whittaker, ed.), Junk, The Hague, pp. 7–50.

Zevenboom, W., 1988, Ecophysiology of nutrient uptake, photosynthesis and growth, in: *Photosynthetic Picoplankton* (T. Platt and W. K. K. Li, eds.), Department of Fisheries and Oceans, Ottawa.

5

Biological Activities of Symbiotic and Parasitic Protozoa and Fungi in Low-Oxygen Environments

ALAN G. WILLIAMS and DAVID LLOYD

1. Introduction

Recent advances in the elucidation of the metabolic capabilities of some protists living in ecosystems where oxygen concentrations are low highlight certain common features of their roles in their environments. In this review we survey the symbiotic protozoa and chytridomycete fungi of the rumen alongside parasitic protozoa infecting the human intestine and urogenital tract: many of these show striking metabolic similarities. We emphasize the putative activities of these organisms *in situ* as inferred by extrapolation from work with isolated organisms or axenic cultures.

Low-Oxygen Environments

Intestinal Tract Ecosystems

Many herbivorous animals have undergone evolutionary physiological and anatomical modifications to regions of the alimentary tract to accommodate extensive and diverse microbial populations which contribute in the digestive processes. Such adaptations to the foregut (Bauchop, 1977) or hindgut (McBee, 1977) function to increase the retention time of the digesta and generate environmental conditions that fulfill the physiological and nutritional requirements of the microbial symbionts. Bacteria are present in all intestinal mutualistic populations, whereas protozoa and fungi occur less widely.

ALAN G. WILLIAMS • Hannah Research Institute, Ayr KA6 5HL, Scotland. DAVID LLOYD • Microbiology Group (PABIO), University of Wales College of Cardiff, Cardiff CF1 3TL, Wales.

Advances in Microbial Ecology, Volume 13, edited by J. Gwynfryn Jones. Plenum Press, New York, 1993.

A variety of evolutionary modifications to the foregut have taken place in different groups of animals, but all serve to reduce ingesta passage rate and separate the resident microbial population from the acid secretions of the stomach. Ruminant animals are the most extensively studied of the groups that possess a prepeptic fermentation. However, a microbial foregut fermentation is known to occur in ten families of plant-eating mammals from four separate orders (Bauchop, 1977; Dehority, 1986). Animals with a foregut fermentation are reliant on the microbial symbionts to digest the feed components into a form that can be absorbed and metabolized in the tissues of the host. However, when the principal site of microbial fermentative activity occurs in the hindgut the initial breakdown is effected by enzymes secreted by the host, and the products are absorbed before microbial intervention. Although some of the products of the postpeptic fermentation are absorbed, most of the microbial metabolites and microbial cell components are not utilized by the host animal and are voided in the feces, unless coprophagy or cecotropy are practiced. The undigested residues of the initial foregut fermentation are subjected to further fermentative action in the hindgut. The products of this additional fermentation and microbial cell components released by the gastric acidic secretions are available for absorption from the intestinal tract of foregut fermenters.

Although ruminants are regarded as being the most successful of large animals with digestive system fermentations, they are dominated numerically by animals having a hindgut adaptation. The diversity of invertebrate and vertebrate genera that possess a hindgut fermentation is greater and hosts include insects, fish, reptiles, birds, and both small and large mammals (McBee, 1977). Smaller animals have an enlarged cecum which retains solute and small particles but indigestible fibrous material has a shorter transit time through the large intestine. In the alternative colonic fermentation (Hume and Warner, 1980), microbial activity occurs in the enlarged proximal colon and cecum. Comparative aspects of fiber digestion in ruminant and nonruminant herbivores have been reviewed by Prins and Kreulen (1990).

Intestinal ecosystems are usually well supplied with nutrients and physiological conditions are relatively constant. The body temperature of the host is strictly regulated and major fluctuations in pH do not occur under normal dietary conditions (Dehority, 1986). The oxidation–reduction (redox) potential in intestinal environments is usually low. The Eh of rumen contents is -350 mV (Smith and Hungate, 1958), but even in termites where digesta volumes are exceptionally small (approx. 1 mm^3) an oxidation–reduction potential of -160 mV is maintained (Bignell, 1984). The Eh of the intestinal contents of piglets ranges from $+265$ mV in the stomach to -214 mV in the cecum (Vervaeke et al., 1973). Such measurements have been used to substantiate the traditionally held view that the intestinal ecosystem is anaerobic and thus completely devoid of oxygen. However, oxygen will enter the alimentary tract during ingestion of feed and liquids, and with the saliva. In addition, the gut wall is well supplied with blood vessels, and a passive diffusion of oxygen into the gut from the bloodstream may occur (Czerkawski, 1969). Although the rapid utilization of oxygen by the microbial population may limit oxygen availability in gut contents, the tract receives a continuous supply of oxygen from various sources and, in consequence, the ecosystem cannot be described accurately as being completely devoid of oxygen.

Limited data are now available to substantiate the description of the gut as a low-oxygen, rather than an oxygen-free, environment. Oxygen was first detected in rumen headspace gases over 30 years ago (McArthur and Miltimore, 1961). A subsequent study by Czerkawski and Clapperton (1968) reported ruminal headspace oxygen levels of up to 6.5%. Direct *in situ* quantitative measurements of dissolved oxygen concentrations in ruminal contents with an oxygen electrode (Scott *et al.*, 1983) and by membrane-inlet quadrupole mass spectrometry (Hillman *et al.*, 1985a) confirmed the presence of oxygen at concentrations of up to 3.2 μmole/liter. Recent studies of oxygen levels along the monogastric intestinal tract indicated that the dissolved concentrations were higher than those reported in the rumen (Hillman *et al.*, 1993). Very high concentrations of oxygen were observed along the length of the porcine alimentary tract, and in some regions of the upper digestive tract values approaching air saturation were observed. In anesthetized unweaned piglets, oxygen concentrations of 108 and 188 μmole/liter were measured polarographically in the stomach and jejunum, respectively; the concentration declined to 85 μmole/liter at the midpoint of the ascending colon.

Microorganisms in intestinal environments have thus adapted to grow on substrates available in plant material at low oxygen tensions over a narrow pH and temperature range. Although it seems likely that these microbes evolved to exploit the opportunities afforded within the intestinal ecosystems, their presence and activities have important consequences for the nutritional well-being of the host. Although a bacterial fermentation occurs at most sites along the intestinal tract of almost all herbivores the occurrence of protists is more limited and is discussed in the following sections.

Urogenital Tract Ecosystems

Several studies have measured conditions in the human vagina. Wagner and Levin (1978) used an oxygen electrode to measure pO_2 at the vaginal surface before, during, and after sexual stimulation. Changes observed were closely correlated with changes in blood flow. The mean basal level of pO_2 in seven healthy subjects was 9.3 mm Hg peaking to 39.4 mm Hg at orgasm. At the same time an increase in pH and in Na^+ and Cl^- concentrations also occurs. More recent investigators have reported lower O_2 levels, with little or no difference between healthy women and those infected with *Trichomonas vaginalis*, although the median pH drops on infection from 6.0 to 4.5 (Rashad *et al.*, 1992). Evidently the vagina should not be regarded as an anaerobic environment.

2. Protists Resident in the Intestinal Tract

2.1. Protozoa in the Intestinal Ecosystem

The role of protozoa in the alimentary tract is generally difficult to assess because hardly any have been grown axenically and studied in detail; the harmful flagellates *Giardia lamblia* and *G. muris* are exceptional in this respect. The rumen ciliates are the only other group that have been subjected to a thorough study (Williams and Coleman, 1991). It is known, however, that wood-eating termites starve when their gut protozoa are removed and under certain dietary conditions ruminants benefit from the activities of the ruminal ciliates. Nevertheless, most of the information available is still restricted to morphological descriptions of protozoa in various host species, and such data have been obtained by the characterization of preserved specimens.

Intestinal protozoa taxonomically occur within 2 phyla, viz. the Sarcomastigophora and the Ciliophora; 6 subphyla are represented (Nakamura, 1990). The organisms from the subphylum Opalinata are symbionts of the large intestine of frogs and toads, although a few have been described from other amphibia, reptiles, and fish. Their role in the digestive activities is unknown. In the subphylum Sarcodina only a few genera are intestinal symbionts. *Entamoeba, Endolimax,* and *Iodamoeba* inhabit the gut of man, while *Endamoeba* spp. occur in association with insects. Six orders of flagellated protozoa from the class Zoomastigophora (subphylum Mastigophora) occur within the intestinal tract of invertebrates and vertebrates. Nakamura (1990) noted that as many as 434 species of flagellates had been reported in the intestines of lower termites and wood-eating roaches. The protozoans of the wood roach are from 3 genera of mastigotes and 9 genera of hypermastigotes; no trichomonads have been reported. The variety of flagellates occurring in termites is also large and includes 4 genera of polymastigotes, 22 genera of hypermastigotes, and 20 genera of trichomonads (Kudo, 1966; Yamin, 1979).

Ciliate protozoa from eight subclasses in three taxonomically separate subphyla inhabit regions of the invertebrate and vertebrate intestinal tract (Nakamura, 1990). The associations are summarized in Table I. Sea urchins and other echinoids harbor at least 56 species of ciliates (Levine, 1972) but their role in the digestion of ingested algal polysaccharides has yet to be evaluated. The occurrence of ciliates in the alimentary tract of herbivorous mammals was comprehensively reviewed by Dehority (1986).

Information on hindgut ciliates is, apart from the horse and elephant, fairly limited. In many hosts (e.g., beaver, human, monkey, pica, pig, porcupine, rabbit, vole) the hindgut fermentation is considered to be completely bacterial (McBee, 1977). However, a wide range of hosts do harbor a hindgut ciliate population (Table II) and new host species continue to be recorded, e.g., bushpig

Table I. Host Specificity and Location of Intestinal Tract Protozoa[a]

Protozoan family	Host family	
	Foregut	Hindgut
Balantidiiae		Amphibia, Reptilia, Caviidae, Muridae, Primates, Suidae, Tayassuidae
Blepharocorythidae	Hippopotamidae, Bovidae, Tragulidae, Antilocapridae	Muridae, Elephantidae, Equidae, Hydrochoeridae
Buetschliidae	Hippopotamidae, Camelidae, Bovidae, Cervidae	Lagomorpha, Sciuridae, Caviidae, Muridae, Equidae, Tapiridae
Cyathodiniidae		Caviidae
Cycloposthiidae	Hippopotamidae, Bovidae	Hydrochoeridae, Elephantidae, Rhinocerotidae, Tapiridae, Equidae
Ditoxidae		Equidae
Isotrichidae	Cervidae, Bovidae, Tragulidae, Giraffidae, Camelidae	Muridae, Primates
Ophryoscolecidae	Camelidae, Tragulidae, Cervidae, Bovidae, Giraffidae, Antilocapridae	Caviidae, Hydrochoeridae, Elephantidae
Paraisotrichidae	Hippopotamidae	Caviidae, Hydrochoeridae, Elephantidae, Equidae
Plagiopylidae	Hippopotamidae	Echinoidea
Polydiniellidae		Elephantidae
Protocaviellidae		Caviidae, Hydrochoeridae
Protohallidae		Hydrochoeridae
Pycnotrichidae		Hydrochoeridae, Ctenodactylidae, Hyracoidae, Primates, Bovidae
Rhinozetidae		Rhinocerotidae
Spirodiniidae		Equidae, Elephantidae
Telamodiniidae		Suidae
Troglodytellidae		Primates (Pongidae)

[a]Data from Dehority (1986), Bonhomme-Florentin (1990a), and Nakamura (1990).

and subterranean naked mole rat (Buffenstein and Yahav, 1991; Van Hoven and Gilchrist, 1991). Dehority (1986) concluded that 60–70 species of protozoa had been identified in the hindgut of the horse, compared with approximately 21 in the elephant, 18 in the capybara, 14 in the zebra, 6–7 in the guinea pig and rhinoceros, and 1–3 in the warthog, tapir, gorilla, and chimpanzee. More recent studies have recorded the occurrence of other genera and extended the species range of the rhinoceros (Van Hoven *et al.*, 1987, 1988) and lowland gorilla (Imai *et al.*, 1991).

Although an extensive microbial fermentation occurs in the foregut of sev-

Table II. Occurrence and Location of Protists in the Intestinal Tracts of Some Vertebrate Hosts[a]

Host	Foregut	Hindgut
Bush pig, capybara, chimpanzee, gorilla, guinea pig, hare, lemming, old world rabbit, pony, tapir, vole, warthog, wood mouse		P[b]
African elephant, Asian elephant, ass, horse, black rhinoceros, Indian rhinoceros, mara, common zebra		P,F
Ruminants (e.g., deer, giraffe, antelope, cattle, sheep, camel, alpaca, guanaco), hippopotamus, macropod marsupials, quokka	P	
Bactrian camel*, bongo*, cattle, gaur*, goat, eastern gray kangaroo, impala, kudu*, llama*, musk-ox, oryx*, red deer, redneck and swamp wallaby, reindeer, roan antelope*, swamp buffalo, vicuna, eastern wallaroo, water buffalo	P,F	
Sheep, cattle	P,F	F

[a]References: Collet et al. (1983), Dehority (1986, 1987), Grenet et al. (1989), Ho et al. (1990b), Imai et al. (1991), Lowe et al. (1987a), Milne et al. (1989), Orpin and Joblin (1988), Van Hoven et al. (1987, 1988), Williams and Coleman (1991).
[b]P, protozoa; F, fungi.
*Fungi present in fecal samples, so intestinal origin uncertain.

eral mammalian hosts, it would appear that these activities in colobid monkeys (Primates), sloths (Edentata), and certain types of whale are bacterial (Bauchop, 1977; Dehority, 1986). Hosts with a symbiotic foregut protozoal population are included in Table II. Since their discovery 150 years ago, over 300 species (30 genera) of rumen ciliates have been described (Williams and Coleman, 1991). The majority of these are members of the Ophryoscolecidae and are restricted to ruminants and camelids. The ruminal ciliate population is normally within the range 10^4–10^6/ml rumen contents; representatives from the Buetschliidae and Blepharocorythidae occur infrequently and the Isotrichidae present normally comprise no more than 5% of the population. The protozoal numbers in the foregut of the hippopotamus and macropod marsupials are similar to those occurring in the rumen (i.e., 10^5–10^6/ml). However, the species present appear to be host-specific (Thurston and Grain, 1971; Thurston and Noirot-Timothee, 1973; Bauchop, 1977; Dehority, 1986). In general, ciliates from the family Ophryoscolecidae occur only in foregut fermenters although other entodiniomorphid families occur in the hindgut. Protozoa are usually not detected in the hindgut of foregut fermenters.

The host specificity and restricted occurrence of protozoa in intestinal ecosystems contrasts with the more widespread occurrence of the principal bacterial inhabitants in gut ecosystems. The specificity of the protozoan–host interaction may reflect divergent evolutionary development of the protozoal ancestors or responses to the subtle differences in environmental conditions in the foregut and hindgut. Although the cause is unknown, it is apparent that transfaunation does not take place between hindgut and foregut fermenters, and likewise transfer does not occur between hosts in either category. Consequently, protozoal families are often host-specific, but when a family does occur in more than one host, then individual genera or species will exhibit host-specificity. Exceptions in hindgut fermenters noted by Dehority (1986) are the occurrence of eight species in the elephant of which five have been detected in the horse, two in the rhinoceros, and one in the tapir. There are also infrequent reports of ciliates occurring in the rumen and foregut or hindgut of other hosts. *Parentodinium africanum* (Cycloposthiidae) occurs both in the stomach of the hippopotamus and in the rumen of Brazilian cattle while both *Charonina equi* (Blepharocorythidae) and *Blepharoconus krugerensis* (Buetschliidae), which have been observed infrequently in the rumen, are known to occur in the large intestine of the horse and elephant, respectively (Williams and Coleman, 1991). There is also a report of the establishment of six species of ruminal ophryoscolecid ciliates in the intestinal tract of a zoo specimen of capybara (Dehority, 1987) and ciliates resembling ruminal isotrichids were present in fixed samples of stomach contents obtained from the neotropical leaf-eating bird, the hoatzin, which has an active foregut fermentation (M. G. Dominguez and C. J. Newbold, personal communication).

2.2. Fungi in the Intestinal Ecosystem

Some yeasts and aerobic fungi are able to grow under anaerobic conditions and have the potential to survive in the alimentary tract (Sivers, 1962; Lund, 1974). Some (e.g., *Sphaerita* and *Sagittospora* spp.) parasitize rumen ciliates and others may cause digestive disorders but the majority are regarded as being transient (Orpin and Joblin, 1988). However, the presence of a saprophytic anaerobic fungal population was discovered in the rumen ecosystem (Orpin, 1975, 1976, 1977), and it has subsequently been confirmed that populations of anaerobic fungi occur in the intestinal tracts of a variety of herbivorous mammals. Several genera have been isolated from the rumen and prepeptic regions of the gut of foregut fermenters and from the large intestine and feces of hindgut fermenting herbivores. All have been classified in the class Chytridiomycetes, but a new family Neocallimasticaceae was invoked (Heath *et al.*, 1983). Recent molecular data indicate that the anaerobic gut fungi belong to the Chytridiomycota which are true fungi (Li and Heath, 1992). Although the gut fungi produce zoospores during their life cycle and had, therefore, been assigned to the kingodm Protoctista or Protista, Li and Heath (1992) concluded that the anaerobic gut fungi were true fungi, not protists. The life cycle of all species that have been examined alternates between a motile flagellated zoospore stage, and a nonmotile plant material-associated vegetative reproductive stage. There is evidence for occurrence of a resistant stage within the life cycle, but the structure has not been identified conclusively (Milne *et al.*, 1989; Wubah *et al.*, 1991). The flagellated zoospores were originally thought to be flagellated protozoa. All the fungi are able to degrade plant cell structural polysaccharides and thus contribute in intestinal fibrolysis and the generation of metabolizable nutrients for the host.

Anaerobic fungi are believed to occur in the rumen of all domesticated ruminants receiving a high-fiber ration. Numbers decline and fungi may be absent from animals fed a high-concentrate (starch) ration, lush young pasture, or seaweed (Orpin, 1989; Orpin and Ho, 1991). Chytridiomycete fungi have also been isolated from ruminal contents and fecal samples of wild and zoo specimens of nondomesticated ruminants (Orpin and Joblin, 1988; Milne *et al.*, 1989; Ho *et al.*, 1990a; Teunissen *et al.*, 1991a) and other nonruminant prepeptic fermenters (Table II). Fungi similar to those present in the rumen have been observed in forestomach contents of various macropodid marsupials (Dellow *et al.*, 1988; Bauchop, 1989), and in fecal samples from small and large hindgut fermenting herbivores (e.g., mara, horse, zebra, rhinoceros, elephant; Orpin, 1981; Gold *et al.*, 1988; Milne *et al.*, 1989; Teunissen *et al.*, 1991a). The host range is summarized in Table II, but it is apparent that the diversity of hosts that harbor an intestinal chytridiomycete population will increase as gut samples from other herbivores are examined.

Anaerobic fungi have been recovered not only from ruminant fecal samples but also from postpeptic regions in the bovine small intestine (duodenum) and large intestine (cecum). However, despite this observation of fungi postruminally in the ruminant intestine, it has not been established whether active growth occurs at these sites (Grenet *et al.*, 1989; Milne *et al.*, 1989). It does seem, however, that anaerobic fungi are restricted to the intestinal tracts of warm-blooded herbivorous vertebrates. Fungi have not been isolated from smaller herbivores like the rabbit and possum or the giant panda which is not a true herbivore although it does consume large amounts of plant material (Orpin and Joblin, 1988; Bauchop, 1989). Attempts to isolate anaerobic chytrids from termites (three species), wood-eating roaches (two species), marine iguana, cane toad, green tree frog, and Australian goanna were unsuccessful (C. G. Orpin, personal communication) and it is possible that these particular fungi are unable to establish in the intestinal tract of small amphibians, reptiles, and insects. The fungi, unlike the protozoa, do not appear to be host-specific and the same species have been isolated from ruminant and nonruminant herbivores. In addition, isolates have been established in alternative host species, and interhost transfer may occur by direct contact, aerosol transmission or ingestion of feed contaminated with saliva or feces which contain viable fungi (Lowe *et al.*, 1987a; Milne *et al.*, 1989; Orpin and Ho, 1991).

Two morphological types of anaerobic chytrid fungi have been described. In the three genera of monocentric fungi, *Neocallimastix*, *Piromyces* (syn. *Piromanas*), and *Caecomyces* (syn. *Sphaeromonas*), each vegetative stage bears a single sporangium on a simple or branched rhizoidal system (Orpin and Joblin, 1988). The three genera are distinguished by ultrastructural and morphological differences. They exhibit similar biochemical characteristics and possess very high (97–99%) 18 S-like rRNA sequence homology (Dore and Stahl, 1991). Ten species have been proposed (Orpin and Joblin, 1988; Gold *et al.*, 1988; Breton *et al.*, 1989, 1991; Orpin and Ho, 1991), although *N. joyonii* was subsequently transferred to the genus *Orpinomyces* (Li *et al.*, 1991). The second morphological grouping contains the polycentric genera *Anaeromyces* (Breton *et al.*, 1990), *Orpinomyces* (Li *et al.*, 1991), and *Ruminomyces* (Ho *et al.*, 1990b). They, like the monocentric genera, produce either uni- or polyflagellated zoospores but differ as numerous sporangia are borne on an extensive highly branched rhizoidal system.

The biomass of chytrid fungi in the intestinal ecosystem cannot be determined accurately. The measurement of unique cellular components such as chitin, tetrahymenol, and C_{24} fatty acids (Kemp *et al.*, 1984) in ingesta or the development of hybridization probes may be of value in quantification, but at present population size is determined by cultivation of zoospores or by enumeration of thallus-forming units (Joblin, 1981; Theodorou *et al.*, 1990). The current assessment, based on the chitin content of the digesta, is that the fungal biomass is less than 10% of the microbial biomass in the rumen.

3. Biochemical Activities and Role of Intestinal Eukaryotes

3.1. Ciliate Protozoa

An understanding of the importance of ciliate protozoa in the intestinal fermentation is dependent on a knowledge of the population size, the biochemical capabilities of the ciliates present, and the consequences of their interactions with other microbial groups present. The characteristics of the ruminal environment, the microbial population present, and the products and extent of the fermentation, for example, differ in faunated and ciliate-free animals (Williams and Coleman, 1991). However, with the exception of a small number of ruminal ciliates, little information is available on the metabolic capabilities of gut ciliates, and this situation is unlikely to change dramatically until methodologies are developed for axenic *in vitro* cultivation. Some ciliates have been grown successfully in the laboratory in cultures with viable bacteria (Bonhomme-Florentin, 1974; Coleman, 1987), but biochemical studies are further complicated by the presence of ingested bacteria, adherent ectobionts, and intracellular endobionts.

Many of the differences between the ruminal fermentation in faunated and ciliate-free ruminants can be attributed to the metabolic activities of the protozoa. The object of the following sections is, therefore, to consider some aspects of protozoal metabolism that are of importance in the overall nutrition of the host.

In domesticated ruminants these effects may have important consequences for animal productivity, and improvements may be gained by the elimination or appropriate manipulation of the size or generic composition of the protozoal population. Examples of the effects of ciliate protozoa on ruminal characteristics and ruminant performance are included in Table III. These effects of the protozoal population were assessed from the comparison of faunated and defaunated animals, and represent the findings most frequently reported. The effects of defaunation on ruminant performance have been studied in detail during the last two decades and have confirmed not only that the protozoa are involved in the digestive processes within the rumen but also that the protozoal activities affect the physical, chemical, and microbiological characteristics of the rumen ecosystem. The protozoa are intimately involved in ruminal function and thereby directly, or indirectly, influence the nutritional status, productivity, and health of the host animal (Veira, 1986; Coleman, 1988; Jouany et al., 1988, Williams and Coleman, 1988, 1991; Bird, 1989, 1991). Although there is no direct evidence, by analogy protozoa in other intestinal ecosystems will have a role in the digestive processes.

The biochemistry of the ruminal ciliates has been the subject of several recent reviews (Coleman, 1980, 1986a; Williams, 1986, 1989a, 1991; Williams and Coleman, 1988, 1991; Bonhomme-Florentin, 1990a,b) and since this group has attracted most attention more emphasis will be given to the metabolic activ-

Table III. Effects of Ruminal Ciliate Protozoa on the Rumen Ecosystem and Fermentation That Influence Animal Productivity

Effects of protozoa on animal performance	
Beneficial	Adverse
Stabilization of ruminal fermentation and pH	Increased:
Physical appearance of host improved	Ammonia concentration
Increased:	Proteolysis
VFA formation	Methanogenesis
Starch digestion	Plasma saturated fatty acid levels
Fiber breakdown	Susceptibility to bloat
Organic matter digestion	Decreased:
Decreased:	Bacterial population
Lactic acid concentration	Nitrogen flow to lower gut
Plasma and hepatic copper levels	Microbial protein synthesis
Susceptibility to lactic acidosis	Plasma polyunsaturated fatty acid levels
Susceptibility to copper toxicity	Live-weight gain
	Wool growth
	Food conversion efficiency

ities of the ruminal ciliates. Although information is limited on other intestinal ciliates, where reliable data exist the biochemical attributes of other groups will be included in the discussion.

3.1.1. Catabolic Activities

The concentrations of soluble fermentable substrates in the intestinal environment are low and increase transiently in the foregut in the immediate postfeed period. The principal substrates available are thus polymeric and include dietary and host-derived proteins and the complex plant structural polysaccharides that the host is unable to utilize directly. The nutritional consequences for the host of the protozoal degradation of proteins and complex polysaccharides are substantially different.

3.1.1a. Polysaccharide Breakdown. The breakdown of cellulose and hemicellulose is higher when protozoa are present in the rumen microbial population (Williams and Coleman, 1991), both as a consequence of the protozoal activities and indirectly through their effects on the activity of the bacterial population, particle retention, and environmental conditions. Fibrolytic enzyme activities are higher in the ruminal contents of faunated animals (Williams and Withers, 1991) and Coleman (1986b) estimated that approximately 60% of the ruminal cellulase activity was associated with the protozoa. Studies *in vitro* indicate that approximately a quarter to a third of fiber breakdown in the rumen is mediated by the protozoa.

The ruminal entodiniomorphid and isotrichid (holotrich) ciliates are attracted by chemotaxis to plant material ingested into the rumen and specific regions of large plant fragments are colonized rapidly (Orpin, 1985; Bauchop, 1989). The retention of the ciliates in the rumen is aided by their sequestration in the plant material. Different attachment mechanisms have been described, but attachment is not a prerequisite for ingestion and intracellular digestion of plant tissue to occur. *Epidinium ecaudatum* secretes extracellular fibrolytic enzymes and the partially digested fragments are subsequently ingested (Akin and Amos, 1979). The cecal ciliates *Didesmis* and *Cycloposthium* spp. also colonize damaged areas on the plant fragments and locate primarily on the epidermis and mesophyll tissues (Bonhomme-Florentin, 1985). Attachment precedes ingestion and intracellular digestion.

Cellulolytic (Bonhomme-Florentin, 1975; Coleman, 1985), hemicellulolytic (Williams and Coleman, 1985), pectolytic (Coleman *et al.,* 1980), and glycoside hydrolase enzymes (Williams *et al.,* 1984) are produced by ruminal ciliates. However, despite the potential importance of these enzymes in ruminal fibrolysis, relatively little is known about their characteristics and modes of action (Williams, 1989a,b) and doubts are still expressed as to the origin of these enzymes because the protozoa used were not obtained from axenic culture. A bacterial origin for the activities has been proposed (Thines-Sempoux *et al.*, 1980). However, evidence from a variety of experimental approaches justifies the assertion that the enzymes are protozoal and not bacterial in origin (Williams, 1989a). It has now been confirmed that both *Polyplastron multivesiculatum* and *Epi. ecaudatum* retain enzymatic activities when grown *in vitro* in the absence of fibrolytic bacteria (Bonhomme-Florentin, 1988a; Bonhomme-Florentin *et al.*, 1986) and the enzymes are located in membrane-bounded subcellular vesicles (Williams and Ellis, 1985; Williams *et al.*, 1986).

Apart from the studies of Bonhomme-Florentin (1990a) on equine hindgut ciliates, there is little known about the occurrence of polysaccharolytic enzymes in other intestinal tract protozoa. *Cycloposthium* spp. were the only ciliates in equine hindgut digesta that were able to survive for 7 days *in vitro* in a medium containing a cellulose energy source. Cell-free extracts exhibited cellulolytic activity against native cellulose and soluble cellulosic derivatives (Bonhomme-Florentin, 1969, 1971, 1974). Hemicellulose and pectin were also degraded by mixed preparations of horse cecal *Cycloposthium* sp. and *Blepharocorys* sp. (Bonhomme-Florentin, 1988b). Significant activities of endoxylanase, three pectolytic enzymes, and the hemicellulolytic glycosidases α-L-arabinofuranosidase and β-D-xylosidase were detected in the protozoan-enriched fraction. The cecal ciliates also contain α- and β-galactosidase and these activities are involved in the hydrolysis of ingested chloroplast mono- and digalactosyldiglycerides (Bonhomme-Florentin, 1986).

Starch is a major reserved carbohydrate of plants. The majority of the rumen ciliates ingest starch but the rates of uptake and digestion are species-dependent (Coleman, 1986a). All ciliates examined contain amylase and α-glucosidase (Williams, 1989a) and Coleman (1986c) estimated that almost 60% of the total ruminal amylase activity could be located in the protozoal population. There have been relatively few studies on the effects of faunation on ruminal amylolysis, but Veira *et al.* (1983) demonstrated that starch was digested effectively in the absence of protozoa, and refaunation only increased the extent of digestion from 84% to 89%. However, the rapid ingestion and controlled metabolism of starch to volatile fatty acids (VFA) by the protozoa suppresses the potentially harmful bacterial lactic fermentation and is important in stabilizing the ruminal fermentation.

Under normal dietary conditions, approximately 10% of the ingested starch reaches the small intestine. The amount of starch reaching the large intestine of hindgut fermenters may likewise be relatively low as dietary starch is subjected to hydrolysis by pancreatic amylase and the degradation products are absorbed from the small intestine. However, some starch may escape digestion in the small intestine and reach the hindgut because it is physically inaccessible in grains or its digestion properties have been altered by processing (Englyst and Macfarlane, 1986). In this respect, Bonhomme-Florentin (1971, 1974) reported that *Cyclo-*

posthium spp. from the horse cecum were amylolytic and able to hydrolyze maltose. Fructosans are also produced as reserve carbohydrates in certain plants. Fructose-containing saccharides, including the polymer inulin, are rapidly metabolized by the ruminal isotrichids (Williams, 1986). It was originally thought that invertase was responsible for the hydrolysis of all fructose-containing carbohydrates. However, the purified enzyme is ineffective against inulin (Dauvrin and Thines-Sempoux, 1989). Nevertheless, the enzyme is one of the few well-characterized ciliate enzymes, and is the most active of the extracellular carbohydrases formed by the ruminal holotrichs (Williams, 1979) which appear to be responsible for much of the free invertase activity in ruminal contents.

    3.1.1b. Protein Breakdown. Protozoal digestion of dietary and microbial proteins influences the nitrogen economy of the host and their involvement, unlike protozoal fibrolysis, is not advantageous for the host. Protozoa as part of the rumen microbial population degrade and assimilate dietary proteins; the microbial proteins are subsequently utilized by the host when the cells are digested in the lower tract. However, because of sequestration the outflow rate of protozoa is only 20–40% of the liquid and bacterial outflow rates and the proportion of protozoa in the biomass is less than in the rumen digesta. The bacterial population is also reduced by the predatory actions of the protozoa. Thus, when protozoa are present in the rumen the efficiency of protein utilization by the host is reduced and ruminal proteolysis is higher; consequently, net microbial synthesis and protein flow to the lower tract are reduced. Biological processes of the host that have a high protein demand are adversely affected in faunated animals particularly when the ration contains inadequate levels of protein (Bird, 1989, 1991).

    Although bacteria are the most important source of nitrogenous nutrients for ruminal ciliates, plant proteins and free amino acids are also utilized. With the exception of bacterial uptake, there is only limited information available on protein uptake (Onodera, 1990; Williams and Coleman, 1991), but studies with mixed preparations and single species have provided information on the proteolytic enzymes present (Williams, 1989a). The entodiniomorphid (Coleman, 1983) and holotrich proteinases (Lockwood *et al.,* 1988a) are active over a wide pH range but the optimum pH in most species is pH 3–4. The enzymes are predominantly aspartic and cysteine proteinases with M_r values ranging from 25 to 200 × 10^3. Marked interspecies variations in the proteinase profiles occur. Equine *Cycloposthium* spp. are actively proteolytic and degrade similar proteins to ruminal *Entodinium* spp. (Bonhomme-Florentin, 1971, 1973, 1974). The proteolytic enzymes have not been characterized.

    3.1.1c. Lipid Metabolism. The role of the ciliate protozoa in rumen lipid metabolism is unclear from the limited number of studies that have been undertaken (Coleman, 1986a). It has been estimated that 30% of the lipolytic activity in the rumen is associated with the protozoal fraction but the evidence for protozoal lipase activity is inconclusive. Mixed entodiniomorphid protozoa do, however, hydrogenate linoleic acid and free unsaturated long-chain fatty acids. Triglycerides and chloroplast galactolipids are degraded, and linolenic acid is biohydrogenated by ciliate preparations from the cecum of the horse (Bonhomme-Florentin, 1976, 1983, 1986).

3.1.1d. Metabolite Formation. The rumen ciliates may account for half of the biomass in the ecosystem and their metabolites are of importance to the host as ruminants derive approximately two-thirds of their dietary energy from microbial short-chain VFA. The concentrations and proportions of ruminal VFA differ in faunated and defaunated animals receiving the same ration (Williams and Coleman, 1991). Although VFA concentrations were lower in pony cecal contents than in bovine rumen fluid, the principal short-chain acids formed were the same (Kern *et al.,* 1973). However, despite the importance of these metabolites to the host, the identity of the products formed, the pathways leading to product formation, and the factors influencing formation are all ill-defined.

3.1.1e. Fermentation Products. The two types of ruminal ciliates occupy different metabolic niches in the rumen. The isotrichid holotrichs utilize soluble carbohydrates whereas the entodiniomorphid ciliates are principally particle feeders; both groups ingest and digest bacteria. The actual range of soluble carbohydrates metabolized, however, is limited. The isotrichids *Isotricha* spp. and *Dasytricha ruminantium* only utilize glucose, fructose, galactose, and more complex carbohydrates containing one or more of these monosaccharides. The range and rate of carbohydrate utilization are genus-dependent, and the ciliates do not appear to control sugar entry into the cell (Williams, 1986). There is little information available on the range of sugars metabolized by the entodiniomorphid ciliates. All but the very smallest *Entodinium* spp. ingest starch grains and all of the species examined will also take up glucose and maltose (Coleman, 1986a). *Entodinium caudatum* can also metabolize ribose, galactose, and sucrose. The rate of glucose uptake by *D. ruminantium* (150 pmole/cell per hr) is well above that of the larger entodiniomorphid genera (15–40 pmole/hr) and *Entodinium* spp. (0.05–2.4 pmole/hr) confirming that the holotrichs are well adapted for a role in the ruminal metabolism of soluble plant carbohydrates.

The principal products of the fermentative metabolism of the ruminal ciliates are short-chain VFA, lactic acid, carbon dioxide, and hydrogen (Table IV). Although the range of metabolites formed by the holotrichs is independent of the substrate supplied, the proportions of the products formed are substrate-dependent and are also affected by substrate concentration, environmental conditions and by metabolic interactions with methanogenic bacteria (Williams and Coleman, 1991; Ellis *et al.,* 1991a). As with the holotrichs, the physiological gas levels affect metabolite formation by the entodiniomorphs (Ellis *et al.,* 1991b,c). An important feature of protozoal metabolism is the assimilation of soluble sugars into a storage carbohydrate; 75–80% of the glucose taken up by *D.*

Table IV. Metabolites Formed by Ruminal Ciliate Protozoa

Ciliate	Metabolites[a]							
Dasytricha ruminantium	A	B	p		L	ala	C	H
Isotricha prostoma	A	B	p		L		C	H
Epidinium ecaudatum	A	B	p	f	L		C	H
Metadinium medium	A	B	p	f	l			
Ophryoscolex caudatus	A	B			L		C	H
Ophryoscolex purkynjei	A	B	P	f	l		C	H
Entodinium caudatum	A	B	p	f			C	H
Eudiplodinium maggii	A	B	P		L	gly	C	H
Polyplastron multivesiculatum	A	B			L	gly	C	H

[a]A, acetate; B, butyrate; P, propionate; F, formate; L, lactate; ala, alanine; gly, glycerol; C, carbon dioxide; H, hydrogen. Lowercase = minor product.

ruminatium is converted into amylopectin, and on some rations, approximately 30% of dietary sugars can be converted into amylopectin by the protozoal population (Coleman, 1979). Protozoal amylopectin synthesis reduces potentially deleterious saccharolytic bacterial activity, and the subsequent utilization of the reserve material both stabilizes and extends the postfeed period in which microbial VFA formation can occur.

Recently identified minor products include glycerol and alanine (Ellis *et al.*, 1991a–c) and although formate has also been identified as a minor metabolite of some ciliates, it was found to be a product of the bacteria associated with *D. ruminantium* rather than the ciliate. The principal acidic metabolite of the isotrichid holotichs is lactic acid, although under certain conditions the acid is consumed (Ellis *et al.*, 1991a); the entodiniomorphid ciliates also consume lactic acid. The ruminal ciliates have an important role in the turnover of ruminal lactate (Nagaraja and Towne, 1990) and in preventing the onset of the ruminant nutritional disorder lactic acid acidosis (Newbold *et al.*, 1986, 1987).

Ruminal ciliates obtain amino acids by *de novo* synthesis, by the breakdown of ingested bacterial and dietary proteins and by uptake from the ecosystem. Although the amino acids are primarily used for protein synthesis, a limited fermentation does take place. A variety of amino acid interconversion and degradation products have been identified (Onodera, 1990). Biochemical mechanisms involve deamination, transamination, decarboxylation, and dethioalkylation (Williams, 1989a); the presence of the ciliates in the rumen is associated with increased ruminal ammonia levels and elevated deaminase activities in the microbial population. The energetic significance of amino acid catabolism to the rumen ciliates is not known.

3.1.1f. Pathways of Product Formation. The intermediary metabolic pathways of carbohydrates in the ruminal isotrichid ciliates (Yarlett *et al.*, 1981, 1982, 1985) are summarized in Fig. 1. Sugars are converted to pyruvate via glycolysis, and hydrogen is formed in a series of hydrogenosomal reactions in which hydrogenase and pyruvate:ferredoxin oxidoreductase participate; the identity of the carriers involved have not been established. Substrate-level phosphorylation results in ATP production during the conversion of acetyl coenzyme A into acetate and butyrate (Williams, 1986; Williams and Coleman, 1991). The metabolic pathways in the entodiniomorphid ciliates have not been identified, although tracer experiments, inhibitor studies, and enzyme assays indicate that in *Ent. caudatum* glucose is also metabolized via glycolysis.

3.1.2. Oxygen and the Rumen Ciliates

The ruminal ciliates are historically described as being obligate anaerobes. However, the rumen ecosystem is not oxygen-free (Scott *et al.*, 1983; Hillman *et al.*, 1985a) and ruminal ciliates that possess hydrogenosomes exhibit some characteristics of aerotolerance (Lloyd *et al.*, 1989a). The hydrogenosome, a microbodylike subcellular organelle, has been detected in isotrichid (Yarlett *et al.*, 1981, 1983a; Paul *et al.*, 1989) and entodiniomorphid ruminal ciliates (Yarlett *et al.*, 1984; Paul *et al.*, 1990). The oxygen-sensitive hydrogen-generating enzymes hydrogenase and pyruvate:ferredoxin oxidoreductase are located within the organelle which functions in the decarboxylation of pyruvate to acetyl coenzyme A; hydrogen is formed by the hydrogenase-mediated reoxidation of reduced electron carriers. The range of enzymes associated with the hydrogenosomes of ruminal ciliates and aerotolerant flagellates differ. The organelle also has the ability to consume oxygen which acts as a terminal electron acceptor during the oxidation of pyruvate to acetate and carbon dioxide (Yarlett *et al.*, 1982). The organelle thus confers some protection for the ciliate against the toxic effects of oxygen. Other protective enzymes detected include NADH oxidase, NADH peroxidase, and catalase (Prins and Prast, 1973; Yarlett *et al.*, 1981, 1983a).

The effects of oxygen on the ruminal ciliates are clearly concentration-dependent. Atmospheric oxygen concentrations are toxic, whereas physiological levels have pronounced, and potentially energetically beneficial, effects. The ciliates are able to survive prolonged periods at low oxygen tensions having K_m values for oxygen in the range 0.3–5.2 μM (Lloyd *et al.*, 1982; Hillman *et al.*, 1985b; Ellis *et al.*, 1989). The presence of physiological levels of oxygen reversibly inhibits hydrogen production by *D. ruminantium* and increases glucose uptake and acetate formation (Yarlett *et al.*, 1983b; Hillman *et al.*, 1985b; Ellis *et al.*, 1991a). Glucose uptake and the proportions of metabolites formed by *Polyplastron multivesiculatum* and *Eudiplodinium maggii* are also influenced by

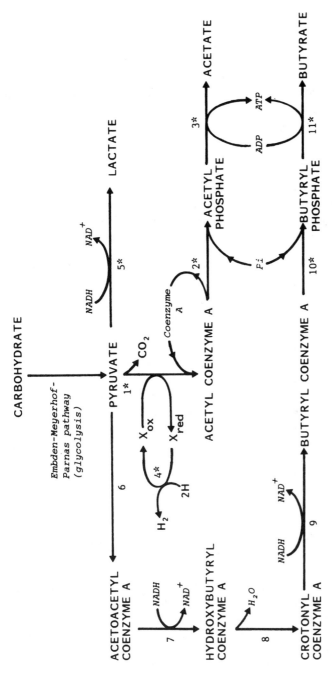

Figure 1. Proposed pathways of intermediary metabolism in *Dasytricha ruminantium* and *Isotricha* spp. The enzymes indicated are: 1, pyruvate synthase (pyruvate:ferredoxin oxidoreductase); 2, phosphoacetyltransferase; 3, acetate kinase; 4, hydrogenase; 5, lactate dehydrogenase; 6, acetyl-CoA:acetyl-CoA acetyltransferase; 7, 3-hydroxybutyryl-CoA dehydrogenase; 8, 3-hydroxyacyl-CoA hydrolase; 9, 3-hydroxyacyl-CoA reductase; 10, phosphobutyryl transferase; 11, butyrate kinase. Some or all of the activity of enzymes marked with an asterisk is present in the hydrogenosomal fraction; the other enzymes are located in the cell cytosol. (Reproduced with permission from Williams and Coleman, 1991.)

ambient oxygen concentrations (Ellis *et al.*, 1991b,c). This ability of the protozoa to consume oxygen is of potential importance in the ruminal ecosystem. The contributions of the protozoal and bacterial populations to ruminal oxygen consumption are approximately the same (Ellis *et al.*, 1989) and their presence can have a protective function for more sensitive organisms (e.g., methanogens, Hillman *et al.*, 1988). The ambient oxygen concentration, which is in part determined by protozoal activity, is an important determinant of the metabolic activities of the ciliate population.

3.1.3. Interactions with Other Microbial Groups

Interactions between the bacterial, fungal, and protozoal populations in the rumen are important in maintaining the stability of the microbial community and determine the final end products of the microbial fermentation (Williams *et al.*, 1993a). Interactions involving ciliate protozoa are discussed in the following sections.

3.1.3a. Protozoa–Bacteria Interactions. The most obvious interaction between the ruminal ciliate protozoa and bacteria is a predator–prey relationship. Bacteria are the most important source of nitrogenous compounds for protozoal growth and are ingested, sometimes selectively, at rates up to 10^5 bacteria/protozoan per hr (Coleman, 1986a, 1989). The rate of bacterial uptake is species-dependent and is affected by the number and physical form of the bacteria, the nutritional status of the protozoa, and environmental conditions. The bacteria are engulfed into, and digested in cytoplasmic vacuoles; some ingested bacteria are resistant to digestion and are expelled at the cytoproct. Equine cecal cycloposthiid ciliates also ingest and envacuolate bacteria; bacterial digestion again provides the principal nitrogen source for the ciliate (Bonhomme-Florentin, 1973). The predatory activity of the ruminal ciliates influences both the population size and relative proportions of the predominant bacterial species present in the rumen. The bacterial population in faunated animals can be 50–90% lower than in ciliate-free animals receiving the same ration. Elimination of the protozoa improves the efficiency of net microbial synthesis and increases the flow of microbial protein from the rumen.

Spherical cystlike inclusions containing numerous bacteria have been observed by electron microscopy in some ruminal ciliates (Fig. 2) and resemble structures originally described as the sporangia of parasitic chytrid fungi (Lubinsky, 1955a,b). Several cyst types differing in wall structure and internal bacteria were observed (Paul, 1990). The relationship of the host cell and the bacteria within the structures is unknown. The presence of free bacteria within the cytoplasm has also been revealed by electron microscopy (Paul, 1990), although it has to be established whether these endobionts are parasitic or symbionts (Fig. 3). Endonuclear cytobionts have been observed in *Entodinium* sp.

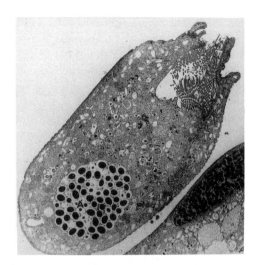

Figure 2. Ruminal *Entodinium* sp. with bacteria enclosed within an endoplasmic thick-walled cystlike vesicle. (Reproduced with permission from Williams and Coleman, 1991.)

(Paul, 1990), *Isotricha intestinalis* (Bretschneider and van Vorstenbosch, 1964), and cecal *Cycloposthium* sp. (Bonhomme-Florentin, 1971).

The relationship between the host protozoa and the free cytobionts is not known although intracellular bacteria do metabolize soluble compounds ingested by the protozoa (Coleman, 1975) and may secrete fibrolytic enzymes that digest cell wall polymers in plant fragments engulfed by the protozoa (Thines-Sempoux

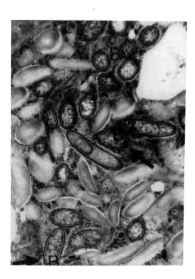

Figure 3. Endospore-forming cytoplasmic bacterial endobionts in the endoplasm of *Dasytricha ruminantium*.

et al., 1980). The close association of the cytobionts with the hydrogenosomes in the ruminal blepharocorytid *Charonina ventriculi* indicates a functional relationship (Paul, 1990). The hydrogenosome-associated endobionts of free-living anaerobic ciliates (Fenchel and Finlay, 1991), flagellates from the termite hindgut (Lee *et al.*, 1987), and endocommensal plagiopylid ciliates in the echinoid gut (Berger and Lynn, 1992) are all methanogenic bacteria. Intracellular methanogenic bacteria are also present in some ruminal ciliate genera, but in others the methanogens are only located on the external surfaces of the ciliate and the endobionts present do not contain fluorescent cofactors typical of methanogenic bacteria and do not react with specific archaebacterial rRNA probes (R. Amman, B. J. Finlay, and A. G. Williams, unpublished observations). The identity and the role of these endobionts in the nonmethanogenic ciliate cell remain undetermined.

Many rumen ciliates also have bacteria attached to the external surfaces of their pellicles (Fig. 4), although the proportion of ciliates colonized and the extent of colonization is variable. Bacteria also adhere to the external surfaces of ciliates in cecal contents of the horse (Bonhomme-Florentin, 1985); bacterial attachment to the ciliates is usually mediated by extracellular carbohydrate-containing polymers (Fig. 5), although more complex attachment structures have been described (Paul, 1990).

Imai and Ogimoto (1978) estimated that the average surface colonization was in the range 15–60 bacteria/200 μm^2 and using immunofluorescence microscopy identified *Streptococcus bovis* and *Ruminococcus albus* in the adherent population. However, a comparison of bright-field and epifluorescence microscopy indicated that virtually all of the bacteria attached to the surface of the ciliates were methanogens (Vogels *et al.*, 1980). It is believed that the methanogenic ectobiont and the ciliate are interacting metabolically, so that both partners benefit from an efficient interspecies transfer of hydrogen. Although

Figure 4. Bacterial ectobionts adhering to the outer surfaces of the ruminal ciliate *Eudiplodinium maggii*.

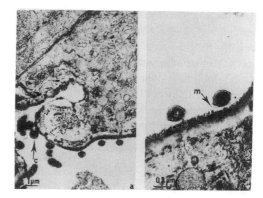

Figure 5. Bacterial attachment to the outer surfaces of equine cecal ciliate *Cycloposthium* sp. is mediated by capsular (c) or a mucilaginous material (m). (Reproduced with permission from Bonhomme-Florentin, 1985.)

Vogels *et al.* (1980) were unable to demonstrate the presence of externally associated methanogens on the pellicle of the isotrichid holotrichs, the only conclusive biochemical evidence for interspecies hydrogen transfer between protozoa and methanogens was obtained with the ruminal holotrichs (Hillman *et al.*, 1988). As a consequence of the metabolic interaction with *Methanosarcina barkeri*, the metabolite profile of *Isotricha* spp. was altered, methane, not hydrogen, accumulated, and the apparent oxygen tolerance of *M. barkeri* was also increased.

   3.1.3b. Protozoa–Eukaryote Interactions.   Protozoal predation on other ruminal ciliates and cannabalistic predation by *P. multivesiculatum* does occur, but has only been studied in detail with *P. multivesiculatum* and *Ent. bursa* (Williams and Coleman, 1991). Predatory species of *Diplodinium, Elytroplastron, Enoploplastron, Entodinium, Metadinium, Ostracodinium,* and *Polyplastron* have been reported. Although *Entodinium* spp. are the most common prey species, many larger organisms are also ingested and some of the larger ciliates are mutually exclusive. The existence of the A- and B-type populations arises because of the predatory activities of *P. multivesiculatum* which engulfs and eliminates epidinia, *Eudiplodinium maggii, Eremoplastron bovis* and *Ostracodinium* spp. Four population types have been characterized on the basis of the protozoal species present (Eadie, 1962; Abou Akkada *et al.*, 1969; Imai *et al.*, 1978).

   The ciliate protozoa and the chytrid fungi both associate with the plant material in the rumen and there is preliminary evidence indicating that some interactions do take place (Joblin, 1990; Williams *et al.*, 1993a). Although there is no direct evidence for protozoal predation of zoospores, ciliates have been observed at sites of mature fungal sporangia and zoospore release in ruminal digesta. Zoospore numbers have been reported to increase on some occasions after defaunation (Romulo *et al.*, 1989). Protozoal ingestion and digestion of fungal biomass has been demonstrated recently (Williams *et al.*, 1993a). Scanning electron microscopy has confirmed that *Eudiplodinium maggii, P. multivesiculatum,* and *Entodinium* spp. are able to ingest fungal rhizoids and occasionally fungal sporangia (Fig. 6). The protozoa possess chitinolytic enzymes and solubilize components from engulfed fungal tissues (A. G. Williams and K. N. Joblin, unpublished results). Fungal protein turnover was reduced by defaunation (Newbold and Hillman, 1990), and protozoal predation may influence fungal biomass development. Although both microbial groups are involved in the digestion of plant matter, the extent of any interactions during fibrolysis appears to be limited. Fungal enzyme formation and xylanolysis were not affected when protozoa were present in the culture, but a mixed entodiniomorphid population reduced fungal cellulolysis. *Lolium perenne* (ryegrass) digestion by *Piromyces communis* was also reduced by the addition of protozoal cell extracts. However, xylanolytic enzymes in cell-free extracts of *Neocallimastix patriciarum* and hemicellulolytic ruminal ciliates interacted synergistically when combined (Fonty and Joblin, 1991; Williams *et al.,* 1993a; A. G. Williams and K. N. Joblin, unpublished results). The extent and consequences of the interactions of the fibrolytic enzymes formed by the ruminal ciliates and chytrid fungi warrant further study in view of their potential importance in ruminal fibrolysis.

3.2. Chytridiomycete Fungi

The rumen chytrid fungi contribute to the nutrition of the host through their degradative activities and by the production of VFA. In foregut fermenters the cellular components of the fungal biomass itself may be of value and absorbed

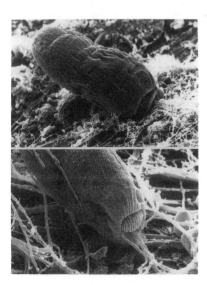

Figure 6. Ingestion of ruminal chytridiomycete fungal rhizoids by *Entodinium* sp.

from the lower tract. The precise contribution of the fungi is a matter of conjecture based on biochemical activities observed in *in vitro* studies (Mountfort, 1987). The fungi are primary invaders of plant material and are able to extensively degrade the dry matter of even highly lignified tissues. A consequence of fungal action is that plant tissues are weakened and the particle size reduced (Fonty and Joblin, 1991). Physical disruption of plant fiber can also occur via growth of the bulbous rhizoid of *Sphaeromonas* (*Caecomyces*) sp. within the plant tissue (Joblin, 1989). However, it has been proposed that the fungi do not have a direct role in particle size reduction, but the associated physical and enzymatic weakening of the plant cell structure enhances the effectiveness of rumination (Wilson and Engels, 1989). Fiber digestion in the rumen (Ford *et al.*, 1987; Calderon-Cortes *et al.*, 1989) and in an artificial rumen (Hillaire and Jouany, 1989; Hillaire *et al.*, 1989) is reduced when fungi are eliminated. These studies and that of Elliott *et al.* (1987) also demonstrated that the proportion of VFA formed were different in the presence and absence of fungi.

There is speculation that the fungal cellular components may be of nutritional value to the host. Fungal proteins contain high levels of sulfur and essential amino acids which are effectively absorbed from the small intestine of sheep (Kemp *et al.*, 1985; Gulati *et al.*, 1989). The fungi may also influence the availability of choline and monounsaturated fatty acids (Kemp *et al.*, 1984) but the benefits of these components to the host are ultimately dependent on the fungal biomass available and its susceptibility to lysis in the lower tract. Chitin is poorly digested in ruminants (Patton and Chandler, 1975) and fungi contributed an insignificant amount of the microbial N reaching the duodenum of sheep on a pelleted hay-grain ration (Faichney *et al.*, 1991).

3.2.1. Catabolic Activities

As with the ciliate protozoa the vast majority of the biochemical studies have utilized fungi isolated from the rumen. However, the fungi are more widespread in foregut and hindgut fermenters and do not appear to exhibit the restricted host specificity of the ciliates. The findings of studies already completed would indicate that the morphological and biochemical characteristics of foregut and hindgut fungi are similar. Because of the perceived importance of the fungi in the degradation of plant material in the gut the major emphasis of the research effort has concentrated on aspects of carbohydrate metabolism.

3.2.1a. Polysaccharide Breakdown. The ruminal chytrid fungi appear to be more able than the fibrolytic bacteria to degrade lignified plant tissues (Borneman and Akin, 1990). Most fungal species are able to utilize cellulose and xylan, but few are pectolytic. Isolates differ in their ability to utilize polysaccharidic substrates; *Sphaeromonas* isolates appear to use a more restricted range of polysaccharides than *Piromyces* and *Neocallimastix* (Phillips and Gordon, 1988). A wide range of polysaccharidase and glycoside hydrolase enzymes are produced by all monocentric and polycentric fungi isolated from the rumen and the hindgut of nonruminant hosts (Williams and Orpin, 1987a,b; Hebraud and Fevre, 1988; Borneman *et al.*, 1989; Teunissen *et al.*, 1991b). In addition to the enzymes required to hydrolyze the structural polysaccharides, the fungi also secrete acetyl xylan esterase and phenolic acid esterases (Borneman *et al.*, 1990; Borneman and Akin, 1990) which solubilize esterified acetyl and phenolic substituents in the plant cell wall structure that impede fibrolysis. Enzyme formation is growth-associated (Pearce and Bauchop, 1985; Lowe *et al.*, 1987b; Teunissen *et al.*, 1991b) and the activity is principally extracellular in location; the zoospores also contain hydrolytic enzymes (Williams and Orpin, 1987a,b).

Characterization of the enzymatic activities in cell lysates and culture supernatants has indicated that the substrate affinities and properties of the enzymes formed by the different isolates are similar with pH optima in the range 5.5–6.5, and temperature optima falling either close to the ruminal value of 39°C or in the range 50–60°C (Mountfort and Asher, 1985, 1989; Lowe *et al.*, 1987b; Williams and Orpin, 1987a,b; Hebraud and Fevre, 1988). Reymond *et al.* (1991) have also demonstrated an apparent homology of enzymes with nonruminal fungi. DNA sequences from *N. frontalis* that are transcribed at high levels under growth conditions that induce enzyme formation, hybridized to a DNA probe which encoded part of the exocellobiohydrolase gene of the aerobic fungus *Trichoderma reesei*.

Several distinct avicelase, carboxymethylcellulase, and β-glucosidase activities have been separated from the enzymatic mix formed by *N. frontalis* (Li and Calza, 1991a). In another strain of the same fungus the enzymes are associated in a cellulosome-type fraction that has the capacity to solubilize hydrogen bond-ordered cellulose (Wilson and Wood, 1992a,b). Fungal enzymes that have been purified and characterized include β-glucosidase (Li and Calza, 1991b,c), β-xylosidase (Hebraud and Fevre, 1990a), a 120-kDa glycoside hydrolase having both β-glucosidase and β-fucosidase activities (Hebraud and Fevre, 1990b), and a *p*-coumaroyl esterase (Borneman *et al.*, 1991).

Polysaccharolytic enzymes are formed during growth on a wide range of carbohydrate substrates, but activities are increased following growth on polysaccharides (Mountfort and Asher, 1985; Williams and Orpin, 1987a,b). Thus, although low levels of hydrolytic enzymes may be formed constitutively, cellulolytic enzyme formation is controlled; synthesis is induced by cellulosic polysaccharides and repressed by glucose, and in some strains by cellobiose and starch (Mountfort and Asher, 1985; Morrison *et al.*, 1990; Calza, 1990, 1991). Xylanase production by a rumen *N. frontalis* isolate was subject to catabolite regulation by xylose and arabinose (Mountfort and Asher, 1989). Enzyme production is also higher when the fungi are grown in coculture with methanogenic bacteria (Bauchop and Mountfort, 1981; Wood *et al.*, 1986; Joblin *et al.*, 1990). Synergism occurs between certain of the hydrolytic activities present in crude enzyme preparations from *N. frontalis* and those in cell extracts of ruminal ciliate protozoa and the hemicelluloytic ruminal bacterium *Butyrivibrio fibrisolvens* (Kopecny and Williams, 1988; Williams *et al.,* 1993a).

The fungi are also able to utilize plant storage polysaccharides as growth substrates. Starch and inulin are utilized by nearly all isolates of *Neocallimastix,* whereas their utilization by *Piromyces* and *Caecomyces* (*Sphaeromonas*) strains is a more variable property (Phillips and Gordon, 1988; Gordon and Phillips, 1989). The formation of amylolytic enzymes was highest when starch was the growth substrate, although low levels of activity were detectable with other carbohydrate growth substrates (Williams and Orpin, 1987a,b; Mountfort and Asher, 1988). Enzyme production is controlled by catabolite regulation as glucose accumulation suppresses α-amylase and α-glucosidase formation. The α-amylase of *N. frontalis* is released mainly into the culture fluid and has pH and temperature optima at 5.5 and 50°C, respectively (Mountfort and Asher, 1988). The characteristics of the amylases of other isolates were very similar (Williams and Orpin, 1987a). The products of α-amylase action are maltitriose, maltotetraose, and higher malto-oligosaccharides; these are degraded to glucose by cell-associated α-glucosidase (Williams and Orpin, 1987b; Mountfort and Asher, 1988). There have been no studies on the fructosan-degrading enzymes in the fungi although the three isolates studied by Williams and Orpin (1987b) formed invertase.

3.2.1b. Proteolysis.   An ovine *N. frontalis* isolate had a high proteolytic activity which became predominantly extracellular during growth. The proteolytic activity was associated with a high molecular-weight metalloprotease which had a broad pH profile with a maximum at pH 7.5 (Wallace and Joblin, 1985). The extracellular proteases may function in provision of amino acids for growth, in the modification of exocellular fibrolytic enzymes, or in the invasion of plant tissues by the fungal rhiziods. Wallace and Jobin (1985) noted that other rumen fungal classes and strains of *N. frontalis* were also proteolytic, but the commonality of the characteristic has to be established, as recent studies (Michael *et al.,* 1993) would indicate that not all fungal isolates are actively proteolytic. However, results of an *in vitro* study implied that rumen fungi had a role in ruminal proteolysis, as the inclusion of *N. frontalis* in a defined bacterial consortium growing on a grass/fishmeal ruminant feed increased the digestiblity of the solid substrate and the proteolytic activity of the culture filtrate doubled (Wallace and Munro, 1986). However, the proteolytic activity associated with the solid material increased almost tenfold. The production of both proteolytic and polysaccharolytic enzymes by the fungi and ciliate protozoa may confer an ecological advantage as the fibrolytic ruminal bacteria are nonproteolytic.

3.2.1c. Metabolite Formation.   All of the fungal strains examined so far metabolize carbohydrates by a mixed acid-type fermentation. However, the importance of fungal metabolites in the nutrition of the host has to be established. Glucose is utilized preferentially by *N. frontalis* and carbohydrate utilization is controlled by catabolite regulatory mechanisms (Mountfort and Asher, 1983). The ability of the fungi to compete with other saccharolytic microorganisms for substrates as they become available in the ecosystem and the metabolic consequences of interactions with other microbial groups will exert an influence on the final metabolite profiles. However, it has been established that the elimination of fungi from the ovine rumen resulted in an increase in the proportion of propionic acid in the metabolites produced by the microbial consortia (Elliott *et al.*, 1987; Calderon-Cortes *et al.*, 1989). The molar proportion of acetate increased at the expense of propionate when fungi were reintroduced into an artificial rumen fermentation which had been initially rendered fungi-free by freezing and treatment with cycloheximide (Hillaire and Jouany, 1989; Hillaire *et al.*, 1989).

   3.2.1d. Fermentation Products.   The fungi are able to ferment a wide range of soluble carbohydrates and all tested can ferment D-fructose, D-glucose, and the disaccharides cellobiose, gentiobiose, and lactose. Among the sugars not utilized are the common plant carbohydrate components arabinose, galactose, and mannose. There are interstrain and interspecies differences in the range of sugars utilized (Phillips and Gordon, 1988; Gordon and Phillips, 1989).

   The principal fermentation end products of monocentric and polycentric fungi and isolates from the rumen and hindgut are the same, although there are some differences in the relative proportions of the products formed and in the nature of the minor metabolites produced (Borneman *et al.*, 1989; Breton *et al.*, 1990; Fonty *et al.*, 1990; Teunissen *et al.*, 1991a). The frequently reported end products are carbon dioxide, hydrogen, acetate, formate, D-(−)- and L-(+)-isomers of lactate and ethanol. Succinate and polyalcohols (e.g., glycerol) are formed as minor products by some isolates (Borneman *et al.*, 1989; Yarlett, 1993). Fungal production of propionate, butyrate, or branched-chain fatty acids has not been reported. Borneman *et al.* (1989) concluded that the ratio of oxidized to reduced products formed by the monocentric isolates was greater than that of the polycentric isolates. The oxidation–reduction balance of monocentric cultures was higher than the theoretical value of 1.0 whereas the balance value of the polycentric isolates studied approximated at unity.

   3.2.1e. Pathways of Metabolite Formation.   The similarity of the fermentation products formed by the different fungal groups would indicate that the fungi have similar intermediary metabolism. Detailed studies have, however, only been undertaken with *N. patriciarum* (Yarlett *et al.*, 1986a) and *N. frontalis* (O'Fallon *et al.*, 1991).

   The proposed pathways of metabolite formation in *N. patriciarum* are summarized in Fig. 7. In the absence of glucose-6-phosphate dehydrogenase activity, glucose is converted by glycolysis into phosphoenolpyruvate; all of the stages in the subsequent conversion of malate into acetate and hydrogen are localized

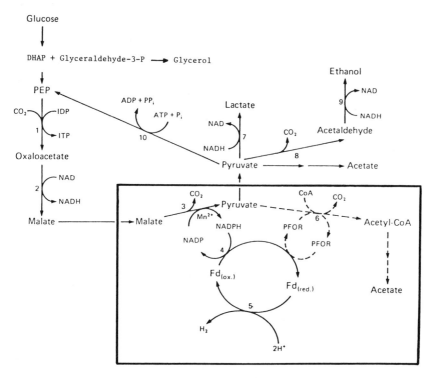

Figure 7. Principal pathways of metabolite formation by *Neocallimastix patriciarum*. Reactions enclosed within the box are believed to occur in hydrogenosomes and pathways marked with a broken line are suppressed during growth under high CO_2 concentrations. The enzymes involved are: 1, phosphoenolpyruvate carboxykinase; 2, malate dehydrogenase; 3, "malic" enzyme; 4, NADPH:-ferredoxin oxidoreductase; 5, hydrogenase; 6, pyruvate:ferredoxin oxidoreductase; 7, lactate dehydrogenase; 8, pyruvate decarboxylase; 9, alcohol dehydrogenase; 10, pyruvate kinase. (Scheme modified from Yarlett *et al.*, 1986a; reproduced with permission.)

within hydrogenosomes. The fungi thus more closely resemble the aerotolerant flagellates than the ruminal ciliates in this respect, as the malic enzyme of the ciliates is located in the cytosol rather than the hydrogenosomes. Acetate is formed in both the cytosol and hydrogenosomes (Yarlett, 1993). Hydrogenosomal acetate is formed from pyruvate via acetyl coenzyme A, but the mechanism of acetate production from acetyl coenzyme A remains to be identified. In the hydrogenosome-containing flagellates and rumen ciliates the energy of the thioester bond is conserved (Müller, 1988). The conversion of pyruvate to formate and acetyl CoA by pyruvate:formate lyase may occur in strains producing appreciable amounts of formate, and the acetyl CoA generated may lead to the cytosolic production of acetate (Yarlett, 1993). Formate is not a major product of

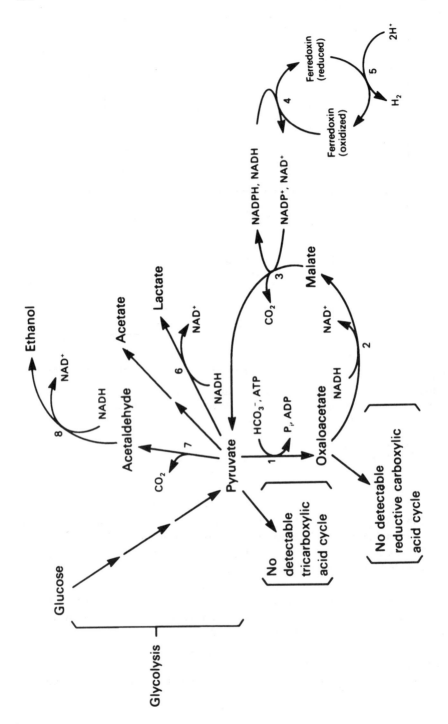

N. patriciarum and Yarlett *et al.* (1986a) were unable to detect any formate dehydrogenase or formate hydrogen lyase activity.

The activities of hydrogenosomal hydrogenase, and NAD(P)H:ferredoxin oxidoreductase in *N. patriciarum* were elevated by growth under CO_2, whereas the activity of pyruvate:ferredoxin oxidoreductase (PFOR) was suppressed. Under these conditions, Yarlett (1993) proposed that NAD(P)H:ferredoxin oxidoreductase activities provided the major reducing power for hydrogen formation. Carbon dioxide can thus suppress hydrogenosomal acetate and cytosolic ethanol production by end product inhibition of PFOR and pyruvate decarboxylase (Orpin and Joblin, 1988). Ambient gas concentrations may thus be important determinants of metabolix fluxes in the ruminal chytrid fungi and ciliate protozoa (Ellis *et al.*, 1991a–c). The activities of some key enzymes in intermediary metabolism are also influenced during cocultivation with methanogenic bacteria (Marvin-Sikkema *et al.*, 1993).

The studies of O'Fallon *et al.* (1991) identified some differences between the pathways in *N. frontalis* and *N. patriciarum*. Pyruvate synthase and PEP carboxykinase were not present in *N. frontalis* and only very low levels of NADPH:ferredoxin oxidoreductase were detected. O'Fallon *et al.* (1991) proposed that pyruvate produced by glycolysis was carboxylated to oxaloacetate by pyruvate carboxylase. Malate formed from the reduction of oxaloacetate by malate dehydrogenase is further metabolized in a series of coupled hydrogenosomal reactions that generate hydrogen, carbon dioxide, and pyruvate. It is proposed that energy is generated by coupling "malic enzyme" oxidation of malate to electron transfer via NADH:ferredoxin oxidoreductase, ferredoxin, and hydrogenase to proton reduction and hydrogen generation (Fig. 8).

Lactate is an important fungal product. D-(−)-Lactate dehydrogenase was detected in *Neocallimastix, Piromonas,* and *Sphaeromonas* isolates by Gleason and Gordon (1990). L-(+)-Lactate dehydrogenase was not detected in any of the isolates which only produced trace amounts of the L-(+)-isomer. Some fungi do, however, produce significant quantities of L-(+)-lactate (Borneman *et al.*, 1989) and obviously enzyme activities should be monitored in these strains. Only three of the strains monitored by Gleason and Gordon (1990) were able to oxidize D-(−)-lactate to pyruvate; the reaction was slowly catalyzed and unlikely to be physiologically significant. The formation of both ethanol and glycerol assists in maintaining the redox balance. It is assumed that they are formed by conventional routes from acetaldehyde and glyceraldehyde-3-phosphate, respectively (Yarlett, 1993).

←———

Figure 8. Principal routes of metabolite formation in *Neocallimastix frontalis*. The enzymes indicated are: 1, pyruvate carboxylase; 2, malate dehydrogenase; 3, "malic" enzyme; 4, NADH (NADPH):ferredoxin oxidoreductases; 5, hydrogenase; 6, lactate dehydrogenase; 7, pyruvate decarboxylase; 8, alcohol dehydrogenase. (Reproduced with permission from O'Fallon *et al.*, 1991.)

3.2.2. Oxygen and Fungal Metabolism

N. patriciarum, in common with other hydrogenosome-containing eukaryotes, is able to survive exposure to low levels of oxygen and exhibits characteristics of aerotolerance (Yarlett *et al.,* 1987). Exposure to oxygen concentrations above 10 μM caused an irreversible inhibition of respiratory activity, but at lower concentrations the stoichiometry of the reaction indicated that water was the principal respiratory product. The respiration was stable when ambient O_2 concentrations were < 10 μM and the apparent K_m for O_2 was 4.0 μM (Yarlett *et al.,* 1987). The effects of oxygen on VFA formation were not determined but an inhibitory effect on hydrogen formation was reported; a 50% inhibition of hydrogen production occurred at an oxygen concentration of 1.4 μM. Superoxide and peroxide radicals were produced during respiration and although an active superoxide dimutase was present, catalase activity could not be detected (Yarlett *et al.,* 1987).

3.2.3. Interactions with Other Microbial Groups

The rumen fungi are able to interact with other ruminal prokaryotes and eukaryotes. Aspects of these interactions have been the subject of several recent reviews (Joblin, 1990; Stewart *et al.,* 1990; Fonty and Joblin, 1991; Williams *et al.,* 1993a,b). Interactions between chytrid fungi and ciliate protozoa were discussed earlier (Section 3.1.3b) and only fungus–bacteria interactions will be discussed in the following section.

3.2.3a. Fungus–Bacteria Interactions. The chytrid fungi are hydrogenogens and are able to interact with hydrogenotrophic bacteria; they do in fact form stable cocultures with methanogenic bacteria which are the principal hydrogenotrophic bacterial group in the rumen ecosystem. The association of fungi and methanogens resulted in increased fungal biomass, a shift in the metabolite profile, and increased activities of polysaccharolytic enzymes and fiber breakdown. Many different combinations of fungal and methanogenic genera and species have been evaluated including representative isolates from nonruminant hosts (Bauchop and Mountfort, 1981; Joblin *et al.,* 1990; Marvin-Sikkema *et al.,* 1990; Teunissen *et al.,* 1992). The *in vitro* fungal degradation of intact plant material is increased when they are cocultured with methanogenic bacteria (Joblin *et al.,* 1989; Joblin and Williams, 1991). Ruminal wheat straw digestion in gnotobiotic lambs harboring only *R. flavefaciens* and ruminal fungi is also increased following ruminal inoculation with methanogenic bacteria (Fonty, Dore, and Williams, unpublished observations).

In coculture with methanogens the fungal fermentation becomes acetogenic; acetic acid production increases while lactate and ethanol formation decreases. Hydrogen and formic acid are methane precursors and do not accumulate. The continuous removal of hydrogen obviates the need for the production of alternative electron sink products, such as lactate and ethanol, since the reduced electron carriers are reoxidized during hydrogen formation; ATP formation is enhanced as a result of the shift to acetate production (Stewart et al., 1990; Williams et al., 1993b). The reason for the stimulation of fungal fibrolysis by the methanogens is complex and suggested contributory factors include changes in fungal growth rate, the metabolic shift away from inhibitory metabolites like ethanol, lactate, and formate, and decreased catabolite repression as soluble sugars do not accumulate in cocultures (Joblin et al., 1990).

The rumen chytrids also interact with nonmethanogenic hydrogenotrophic bacteria. *Selenomonas ruminantium* does not degrade cellulose but can utilize hydrogen and other fungal fermentation products. However, the extent of the interactions is dependent on the bacterial and fungal strains involved. For example, the association of *N. frontalis* MCH3 or *Piromyces communis* RL with *Selenomonas ruminantium* WPL depressed the fungal cellulolysis, whereas cellulose breakdown by *Sphaeromonas communis* was more efficient in association with this bacterial strain (Bernalier et al., 1991). Interaction of other *Neocallimastix* sp. with lactate-utilizing or nonlactilytic *Selenomonas ruminantium* strains stimulated the rate and extent of filter paper cellulose degradation (Marvin-Sikkema et al., 1990; Richardson and Stewart, 1990), and xylanolysis (Williams et al., 1991). Interspecies hydrogen transfer occurred in the associative fermentation, hydrogen did not accumulate, and lactate formation was suppressed. Cocultures of the chytrids and the acetogenic hydrogenotroph *Eubacterium limosum* have also been established (Williams et al., 1993b). Although cellulolysis was not improved, interspecies hydrogen transfer resulted in increased acetate accumulation and a concomitant decreased formation of formate and lactate (Bernalier and Fonty, unpublished data).

Interspecies cross-feeding of fungal catabolic products and other metabolites can occur and will influence the fibrolytic activities of the fungi. Nutrient cross-feeding interactions support the growth and survival of species in the ecosystem that are not primary degraders. With the exception of acetate, all of the fungal metabolites can be metabolized further by other microbial groups (Williams et al., 1993b). *Selenomonas ruminantium* strains are not only involved in interspecies hydrogen transfer but some species will also metabolize released sugars and the metabolites lactate and succinate. The effects of cocultivation with either *Megasphaera elsdenii* or *Veillonella parvula*, other lactate-utilizing bacteria, on fungal cellulolysis and hemicellulolysis are strain-dependent as stimulatory and inhibitory effects have been observed (Stewart et al., 1986; Williams et al., 1991). Saccharolytic bacteria such as *Succinivibrio dextrinosolvens* utilize carbohydrates that are released from plant polymers by fungal enzymes. Hemicellulolysis by *N. frontalis* doubled on cocultivation with *S. dextrinosolvens* as the hemicellulose degradation products which could repress fungal activity were utilized by the bacterial partner and did not accumulate (Williams *et al.,* 1991).

Some limited interactions occur between enzyme preparations from ruminal fungi and fibrolytic bacteria (Kopecny and Williams, 1988), and cocultivation with *Prevotella (Bacteroides) ruminicola, Butyrivibrio fibrisolvens,* and *Fibrobacter succinogenes* improved, or did not impede, cellulolysis and hemicellulolysis. However, the overall degradation of both polysaccharides was depressed by *Ruminococcus albus* and *R. flavefaciens* even in the presence of methanogenic bacteria (Stewart *et al.,* 1986; Bernalier *et al.,* 1988; Irvine and Stewart, 1991; Williams *et al.,* 1991). It was proposed that the adverse effects of the ruminococci on fungal growth and polymer breakdown were a consequence of interspecies competition for colonization sites on the plant tissue and released carbohydrate substrates. However, it has been established recently that the antagonistic effects of *R. flavefaciens* on cellulolysis by both *P. communis* and *N. frontalis* are related to the inhibitory activity of a protein released by the bacterium (Stewart *et al.,* 1992; Bernalier *et al.,* 1993).

3.3. *Giardia lamblia*—A Flagellate Parasite

Parasitic protozoa of the genus *Giardia* infect a wide range of vertebrate hosts, and the extent to which infection from animal reservoirs to humans can occur is uncertain (Meyer, 1990). Transmission occurs when viable cysts are injested (Adam, 1991); excystation in the upper intestine produces trophozoites which attach themselves to the mucosal lining. The human pathogen, *G. lamblia,* is numerically the most important cause of waterborne infection worldwide, and results in severe and often persistent diarrheal disease. Cysts are shed with the feces.

Trophozoite attachment, a key event in infection, is resistant to the sloughing of mucosal cells, and the special ventral disk has cysteine-rich proteins (Aggarwal *et al.,* 1989) of importance for parasite retention (Gillin, 1984). Closely apposed to the epithelial lining of the gut, the parasite has to compete for nutrients, not only with the microbial flora, but also with the host mucosa.

3.3.1. *Catabolic Activities*

Glucose is the only natural sugar utilized (Jarroll *et al.,* 1989a). Arginine is also a major energy source (Schofield *et al.,* 1990), and the availability of this amino acid may limit growth *in situ,* as, under anaerobic conditions at least, cultured organisms use it in preference to glucose (Schofield *et al.,* 1991). Purines, pyrimidines, and lipids are scavenged from the environment (Jarroll *et al.,* 1989a) and amino acids other than alanine and valine are not synthesized *de novo* (Paget *et al.,* 1993).

3.3.1a. Proteinase. It seems unlikely that the lysosomal proteases found in *G. lamblia* are involved in pathogenicity (Jarroll *et al.*, 1989b); a role in cytodifferentiation during encystation seems more feasible. However, extracellular release of a thiol proteinase activity has been reported (Parenti, 1989). The extent to which the organism can utilize extracellular proteins and peptides is unknown.

3.3.1b. Fermentation Pathways and Products. The pathways leading to major products of carbohydrate breakdown in *G. lamblia* were elucidated by Lindmark (1980). Pyruvate produced by glycolysis is either decarboxylated by pyruvate:acceptor oxidoreductase to give acetyl CoA, and hence acetate and ATP by acetate thiokinase, or else gives rise to ethanol, presumably by way of the NADPH-linked dehydrogenase detected in extracts; the route of ethanol formation is still ill-defined (Schofield and Edwards, 1991). Inorganic pyrophosphate is the phosphoryl group donor during glycolytic fructose 1,6-bisphosphate formation (Mertens, 1990). The organism possesses neither mitochondria nor hydrogenosomes.

Similar pathways and lack of intracellular compartmentation are also found in *Entamoeba histolytica,* a parasite of the large intestine (Reeves *et al.*, 1977, 1980). In this organism, inorganic pyrosphosphate plays an even more pivotal role than in *G. lamblia,* as in addition to PP_i-phosphofructokinase, the role of pyruvate kinase is assumed by an AMP, PP_i-pyruvate dikinase (Reeves, 1984).

The importance of arginine as an energy source for *G. lamblia* was revealed when alanine was discovered as the major product of cultured organisms under anaerobic conditions (Edwards *et al.*, 1989). *In situ,* where conditions are not anaerobic, it seems unlikely that alanine is excreted (Paget *et al.*, 1990).

3.3.2. Oxygen and G. lamblia

At the mucosal lining of the small intestine, surprisingly high O_2 concentrations have been measured in both sheep and gerbils (J. Finney, C. Preston-Meek, K.-W. Thong, and D. Lloyd, unpublished results). In sheep, values lie within the range 25–135 μM O_2 and in gerbils 12–30 μM O_2. Studies to determine the effects of O_2 on growth of *G. lamblia* in culture are hindered by the parasites' requirement for cysteine, but using washed nonproliferating cell suspensions, it has been shown that the biochemistry of the organism is profoundly affected by O_2 (Paget *et al.*, 1990, 1993). Thus, the balance of products shifts dramatically away from alanine and toward acetate as O_2 concentrations are increased. Ethanol formation is stimulated by low levels of dissolved O_2 (< 3 μM), but is diminished at higher concentrations (Lloyd and Paget, 1991). Changes in intracellular redox states, as observed by alterations of $NAD(P)H/NAD(P)^+$ ratios, accompany alternative product formation (Lloyd *et al.*, 1989b). Clearly, the biochemistry of the organism *in situ* is very dependent on ambient conditions of oxygenation (Paget *et al.,* 1993). Oxygen consumption by trophozoites both of *G. lamblia* and of the murine parasite *G. muris* is maximal at 3.5–7.0 μM O_2; whereas respiratory activity in the former is inhibited by O_2 above 80 μM, in the mouse parasite this threshold is at 15 μM (Paget *et al.,* 1989). The parasite is evidently well tuned to its highly specialized niche. Metronidazole chemotherapy and resistance must take account of intestinal O_2 levels (Boreham *et al.,* 1984; Ellis *et al.,* 1993). Triggers for encystation are thought to include pH, pCO_2, and bile salts (Jarroll *et al.,* 1989a).

3.4. Other Intestinal Protists

A number of other protists inhabit the human intestinal tract. With few exceptions (e.g., *Entamoeba histolytica,* Diamond and Cunnick, 1991; *Blastocystis hominis,* Zierdt *et al.,* 1988) these organisms have not yet been cultured under axenic conditions, so that detailed information on their biological activities is lacking. It should be stressed that prolonged *in vitro* cultivation, especially in the absence of other organisms, may result in loss of important characteristics of fresh isolates. Thus, the virulence of the intestinal parasite *E. histolytica* and its conversion from a harmless commensal to an aggressive invader depends on factors that are lost during successive subculturing (Bracha and Mirelman, 1984).

4. Biochemical Activities of Protists in the Urogenital Tract

Trichomonads

The biochemistry of *Trichomonas vaginalis,* a sexually transmitted flagellate which inhabits the vagina, male urethra and prostrate gland, is the best documented of all of the protists living at low oxygen tensions. This is because differences between parasite and host provide targets for chemotherapeutic attack. The economically important parasite *Tritrichomonas foetus,* responsible for abortion in cattle, has also received much attention; both organisms can be grown axenically in large quantities.

Metabolic Activities

The main energy sources for *T. vaginalis* are carbohydrates, but the organism also produces extracellular proteinases, and can thus satisfy its amino acid requirements from peptides and proteins. Arginine can also serve as an important energy source (Linstead and Cranshaw, 1983; Yarlett, 1988), and other amino acids rapidly utilized include methionine, leucine, and threonine (Lockwood and Coombs, 1989). The organism cannot use fatty acids as energy sources (Holz *et al.,* 1986). Considerable stores of glycogen are accumulated, but control of mobilization has not been studied. Although capable of consuming oxygen very rapidly, even at low oxygen concentrations (e.g., 1 µM, Lloyd et al., 1982), trichomonads have only fermentative energy production (Müller, 1988). This is a consequence of the fact that they are devoid of mitochondria (Brugerolle, 1972), and lack cytochromes (Lloyd et al., 1979). The major site of oxygen reduction is within hydrogenosomes, organelles which under anaerobic conditions produce H_2 (Müller and Lindmark, 1978; Cerkasov et al., 1978).

A variety of fermentation products accumulate in cultures: carbon flow between terminal alternative pathways is highly dependent on intracellular redox state and hence external conditions, especially with respect to ambient concentrations of O_2 (Ellis et al., 1992).

As is typically the case for parasites, biosynthetic machinery has become simplified wherever feasible. Thus, de novo purine synthesis does not occur, and salvage pathways permit their reutilization from the degradation of nucleic acids or nucleotides (Hassan and Coombs, 1988). Trichomonads can be regarded as fatty acid and sterol auxotrophs (Beach et al., 1990; Lindmark et al., 1991), and it is known that palmitic, stearic, and oleic acid, together with cholesterol (all complexed to bovine serum albumin), can satisfy the requirements of T. vaginalis (Linstead, 1981). It seems likely that in situ, the endocytosis of low-density human lipoproteins is receptor-mediated; subsequent digestion provides an adequate source of lipids for growth (Peterson and Alderete, 1984).

Proteinases. Recent years have seen a burgeoning interest in the proteinases of parasitic protists. The recognition of multiple types of proteinases, and the availability of specific inhibitors, has focused attention on the roles of these enzymes in the host–parasite relationship, pathogenicity, and parasite invasiveness. The continuous release of highly active cysteine proteinases (at least 50% of the total) into the medium of axenic cultures of T. vaginalis alongside N-acetyl-β-D-glucosaminidase, acid phosphatase, and α-mannosidase (Lockwood et al., 1988b) suggests important functions for enzyme secretion from a specific high-density lysosomal population. As well as the production of monomers of nutritional benefit, it has been shown that degradation of certain components (e.g., IgA1) of the host immune system is facilitated (Parenti, 1989). Other possible roles include erosion of host mucosa to help parasite adhesion (Silva Filho and de Souza, 1988; Arroyo and Alderete, 1989) and release of amino acids for amine production to offset low vaginal pH (North, 1991).

Lipid Metabolism. Trichomonads cannot synthesize fatty acids and rely on uptake of unesterified and esterified, medium- and long-chain, saturated and unsaturated fatty acids. As well as not being used as energy sources, fatty acids are not shortened or elongated, saturated or desaturated. They are used in unmodified form for the production of phosphoglycerides and sphingolipids. Free cholesterol and cholesterol esters must also be obtained from external sources; deacylation provides precursor acyl groups for phosphoglyceride synthesis (Lindmark et al., 1991).

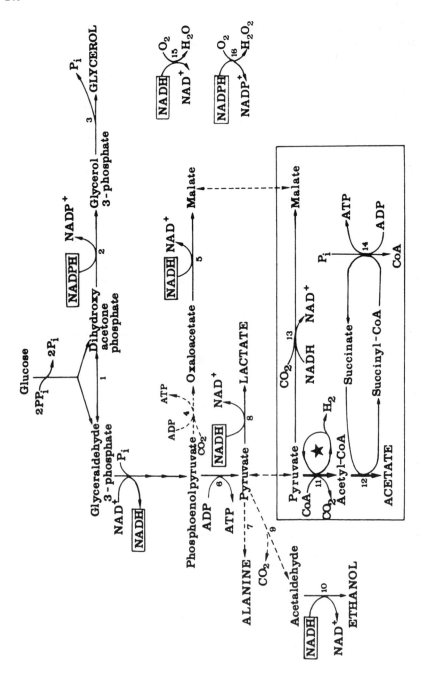

Metabolite Formation.   Arginine utilization results in the production of orthinine (Linstead and Cranshaw, 1983), a precursor of putrescine (Yarlett and Bacchi, 1988) which accumulates, together with lower amounts of spermidine and spermine, in the growth medium. The disappearance of arginine and the occurrence of polyamines in vaginal fluid is correlated with infections by *T. vaginalis* (Chen *et al.*, 1982). These observations point to the probable importance of arginine as an energy source *in situ* where the supply of carbohydrates may be limited (Yarlett and Bacchi, 1991). As well as providing pH buffering capacity, putrescine may inhibit the natural defenses of the vaginal tissues, as it acts as a powerful anti-inflammatory agent in model systems (Bird *et al.*, 1983). Cadaverine, the decarboxylation product of lysine, has also been detected in vaginal fluids of infected patients (Sanderson *et al.*, 1983).

The metabolism of sulfur-containing amino acids leads to the formation of H_2S and the volatile thiol, methanethiol (Thong *et al.*, 1987); it has been suggested that these noxious products may help the organism compete with other pathogens. Leucine and threonine catabolism leads to excretion of α-hydroxyisocaproate and α-hydroxybutyrate, respectively (Lockwood and Coombs, 1989). Indole, produced from tryptophan, as well as dimethyl disulfide predominate the highly complex mass spectra of culture filtrates; many minor volatile products remain to be identified (Lloyd *et al.*, 1991). Both indole and thiols are free radical scavengers and may protect against oxidative stress.

Fermentation Pathways and Products.   Glucose or glycogen catabolism leads to the production of phosphoenolpyruvate or pyruvate and as *T. vaginalis* has no tricarboxylic acid cycle, decarboxylation and transacylation of the acetyl-CoA generated within the hydrogenosomes, yield acetate as end product (Müller, 1989). Under anaerobic conditions, electrons from pyruvate are transported via a chain of iron–sulfur clusters and flavins to produce hydrogen. Lactate can also be formed directly from pyruvate, and glycerol is yet another product (Chapman *et al.*, 1985). An NAD^+-linked alcohol dehydrogenase is involved in ethanol production (Ellis *et al.*, 1992). The pathways implicated in these fermentative reactions are shown in Fig. 9. Several steps show characteristic features; phos-

←──

Figure 9. Principal routes of metabolite formation in *Trichomonas vaginalis*. The enzymes indicated are: 1, triose P-isomerase; 2, glycerol 3-P dehydrogenase; 3, glycerol 3-phosphatase; 4, phosphoenolpyruvate carboxykinase; 5, malate dehydrogenase; 6, pyruvate kinase; 7, alanine aminotransferase; 8, lactate dehydrogenase; 9, pyruvate decarboxylase; 10, alcohol dehydrogenase; 11, pyruvate:ferredoxin oxidoreductase; 12, acetate:succinate CoA transferase; 13, malate dehydrogenase (decarboxylating); 14, succinate thiokinase; 15, NADH oxidoreductase; 16, NADPH oxidoreductase. Heavy arrows denote the pathway predominant at vaginal O_2 concentrations. The cytosolic pool of reduced nicotinamide nucleotides is indicated by boxes, and the reactions occurring within hydrogenosomes are drawn in a box. The asterisk indicates the electron transport chain of hydrogenosomes consisting of a series of iron sulfur clusters and flavins. Dashed arrows denote enzymes unconfirmed in this organism (Ellis *et al*, 1992).

phofructokinase is unusual in that it is pyrophosphate- rather than ATP-linked (Mertens *et al.*, 1989; Mertens, 1990). This has interesting implications for glycolytic flux control and also for energetic efficiency. Pyruvate:ferredoxin oxidoreductase (Williams *et al.*, 1987) uses a [2FE–2S] ferredoxin (Gorrell *et al.*, 1984). Substrate-level phosphorylation of ADP to ATP is driven by hydrogenosomal succinate thiokinase.

Oxygen and T. vaginalis

Although *T. vaginalis* grows well in the absence of oxygen and has been traditionally studied as if it were a strict anaerobe, it has been known for some time that a restricted oxygen supply does not completely inhibit growth (Mack and Müller, 1978). The recent observation that growth is most rapid at high CO_2 (5 mM), in the presence of traces of O_2 (< 0.25 μM), indicates that *T. vaginalis* should be regarded as a microaerophilic organism (Paget and Lloyd, 1990). Apportionment of metabolic fluxes between pathways resulting in formation of acetate, lactate, and glycerol shows complex dependence on dissolved O_2 and CO_2. Thus, whereas under the usual conditions of growth in sealed bottles, roughly equimolar concentrations of the three major products accumulate, acetate production is enhanced by O_2; the formation of both lactate and glycerol increase at 5 mM CO_2. Hydrogen evolution is very oxygen-sensitive (K_i 1.1–2.3 μM O_2 for five different strains, Yarlett *et al.*, 1986b). The remarkable oxygen-consumption capacity of *T. vaginalis* provides high-affinity O_2-scavenging systems (K_m 3–49 μM O_2 for five different strains): H_2O_2 as well as water is produced (Chapman, 1986). These characteristics have important implications for metronidazole chemotherapy (Lloyd and Petersen, 1985), as the presence of O_2 in the vagina (and hence intracellularly in the parasite) can quench the nitroradical anion production necessary for the killing of *T. vaginalis*. Metronidazole-resistance, sometimes detected in clinical isolates, is correlated with altered hydrogenosome properties (Kulda *et al.*, 1989) and O_2 responses (Ellis *et al.*, 1992). Thus, in summary, *T. vaginalis* is well adapted to the conditions it experiences *in situ* in the vagina (traces of O_2, high CO_2), and a detailed appreciation of its natural habitat is of great clinical significance.

References

Abou Akkada, A. R., Bartley, E. E., and Fina, L. R., 1969, Ciliate protozoa in the rumen of the lactating cow, *J. Dairy Sci.* **52:**1088–1091.

Adam, R. D., 1991, The biology of *Giardia* spp., *Microbiol. Rev.* **55:**706–732.

Aggarwal, A., Merritt, J. W., Jr., and Nash, T. E., 1989, Cysteine-rich variant surface proteins of *Giardia lamblia, Mol. Biochem. Parasitol.* **32:**39–48.

Akin, D. E., and Amos, H. E., 1979, Mode of attack on orchardgrass leaf blades by rumen protozoa, *Appl. Environ. Microbiol.* **37:**332–338.

Arroyo, R., and Alderete, J. F., 1989, *Trichomonas vaginalis* surface proteinase activity is necessary for parasite adherence to epithelial cells, *Infect. Immun.* **57**:1849–1853.

Bauchop, T., 1977, Foregut fermentation, in: *Microbial Ecology of the Gut* (R.T.J. Clarke, and T. Bauchop, eds.), Academic Press, New York, pp. 223–250.

Bauchop, T., 1989, Colonization of plant fragments by protozoa and fungi, in: *The Roles of Protozoa and Fungi in Ruminant Digestion* (J. V. Nolan, R. A. Leng, and D. I. Demeyer, eds.), Penambul Books, Armidale, pp. 83–96.

Bauchop, T., and Mountfort, D. O., 1981, Cellulose fermentation by a rumen anaerobic fungus in both the absence and presence of rumen methanogens, *Appl. Environ. Microbiol.* **42**:1103–1110.

Beach, D. H., Holz, G. G., Jr., Singh, B. N., and Lindmark, D. G., 1990, Fatty acid and sterol metabolism of cultured *Trichomonas vaginalis* and *Tritrichomonas foetus*, *Mol. Biochem. Parasitol.* **38**:175–190.

Berger, J., and Lynn, D. H., 1992, Hydrogenosome–methanogen assemblages in the echinoid endocommensal plagiopylid ciliates, *Lechriopyla mystax* Lynch, 1930 and *Plagiopyla minuta* Powers, 1933, *J. Protozool.* **39**:4–8.

Bernalier, A., Fonty, G., and Gouet, P., 1988, Dégradation et fermentation de la cellulose par *Neocallimastix* sp. seul ou associé à quelques bactériennes du rumen, *Reprod. Nutr. Dev.* **28**(Suppl):75–76.

Bernalier, A., Fonty, G., and Gouet, P., 1991, Cellulose degradation by two rumen anaerobic fungi in monoculture or in coculture with rumen bacteria, *Anim. Feed Sci. Technol.* **32**:131–136.

Bernalier, A., Fonty, G., Bonnemoy, F., and Gouet, P., 1993, Inhibition of the cellulolyte activity of *Neocallimastix frontalis* by *Ruminococcus flavefaciers*, *J. Gen. Microbiol.* **139**:873–880.

Bignell, D. E., 1984, Direct potentiometric determination of redox potentials of gut contents in the termites, *Zootermopsis nevadensis* and *Cubitermes severans,* and three other arthropods, *J. Insect Physiol.* **30**:169–174.

Bird, J., Mohd-Hidir, S., and Lewis, D. A., 1983, Putrescine—A potent anti-inflammatory substance in inflammatory exudates, *Agents Actions* **13**:342–347.

Bird, S. H., 1989, Production from ciliate-free ruminants, in: *The Roles of Protozoa and Fungi in Ruminant Digestion* (J. V. Nolan, R. A. Leng, and D. I. Demeyer, eds.), Penambul Books, Armidale, pp. 233–246.

Bird, S. H., 1991, Role of protozoa in relation to the nutrition of the host animal, in: *Recent Advances on the Nutrition of Herbivores* (Y. W. Ho, H. K. Wong, N. Abdullah, and Z. A. Tajuddin, eds.), Malaysian Society of Animal Production, Selangor, pp. 171–180.

Bonhomme-Florentin, A., 1969, Essais de culture in vitro des Cycloposthiidae, ciliés commensaux de l'intestin du cheval role de ces ciliés dans la dégradation de la cellulose, *Protistologica* **5**:519–522.

Bonhomme-Florentin, A., 1971, Étude des métabolismes azoté et glucidique des ciliés oligotriches du genre Cycloposthium du caecum des équidés, *Protistologica* **7**:411–419.

Bonhomme-Florentin, A., 1973, Role des bactéries dans la physiologie des ciliés entodiniomorphes. Métabolisme azoté de ces ciliés, *Ann. Biol.* **12**:535–564.

Bonhomme-Florentin, A., 1974, Contribution a l'étude de la physiologie des ciliés entodiniomorphes endocommensaux des ruminants et des équidés, *Ann. Sci. Nat. Zool. Biol. Anim.* **16**:155–283.

Bonhomme-Florentin, A., 1975, Activité cellulolytique des ciliés entodiniomorphes, *J. Protozool.* **22**:445–451.

Bonhomme-Florentin, A., 1976, Activité lipolytique des ciliés et des bactéries du caecum des équidés, *C.R. Acad. Sci. Ser. D* **282**:1605–1608.

Bonhomme-Florentin, A., 1983, Biohydrogénation des acides gras insaturés de chloroplastes, par les protozoaires et les bactéries du contenu du caecum de cheval, *Arch. Protistenkd.* **127**:399–404.

Bonhomme-Florentin, A., 1985, Attachement des ciliés du caecum de cheval aux fragments végétaux-dégradation des chloroplastes. Attachment des bactéries aux ciliés du caecum, *Reprod. Nutr. Dev.* **25**:127–139.

Bonhomme-Florentin, A., 1986, Dégradation des galactolipides par les protozoaires et les bactéries du contenu du caecum de cheval, *Reprod. Nutr. Dev.* **26**:291–292.

Bonhomme-Florentin, A., 1988a, Endo-1,4-β-glucanase and endo-1,4-β-xylanase of the ciliate *Epidinium ecaudatum* free of cellulolytic and hemicelluloytic bacteria, *Jpn. J. Vet. Sci.* **50**:543–547.

Bonhomme-Florentin, A., 1988b, Degradation of hemicellulose and pectin by horse caecum contents, *Br. J. Nutr.* **60**:185–192.

Bonhomme-Florentin, A., 1990a, Fibre digestion by symbiotic protozoa of mammalian herbivores gut, *Comp. Physiol.* **5**:254–268.

Bonhomme-Florentin, A., 1990b, Rumen ciliates: Their metabolism and relationships with bacteria and their hosts, *Anim. Feed Sci. Technol.* **30**:203–266.

Bonhomme-Florentin, A., Fonty, G., Foglietti, M. J., and Weber, M., 1986, Endo-1,4-glucanase and β-glucosidase of the ciliate *Polyplastron multivesiculatum* free of cellulolytic bacteria, *Can. J. Microbiol.* **32**:219–225.

Boreham, P.F.L., Phillips, R. E., and Shepherd, R. W., 1984, The sensitivity of *Giardia intestinalis* to drugs *in vitro*, *J. Antimicrob. Chemother.* **14**:449–461.

Borneman, W. S., and Akin, D. E., 1990, Lignocellulose degradation by rumen fungi and bacteria: Ultrastructure and cell wall degrading enzymes, in: *Microbial and Plant Opportunities to Improve Lignocellulose Utilization by Ruminants* (D. E. Akin, L. G. Ljungdahl, J. R. Wilson, and P. J. Harris, eds.), Elsevier, Amsterdam, pp. 325–339.

Borneman, W. S., Akin, D. E., and Ljungdahl, L. J., 1989, Fermentation products and plant cell wall degrading enzymes produced by monocentric and polycentric anaerobic ruminal fungi, *Appl. Environ. Microbiol.* **55**:1066–1073.

Borneman, W. S., Hartley, R. D., Morrison, W. H., Akin, D. E., and Ljungdahl, L. J., 1990, Feruloyl and p-coumaroyl esterase from anaerobic fungi in relation to plant cell wall degradation, *Appl. Microbiol. Biotechnol.* **33**:345–351.

Borneman, W. S., Ljungdahl, L. J., Hartley, R. D., and Akin, D. E., 1991, Isolation and characterisation of p-coumaroyl esterase from the anaerobic fungus *Neocallimastix* strain MC-2, *Appl. Environ. Microbiol.* **57**:2337–2334.

Bracha, R., and Mirelman, D., 1984, Virulence of *Entamoeba histolytica* trophozoites, *J. Exp. Med.* **160**:353–368.

Breton, A., Bernalier, A., Bonnemoy, F., Fonty, G., Gaillard, B., and Gouet, P., 1989, Morphological and metabolic characterization of a new species of strictly anaerobic fungus, *Neocallimastix joyonii*, *FEMS Microbiol. Lett.* **58**:309–314.

Breton, A., Bernalier, A., Dusser, M., Fonty, G., Gaillard-Martinie, B., and Guillot, J., 1990, *Anaeromyces mucronatus* nov. gen., nov. sp. A new strictly anaerobic fungus with polycentric thallus, *FEMS Microbiol. Lett.* **70**:177–182.

Breton, A., Dusser, M., Gaillard-Martinie, B., Guillot, J., Millet, L., and Prensier, G., 1991, *Piromyces rhizinflata* nov. sp., a strictly anaerobic fungus from faeces of Saharian ass: A morphological, metabolic and ultrastructural study, *FEMS Microbiol. Lett.* **82**:1–8.

Bretschneider, L. N., and van Vorstenbosch, C.J.A., 1964, Das vorkommen von intraplasmatischen und intranuklearen mikroorganismen in eingen pansenciliaten, *Proc. K. Ned. Akad. Wet. Ser. C* **67**:313–319.

Brugerolle, G., 1972, Characterisation, ultrastructurale et cytochimique de 2 types de granules cytoplasmiques chez les Trichomonas, *Protistologica* **8**:352–363.

Buffenstein, R., and Yahav, S., 1991, The effect of diet on microfaunal population and function in the caecum of a subterranean naked mole-rat, *Heterocephalus glaber, Br. J. Nutr.* **65**:249–258.

Calderon-Cortes, J. F., Elliott, R., and Ford, C. W., 1989, Influence of rumen fungi on the nutrition of sheep fed forage diets, in: *The Roles of Protozoa and Fungi in Ruminant Digestion* (J. V. Nolan, R. A. Leng, and D. I. Demeyer, eds.), Penambul Books, Armidale, pp. 181–187.

Calza, R. E., 1990, Regulation of protein and cellulase excretion in the ruminal fungus *Neocallimastix frontalis* EB 188, *Curr. Microbiol.* **21:**109–115.

Calza, R. E., 1991. Carbon source, cyclic nucleotide, and protein inhibitor effects on protein and cellulase secretions in *Neocallimastix frontalis* EB 188, *Curr. Microbiol.* **22:**213–219.

Cerkasov, J., Cerkasovová, A., Kulda, J., and Vilhelmová, D., 1978, Respiration of hydrogenosomes of *Tritrichomonas foetus* 1. ADP-dependent oxidation of malate and pyruvate, *J. Biol. Chem.* **253:**1207–1214.

Chapman, A., 1986, Biochemistry of *Trichomonas vaginalis,* Ph.D. thesis, University of Wales, Cardiff.

Chapman, A., Linstead, D. J., Lloyd, D., and Williams, J., 1985, ^{13}C-nmr reveals glycerol as an unexpected major metabolite of the protozoan parasite, *Trichomonas vaginalis, FEBS Lett.* **191:**287–292.

Chen, K.C.S., Amscib, R., Eschenbach, D. A., and Holmes, K. K., 1982, Biochemical diagnosis of vaginitis: Determination of diamines in vaginal fluid, *J. Infect. Dis.* **134:**337–345.

Coleman, G. S., 1975, The interrelationship between rumen ciliate protozoa and bacteria, in: *Digestion and Metabolism in the Ruminant* (I. W. McDonald and A. C. Warner eds.), University of New England Publishing Unit, Armidale, pp. 149–164.

Coleman, G. S., 1979, The role of rumen protozoa in the metabolism of ruminants given tropical feeds, *Trop. Anim. Prod.* **4:**199–213.

Coleman, G. S., 1980, Rumen ciliate protozoa, *Adv. Parasitol.* **18:**121–173.

Coleman, G. S., 1983, Hydrolysis of fraction 1 leaf protein and casein by rumen entodiniomorphid protozoa, *J. Appl. Bacteriol.* **55:**111–118.

Coleman, G. S., 1985, The cellulase content of 15 species of entodiniomorphid protozoa, mixed bacteria and plant debris isolated from the ovine rumen, *J. Agric. Sci.* **104:**349–360.

Coleman, G. S., 1986a, The metabolism of rumen ciliate protozoa, *FEMS Microbiol. Rev.* **39:**321–344.

Coleman, G. S., 1986b, The distribution of carboxymethylcellulase between fractions taken from the rumen of sheep containing no protozoa or one of five different protozoal populations, *J. Agric. Sci.* **106:**121–127.

Coleman, G. S., 1986c, The amylase activity of 14 species of entodiniomorphid protozoa and the distribution of amylase in digesta fractions of sheep containing no protozoa or one of seven different protozoal populations, *J. Agric. Sci.* **107:**709–721.

Coleman, G. S., 1987, Rumen entodiniomorphid protozoa, in: *In Vitro Methods for Parasite Cultivation* (A.E.R. Taylor and J. R. Baker, eds.), Academic Press, New York, pp. 29–51.

Coleman, G. S., 1988, The importance of rumen ciliate protozoa in the growth and metabolism of the host ruminant, *Int. J. Anim. Sci.* **3:**75–95.

Coleman, G. S., 1989, Protozoal–bacterial interaction in the rumen, in: *The Role of Protozoa and Fungi in Ruminant Digestion* (J. V. Nolan, R. A. Leng, and D. I. Demeyer, eds.), Penambul Books, Armidale, pp. 13–27.

Coleman, G. S., Sandford, D. C., and Beahon, S., 1980, The degradation of polygalacturonic acid by rumen ciliate protozoa, *J. Gen. Microbiol.* **120:**295–300.

Collet, J. Y., Garin, Y., Tulin, C. G., and Fernandez, M., 1983, The intestinal entodiniomorph ciliates of wild lowland gorillas in Gabon West Africa, *J. Med. Primatol.* **12:**239–249.

Czerkawski, J. W., 1969, Methane production in ruminants and its significance, *World Rev. Nutr. Diet.* **11:**240–282.

Czerkawski, J. W., and Clapperton, J. L., 1968, Analysis of gases produced by metabolism of microorganisms, *Lab. Pract.* **17:**994–996.

Dauvrin, T., and Thines-Sempoux, D., 1989, Purification and characterization of a heterogeneous glycosylated invertase from the rumen holotrich ciliate *Isotricha prostoma*, *Biochem. J.* **264:**721–727.

Dehority, B. A., 1986, Protozoa of the digestive tract of herbivorous mammals, *Insect Sci. Appl.* **7:**279–296.

Dehority, B. A., 1987, Rumen ophryoscolecid protozoa in the hindgut of the capybara (*Hydrochoerus hydrochoeris*), *J. Protozool.* **34:**143–145.

Dellow, D. W., Hume, I. D., Clarke, R.T.J., and Bauchop, T., 1988, Microbial activity in the forestomach of free living macropodid marsupials: Comparison with laboratory studies, *Aust. J. Zool.* **36:**383–395.

Diamond, L. S., and Cunnick, C. C., 1991, A serum-free partly defined medium PDM-805 for axenic activation of *Entamoeba histolytica*, Schaudinn 1903 and other *Entamoeba, J. Protozool.* **38:**211–216.

Dore, J., and Stahl, D. A., 1991, Phylogeny of anaerobic chytridiomycetes inferred from small subunit ribosomal RNA sequence comparisons, *Can. J. Bot.* **69:**1964–1971.

Eadie, J. M., 1962, Inter-relationships between certain rumen ciliate protozoa, *J. Gen. Microbiol.* **29:**579–588.

Edwards, M. R., Gilroy, F. V., Jimenez, M. B., and Sullivan, W. J., 1989, Alanine is a major product of metabolism of *Giardia lamblia:* A proton nuclear magnetic resonance study, *Mol. Biochem. Parasitol.* **37:**19–26.

Elliott, R., Ash, A. J., Calderon-Cortes, F., and Norton, B. W., 1987, The influence of anaerobic fungi on rumen volatile fatty acid concentrations in vivo, *J. Agric. Sci.* **109:**13–17.

Ellis, J. E., Williams, A. G., and Lloyd, D., 1989, Oxygen consumption by rumen microorganisms: Protozoal and bacterial contributions, *Appl. Environ. Microbiol.* **55:**2583–2587.

Ellis, J. E., McIntyre, P. S., Saleh, M., Williams, A. G., and Lloyd, D., 1991a, Influence of CO_2 and low concentrations of O_2 on fermentative metabolism of the rumen ciliate *Dasytricha ruminatium, J. Gen. Microbiol.* **137:**1409–1417.

Ellis, J. E., McIntyre, P. S., Saleh, M., Williams, A. G., and Lloyd, D., 1991b, Influence of CO_2 and low concentrations of oxygen on fermentative metabolism of the ruminal ciliate *Polyplastron multivesiculatum, Appl. Environ. Microbiol.* **57:**1400–1407.

Ellis, J. E., McIntyre, P. S., Saleh, M., Williams, A. G., and Lloyd, D., 1991c, The influence of ruminal concentrations of O_2 and CO_2 on fermentative metabolism of the rumen entodiniomorphid ciliate *Eudiplodinium maggii, Curr. Microbiol.* **23:**245–251.

Ellis, J. E., Cole, D., and Lloyd, D., 1992a, Influence of oxygen on the fermentative metabolism of metronidazole-sensitive and resistant strains of *Trichomonas vaginalis, Mol. Biochem. Parasitol.* **56:**79–88.

Ellis, J. E., Wingfield, J. M., Cole, D., Boreham, P.F.L., and Lloyd, D., 1992b, Oxygen affinities of metronidazole-resistant and sensitive stocks of *Giardia intestinalis, Int. J. Parasitol.* **23:**35–39.

Englyst, H. N., and Macfarlane, G. T., 1986, Breakdown of resistant and readily digestible starch by human gut bacteria, *J. Sci. Food Agric.* **37:**699–706.

Faichney, G. J., Brownlee, A. G., Gordon, G.L.R., Phillips, M. W., and Welch, R. J., 1991, Contribution of protozoa and anaerobic fungi to digesta N in sheep given a pelleted hay/grain diet, *Proc. Nutr. Soc. Aust.* **16:**209.

Fenchel, T., and Finlay, B. J., 1991, The biology of free-living anaerobic ciliates, *Eur. J. Protistol.* **26:**201–215.

Fonty, G., and Joblin, K. N., 1991, Rumen anaerobic fungi: Their role and interactions with other rumen microorganisms in relation to fiber digestion, in: *Physiological Aspects of Digestion and Metabolism in Ruminants* (T. Tsuda, Y. Sasaki, and R. Kawashima, eds.), Academic Press, New York, pp. 655–680.

Fonty, G., Joblin, K. N., and Brownlee, A., 1990, Contribution of anaerobic fungi to rumen functions, in: *The Rumen Ecosystem: The Microbial Metabolism and Its Regulation* (S. Hoshino, R. Onodera, H. Minato, and H. Itabashi, eds.), Japan Scientific Societies Press, Tokyo, pp. 93–100.

Ford, C. W., Elliott, R., and Maynard, P. J., 1987, The effect of chlorite delignification on digestibility of some grass forages and on intake and rumen microbial activity in sheep fed barley straw, *J. Agric. Sci.* **108:**129–136.

Gillin, F. D., 1984, The role of reducing agents and the physiology of trophozoite attachment, in: *Giardia and Giardiasis* (S. L. Erlandsen and E. A. Meyer, eds.), Plenum Press, New York, pp. 111–132.

Gleason, F. H., and Gordon, G.L.R., 1990, Lactate dehydrogenases in obligately anaerobic chytridiomycetes from the rumen, *Mycologia* **82:**261–263.

Gold, J. J., Heath, I. B., and Bauchop, T., 1988, Ultrastructural description of a new chytrid genus of caecum anaerobe, *Caecomyces equi* gen. nov., sp. nov., assigned to the Neocallimasticaceae, *BioSystems* **21:**403–415.

Gordon, G.L.R., and Phillips, M. W., 1989, Comparative fermentation properties of anaerobic fungi from the rumen, in: *The Roles of Protozoa and Fungi in Ruminant Digestion* (J. V. Nolan, R. A. Leng, and D. I. Demeyer, eds.), Penambul Books, Armidale, pp. 127–138.

Gorrell, T. E., Yarlett, N., and Müller, M., 1984, Isolation and characterisation of *Trichomonas vaginalis* ferredoxin, *Carls. Res. Commun.* **49:**259–268.

Grenet, E., Fonty, G., Jamot, J., and Bonnemoy, F., 1989, Observation of anaerobic fungi in the ruminant intestine, *Proc. Nutr. Soc.* **49:**125A.

Gulati, S. K., Ashes, J. R., Gordon, G.L.R., Connell, P. J., and Rogers, P. L., 1989, Nutritional availability of amino acids from the rumen anerobic fungus *Neocallimastix* sp. LM1 in sheep, *J. Agric. Sci.* **113:**383–387.

Hassan, H. F., and Coombs, G. H., 1988, Purine and pyrimidine metabolism in parasitic protozoa, *FEMS Microbiol. Rev.* **54:**47–84.

Heath, I. B., Bauchop, T., and Skipp, R. A., 1983, Assignment of the rumen anaerobe *Neocallimastix frontalis* to the Spizellomycetales (Chytridiomycetes) on the basis of its polyflagellate zoospore ultrastructure, *Can. J. Bot.* **61:**295–307.

Hebraud, M., and Fevre, M., 1988, Characterization of glycoside and polysaccharide hydrolases secreted by the rumen anaerobic fungi *Neocallimastix frontalis*, *Sphaeromonas communis* and *Piromonas communis*, *J. Gen. Microbiol.* **134:**1123–1129.

Hebraud, M., and Fevre, M., 1990a, Purification and characterization of an extracellular β-xylosidase from the rumen anaerobic fungus *Neocallimastix frontalis*, *FEMS Microbiol. Lett.* **72:**11–16.

Hebraud, M., and Fevre, M., 1990b, Purification and characterization of an aspecific glycoside hydrolase from the anaerobic ruminal fungus *Neocallimastix frontalis*, *Appl. Environ. Microbiol.* **56:**3164–3169.

Hillaire, M. C., and Jouany, J. P., 1989, Effects of anaerobic fungi on the digestion of wheat straw and the end products of microbial metabolism: Studies in a semi-continuous in vitro system, in: *The Roles of Protozoa and Fungi in Ruminant Digestion* (J. V. Nolan, R. A. Leng, and D. I. Demeyer, eds.), Penambul Books, Armidale, pp. 269–271.

Hillaire, M. C., Jouany, J. P., and Fonty, G., 1989, Wheat straw degradation, in Rusitec, in the presence or absence of anaerobic fungi, *Proc. Nutr. Soc.* **49:**127A.

Hillman, K., Lloyd, D., and Williams, A. G., 1985a, Use of a portable quadrupole mass spectrometer for the measurement of dissolved gas concentrations in ovine rumen liquor in situ, *Curr. Microbiol.* **12:**335–340.

Hillman, K., Lloyd, D., Scott, R. I., and Williams, A. G., 1985b, The effects of oxygen on hydrogen production by rumen holotrich protozoa, as determined by membrane inlet mass spectrometry, in: *Microbial Gas Metabolism: Mechanistic, Metabolic and Biotechnological Aspects* (R. K. Poole and C. S. Dow, eds.), Academic Press, New York, pp. 271–277.

Hillman, K., Lloyd, D., and Williams, A. G., 1988, Interactions between the methanogen *Methanosarcina barkeri* and rumen holotrich ciliate protozoa, *Lett. Appl. Microbiol.* **7**:49–53.

Hillman, K., Whyte, A. L., and Stewart, C. S., 1992, Dissolved oxygen in the porcine gastrointestinal tract, *Lett. Appl. Microbiol.* **16**:299–302.

Ho, Y. W., Abdullah, N., and Jalaludin, S., 1990a, Invasion and colonization by anaerobic rumen fungi, in: *The Rumen Ecosystem: The Microbial Metabolism and Its Regulation* (S. Hoshino, R. Onodera, H. Minato, and H. Itabashi eds.), Japan Scientific Societies Press, Tokyo, pp. 101–107.

Ho, Y. W., Bauchop, T., Abdullah, N., and Jalaludin, S., 1990b, *Ruminomyces elegans* gen. et sp. nov., a polycentric anaerobic rumen fungus from cattle, *Mycotaxon* **38**:397–405.

Holz, G. G., Lindmark, D. G., Beach, D. H., Neale, K. A., and Singh, B. N., 1986, Lipids and lipid metabolism of trichomonads, *Acta Univ. Carol. Biol.* **30**:229–311.

Hume, I. D., and Warner, A.C.I., 1980, Evolution of microbial digestion in mammals, in: *Digestive Physiology and Metabolism in Ruminants* (Y. Ruckebusch and P. Thivend eds.), MTP Press, Lancaster, pp. 665–684.

Imai, S., and Ogimoto, K., 1978, Scanning electron and fluorescent microscopic studies on the attachment of spherical bacteria to ciliate protozoa in the ovine rumen, *Jpn. J. Vet. Sci.* **40**:9–19.

Imai, S., Katsuno, M., and Ogimoto, K., 1978, Distribution of rumen ciliate protozoa in cattle, sheep and goat and experimental transfaunation of them, *Jpn. J. Zootech. Sci.* **49**:494–505.

Imai, S., Ikeda, S. I., Collet, Y. Y., and Bonhomme, A., 1991, Entodiniomorphid ciliates from the wild lowland gorilla with the description of a new genus and three new species, *Eur. J. Protistol.* **26**:270–278.

Irvine, H. L., and Stewart, C. S., 1991, Interactions between anaerobic cellulolytic bacteria and fungi in the presence of *Methanobrevibacter smithii*, *Lett. Appl. Microbiol.* **12**:62–64.

Jarroll, E. J., Manning, P., Berrada, A., Hare, D., and Lindmark, D. G., 1989a, Biochemistry and metabolism of *Giardia*, *J. Protozool.* **36**:190–197.

Jarroll, E. J., Gaspano, J., Hare, D., and Lindmark, D., 1989b, Proteinases of *Giardia*, in: *Biochemistry and Molecular Biology of "Anaerobic Protozoa"* (D. Lloyd, G. H. Coombs, and T. A. Paget, eds.), Harwood, Chur, pp. 202–216.

Joblin, K. N., 1981, Isolation, enumeration and maintenance of rumen anaerobic fungi in roll tubes, *Appl. Environ. Microbiol.* **42**:1119–1122.

Joblin, K. N., 1989, Physical disruption of plant fibre by rumen fungi of the *Sphaeromonas* group, in: *The Roles of Protozoa and Fungi in Ruminant Digestion* (J. V. Nolan, R. A. Leng, and D. I. Demeyer, eds.), Penambul Books, Armidale, pp. 259–260.

Joblin, K. N., 1990, Bacterial and protozoal interactions with ruminal fungi, in: *Microbial and Plant Opportunities to Improve Lignocellulose Utilization by Ruminants* (D. E. Akin, L. G. Ljungdahl, J. R. Wilson, and P. J. Harris, eds.), Elsevier, Amsterdam, pp. 311–326.

Joblin, K. N., and Williams, A. G., 1991, Effects of cocultivation of ruminal chytrid fungi with *Methanobrevibacter smithii* on lucerne stem degradation and extracellular fungal enzyme activities, *Lett. Appl. Microbiol.* **12**:121–124.

Joblin, K. N., Campbell, G. P., Richardson, A. J., and Stewart, C. S., 1989, Fermentation of barley straw by anaerobic rumen bacteria and fungi in axenic culture and in co-culture with methanogens, *Lett. Appl. Microbiol.* **9**:195–197.

Joblin, K. N., Naylor, G. E., and Williams, A. G., 1990, Effect of *Methanobrevibacter smithii* on xylanolytic activity of ruminal fungi, *Appl. Environ. Microbiol.* **56**:2287–2295.

Jouany, J. P., Demeyer, D. I., and Grain, J., 1988, Effects of defaunating the rumen, *Anim. Feed Sci. Technol.* **21**:229–265.

Kemp, P., Lander, D. J., and Orpin, C. G., 1984, The lipids of the rumen fungus *Piromonas communis*, *J. Gen. Microbiol.* **130**:27–37.

Kemp, P., Jordan, D. J., and Orpin, C. G., 1985, The free- and protein-amino acids of the rumen phycomycete fungi *Neocallimastix frontalis* and *Piromonas communis*, *J. Agric. Sci.* **105:**523–526.

Kern, D. L., Slyter, L. L., Weaver, J. M., Leffel, E. C., and Samuelson, G., 1973, Pony cecum vs steer rumen: The effect of oats and hay on the microbial ecosystem, *J. Anim. Sci.* **37:**463–469.

Kopecny, J., and Williams, A. G., 1988, Synergism of rumen microbial hydrolases during degradation of plant polymers, *Folia Microbiol.* **33:**208–212.

Kudo, R. R., 1966, *Protozoology*, 5th ed., Thomas, Springfield.

Kulda, J., Kabičková, H., Tachezy, A., Čerkasovová, A., and Čerkasov, J., 1989, Metronidazole-resistant trichomonads: Mechanism of *in vitro* developed anaerobic resistance, in: *Biochemistry and Molecular Biology of Anaerobic Protozoa* (D. Lloyd, G. H. Coombs, and T. A. Paget, eds.), Harwood, Chur, pp. 137–160.

Lee, M. J., Schreurs, P. J., Messer, A. C., and Zinder, S. H., 1987, Association of methanogenic bacteria with flagellated protozoa from a termite hindgut, *Curr. Microbiol.* **15:**337–341.

Levine, N. D., 1972, Relationship between certain protozoa and other animals, in: *Research in Protozoology,* Volume 4 (T. Chen, ed.), Pergamon Press, Elmsford, N.Y., 292–350.

Li, J., and Heath, I. B., 1992, The phylogenetic relationships of the anaerobic chytridiomycetous gut fungi (Neocallimasticacea) and the Chytridiomycota. 1. Cladistic analysis of rRNA sequences, *Can. J. Bot.* **70:**1738–1746.

Li, J., Heath, I. B., and Cheng, K.-J., 1991, The development and zoospore ultrastructure of a polycentric gut fungus, *Orpinomyces joyonii* comb. nov., *Can. J. Bot.* **69:**580–589.

Li, X., and Calza, R. E., 1991a, Fractionation of cellulases from the ruminal fungus *Neocallimastix frontalis* EB 188, *Appl. Environ. Microbiol.* **57:**3331–3336.

Li, X., and Calza, R. E., 1991b, Kinetic study of a cellobiase purified from *Neocallimastix frontalis* EB 188, *Biochim. Biophys. Acta* **1080:**148–154.

Li, X., and Calza, R. E., 1991c, Purification and characterization of an extracellular β-glucosidase from the rumen fungus *Neocallimastix frontalis* EB 188, *Enzyme Microb. Technol.* **13:**622–628.

Lindmark, D. G., 1980, Energy metabolism of the anaerobic protozoan *Giardia lamblia, Mol. Biochem. Parasitol.* **1:**1–12.

Lindmark, D. G., Beach, D. H., Singh, B. N., and Holz, G. G., Jr., 1991, Lipids and lipid metabolism of trichomonads (*Tritrichomonas foetus* and *Trichomonas vaginalis*), in: *Biochemical Protozoology* (G. H. Coombs and M. J. North, eds.), Taylor & Francis, London, pp. 329–335.

Linstead, D., 1981, New defined and semidefined media for cultivation of the flagellate *Trichomonas vaginalis, Parasitology* **83:**125–137.

Linstead, D., and Cranshaw, M., 1983, The pathway of arginine catabolism in the parasitic flagellate *Trichomonas vaginalis, Mol. Biochem. Parasitol.* **8:**241–252.

Lloyd, D., and Paget, T. A., 1991, The effects of environmental factors on the metabolism of *Giardia* and *Trichomonas*, in: *Biochemical Protozoology* (G. H. Coombs and M. J. North, eds.), Taylor & Francis, London, pp. 92–101.

Lloyd, D., and Petersen, J. Z., 1985, Metronidazole radical anion generation *in vivo* in *Trichomonas vaginalis:* O_2 quenching is enhanced in a drug-resistant strain, *J. Gen. Microbiol.* **131:**87–92.

Lloyd, D., Lindmark, D. G., and Müller, M., 1979, Respiration of *Tritrichomonas foetus:* Absence of detectable cytochromes, *J. Parasitol.* **65:**466–469.

Lloyd, D., Williams, J., Yarlett, N., and Williams, A. G., 1982, Oxygen affinities of the hydrogenosome-containing protozoa *Tritrichomonas foetus* and *Dasytricha ruminantium* and two aerobic protozoa determined by bacterial bioluminescence, *J. Gen. Microbiol.* **128:**1019–1022.

Lloyd, D., Hillman, K., Yarlett, N., and Williams, A. G., 1989a, Hydrogen production by rumen holotrich protozoa: Effects of oxygen and implications for metabolic control by in situ conditions, *J. Protozool.* **36:**205–213.

Lloyd, D., Yarlett, N., Hillman, K., Paget, T. A., Chapman, A., Ellis, J. E., and Williams, A. G., 1989b, Oxygen and aerotolerant protozoa: studies using non-invasive techniques, *Biochemistry and Molecular Biology of Anaerobic Protozoa* (D. Lloyd, G. H. Coombs, and T. A. Paget, eds.), Harwood, Chur, pp. 1–21.

Lloyd, D., Lauritsen, F. R., and Degn, H., 1991, The parasitic flagellates *Trichomonas vaginalis* and *Tritrichomonas foetus* produce indole and dimethyl disulphide: Direct characterization by membrane inlet tandem mass spectrometry, *J. Gen. Microbiol.* **137:**1743–1747.

Lockwood, B. C., and Coombs, G. H., 1989, The catabolism of amino acids by *Trichomonas vaginalis*, in: *Biochemistry and Molecular Biology of Anaerobic Protozoa* (D. Lloyd, G. H. Coombs, and T. A. Paget, eds.), Harwood, Chur, pp. 93–111.

Lockwood, B., Coombs, G. H., and Williams, A. G., 1988a, Proteinase activity in rumen ciliate protozoa, *J. Gen. Microbiol.* **134:**2605–2614.

Lockwood, B. C., North, M. J., and Coombs, G. H., 1988b, The release of hydrolases from *Trichomonas vaginalis* and *Tritrichomonas foetus, Mol. Biochem. Parasitol.* **30:**135–142.

Lowe, S. E., Theodorou, M. K., and Trinci, A.P.J., 1987a, Isolation of anaerobic fungi from saliva and faeces of sheep, *J. Gen. Microbiol.* **133:**1829–1834.

Lowe, S. E., Theodorou, M. K., and Trinci, A.P.J., 1987b, Cellulases and xylanase of an anaerobic fungus grown on wheat straw, wheat straw holocellulose, cellulose, and xylan, *Appl. Environ. Microbiol.* **53:**1216–1223.

Lubinsky, G., 1955a, On some parasites of parasitic protozoa. 1. *Sphaerita hoari* sp. n. A chytrid parasitizing *Eremoplastron bovis, Can. J. Microbiol.* **1:**440–450.

Lubinsky, G., 1955b, On some parasites of parasitic protozoa. 2. *Sagittospora cameroni*, gen. n., sp. n. A phycomycete parasitizing Ophryoscolecidae, *Can. J. Microbiol.* **1:**675–684.

Lund, A., 1974, Yeasts and moulds in the bovine rumen, *J. Gen. Microbiol.* **81:**453–462.

McArthur, J. M., and Miltimore, J. E., 1961, Rumen gas analysis by gas–solid chromatography, *Can. J. Anim. Sci.* **41:**187–196.

McBee, R. H., 1977, Fermentation in the hindgut, in: *Microbial Ecology of the Gut* (R.T.J. Clarke and T. Bauchop, eds.), Academic Press, New York, pp. 185–222.

Mack, S. R., and Müller, M., 1978, Effect of oxygen and carbon dioxide on the growth of *Trichomonas vaginalis* and *Tritrichomonas foetus, J. Parasitol.* **64:**927–929.

Marvin-Sikkema, F. D., Richardson, A. J., Stewart, C. S., Gottschal, J. C., Prins, R. A., 1990, Influence of hydrogen-consuming bacteria on cellulose degradation by anaerobic fungi, *Appl. Environ. Microbiol.* **56:**3793–3797.

Marvin-Sikkema, F. D., Rees, E., Kraak, M. N., Gottschel, J. C., and Prins, R. A., 1993, Influence of metronidazole, CO, CO_2, and matharogens on the fermentative metabolism of the anaerobic fungus *Neocallimastix* sp. L2, *Appl. Environ Microbiol.* **59:**2678–2683.

Mertens, E., 1990, Occurrence of pyrophosphate fructose-6-phosphate 1-phosphotransferase in *Giardia lamblia* trophozoites, *Mol. Biochem. Parasitol.* **40:**147–150.

Mertens, E., Van Schaftingen, E., and Müller, M., 1989, Presence of a fructose-2,6-biphosphate-insensitive pyrophosphate: fructose-6-phosphotransferase in the anaerobic protozoa *Tritrichomonas vaginalis* and *Isotricha prostoma, Mol. Biochem. Parasitol.* **37:**183–190.

Meyer, E. A. (ed.), 1990, *Human Parasitic Diseases*, Volume 3, Elsevier, Amsterdam.

Michel, V., Fonty, G., Millet, L., Bonnemoy, F., and Gouet, P., 1993, In vitro study of the proteolytic activity of rumen anaerobic fungi, *FEMS Microbiol. Lett.,* **110:**5–10.

Milne, A., Theodorou, M. K., Jordan, M.G.C., King-Spooner, C., and Trinci, A.P.J., 1989, Survival of anaerobic fungi in feces, in saliva, and in pure culture, *Exp. Mycol.* **13:**27–37.

Morrison, M., Mackie, R. I., and Kistner, A., 1990, Evidence that cellulolysis by an anaerobic ruminal fungus is catabolite regulated by glucose, cellobiose and soluble starch, *Appl. Environ. Microbiol.* **56:**3227–3229.

Mountfort, D. O., 1987, The rumen anaerobic fungi, *FEMS Microbiol. Rev.* **46:**401–408.

Mountfort, D. O., and Asher, R. A., 1983, Role of catabolite regulatory mechanisms in control of carbohydrate utilization by the rumen anaerobic fungus *Neocallimastix frontalis, Appl. Environ. Microbiol.* **46:**1331–1338.

Mountfort, D. O., and Asher, R. A., 1985, Production and regulation of cellulase by two strains of the rumen anaerobic fungus *Neocallimastix frontalis, Appl. Environ. Microbiol.* **49:**1314–1322.

Mountfort, D. O., and Asher, R. A., 1988, Production of α-amylase by the ruminal anaerobic fungus *Neocallimastix frontalis, Appl. Environ. Microbiol.* **54:**2293–2299.

Mountfort, D. O., and Asher, R. A., 1989, Production of xylanase by the ruminal anaerobic fungus *Neocallimastix frontalis, Appl. Environ. Microbiol.* **55:**1016–1022.

Müller, M., 1988, Energy metabolism of protozoa without mitochondria, *Annu. Rev. Microbiol.* **42:**465–488.

Müller, M., 1989, Biochemistry of *Trichomonas vaginalis,* in: *Trichomonads Parasitic in Humans* (B. M. Honigberg, ed.), Springer, Berlin, pp. 53–83.

Müller, M., and Lindmark, D. G., 1978, Respiration of hydrogenosomes in *Trichomonas foetus.* II. Effect of CoA and pyruvate, *J. Biol. Chem.* **253:**1215–1218.

Nagaraja, T. G., and Towne, G., 1990, Ciliated protozoa in relation to ruminal acidosis and lactic acid metabolism, in: *The Rumen Ecosystem: The Microbial Metabolism and Its Regulation* (S. Hoshino, R. Onodera, H. Minato, and H. Itabashi, eds.), Japan Scientific Societies Press, Tokyo, pp. 187–194.

Nakamura, K., 1990, Evolutionary considerations on the distribution of protozoa in herbivores, in: *The Rumen Ecosystem: The Microbial Metabolism and Its Regulation* (S. Hoshino, R. Onodera, H. Minato, and H. Itabashi, eds.), Japan Scientific Societies Press, Tokyo, pp. 13–21.

Newbold, C. J., and Hillman, K., 1990, The effect of ciliate protozoa on the turnover of bacterial and fungal protein in the rumen of sheep, *Lett. Appl. Microbiol.* **11:**100–102.

Newbold, C. J., Chamberlain, D. G., and Williams, A. G., 1986, The effects of defaunation on the metabolism of lactic acid in the rumen, *J. Sci. Food Agric.* **37:**1083–1090.

Newbold, C. J., Williams, A. G., and Chamberlain, D. G., 1987, The in vitro metabolism of D,L-lactic acid by rumen microorganisms, *J. Sci Food Agric.* **38:**9–18.

North, M. J., 1991, Proteinases of trichomonads and Giardia, in: *Biochemical Protozoology* (G. H. Coombs and M. J. North, eds.), Taylor & Francis, London, pp. 234–244.

O'Fallon, J. V., Wright, R. W., and Calza, R. E., 1991, Glucose metabolic pathways in the anaerobic rumen fungus *Neocallimastix frontalis* EB 188, *Biochem. J.* **274:**595–599.

Onodera, R., 1990, Amino acid and protein metabolism by rumen ciliate protozoa, in: *The Rumen Ecosystem: The Microbial Metabolism and Its Regulation* (S. Hoshino, R. Onodera, H. Minato, and H. Itabashi, eds.), Japan Scientific Societies Press, Tokyo, pp. 33–42.

Orpin, C. G., 1975, Studies on the rumen flagellate *Neocallimastix frontalis, J. Gen. Microbiol.* **91:**249–262.

Orpin, C. G., 1976, Studies on the rumen flagellate *Sphaeromonas communis, J. Gen. Microbiol.* **94:**270–280.

Orpin, C. G., 1977, The rumen flagellate *Piromonas communis:* Its life history and invasion of plant material in the rumen, *J. Gen. Microbiol.* **99:**107–117.

Orpin, C. G., 1981, Isolation of cellulolytic phycomycete fungi from the caecum of the horse, *J. Gen. Microbiol.* **123:**187–196.

Orpin, C. G., 1985, Association of rumen ciliate populations with plant particles in vitro, *Microb. Ecol.* **11:**59–69.

Orpin, C. G., 1989, Ecology of rumen anaerobic fungi in relation to the nutrition of the host animal, in: *The Roles of Protozoa and Fungi in Ruminant Digestion* (J. V. Nolan, R. A. Leng, and D. I. Demeyer, eds.), Penambul Books, Armidale, pp. 29–38.

Orpin, C. G., and Ho, Y. W., 1991, Ecology and function of the anaerobic rumen fungi, in: *Recent*

Advances on the Nutrition of Herbivores (Y. W. Ho, H. K. Wong, N. Abdullah, and Z. A. Tajuddin, eds.), Malaysian Society of Animal Production, Selangor, pp. 163–170.

Orpin, C. G., and Joblin, K. N., 1988, The rumen anaerobic fungi, in: *The Rumen Microbial Ecosystem* (P. N. Hobson, ed.), Elsevier, Amsterdam, pp. 129–150.

Paget, T. A., and Lloyd, D., 1990, *Trichomonas vaginalis* requires traces of oxygen and high concentrations of carbon dioxide for optimal growth, *Mol. Biochem. Parasitol.* **41:**65–72.

Paget, T. A., Jarroll, E. L., Manning, P., Lindmark, D. G., and Lloyd, D., 1989, Respiration in cysts and trophozoites of *Giardia muris, J. Gen. Microbiol.* **135:**145–154.

Paget, T. A., Raynor, M. J., Shipp, D.W.E., and Lloyd, D., 1990, *Giardia lamblia* produces alanine anaerobically but not in the presence of oxygen, *Mol. Biochem. Parasitol.* **42:**63–68.

Paget, T. A., Kelly, M., Jarroll, E. L., Lindmark, D. G., and Lloyd, D., 1993, The effects of oxygen on the fermentation in the intestinal parasite *Giardia lamblia, Mol. Biochem. Parasitol.* **57:**65–72.

Parenti, D. M., 1989, Characterization of a thiol proteinase in *Giardia lamblia, J. Infect. Dis.* **160:**1076–1080.

Patton, R. S., and Chandler, P. T., 1975, In vivo digestibility evaluation of chitinous materials, *J. Dairy Sci.* **58:**397–403.

Paul, R. G., 1990, The digestion and metabolism of rumen ciliates, Ph.D. thesis, University of Manchester.

Paul, R. G., Butler, R. D., and Williams, A. G., 1989, Ultrastructure of the rumen holotrich ciliate *Dasytricha ruminantium, Eur. J. Protistol.* **24:**204–215.

Paul, R. G., Williams, A. G., and Butler, R. D., 1990, Hydrogenosomes in the rumen entodiniomorphid ciliate *Polyplastron multivesiculatum, J. Gen. Microbiol.* **136:**1981–1989.

Pearce, P. D., and Bauchop, T., 1985, Glycosidases of the rumen anaerobic fungus *Neocallimastix frontalis* grown on cellulosic substrates, *Appl. Environ. Microbiol.* **49:**1265–1269.

Peterson, K. M., and Alderete, J. F., 1984, Selective acquisition of plasma proteins by *Trichomonas vaginalis* and human lipoproteins as a growth requirement of this species, *Mol. Biochem. Parasitol.* **12:**37–48.

Phillips, M. W., and Gordon, G.L.R., 1988, Sugar and polysaccharide fermentation by rumen anaerobic fungi from Australia, Britain and New Zealand, *BioSystems* **21:**377–383.

Prins, R. A., and Kreulen, D. A., 1990, Comparative aspects of plant cell wall digestion in mammals, in: *The Ecosystem: The Microbial Metabolism and Its Regulation* (S. Hoshino, R. Onodera, H. Minato, and H. Itabashi, eds.), Japan Scientific Societies Press, Tokyo, pp. 109–120.

Prins, R. A., and Prast, E. R., 1973, Oxidation of NADH in a coupled oxidase–peroxidase reaction and its significance for the fermentation in the rumen protozoa of the genus *Isotricha, J. Protozool.* **20:**471–477.

Rashad, A. L., Toffler, W. L., Wolf, R. N., Thornbur, K., Kirk, E. P., Ellis, G., and Whitehead, W. E., 1992, Vaginal pO_2 in healthy women and in women infected with *Trichomonas vaginalis:* Potential implications for metronidazole therapy, *Am. J. Obstet. Gynecol.* **166:**620–624.

Reeves, R. E., 1984, Metabolism of *Entamoeba histolytica* Schaudinn 1903, *Adv. Parasitol.* **23:**105–142.

Reeves, R. E., Warren, L. G., Surstind, B., and Lo, H.-S., 1977, An energy-conserving pyruvate-to-acetate pathway in *Entamoeba histolytica.* Pyruvate synthetase and a new acetate thiokinase, *J. Biol. Chem.* **252:**726–731.

Reeves, R. E., Guthrie, J. D., and Lobelle-Rich, P., 1980, *Entamoeba histolytica:* Isolation of ferredoxin, *Exp. Parasitol.* **49:**83–88.

Reymond, P., Durand, R., Hebraud, M., and Fevre, M., 1991, Molecular cloning of genes from the rumen anaerobic fungus *Neocallimastix frontalis:* Expression during hydrolase induction, *FEMS Microbiol. Lett.* **77:**107–112.

Richardson, A. J., and Stewart, C. S., 1990, Hydrogen transfer between *Neocallimastix frontalis* and *Selenomonas ruminantium* grown in mixed culture, in: *Microbiology and Biochemistry of Strict*

Anaerobes Involved in Interspecies Hydrogen Transfer (J.-P. Belaich, M. Bruschi, and J.-L. Garcia, eds.), Plenum Press, New York, pp. 463–465.

Romulo, B., Bird, S. H., and Leng, R. A., 1989, Effects of defaunation and protein supplementation on intake, digestibility, N-retention, and fungal numbers in sheep fed straw-based diets, in: *The Roles of Protozoa and Fungi in Ruminant Digestion* (J. V. Nolan, R. A. Leng, and D. I. Demeyer, eds.), Penambul Books, Armidale, pp. 285–288.

Sanderson, B. E., White, E., and Balsdon, M. J., 1983, Amine content of vaginal fluid from patients with trichomoniasis and gardnerella associated non-specific vaginitis, *Br. J. Vener. Dis.* **59:**302–305.

Schofield, P. J., and Edwards, M. R., 1991, Energy metabolism in *Giardia intestinalis,* in: *Biochemical Protozoology* (G. H. Coombs and M. J. North, eds.), Taylor & Francis, London, pp. 102–112.

Schofield, P. J., Costello, M., Edwards, M. R., and O'Sullivan, W. J., 1990, The arginine dihydrolase pathway is present in *Giardia intestinalis, Int. J. Parasitol.* **20:**697–699.

Schofield, P. J., Edwards, M. R., and Kranz, P., 1991, Glucose metabolism in *Giardia intestinalis:* A re-evaluation, *Mol. Biochem. Parasitol.* **45:**39–48.

Scott, R. I., Yarlett, N., Hillman, K., Williams, T. N., Williams, A. G., and Lloyd, D., 1983, The presence of oxygen in rumen liquor and its effects on methanogenesis, *J. Appl. Bacteriol.* **55:**143–149.

Silva Filho, F. C., and de Souza, W., 1988, The interaction of *Trichomonas vaginalis* and *Tritrichomonas foetus* with epithelial cells *in vitro, Cell Struct. Funct.* **13:**301–310.

Sivers, V. S., 1962, Fungi of the order Mucorales in the rumen of cattle, *Mikrobiol. Zh.* **24:**14–19.

Smith, P. H., and Hungate, R. E., 1958, Isolation and characterization of *Methanobacterium ruminantium* n. sp. *J. Bacteriol.* **75:**713–718.

Stewart, C. S., Gilmour, J., and McConville, M. L., 1986, Microbial interactions, manipulation and genetic engineering, in: *New Developments and Future Prospects for Research into Rumen Function,* Report EUR 10054 Committee of European Communities, pp. 243–257.

Stewart, C. S., Richardson, A. J., Douglas, R. M., and Rumney, C. J., 1990, Hydrogen transfer in mixed cultures of anaerobic bacteria and fungi with *Methanobrevibacter smithii,* in: *Microbiology and Biochemistry of Strict Anaerobes Involved in Interspecies Hydrogen Transfer* (J.-P. Belaich, M. Bruschi, and J.-L. Garcia, eds.), Plenum Press, New York, pp. 121–131.

Stewart, C. S., Duncan, S. H., Richardson, A. J., Backwell, C., and Begbie, R., 1992, The inhibition of fungal cellulolysis by cell-free preparations from ruminococci, *FEMS Microbiol. Lett.,* **97:**83–88.

Teunissen, M. J., Op den Camp, H.J.M., Orpin, C. G., Huis in 't Veld, J.H.J., and Vogels, G. D., 1991a, Comparison of growth characteristics of anaerobic fungi isolated from ruminant and non-ruminant herbivores during cultivation in a defined medium, *J. Gen. Microbiol.* **137:**1401–1408.

Teunissen, M. J., Smits, A. A., Op den Camp, H.J.M., Orpin, C. G., Huis in 't Veld, J.H.J., and Vogels, G. D., 1991b, Fermentation of cellulose and production of cellulolytic and xylanolytic enzymes by anaerobic fungi from ruminant and non-ruminant herbivores, *Arch. Microbiol.* **156:**290–296.

Teunissen, M. J., Kets, E.P.W., Op den Camp, H.J.M., Huis in 't Veld, J.H.J., and Vogels, G. D., 1992, Effect of coculture of anaerobic fungi isolated from ruminants and non-ruminants with methanogenic bacteria on cellulolytic and xylanolytic enzyme activities, *Arch. Microbiol.* **157:**176–182.

Theodorou, M. K., Gill, M., King-Spooner, C., and Beever, D. E., 1990, Enumeration of anaerobic chytridiomycetes as thallus-forming units: Novel methods for quantification of fibrolytic fungal populations from the digestive tract ecosystem, *Appl. Environ. Microbiol.* **56:**1073–1078.

Thines-Sempoux, D., Delfosse-Debusscher, J., Lefebvre, V., Absil, J. P., and Hellings, P., 1980, Aspects of bacterial–ciliates symbiosis in the rumen: Postulated role of bacteria in the digestive system of the ciliates, in: *Endocytobiology–Endosymbiosis and Cell Biology, a Synthesis of Recent Research* (W. Schwemmler and H.E.A. Schenk, eds.), de Gruyter, Berlin, pp. 371–379.

Thong, K.-W., Coombs, G. H., and Sanderson, B. E., 1987, L-Methionine catabolism in trichomonads, *Mol. Biochem. Parasitol.* **23:**223–231.

Thurston, J. P., and Grain, J., 1971, Holotrich ciliates from the stomach of *Hippopotamus amphibius*, with descriptions of two new genera and four new species, *J. Protozool.* **18:**131–141.

Thurston, J. P., and Noirot-Timothee, C., 1973, Entodiniomorph ciliates from the stomach of *Hippopotamus amphibius* with descriptions of two new genera and three new species, *J. Protozool.* **20:**562–565.

Van Hoven, W., and Gilchrist, F.M.C., 1991, First record of ciliated protozoan endocommensals in the gut of bushpig, *S. Afr. J. Wildlife* **21:**28–29.

Van Hoven, W., Gilchrist, F.M.C., and Hamilton-Attwell, V. L., 1987, Intestinal ciliated protozoa of African rhinoceros: Two new genera and five new species from the white rhino (*Ceratotherium simmum* Burchell, 1817), *J. Protozool.* **34:**338–342.

Van Hoven, W., Gilchrist, F.M.C., and Hamilton-Attwell, V. L., 1988, A new family, genus and seven new species of entodiniomorphida (Protozoa) from the gut of African rhinoceros, *J. Protozool.* **35:**92–97.

Veira, D. M., 1986, The role of ciliate protozoa in the nutrition of the ruminant, *J. Anim. Sci.* **63:**1547–1560.

Veira, D. M., Ivan, M., and Jui, P. Y., 1983, Rumen ciliate protozoa effects on digestion in the stomach of sheep, *J. Dairy Sci.* **66:**1015–1022.

Vervaeke, I. J., Van Nevel, C. J., Decuypere, J. A., and Van Assche, P. F., 1973, A comparison of two methods for obtaining anaerobic counts in different segments of the gastro-intestinal tract of piglets, *J. Appl. Bacteriol.* **36:**397–405.

Vogels, G. D., Hoppe, W. F., and Stumm, C. K., 1980, Association of methanogenic bacteria with rumen ciliates, *Appl. Environ. Microbiol.* **40:**608–612.

Wagner, G., and Levin, R., 1978, Oxygen tension of the vaginal surface during sexual stimulation in the human, *Fertil. Steril.* **30:**50–53.

Wallace, R. J., and Joblin, K. N., 1985, Proteolytic activity of a rumen anaerobic fungus, *FEMS Microbiol. Lett.* **29:**19–25.

Wallace, R. J., and Munro, C. A., 1986, Influence of the rumen anaerobic fungus *Neocallimastix frontalis* on the proteolytic activity of a defined mixture of rumen bacteria growing on a solid substrate, *Lett. Appl. Microbiol.* **3:**23–26.

Williams, A. G., 1979, Exocellular carbohydrase formation by rumen holotrich ciliates, *J. Protozool.* **26:**665–672.

Williams, A. G., 1986, Rumen holotrich ciliate protozoa, *Microbiol. Rev.* **50:**25–49.

Williams, A. G., 1989a, The metabolic activities of rumen protozoa, in: *The Roles of Protozoa and Fungi in Ruminant Digestion* (J. V. Nolan, R. A. Leng, and D. I. Demeyer, eds.), Penambul Books, Armidale, pp. 97–126.

Williams, A. G., 1989b, Hemicellulose utilization by microorganisms in the alimentary tract of ruminant and non-ruminant animals, in: *Enzyme Systems for Lignocellulose Degradation* (M. P. Coughlan, ed.), Elsevier, Amsterdam, pp. 183–219.

Williams, A. G., 1991, The biochemical activities and importance of the ciliate protozoa in the rumen ecosystem, in: *Biochemical Protozoology* (G. H. Coombs and M. J. North, eds.), Taylor & Francis, London, pp. 61–79.

Williams, A. G., and Coleman, G. S., 1985, Hemicellulose degrading enzymes in rumen ciliate protozoa, *Curr. Microbiol.* **12:**85–90.

Williams, A. G., and Coleman, G. S., 1988, Rumen ciliate protozoa, in: *The Rumen Microbial Ecosystem* (P. N. Hobson, ed.), Elsevier, Amsterdam, pp. 77–128.

Williams, A. G., and Coleman, G. S., 1991, *The Rumen Protozoa*, Springer-Verlag, Berlin.

Williams, A. G., and Ellis, A. B., 1985, Subcellular distribution of glycoside hydrolase and polysaccharide depolymerase enzymes in the rumen entodiniomorphid ciliate *Polyplastron multivesiculatum, Curr. Microbiol.* **12:**175–182.

Williams, A. G., and Orpin, C. G., 1987a, Polysaccharide-degrading enzymes formed by three species of anaerobic rumen fungi grown on a range of carbohydrate substrates, *Can. J. Microbiol.* **33:**418–426.

Williams, A. G., and Orpin, C. G., 1987b, Glycoside hydrolase enzymes present in the zoospore and vegetative growth stages of the rumen fungi *Neocallimastix patriciarum, Primonas communis,* and an unidentified isolate, grown on a range of carbohydrates, *Can. J. Microbiol.* **33:**427–434.

Williams, A. G., and Withers, S. E., 1991, Effect of ciliate protozoa on the activity of polysaccharide-degrading enzymes and fibre breakdown in the rumen ecosystem, *J. Appl. Bacteriol.* **70:**144–155.

Williams, A. G., Withers, S. E., and Coleman, G. S., 1984, Glycoside hydrolases of rumen bacteria and protozoa, *Curr. Microbiol.* **10:**287–294.

Williams, A. G., Ellis, A. B., and Coleman, G. S., 1986, Subcellular distribution of polysaccharide depolymerase and glycoside hydrolase enzymes in rumen ciliate protozoa, *Curr. Microbiol.* **13:**139–147.

Williams, A. G., Withers, S. E., and Joblin, K. N., 1991, Xylanolysis by cocultures of the rumen fungus *Neocallimastix frontalis* and ruminal bacteria, *Lett. Appl. Microbiol.* **12:**232–235.

Williams, A. G., Joblin, K. N., Butler, R. D., Fonty, G., and Bernalier, A., 1993a, Bacteria–protist interactions in the rumen, *Ann. Biol.* **32:**13–30.

Williams, A. G., Joblin, K. N., and Fonty, G., 1993b, Interactions between rumen chytrid fungi and other rumen microorganisms, in: *Anaerobic Fungi* (D. O. Mountfort and C. G. Orpin, eds.), Dekker, New York (in press).

Williams, K., Lowe, P. N., and Leadlay, P. F., 1987, Purification and characterisation of pyruvate: ferredoxin oxidoreductase from anaerobic protozoon *Trichomonas vaginalis, Biochem. J.* **246:**529–536.

Wilson, C. A., and Wood, T. M., 1992a, The anaerobic fungus *Neocallimastix frontalis:* Isolation and properties of a cellulosome-type enzyme fraction with the capacity to solubilize hydrogen bond-ordered cellulose, *Appl. Microbiol. Biotechnol.* **37:**125–129.

Wilson, C. A., and Wood, T. M., 1992b, Studies on the cellulase of the rumen anaerobic fungus *Neocallimastix frontalis,* with special reference to the capacity of the enzyme to degrade crystalline cellulose, *Enzyme Microb. Technol.* **14:**258–264.

Wilson, J. R., and Engels, F. M., 1989, Do rumen fungi have a significant role in particle size reduction, in: *The Roles of Protozoa and Fungi in Ruminant Digestion* (J. V. Nolan, R. A. Leng, and D. I. Demeyer, eds.), Penambul Books, Armidale, pp. 255–257.

Wood, T. M., Wilson, C. A., McCrae, S. I., and Joblin, K. N., 1986, A highly active extracellular cellulase from the anaerobic rumen fungis *Neocallimastix frontalis, FEMS Microbiol. Lett.* **34:**37–40.

Wubah, D. A., Fuller, M. S., and Akin, D. E., 1991, Resistant body formation in *Neocallimastix* sp., an anaerobic fungus from the rumen of a cow, *Mycologia* **83:**40–47.

Yamin, M. A., 1979, Flagellates of the orders Trichomonadida Kirby, Oxymonadida Grassé and Hypermastigida Grassi & Foà reported from lower termites (Isoptera families Mastotermitidae, Kalotermitidae, Hodotermitidae, Termopsidae, Rhinotermitidae, and Serritermitidae) and from the wood-feeding roach *Cryptocercus* (Dictyoptera: Cryptocericidae), *Sociobiol* **4:**3–117.

Yarlett, N., 1988, Polyamine biosynthesis and inhibition in *Trichomonas vaginalis, Parasitol. Today* **4:**357–360.

Yarlett, N., 1993, Fermentation product generation in rumen phycomycetes, in: *Anaerobic Fungi* (D. O. Mountfort and C. G. Orpin, eds.), Dekker, New York (in press).

Yarlett, N., and Bacchi, C. J., 1988, Effect of DL-α-difluoromethylornithine on polyamine synthesis and interconversion in *Trichomonas vaginalis* grown in a semi-defined medium, *Mol. Biochem. Parasitol.* **31:**1–10.

Yarlett, N., and Bacchi, C. J., 1991, Polyamine metabolism in anaerobic protozoa, in: *Biochemical Protozoology* (G. H. Coombs and M. J. North, eds.), Taylor & Francis, London, pp. 458–468.

Yarlett, N., Hann, A. C., Lloyd, D., and Williams, A. G., 1981, Hydrogenosomes in the rumen protozoon *Dasytricha ruminantium* Schuberg, *Biochem. J.* **200:**365–372.

Yarlett, N., Lloyd, D., and Williams, A. G., 1982, Respiration of the rumen ciliate *Dasytricha ruminantium* Schuberg, *Biochem. J.* **206:**259–266.

Yarlett, N., Hann, A. C., Lloyd, D., and Williams, A. G., 1983a, Hydrogenosomes in a mixed isolate of *Isotricha prostoma* and *Isotricha intestinalis* from ovine rumen contents, *Comp. Biochem. Physiol.* **74B:**357–364.

Yarlett, N., Scott, R. I., Williams, A. G., and Lloyd, D., 1983b, A note on the effects of oxygen on hydrogen production by the rumen protozoon *Dasytricha ruminantium*, *J. Appl. Bacteriol.* **55:**359–361.

Yarlett, N., Coleman, G. S., Williams, A. G., and Lloyd, D., 1984, Hydrogenosomes in known species of rumen entodiniomorphid protozoa, *FEMS Microbiol. Lett.* **21:**15–19.

Yarlett, N., Lloyd, D., and Williams, A. G., 1985, Butyrate formation from glucose by the rumen protozoon *Dasytricha ruminantium*, *Biochem. J.* **228:**187–192.

Yarlett, N., Orpin, C. G., Munn, E. A., Yarlett, N. C., and Greenwood, C. A., 1986a, Hydrogenosomes in the rumen fungus *Neocallimastix patriciarum*, *Biochem. J.* **236:**729–739.

Yarlett, N., Yarlett, N. C., and Lloyd, D., 1986b, Metronidazole-resistant clinical isolates of *Trichomonas vaginalis* have lowered oxygen affinities, *Mol. Biochem. Parasitol.* **19:**111–116.

Yarlett, N., Rowlands, C., Yarlett, N. C., Evans, J. C., and Lloyd, D., 1987, Respiration of the hydrogenosome-containing fungus *Neocallimastix patriciarum*, *Arch. Microbiol.* **148:**25–28.

Zierdt, C. H., Donnolley, C. T., Muller, J., and Constantopoulos, G., 1988, Biochemical and ultrastructural study of *Blastocystis hominis*, *J. Clin. Microbiol.* **26:**965–970.

6

Intraclonal Polymorphism in Bacteria

PAUL B. RAINEY, E. RICHARD MOXON and
IAN P. THOMPSON

Before the invention of pure culture methods, bacteria were believed to be fantastically variable—indeed, all the different types observed were thought by some biologists (the pleomorphists) to represent different stages in the life cycles of a few kinds of microbe. Koch's demonstration that each type of bacterium breeds true when grown in pure culture caused the pendulum to swing the other way; it became the majority opinion that bacteria were monomorphic. At the beginning of the twentieth century, however, it became recognized that even the most impeccably pure cultures were able to change, and many bacteriologists began to study the mechanism of such variations.

Stanier, Dourdoroff, and Adelberg (1958)

1. Introduction

Bacteria occupy an extremely diverse range of habitats: from deep-sea volcanic vents to arctic soils and from animal organs to air-conditioning systems in modern buildings (Krieg and Holt, 1984). Given the diversity of genotypes within the eubacteria and archaebacteria this ubiquitous distribution is not surprising, but even at the genus level the ability to occupy disparate environments is often encountered. Moreover, this ability extends even to the species level, where, for example, *Pseudomonas aeruginosa* may be isolated from soil, water, and the lungs of humans compromised by cystic fibrosis (Palleroni, 1984). Evidently, the potential for adaptation within bacterial populations is prodigious. Even among genetically related bacteria, the ability to survive rapid and extensive changes in the environment is striking, reflecting in part the capacity for phenotypic variation or plasticity. Phenotypic plasticity has been defined as the ability of a single genotype to produce more than one alternative form of morphology, physiological state, and/or behavior in response to environmental conditions (West-

Paul B. Rainey and Ian P. Thompson • Institute of Virology and Environmental Microbiology, Oxford OX1 3SR, England.   **E. Richard Moxon** • Molecular Infectious Diseases Group, Institute of Molecular Medicine, Oxford University, John Radcliffe Hospital, Oxford OX3 9DU, England.
Advances in Microbial Ecology, Volume 13, edited by J. Gwynfryn Jones. Plenum Press, New York, 1993.

Eberhard, 1989). Ultimately, however, phenotypic plasticity reflects altered gene expression and it is the essence and subtleties of these genetically determined adaptations which are addressed in this chapter.

The majority of bacteria inhabit heterogeneous environments which are subject to constant and often unpredictable change. Upon encountering an unfavorable environment, bacteria have two options: either to escape (temporally or spatially) or to adapt. Several strategies for temporal escape have been described (Roszak and Colwell, 1987) and include spore formation in *Bacillus* (Losick and Youngman, 1984) and fruit body formation in *Myxobacteria* (Kaiser, 1984). Spatial escape may be possible for motile bacteria (Gammack *et al.*, 1992).

Bacteria are able to adapt to an extensive range of external stimuli by coordinated regulation of gene expression, which enables bacteria to optimize the level of gene expression for a particular set of environmental conditions. For example, many bacteria are able to respond to iron starvation by synthesis of siderophores and their cognate receptors (Leong, 1986). The ability to respond in this manner to fluctuations in external parameters is essential for survival, but it is limited in that it can only ensure adaptation to conditions which have been previously encountered by ancestral bacteria and to which a genetic response has previously evolved. It does not necessarily provide a means of responding to novel, unfavorable environments.

Strategies by which bacteria adapt to unpredictable environments are not well understood. Adaptation to novel, inhospitable environments is unlikely to be achieved by coordinated regulation of gene expression alone. In many higher organisms, adaptation occurs as a result of the action of natural selection on preexisting genetic variation within a species. This may also occur within bacterial populations, but the concept that genetic variability within a species population is important for adaptation and long term evolutionary success is not so obviously applicable to bacteria. This is because bacteria are not dependent upon sex (intergenomic transfer of DNA) with related bacteria (same species) to generate progeny, and neither are they dependent on sex with related bacteria to generate variation. Progeny are produced by binary fission and variation can be generated by several mechanisms, including exchange of DNA with quite unrelated organisms. Hence, the concept of a variable pool of genotypes that is confined to members of a species and upon which natural selection can operate, is not a useful paradigm. Subsequently, it is possible to consider a bacterial genotype as an entity that is concerned with its own survival, rather than with contributing to the long term evolutionary success of a "species" by enhancing variation within a gene pool. In this context, it is important to distinguish between independent and cooperative action of bacteria (Moxon and Murphy, 1978); a population of bacteria may exhibit properties *en masse* that are denied to single organisms. Confronted with the same problem of adapting to change as are higher organisms (and yet confined to a predominantly asexual mode of reproduction), it is likely that bacteria have evolved novel strategies for generating variation independently of sex. It is our opinion that intraclonal polymorphism reflects such an ability. This chapter seeks to emphasize the importance of intraclonal polymorphism in bacteria and does so in several parts. Following a discussion of definitions and terminology, colony sectoring, a commonly encountered manifestation of intraclonal polymorphism, is examined from first principles. Conclusions from this section are combined with information on genetic mechanisms and a hypothesis concerning the significance of intraclonal polymorphism in bacteria is presented. Results from an experiment designed to test the hypothesis are outlined and finally, the implications of intraclonal polymorphic variation are considered.

We have drawn examples from a variety of subject areas in order to demonstrate the ubiquitous occurrence of intraclonal polymorphism in bacteria. Where possible we have selected examples from both nonpathogenic and pathogenic bacteria, but because of the scarcity of information concerning certain aspects of intraclonal polymorphism in nonpathogenic bacteria, this has not always been feasible. Our primary intention has not been to recount the many documented instances of intraclonal bacterial polymorphism, but to develop a conceptual framework on which a hypothesis concerning the significance of intraclonal polymorphism in bacteria can be developed.

2. Definitions and Terminology

An understanding of how organisms interact with their environment is necessary before the biology of any organism can be fully realised. This requirement has led to an enormous interest in strategies for responding to environmental change. Most of this interest has been directed toward higher organisms and some of these ideas and concepts are applicable to bacteria (Andrews, 1991).

2.1. A Working Definition of Intraclonal Polymorphism

A useful starting point for the development of a working definition of intraclonal polymorphism in bacteria is provided by studies on phenotypic variation strategies in plants (Sultan, 1987; Schlichting, 1986; Lloyd, 1984; Bradshaw, 1965). Lloyd (1984) recognized that plant structures exhibit five principal classes of variation in heterogeneous environments, namely, uniformity, continuous lability, genetic polymorphism, conditional choices, and multiple strategies. The third of these classes, genetic polymorphism, which is defined by the occurrence of distinct, genetically determined phenotypes within natural populations (Ford, 1971), most closely portrays intraclonal polymorphism in bacteria.

The main difficulty with this definition, which prevents it from accurately defining intraclonal bacterial polymorphism, arises from the fact that plant populations, with few exceptions, are not exclusively clonal and usually exhibit some form of sexual reproduction. We therefore define intraclonal bacterial polymorphism as the occurrence of phenotypically distinct individuals within an asexually reproducing population. While realizing that the term *polymorphism* has been widely used, we feel that this restricted definition accurately describes the subject of this chapter.

Intraclonal polymorphism in bacteria is not a new concept and reports of phenotypic variation span more than a century. Over this time a number of terms have been employed to describe instances of this behavior, including dissociation (Henry, 1933), clonal polymorphism/dimorphism (Simon and Silverman, 1983), colony polymorphism/dimorphism (Sylvester-Bradley *et al.*, 1988), phenotypic switching (Schrader and Holmes, 1988), phenotypic variation (Rainey, 1991), colonial heterogeneity (Claassen *et al.*, 1986), morphological variation (Coetzee and Sacks, 1960), phase variation (Stocker, 1949), and antigenic variation (Bhaskaran and Gorrill, 1957). These different terminologies have tended to reflect the view that each instance of intraclonal polymorphism is distinct and has led to the development of a diverse range of opinions which have hampered full realization of the universal nature and fundamental significance of this phenomenon.

2.2. Phase Variation and Antigenic Variation

Phase variation and antigenic variation are two terms in common usage which describe specific instances of intraclonal bacterial polymorphism, especially among medically important pathogens. Phase variation refers to alterations in phenotype which are controlled by an ON/OFF switch. In contrast, antigenic variation refers to qualitative alterations in the expression of particular determinants. For example, phase variation in *Mycoplasma hyorhinis* results from ON/OFF expression of three surface lipoproteins and manifests as alterations in both colony opacity and morphology. The lipoproteins are themselves subject to antigenic variation in which the size of the proteins vary depending on the number of repetitive intragenic coding sequences (Yogev *et al.*, 1991).

2.3. Mechanisms of Altered Gene Expression

Central to the concepts and ideas presented below is an emphasis on the role of stochastic mechanisms, the nature and timing of which, within the constraints of the genotype, are probabilistic, rather than stereotypic. These mechanisms generate diversity within bacterial populations and this "blind" variation can be adaptive.

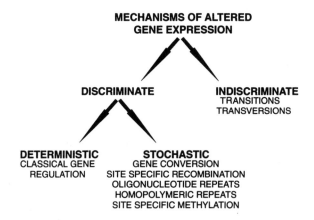

Figure 1. Mechanisms of altered gene expression.

Intraclonal polymorphic variation must occur as a result of altered gene expression which is governed either by alterations in DNA sequence, or by alterations in DNA conformation. Changes in DNA sequence may result from intergenomic or intragenomic events. Intergenomic events and their evolutionary consequences for bacteria are reviewed elsewhere (see, for example, Maynard-Smith, 1990; Maynard-Smith *et al.*, 1991). Intragenomic alterations in gene expression which occur as a result of either conformational or sequence changes in DNA can be further differentiated depending upon the discriminatory nature of the regulatory event (Fig. 1). Indiscriminate alterations in gene expression result primarily from random DNA sequence changes (transitions and transversions; also referred to as mutation, incidental mutation, or unprogrammed mutation; Borst and Greaves, 1987; Robertson and Meyer, 1992) which occur throughout the genome. Such alterations include errors which result from DNA replication, repair, or recombination; movement of mobile genetic elements; or from the insertion or excision of immigrant DNA. In contrast, discriminate alterations in gene expression include those mutations and alterations in DNA conformation which are restricted to particular genetic loci (genes, operons, regulons, stimulons, etc.). The majority of coordinated gene regulatory mechanisms are of this type and involve alterations in DNA conformation at precise genomic locations without sequence change. For example, binding of the *lac* repressor to the *lac* operator in the absence of an inducer molecule prevents transcription of the *lac* operon. An important aspect of this type of regulatory mechanism is that the outcome is predictable, that is, deterministic. This contrasts markedly with an additional category of discriminate regulatory mechanisms where the outcome of each regulatory event is governed by stochastic mechanisms.

Discriminate stochastic mechanisms of gene regulation which involve DNA sequence alterations have been called "programmed" rearrangements (Borst and

Greaves, 1987; Robertson and Meyer, 1992). Unfortunately this term is confusing because these mechanisms are not programmed in the sense that specific mutations (and the phenotypic changes they engender) do not occur more often when they are useful than when they are not, nor are they deterministic. Such rearrangements are confined to particular regions of the chromosome and are characterized by certain arrangements of nucleotides, such as oligonucleotide repeats, or homopolymeric repeats (Fig. 1). Through slipped-strand mispairing, polymerase slippage, or recombination between homologous repeats, such arrangements can alter transcription or translation (frame-shifts). As a consequence, these loci can generate phenotypic variation at high frequency. Discriminate stochastic regulation of gene expression can also occur without sequence change and as a result of changes in DNA conformation which arise through the positioning of potential methylation sites. Discriminate stochastic mechanisms of gene regulation are described more fully below (see genetic mechanisms controlling intraclonal polymorphism).

2.4. Phenotypic Plasticity

Intraclonal polymorphism in bacteria is not synonymous with the term *phenotypic plasticity* as described and discussed by Brown and Williams (1985) or Costerton (1988). Phenotypic plasticity results from coordinated genetic responses to precise signals, such as iron starvation, whereas we argue that a component of intraclonal polymorphic variation is independent of environmental variation *per se,* occurs as a result of random (stochastic) mechanisms, and does not represent an individual genotype's response. While such a distinction suggests that phenotypic plasticity and intraclonal polymorphic variation are separable, they are not mutually exclusive; indeed, it is advantageous for both coordinated and random processes to operate together.

3. Variation of Colony Morphology

Since the days of Robert Koch, the agar plate colony has played a crucial role in the methodology of microbiology and still provides the main basis for the isolation of pure cultures (Brock, 1961). Individual well-isolated colonies develop from the growth of individual bacterial cells. Since bacteria reproduce asexually, by binary fission, all bacteria within a colony are frequently assumed to be genetically and phenotypically identical (Atlas and Bartha, 1987). Closer inspection of a colony often reveals this assumption to be incorrect; individual cells may differ genetically and/or phenotypically for a variety of reasons, including mutation, and differences arising from chance fluctuations in the synthesis, or partitioning of critical macromolecules (Koch, 1987; Simon and Silverman, 1983). One of the most common and striking ways this heterogeneity can express itself in laboratory studies is colony sectoring.

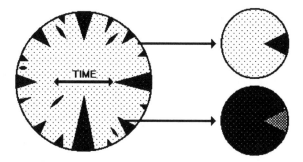

Figure 2. Diagrammatic representation of a typical polymorphic colony showing variant sectors (both dots and sectors), and phenotype of subcultured sectors. Note the relationship between sectoring and time.

4. Colony Sectoring

Colony sectoring has been observed in a wide range of bacteria (Simon and Silverman, 1983) and probably overlooked in many others. Almost all instances of intraclonal polymorphism in bacteria have been detected initially as a result of the gain, loss, or alteration of observable characteristics, such as colony morphology, or virulence.

Sectoring usually occurs after several days' growth on agar plates and appears as a morphologically distinct, subclonal region within a single colony (Shapiro, 1986) (Fig. 2). Observations on colony growth indicate that this region arises as a result of the *de novo* appearance and subsequent growth of a single phenotypic variant cell within the actively growing regions of a colony. The type of sector, either "wedge" or "dot," depends on whether the phenotypic variant cell arises among actively dividing cells at the colony periphery, in which case a wedge will result, or within cells involved in upward expansion of the colony, in which case a dot-shaped sector will appear (Shapiro, 1986). Frequently a wedge sector will extend beyond the margin of the colony indicating more rapid growth of the variant cells and it is common to observe more than one sector per colony, and more than one variant sector type (Fig. 2).

A typical characteristic of the cells of variant sectors is that when selected and subcultured they yield colonies predominantly with the morphology of the variant sector. Similarly, when cells of an unsectored region are subcultured they produce colonies true to the original form (Fig. 2). While it is not often reported, variant colonies will themselves sector in time, giving rise to a third variant and so this process will continue. However, sectoring of variant colonies usually takes much longer than the 2–3 days required for sectoring of wild-type colonies and drying agar plates may render detection difficult. Occasionally, variant colonies will give rise to the original wild-type form, but among nonpathogenic bacteria this is uncommon and usually back reversion is not detected on agar plates. Among pathogenic bacteria, switching between a range of variants is often encountered *in vitro* (Saunders, 1986).

5. Examples of Intraclonal Polymorphism

There are many reports of colony sectoring which result in a polymorphic population of genetically related cells. Examples of intraclonal polymorphism in three diverse bacterial species are described below and numerous examples are recorded in Table I.

5.1. Intraclonal Polymorphism in Luminescent Marine Bacteria

Intraclonal polymorphism among luminescent marine bacteria, including *Photobacterium phosphorium, P. leiognathi,* and *Vibrio harveyi,* highlights polymorphism as manifest by colony sectoring. Initial observations made in the last century revealed that luminous cultures give rise to colonies which emit little or no light (Beijerinck, 1889). Loss of light production is heritable, but non-light-emitting colonies occasionally yield colonies with the original luminescence phenotype. Luminescence is reported to be very unstable in old cultures, and bacteria grown in nonshaken broth cultures at elevated temperatures also show high numbers of non-light-emitting variants (Keynan and Hastings, 1961). Instability of the luminescence phenotype is also marked in strains freshly isolated from the natural environment (Nealson, 1972). The frequency of switching in some strains can occur at rates as high as 10^{-1} to 10^{-2} event per cell per generation (Silverman *et al.,* 1989). Careful characterization of the variants with respect to light emission has shown that at least four variants are produced (Silverman *et al.,* 1989).

Recent studies have shown that variation of several other characteristics also occurs, including flagellation, colony morphology, bacteriophage sensitivity, outer membrane protein composition, and cell adhesiveness (Nealson, 1972; Silverman *et al.,* 1989).

5.2. Intraclonal Polymorphism in *Pseudomonas tolaasii*

Pseudomonas tolaasii, causal organism of brown blotch disease of the cultivated mushroom, provides another good example of a bacterium which displays marked intraconal polymorphism.

Opaque wild-type *P. tolaasii* colonies produce a low-molecular-weight peptide toxin (tolaasin) which causes disruption of hyphal cell membranes and typical disease symptoms (Rainey *et al.,* 1992, 1993). When cultured on agar plates, wild-type colonies rapidly sector and produce translucent variants which are avirulent (Olivier *et al.,* 1978; Cutri *et al.,* 1984; Rainey, 1989). Avirulent variants do not produce tolaasin and also differ from the wild-type form with respect to a

Table I. Examples of Intraclonal Polymorphism in Bacteria

Organism	Variable phenotype	Mechanism*	Reference
Anaplasma marginale	Surface antigen	Oligonucleotide repeat	Allred et al. (1990)
Bacteroides nodosus	Pilin		McKern et al. (1985)
Bordetella avium	Colony morphology		Jackwood et al. (1991)
B. pertussis	Fimbriae		Coote (1991)
Borellia hermsii	Lipoprotein (Vmp)	Homopolymeric repeats	Plasterk et al. (1991)
Bradyrhizobium spp.	Colony morphology	Homologous recombination	Sylvester-Bradley et al. (1988)
Brucella spp.	Colony morphology		Henry (1933)
Campylobacter coli	Flagellin		Guerry et al. (1988)
C. jejuni	Flagellin		King and Clayton (1991)
Citrobacter freundii	Vi antigen	Insertion/deletion of IS	Snellings et al. (1981)
Enterobacter aerogenes	Colony morphology		Strange and Hunter (1966)
	Polysaccharide		
	Surface antigen		
Escherichia coli	Pap pilin	Methylation blocking factor	Braaten et al. (1991)
	Fimbriae	Site-specific recombination	Glasgow et al. (1989)
	Autoaggregation		Warne et al. (1990)
Haemophilus influenzae b	LPS	Oligonucleotide repeats	Weiser et al. (1989)
	Capsulation	Gene deletion	Brophy et al. (1991)
Legionella pneumophilia	Surface antigen		Harrison et al. (1990)
	Plasmid content		
Moraxella bovis	Pilin	Site-specific recombination	Marrs et al. (1988)
Mycoplasma hyorhinis	Lipoproteins (Vlp)	Oligonucleotide repeats	Yogev et al. (1991)
		Homopolymeric repeats	Yogev et al. (1991)
Myxococcus xanthus	Pigment	DNA rearrangement	Yee and Inouye (1984)
Neisseria gonorrhoeae	Pilin	Homopolymeric repeats	James and Swanson (1978)
	Opacity protein		Swanson and Barrera (1983)
N. meningitidis	Pilin	Oligonucleotide repeats	Olafson et al. (1985)
Proteus hauseri	Colony morphology		Weil and Felix (1917)

(continued)

Table I. (*Continued*)

Organism	Variable phenotype	Mechanism*	Reference
Pseudomonas sp.	Utilization of meta-chlorobenzoate	Gene amplification	Rangnekar (1988)
P. aeruginosa	Pilin		Sastry et al. (1983)
	EPS		Govan (1989)
P. atlantica	EPS	Insertion/deletion of IS	Bartlett et al. (1988)
P. gingeri	Pathogenicity		Cutri et al. (1984)
P. lachrymans	Pathogenicity		Lucas and Grogan (1969)
	Attachment		Rainey (1991)
P. putida	Chemotaxis		Grewal and Rainey (1991)
P. solanacearum	Pathogenicity	Oligonucleotide repeat	Brumbley et al. (1993)
	Chemotaxis		Kelman and Hruschka (1973)
P. stutzeri	Dentrification		Stanier et al. (1966)
P. syringae	Pathogenicity		Gross and DeVay (1977)
P. tolaasii	Pathogenicity		Olivier et al. (1978)
	Chemotaxis		Grewal and Rainey (1991)
	Attachment		Rainey (1991)
Rhizobium CB756	Symbiotic efficiency		Herridge and Roughley (1975)
R. japonicum	Nutritional diversity		Kuykendall and Elkan (1976)
R. melliloti	Colony morphology		Jensen (1942)
R. phaseoli	Symbiotic efficiency		Flores et al. (1988)
R. trifolii			
Rhodopseudomonas spheroides	Pigment		Griffiths and Stanier (1956)
Salmonella typhimurium	Flagellin	Site-specific recombination	Glasgow et al. (1989)
Serratia marcescens	Pigment		Paruchuri and Harshey (1987)
Staphylococcus aureus	Flagellin		Smith et al. (1977)
S. epidermis	EPS		Christensen et al. (1987)

Organism	Trait	Mechanism*	Reference
Streptococci group A	Colony morphology		Deighton et al. (1992)
	Hemolysis		
Streptococcus gordonii	M protein	Oligonucleotide repeat	Fischetti (1991)
S. pyrogenes	Glucosyltransferase		Vickerman et al. (1991)
	Colony opacity		Pincus et al. (1992)
Streptomyces reticuli	Pigment		Schrempf (1983)
Thiobacillus ferrooxidans	Colony morphology		Schrader and Holmes (1988)
	Iron oxidation		
T. versutus	Surface antigen		Claassen et al. (1986)
	EPS		
Vibrio cholerae	Antigenicity		Bhaskaran and Gorrill (1957)
V. harveyi	Bioluminescence		Keynan and Hastings (1961)
Xanthomonas campestris	Pathogenicity		Kamoun and Kado (1990)
	Chemotaxis		
	Xanthan production		
X. phaseoli	Pathogenicity		Corey and Starr (1957)
Xenorhabdus luminescens	Colony morphology		Hurlbert et al. (1989)
	Bioluminescence		
	Swarming		
	Antibiotic		
Yersinia spp.	YopA, invasin	Homopolymeric repeat	Rosqvist et al. (1991)
Incl1 Plasmid R721	Pilin	Site-specific recombination	Kim and Komano (1992)

*where known

number of additional characteristics. These include motility and chemotaxis (Grewal and Rainey, 1991), cell adhesion (Rainey, 1991), siderophore production, respiration rate, and total soluble protein (Rainey, 1989, and unpublished).

Sectoring in *P. tolaasii* also occurs at a higher rate in freshly isolated strains (approximately 10^{-3} per cell per generation) than in laboratory strains, and sectoring is also more prevalent in old colonies which have grown on an uncrowded plate. Interestingly, when *P. tolaasii* is cultured in unshaken broth for several days before streaking onto solid media, an extensive array of intricately sculptured phenotypic forms are produced. Such variants are not apparent when the bacterium is cultured on solid media (Rainey, 1989).

5.3. Intraclonal Polymorphism in *Neisseria gonorrhoeae*

A large number of human pathogenic bacteria also undergo phenotypic variation when cultured *in vitro* (Table I). *Neisseria gonorrhoeae,* a gram-negative diplococcus which causes sexually transmitted disease in humans, produces a range of phenotypically distinct colonies when cultured on clear media. These colonies differ in size, edge morphology, and opacity and also in a range of biological characters such as virulence, adhesion to host cells, and susceptibility to killing (Saunders, 1989). Because phenotypic switching affects virulence determinants, the mechanisms by which these changes are controlled have received considerable attention. This is also true of a number of other medically important pathogens (Table I).

Changes in colony morphology correlate with independent variation of two surface components, pili and the principal outer membrane protein (P.II, or opacity protein). Piliated colonies (P⁺) are generally small in diameter and have sharp edges and sector to produce nonpiliated variants (P⁻) which form larger colonies with indistinct boundaries (Swanson and Barrera, 1983). The switch is reversible and the frequency of P⁺ to P⁻, and from P⁻ to P⁺ is approximately 10^{-2} to 10^{-3}, and 10^{-5} per cell per generation, respectively (Swanson, 1987).

Small and large colonies also differ in their degree of opacity and range from translucent to white, with a number of degrees of opacity in between. This variation is caused by alterations in the number of P.II polypeptides which ranges from several to none (Swanson, 1982). In addition to phase variation, both pili and P.II are subject to antigenic variation which is discernible following antibody reactions (Saunders, 1989). The presence of variable factors which are not immediately visible raises the possibility that the number of characteristics known to show transitional behavior is an underestimate.

6. Intraclonal Polymorphism in Bacteria: Development of a Hypothesis

The above descriptions of colony sectoring and examples of intraclonal polymorphism provide a number of clues to the possible significance of variant production. These are outlined below and provide a basis for the development of a hypothesis.

6.1. A Genetic Mechanism

Genetic mechanisms involved in the production of phenotypic variants must accommodate the following characteristics: (1) the frequency with which phenotypic variants typically arise, (2) the number of behavioral, physiological, and morphological alterations, and (3) the reversibility of switching.

Recent examination of the basis of variant production in several different genera of pathogenic bacteria has shown a variety of genetic mechanisms involved in phenotypic switching. These are considered in more detail below.

6.2. Regulation by Environmental Stimuli

Observations of the occurrence of sectors in colonies indicate that in many bacterial species they arise in a time-dependent manner. Few variants, if any, are produced during the early stages of colony growth, but as a colony matures (2–3 days) the frequency of sectoring greatly increases (Fig. 2). This behavior suggests that variants are not produced independently of external stimuli. A degree of regulation is also suggested by the different frequencies with which variants interconvert, for example, the rate of switching between P^+ and P^- pilation states in *N. gonorrhoeae* (see above).

The nature of the stimuli are in most instances unknown; however, the apparently random manner in which sectors arise indicates that cells do not respond to stimuli in a uniform manner. We suggest that the key stimulus is stress. As a functional correlate, stress may be said to occur when classical regulation of gene expression can no longer provide an adequate response to changing environmental conditions (see Hoffmann and Parsons, 1991). The possible involvement of stress is consistent with reports of a greater frequency of sectoring in colonies resulting from the growth of freshly isolated bacteria, and in mature colonies; in both these situations bacteria are likely to be in a state of increased stress.

Apart from visual observations, there is little direct evidence to support the idea that stress regulates variant production, however, recent work has shown that variation of both Pap pili and the major fimbrial subunit of *Escherichia coli* are subject to external influences. In fimbrial phase variation this is affected by *osmZ,* the gene product of which influences DNA supercoiling in response to osmotic stress (Higgins *et al.,* 1988). It is possible that intraclonal polymorphic variation is regulated at a basal level by a global stress-responsive mechanism, such as the degree of DNA supercoiling (Higgins *et al.,* 1990; Dorman and Ni Bhriain, 1992). However, having raised this possibility we urge caution and emphasize that stress is only one potential factor. Rigorous examination of the involvement of stress in regulating the production of phenotypic variants must now follow, with particular attention being given to experiments that clearly separate the effects of selection from those of mutation (Lenski and Mittler, 1993).

In some bacteria it is possible that the production of phenotypic variants will not be controlled by environmental signals, although this would only be expected in bacteria which inhabit an environment which fluctuates in an unpredictable manner. Under such conditions the continuous production of variants may be necessary for survival; however, under conditions of environmental stasis the production of progeny unsuited to the prevailing conditions could incur a significant cost. A degree of control over whether variants are produced would enable bacteria to optimize population fitness by regulating the balance between individual flexibility and fitness (this is considered in more detail below). Some pathogenic bacteria appear to generate variant forms in an unregulated manner (Borst and Greaves, 1987), and while this may be true (and in some instances necessary), it is also possible that high-frequency switching is a response to the stress of growing on an agar plate.

6.3. Adaptation of Phenotypic Variants to New Environmental Conditions

The time taken before sectoring in variant, versus wild-type colonies on solid media (7–10 versus 2–3 days, respectively) suggests the possibility that variant colonies are more suited to survival under the environmental conditions in which they were produced.

Characteristics of the variant forms also suggest that they are adapted to a different set of environmental conditions than the wild-type forms. For example, in both *V. harveyi* and *P. tolaasii*, the variant forms possess particular traits which indicate that they may occupy different ecological niches than the wild-type forms (Kelman and Hruschka, 1973; Bartlett *et al.*, 1988; Schrader and Holmes, 1988; Silverman *et al.*, 1989; Kamoun and Kado, 1990; Grewal and Rainey, 1991; Rainey, 1991; Durbin, 1992). In *P. tolaasii*, the virulent form appears adapted to life in association with mushroom tissue; its membrane-disrupting toxin ensuring a readily available source of nutrients and its ability to attach to mycelium guaranteeing its persistence within the mushroom environment. In contrast, the avirulent variant appears adapted to life in the absence of a nutrient source (mushroom), where location of new nutrient reserves is of prime importance; it no longer produces tolaasin, is highly motile, responds rapidly to chemoattractants, and does not attach to mushroom mycelium.

A number of other studies have shown similar pronounced behavioral differences between wild-type and variant forms. *Xanthomonas campestris* causes disease in cauliflower and radish and when cultured *in vitro* produces a variant form with reduced virulence, which unlike the virulent form, is chemotactic and does not produce extracellular polysaccharide (EPS) (Kamoun and Kado, 1990). These traits suggest, as with *P. tolaasii,* that the virulent form of *X. campestris* is adapted to life in association with its host, while the phenotype with reduced virulence is produced once the host plant no longer provides a source of nutrients. This form appears adapted to survival in the absence of the host.

A further example is provided by studies on the colonization of tooth surfaces by *Streptococcus gordonii* (Vickerman *et al.*, 1991). *S. gordonii* switches between two phenotypic forms which differ in the production of extracellular glucosyltransferase (GTF) which is involved in the synthesis of glucans. Spp$^+$ variants produce GTF and as a result of glucan production form hard cohesive colonies on sucrose-containing agar while Spp$^-$ variants produce 80% less GTF and form soft colonies on agar plates. When cultured in broth in the presence of sucrose and glass beads, the Spp$^+$ variants adhere to the beads and form "plaque" layers, but give rise to Spp$^-$ forms which are liberated from the plaque layers and colonize the broth phase. When Spp$^-$ variants are inoculated into the same environment they give rise to Spp$^+$ variants which attach to the bead surface. These results are consistent with the ecological scenario that for bacteria like *S. gordonii* which colonize the nonshedding surface of the tooth, the production of less-adhesive forms would be ecologically advantageous when the niche becomes overpopulated, or otherwise unfavorable for growth.

Antigenic variation by a range of medically important pathogens can also be viewed in a similar manner, but, because the host immune response creates an extremely variable environment, the duration of each phenotypic phase may be very brief. Nevertheless, some variants must escape detection by the host immune response for infection to occur and as such, these variants are adapted to the prevailing conditions.

Not only does antigenic variation provide a strategy for evading the host immune response, but it also allows optimization of receptor–ligand interactions, which, like the immune response, cannot be predicted in advance (Robertson and Meyer, 1992). In the pathogenesis of an infection, for example, meningitis, it is necessary for bacteria to migrate from the nasopharynx to the brain via the blood and it is possible that polymorphic variation may facilitate adaptation to the different stages of the infection process. It is also possible that polymorphism in pathogenic bacteria may serve other purposes, such as adaptation to various environmental conditions (Seifert and So, 1988). This may be particularly important for those pathogens which are capable of surviving outside of the host.

6.4. The Extent of Variation

Most of the examples of intraclonal polymorphism given above refer to only a small number of distinct phenotypic forms, but it is likely that the true extent of variation is much greater. The existence of variants which display no visible morphological change has already been raised, but in addition, it is probable that even within a colony with only a single distinct sector a variety of morphologically distinct variants will be present. The reasons for postulating this will become apparent after further reading, but it is clear that variants will only give rise to sectors if their growth rate is either equal to, or more rapid than, the wild type, and/or the variants produce cells of a larger size. If they do not, then they will be swamped.

Evidence that colonies contain a more extensive range of variant cell types than immediately visible is shown by the experiments of Shapiro (1986). Shapiro took samples from old sectored colonies growing on agar plates, suspended them in broth, and then spread appropriate dilutions back onto agar plates. The resulting colonies revealed a range of morphologies far greater than detected within the old colonies by visual observation of sectors.

6.5. Intraclonal Polymorphism *in Situ*

Few studies have examined intraclonal polymorphism *in situ*. Variation in both pili (Lambden *et al.*, 1981) and P.II (McBride *et al.*, 1981) occurs during natural infection by *N. gonorrhoeae* and variation of slime production by *Staphylococcus epidermis* associated with infection of indwelling medical devices has been shown to occur *in situ* (Baddour *et al.*, 1990). Antigenic variation has also been shown to occur in *Borrelia recurrentis* var. *turicate* when injected into rats (Schuhardt and Wilkerson, 1951).

The apparent irreversibility of some phenotypic transitions *in vitro*, particularly between avirulent and virulent forms of phytopathogenic bacteria, has resulted in suggestions that the transition is caused by loss of a plasmid, or some other irreversible genetic rearrangement (e.g., see Cutri *et al.*, 1984). This view has been challenged by those who consider the environment to be a significant factor in phenotypic switching and two studies have now been conducted which show production of virulent variants from avirulent variants *in situ*. Phenotypic variants of *X. campestris* which show reduced virulence do not revert to wild type *in vitro*. However, after growth on radish plants, reduced virulence forms produce fully virulent, nonchemotactic, EPS-producing variants (Kamoun and Kado, 1990). Similar results were obtained when a genetically marked avirulent variant of *P. tolaasii* was released into a mushroom cropping house. Avirulent *P. tolaasii* rarely ever produces detectable virulent forms *in vitro*, but after growth *in situ* virulent variants were detected after 18 hr (R.-M. Wu, P. B. Rainey, B. Palmer, M. J. Bailey, and A.L.J. Cole, unpublished).

7. Genetic Mechanisms Controlling Intraclonal Polymorphism

This section describes genetic mechanisms controlling intraclonal polymorphism, the main purpose of which is to emphasize the evolution of discriminate stochastic mechanisms of gene regulation. Characteristically, these mechanisms operate independently of precise signals *per se*, are often reversible, multidimensional, and most importantly, as a result of the stochastic nature of the switch, generate both novelty and population heterogeneity. With the exception of Pap pili regulation, the mechanisms described involve rearrangements in DNA sequence. Pap pili regulation involves random changes in the conformation of DNA.

The importance and novelty of these gene regulatory mechanisms has resulted in many recent reviews. We provide only a single example of each mechanism and recommend that the excellent reviews cited below be consulted for more detailed information and reference lists.

7.1. Variation by General Homologous Recombination (Gene Conversion)

A number of examples of intraclonal polymorphism (phase and antigenic variation) employing homologous recombination have been described, all of which are dependent on functional *recA* (Table I). The most widely studied example occurs in *N. gonorrhoeae* which possesses several systems which generate variation in a number of independent components, including pili, opacity protein, and lipopolysaccharide. Each of these components is important in establishing and maintaining bacteria–bacteria and bacteria–host cell interactions. Pilin variation provides a good example of the homologous recombination mechanism (Meyer *et al.*, 1990; Saunders, 1986; Swanson and Koomey, 1989).

Pili from *N. gonorrhoeae,* and from other gonococci and meningococci, are formed of proteins approximately 160 amino acid residues long and contain two distinct regions. The N-terminal region of approximately 50 amino acids is hydrophobic and highly conserved. The remainder of the molecule is variable and consists of six short regions, known as minicassettes (mc). Of these, mc2, which is situated at the C-terminal end, is highly variable and contains the immunodominant epitopes. The minicassettes are separated by short, highly conserved sequences, both at the protein and DNA level, and are essential prerequisites for the mechanism by which pilin variation occurs.

The genome of *N. gonorrhoeae* contains, in addition to the complete pilin coding region *pilE,* silent pilin loci (*pilS*) which are transcriptionally inactive. These loci, which may contain between 12 and 20 tandemly arranged partial pilin genes, are located on either side of the complete pilin gene. The partial gene copies are partly homologous to internal portions of the complete *pilE* gene and show the same arrangement as the variable minicassettes found in *pilE;* however, they are promoterless and also lack the conserved N-terminal region.

Sequence analysis of pilin transcripts from strains expressing different pilin types suggested that variation is caused by recombination events in *pilE*. Subsequent work has shown that recombination occurs between the variable minicassettes within the silent *pilS* loci, and *pilE*. An interesting and significant feature of this system is that *pilE* usually acquires only some of the variable minicassettes from *pilS* and thus an extensive variety of new sequences can be generated (Fig. 3).

The precise mechanism of gene exchange is not understood, but involves

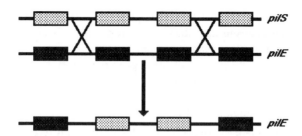

Figure 3. Pilin variation in *N. gonorrhoeae* involves recombinatorial exchange of variable mini-cassettes between the silent pilin gene *pilS* and the expressed pilin gene *pilE*. Crossover occurs between the highly conserved sequences separating the minicassettes and results in new combinations of minicassettes within *pilE*. Additional variation is gained by recombination between the *pilE* gene and *pilS* sequences which have been acquired by uptake of DNA from lysed bacteria.

nonreciprocal exchange of DNA from partial pilin genes (donor) to the complete pilin gene (recipient). Because of the unequal recovery of pilin alleles following recombination, this event has been termed gene conversion (Swanson and Koomey, 1989).

   N. gonorrhoeae is also thought to be able to acquire novel *pil* sequences by intergenomic transfer of DNA from lysed bacteria. This can occur *in vivo* because *N. gonorrhoeae* is constitutively competent. Transformation-mediated recombination of exogenous homologous DNA could be used to replace the pilin expression gene, thus providing an additional source of *pil* sequences (Seifert *et al.*, 1988; Gibbs *et al.*, 1989).

7.2. Variation by Site-Specific Recombination

   A more precise homologous recombination mechanism is used to control the expression of surface structures in a number of bacteria. While more precise, this type of control is limited in terms of the variability it generates and is usually confined to two-way, ON/OFF switches.

   Type 1 mannose-sensitive fimbriae of *E. coli* play an important part in virulence and undergo rapid phenotypic switching by specialized site-specific recombination (Glasgow *et al.*, 1989; Robertson and Meyer, 1992). Three *fim* genes are required for formation of type 1 fimbriae, but only *fimA* encodes the fimbrial subunit. Upstream of *fimA* is a consensus binding site for integration host factor (IHF) and a promoter which is flanked by 9-bp inverted repeats (Fig. 4). The orientation of the promoter determines whether or not *fimA* will be transcribed, thus controlling the switch. FimB directs inversion of the DNA segment to the ON orientation and FimE directs switching to the OFF orientation.

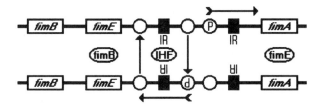

Figure 4. Type 1 fimbrial expression in *E. coli* is controlled by inversion of a promoter-containing element. The promoter element is bounded by 9-bp inverted repeats (IR) and the two binding sites for the integration host factor (IHF) are shown by open circles. Inversion of the promoter element to the ON and OFF orientations are directed by *fimB* and *fimE*, respectively. (Glasgow *et al.*, 1989, as adapted by Robertson and Meyer, 1992.)

7.3. Variation by Oligonucleotide Repeats

Lipopolysaccharide (LPS) is a major virulence determinant of *Haemophilus influenzae*, a common commensal of the upper respiratory tract. *H. influenzae* LPS shows rapid phase variation as defined by reactivity with monoclonal antibodies and LPS size. Three loci have been identified as being involved in this variation (*lic1*, *lic2*, and *lic3*) (Moxon and Maskell, 1992). The *lic1* locus is involved in oligosaccharide biosynthesis, codes for four genes, and is responsible for the expression of two epitopes. The first open-reading frame (ORF) of *lic1* mediates phase variation via tandem repeats of the tetranucleotide 5'-CAAT-3' (approximately 30 repeats). It is thought that by slip stranded mispairing (Levinson and Gutman, 1987), copies of CAAT are either lost or gained (Fig. 5). Gain or loss of CAAT is thought to induce frame shifts with respect to upstream initiation codons resulting in altered translation and epitope expression through the effects of downstream genes (Weiser *et al.*, 1989).

Figure 5. Variation of *H. influenzae* LPS epitopes expressed by *lic1*. A translational switch modulates between three expression states. Dependent on the number of CAAT repeats, either one, two, or no ATG initiation codons are in-frame (Weiser *et al.*, 1989).

7.4. Variation by Homopolymeric Repeats

Insertions or deletions are likely to occur in regions with reiterated bases and homopolymeric repeats therefore provide opportunities for random control of gene expression (Streisinger and Owen, 1985).

Wall-less mycoplasma pathogens show a remarkable degree of phenotypic and genotypic variation (Dybvig, 1990). In the swine pathogen *Mycoplasma hyorhinis,* antigenic and phase variation of variant lipoproteins (Vlps) have been extensively studied (Rosengarten and Wise, 1990, 1991; Yogev *et al.,* 1991) and shown to be controlled by two independent but complementary systems. One system controls antigenic variation via alterations in oligonucleotide repeats (as described above) and the other controls phase variation by a mechanism involving loss, or gain, of adenine nucleotides in a polyA tract.

Phase variation of the Vlps appears to be controlled at the level of transcription by the length of poly(A) tract which lies within the *vlp* promoter region, between putative -10 and -35 boxes. Gain, or loss, of adenine nucleotides within the poly(A) tract is thought to influence the positioning of RNA polymerase, or other factors, on the DNA, thus affecting transcription (Fig. 6). A length of 17 residues switches the *vlpA* and *vlpB* genes ON, while a length of 18 residues switches them OFF. In *vlpC,* up to 20 residues are associated with the OFF state (Yogev *et al.,* 1991).

7.5. Variation by Extrinsic Alterations in DNA Conformation

A novel phase variation control mechanism is involved in regulation of the pyelonephritis-associated pilus (*pap*) operon of *E. coli.* Phase variation, between an OFF and ON state, involves differential inhibition of deoxyadenosine methylase (Dam) methylation of two *pap* GATC sites (GATC$_{1028}$ and GATC$_{1130}$) located in the regulatory region of *papA,* the gene encoding the major subunit pilin. When in the OFF state, the GATC$_{1130}$ site is unmethylated and the GATC$_{1028}$ site is methylated, while when in the ON state the GATC$_{1028}$ is unmethylated and GATC$_{1130}$ is methylated (Blyn *et al.,* 1989, 1990; Braaten *et al.,* 1991; Robertson and Meyer, 1992).

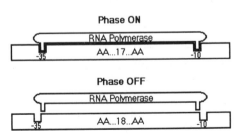

Figure 6. Phase variation of variable lipoprotein (Vlp) in *M. hyorhinis* is controlled at the level of transcription by the length of poly(A) tract which lies between putative -10 and -35 RNA polymerase binding sites. When the number of A residues is 17, RNA polymerase is able to bind, but when greater than this number, correct positioning of the polymerase is prevented (Yogev *et al.,* 1991).

The presence of unmethylated GATC sites in *E. coli* is unusual and investigation into this phenomenon revealed the presence of a methylation-blocking factor (Mbf) which in association with an additional gene product encoded by the Pap operon, PapI, inhibits methylation at $GATC_{1028}$. It is thought that PapI and Mbf bind and inhibit Dam methylation at $GATC_{1028}$ by steric hindrance. Inhibition of Dam methylation at the $GATC_{1130}$ site is brought about solely by the effect of Mbf.

The model presented by Blyn *et al.* (1990) and Braaten *et al.* (1991) to explain phase variation assumes the methylation protection factors (Mab and PapI) have a higher affinity for unmethylated or hemimethylated DNA than methylated DNA (Fig. 7). During DNA replication, protected sites are not affected by Dam. If the hemimethylated and unmethylated sites are protected with equal efficiency, then, as only one site can be protected at any one time, there is an equal chance that switching will occur. When only unmethylated sites are protected, the pilus status remains fixed, but if a hemimethylated site is protected, then switching occurs; subject to two rounds of DNA replication involving a transition stage with one methylated and one hemimethylated site.

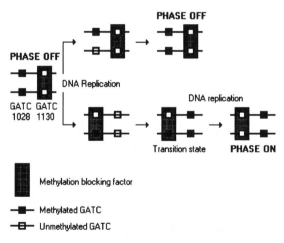

Figure 7. Model of phase variation of *E. coli* Pap pili as proposed by Blyn *et al.* (1990) and Braaten *et al.* (1991) and adapted from Robertson and Meyer (1992). Methylation blocking factor (Mbf) binds preferentially to hemimethylated DNA rather than unmethylated DNA and prevents methylation of site $GATC_{1028}$ or $GATC_{1130}$. During DNA replication, either the unmethylated and/or hemimethylated site is protected. If Mbf protects the hemimethylated and unmethylated sites with equal efficiency, then there will be an equal chance of a switch occurring (assuming both sites cannot be protected simultaneously). Any bias toward either hemimethylated or unmethylated sites will be reflected in a tendency always to switch in the first instance, and never to switch in the second. The phase status of the transition state is unknown.

7.6. Variation by Other Mechanisms

Little progress has been made in understanding the genetic basis of intraclonal polymorphism in bacteria which are not of medical significance. While it cannot be assumed that identical mechanisms will operate in all bacteria, it is likely, given the requirement for randomness (see below), that mechanisms similar to those described above will be found in other bacteria. The studies described below do indicate this.

Rhizobium strains contain a range of reiterated sequences which are dispersed throughout both the chromosome and plasmid(s) (Quinto *et al.*, 1982; de Lourdes Girard *et al.*, 1991). High-frequency rearrangements (deletions, amplifications, inversions) have been shown to occur between these sequences and it has been suggested that such recombinational events may account for the production of phenotypic variants (Flores *et al.*, 1988; de Lourdes Girard *et al.*, 1991). In *Thiobacillus ferrooxidans*, multiple copies of two insertion elements are found dispersed throughout the genome and it is thought that transposition of these may be involved in the switching between wild-type colonies and large spreading colonies (LSC) (Schrader and Holmes, 1988; Yates *et al.*, 1988). In *Pseudomonas* sp. (strain B13) the ability to utilize *meta*-chlorobenzoate is associated with the tandem amplification and deamplification of a 4.3-kbp DNA region which encodes three key enzymes in the chlorocatechol pathway (Rangnekar, 1988). Studies on switching between mucoid and nonmucoid strains of *P. atlantica* have shown that it occurs by precise insertion and deletion of a 1.2-kbp IS element into the *eps* gene (Bartlett *et al.*, 1988).

Pseudomonas solanacearum, causal agent of bacterial wilt disease, produces a range of nonmucoid, avirulent variants which encompass an extensive array of biochemical phenotypes. A gene (*epsR*) encoding a 25-kDa protein was isolated from a phenotypic variant which when introduced into the wild-type strain on a low-copy-number plasmid triggered the phenotypic switch (Huang and Sequeira, 1990; Gosti *et al.*, 1991). Interestingly, when an equivalent gene isolated from the wild-type strain was reintroduced back into the wild-type strain in *trans* on a multicopy vector, the same phenotypic switch was observed. The *epsR* gene has been sequenced recently and shown to be homologous to RcsB, a A-binding protein which positively regulates capsule production in enteric bacteria (C. C. Kao and L. Sequeira, unpublished). The precise mechanism of *epsR* activity remains to be determined, but it is thought that modulation of *epsR* activity occurs by a post-translational mechanism (C. C. Kao and L. Sequeira, unpublished). More recently, a locus (*phcA*; phenotype conversion) was identified in *P. solanacearum* that controls phenotype switching. This locus is homologous to the LysR family of transcriptional activators and is subject to frameshifts which occur as a result of insertions within a short region of GC repeats near the carboxyl terminus of PhcA. Duplication of a single GC repeat unit resulted in switching from a virulent to an avirulent phenotype (Brumbley *et al.*, 1993).

Irreversible switches make little sense from an evolutionary perspective, yet there are examples among the plant pathogenic pseudomonads of polymorphism being caused by spontaneous deletion and apparently irreversible loss of toxin genes (Durbin, 1992; Gross, 1991; Willis *et al.*, 1991). Recent evidence has indicated that restoration of toxin production may occur by plasmid-mediated uptake of toxin genes (Durbin, 1992). Loss of capsule production in *H. influenzae* also appears to be irreversible and the capsule-deficient phenotype occurs as a result of a two-step deletion of DNA within the *cap* locus (Brophy *et al.*, 1991). It is possible that as a result of the natural competence of *H. influenzae,* restoration of capsule production may occur *in situ* via uptake of DNA from lysed bacteria.

8. Intraclonal Bacterial Intraclonal Polymorphism: A Hypothesis

On the basis of the information presented above we postulate the following:

1. The emergence of phenotypically distinct variants within clonal bacterial populations occurs in response to stress.
2. Variants are produced in a random manner (no adaptive value is attached to the changes, that is, variants provide the raw material upon which natural selection can act).
3. The presence of a range of distinct phenotypes facilitates rapid adaptation to environmental change and is an evolved response to environmental variation.
4. This adaptive response is controlled by discriminate stochastic mechanisms which facilitate high-frequency alterations in DNA sequence and/- or DNA conformation.

8.1. A Conceptual Model

The following model is presented to account for the random production of a range of phenotypically distinct variants in response to stress. Our intention is to provide a general framework on which an understanding of intraclonal bacterial polymorphism can be developed.

In proposing a general model, it is necessary to account for alterations in a wide variety of characteristics, such as chemotaxis, motility, adherence, toxin production, sensitivity to antibiotics, resistance to desiccation, and acquisition of nutrients. Studies of pathogenic bacteria have shown that surface components, such as pili, fimbriae, outer membrane proteins, and LPS, are subject to variation. As surface components (among other factors) influence how cells interact with their environment and with each other, it is quite possible that alterations in key surface components are sufficient to generate a range of phenotypes (see Birkbeck and Penn, 1986). For example, alterations in almost any outer membrane component are likely to affect attachment (Brown and Williams, 1985; Costerton, 1988). Similarly, motility, chemotaxis, resistance and susceptibility to external factors, acquisition of nutrients, etc., are all likely to be affected by changes in surface components. Whether such changes can also affect toxin production is less certain, but in *P. tolaasii,* loss of toxin production is associated with truncation of a periplasmic associated synthetase (P. B. Rainey, unpublished).

The model must also account for the ability to generate variation in a random manner and at a high frequency. Random variation provides the most effective mechanism by which bacteria can generate the variation necessary for successful adaptation to novel unpredictable environments (Robertson and Meyer, 1992; Seifert and So, 1988; Koch, 1987; DiRita and Mekalanos, 1989). In addition, the model must explain how stress may regulate variant production.

The model presented in Fig. 8 is based on discriminate stochastic genetic mechanisms which facilitate high-frequency DNA sequence rearrangements as a result of the organization of nucleoties within particular regions of the chromo-

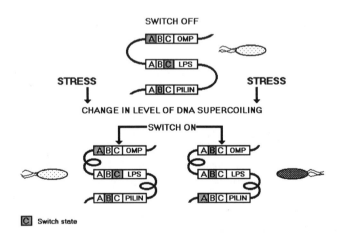

Figure 8. General model to account for production of phenotypic variants in bacteria. Three independent genes encoding surface components [outer membrane protein (OMP), lipopolysaccharide (LPS), and pilin] contain discrete regions which are able to undergo random switching in a manner analogous to those previously described (see Section 7). Switching is regulated by the level of DNA supercoiling which is responsive to environmental stress. In this simple three-gene, three-switch-per-gene model, 27 distinct variants can be produced. The adaptive value of each variant is unknown and each will be subject to selection by the prevailing environmental conditions.

some (see Section 7). In this model, the likelihood that these rearrangements will occur is regulated by environmental stress through its effect on the level of DNA supercoiling. The mechanism by which the level of DNA supercoiling may regulate variant production is not known, but evidence indicates that alterations in the topology of DNA which increase torsional strain favor reactions such asrecombination and transposition (Fisher, 1984). Such genetic rearrangements are likely to be required for phenotypic switching to occur. We again emphasize that the rearrangements which occur in response to the level of DNA supercoiling do so in a stochastic manner.

Three independent genes involved in synthesis of surface components are depicted in the model; one is involved in synthesis of a major outer membrane protein (OMP), one in synthesis of LPS, and the other in synthesis of pili. Rearrangements within the variable region of each gene occur at a high frequency following alterations in the level of DNA supercoiling and produce one of three possible switch positions. As a result, each gene can give rise to three variant forms of OMP, LPS, and pili, respectively. In this simple model, random rearrangements can generate one of 27 (3^3) different phenotypes, but the outcome of each cycle of rearrangements cannot be predicted with certainty. If four switching states existed, then the total number of phenotypes would be 81 (3^4). In *M. hyorhinis*, more than 10^4 possible phenotypes can be generated (Yogev *et al.*, 1991). Using this model, more complex scenarios can be accommodated; for example, toxin production could be included by either an additional set of switches and structural gene(s), or could be regulated by the "OMP switch" by placement of toxin structural gene(s) downstream of OMP. Addition of genes to discrete switches in this manner has important evolutionary implications which are considered below. A further degree of complexity could involve supercoiling-sensitive promoters which may facilitate DNA rearrangements when activated.

This model shows how it is potentially possible to generate a range of distinct phenotypes at a high frequency by employing a simple stochastic mechanism. It fulfills the requirements for random generation of variation in response to environmental stress and shows how this can occur without an organism having to evolve a unique set of genes for each set of environmental conditions. Such a scenario provides a hypothetical example of a genetic mechanism which has evolved a capacity to utilize random fluctuations in a constructive manner, thus providing access to novelty and variation.

8.2. Costs of Phenotypic Variation

Generation of random variation is unlikely to occur without some cost. There are two probable costs. The first arises as a result of the process of DNA recombination which is likely to be a necessary part of a switch mechanism (see Section 7). No DNA recombination system is error-free and the more frequently a switch is operated, the greater is the opportunity for error. Evidence for a cost associated with continual switching is found in *Saccharomyces cerevisiae* where high-frequency switching of mating type generates aberrant recombinations of mating-type sequences (Beach and Klar, 1984).

The second cost arises as a result of the production of variants which are not optimally suited to a particular environment. In a sense this is not a true cost, but rather concerns the balance between fitness and flexibility; fitness being best served by the production of progeny optimal for the immediate circumstances and flexiblity by the provision of variants which may be optimal for environments only to be encountered elsewhere (Mather, 1943). This balance will be primarily determined by the nature of the environment in which an organism lives. In a highly variable environment, such as that encountered by a pathogen attempting to infect the human body, a flexible population is needed in order to evade the host immune response (Borst and Greaves, 1987; Seifert and So, 1988; Robertson and Meyer, 1992). A pathogen, such as the African trypanosome, which exists permanently within the bloodstream and which is forever subject to attack by the host immune response, may not possess any means of regulating phenotypic switching, but pathogens which manage to avoid the host immune response and adopt latent or commensal associations are likely to be able to regulate variant production.

In environments where periods of drastic change are interspersed with periods of relative stasis, natural selection is unlikely to favor the generation of phenotypic variation which may actually reduce the fitness of individual clones during periods of stasis. Hence, selection will favor a strategy whereby variants are produced only under conditions of environmental change.

9. Testing the Hypothesis

A recent set of experiments designed to address aspects of the hypothesis presented above concerns the production of phenotypic variants by *P. fluorescens* SBW25, a saprophyte originally isolated from the phylloplane of sugar beet (P. B. Rainey, unpublished).

When cultured on agar plates this bacterium produces a small number of indistinct sectors; however, when cultured in a stationary broth environment an extensive variety of phenotypic variants are produced. These become evident once appropriate dilutions have been made from the broth culture and spread on agar plates. This behavior is not confined to *P. fluorescens,* but is encountered in a range of pseudomonads, including *P. putida* and *P. tolaasii* (Rainey, 1989).

The production of variant forms within a stationary broth culture of *P. fluorescens* was determined by daily monitoring of changes in the behavior of a randomly selected sample of colonies with respect to a quantifiable characteristic with perceivable ecological significance, that is, swarm diameter in semisolid agar.

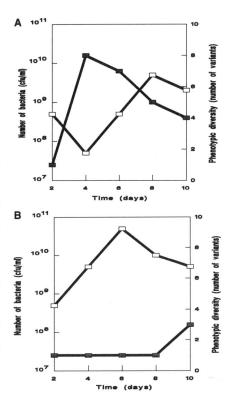

Figure 9. Survival (clear blocks) and phenotypic diversity (filled blocks) of *P. fluorescens* in broth culture. (A) Wild-type *P. fluorescens* does not survive well in broth culture and after day 1 the number of viable cells declines. Concomitant with this decline (an indication of stress) is a marked increase in the diversity of phenotypic variants which correlates with a corresponding increase in the number of viable bacteria. By day 6 the culture is dominated by one variant form and wild-type forms are no longer detectable. (B) Inoculation of the most abundant phenotypic variant from (A), a surface colonizing variant, back into broth, reveals that the variant is well suited to growth in this environment and the number of viable bacteria continues to increase until day 6. No phenotypic variants are detected during this period, but once the number of viable bacteria begins to decline, variants are once again produced.

When the wild-type form (which had not previously been subjected to growth in broth) was introduced into broth culture the total number of bacteria rapidly declined, but this decline was marked by a concomitant increase in the diversity of phenotypic variants (Fig. 9A). A significant increase in the total number of bacteria accompanied variant diversification and the population was eventually dominated by one variant form. Examination of the habitat preference of each phenotypic variant revealed distinct niches within the broth environment where each variant grew. The phenotypic form which grew best (greatest cell density) in broth culture grew solely at the broth–air interface where it formed a dense mat of cells; other variants grew within the broth, while others colonize the bottom of the vial. When inoculated into broth, the broth–air colonizing variant grew well and cell numbers continued to increase until day 6. Unlike the wild type, no phenotypic variants were produced until day 8, and when they did eventually arise, they did so following a decrease in cell numbers (Fig. 9B). Other phenotypic forms grew very poorly when inoculated individually back into broth.

Several results from these experiments are consistent with our hypothesis. First, production of phenotypic variants by both the wild type and broth-adapted form coincided with a period of stress (as indicated by a decline in the number of viable bacteria. The unequivocal involvement of stress remains to be established due to the inherent difficulties in separating the effects of intensified selection from those of increased mutation). Second, the variants appeared to be generated in a random manner, because replicate populations (founded from a single bacterium) showed substantial differences in the polymorphisms that arose. Third, adaptation to growth in broth occurred following the generation of phenotypic variants (which presumably constituted the raw material upon which natural selection could operate).

10. The Significance and Implications of Intraclonal Polymorphism in Bacteria

Generation of a random array of phenotypically distinct progeny in response to stress is a strategy for responding to unpredictable environmental change. The ability to respond to unforeseen circumstances is likely to be essential for the many bacteria which inhabit environments where conditions fluctuate in unpredictable ways.

Not only does a discriminate stochastic switching mechanism facilitate rapid adaptation, but it also has important evolutionary consequences, particularly as a factor which contributes to the origin of novel traits and to new directions of change (see recent reviews: Lloyd, 1984; Schlichting, 1986; Sultan, 1987; West-Eberhard, 1989; Thompson, 1991). A polymorphic population provides more than one phenotype on which natural selection can act. Should variants be subjected to different selective forces (because of different environmental conditions), then phenotypic divergence can occur. Consider a bacterium which exhibits variation in the antigenicity of its LPS. In environment A, hydrophobic LPS offers an advantage because it causes cells to aggregate, while in environment B, hydrophilic LPS is beneficial because aggregation is detrimental to dispersal. If a period of stasis follows, then selection, acting on expressed phenotypes, will favor cells in environment A with mutations which enhance the hydrophobicity of the LPS, while in environment B, any increase in hydrophilicity will be favored. Should the period of stasis continue, then it is possible that the phenotype of each may become fixed and so the potential exists for both micro- and macroevolutionary change (West-Eberhard, 1989). In higher organisms this scenario is considered sufficient to initiate the process of speciation and hence it is likely that intraclonal polymorphism in bacteria could have similar consequences. Perhaps the marked genotypic and phenotypic heterogeneity among members of a bacterial "species" is partly the result of this process.

A discrete switch has additional implications for evolutionary change. Until recently, phenotypic plasticity has been considered to retard the rate of evolutionary change because of its uncoupling effect on the genotype (Wright, 1931; Stebbins, 1950). However, it is clear that in many organisms, including bacteria, the response itself is subject to selection and thus any genetically based variation in response can provide a template for evolutionary change (Thompson, 1991; West-Eberhard, 1989; Sultan, 1987). For example, it is possible that in a heterogeneous environment, selection will favor mutations which enhance the breadth of plasticity, or perhaps reduce response time. A further evolutionary implication of a discrete switch arises as a result of the opportunity to accumulate modifiers sensitive to it, or to make additions to the sets of developmental or behavioral events initiated by the switch (Turner, 1977). Recombination between *pilS* and *pilE* in *N. gonorrhoeae* provides an excellent example of this.

The implications which discriminate stochastic gene regulatory mechanisms have for evolutinary change suggest the possibility that these mechanisms have evolved to facilitate the evolutionary process. This concept was recently addressed by Wills (1989) who provides many convincing arguments in its support. It is possible that genome organization facilitating rapid change has evolved because of the pressure on bacteria (and many other organisms) to develop strategies for responding to unpredictable environmental change.

10.1. Implications for Taxonomy

The occurrence of phenotypic variants may create problems for microbiologists, especially taxonomists who are often concerned with the establishment of order. The desire to establish order may explain why phenotypic variation in many bacteria has been overlooked and why the majority of work on the subject has been confined to studies concerned with the variation of virulence factors in pathogenic bacteria.

It is important that microbiologists are aware of phenotypic variation and of the potential consequences of this behavior. The ability of a single cell to give rise to variants which may be both phenotypically and genotypically distinct further undermines the frequently held assumption that colonies are a collection of identical cells (Koch, 1987).

Bacterial taxonomy has traditionally relied on cells within a colony possessing an identical genotype and phenotype (Sokal, 1985). The fact that this may not always be true highlights the importance of developing taxonomic methods which consider the variability of the individual bacterium. Methods which rely solely on phenotypic characteristics are particularly susceptible to the effects of intraclonal polymorphism. Such methods include dichotomous keys, where those based on single characters are especially prone to the potentially misleading effects of phenotypic variation. An example of this problem occurs in identification of phytopathogenic pseudomonads, many of which are identified either by their ability to cause disease in a particular host or by their ability to produce a particular metabolite. *P. tolaasii*, for example, is identified primarily by its ability to produce tolaasin toxin. Avirulent variants do not produce tolaasin and therefore are prone to mis-identification as the saprophyte *P. fluorescens* (Goor *et al.*, 1986). Clearly, incorrect identification of pathogenic bacteria, because they do not display a certain characteristic *in vitro,* could have serious consequences.

More reliable methods for identification of bacteria on the basis of phenotypic characteristics are provided by strategies, such as probabilistic identification matrices, where information on the variance of selected features within a population can be incorporated (Sneath, 1985).

10.2. Implications for Biotechnology

Biotechnology is an area where ignorance of phenotypic variation and it consequences could have serious implications. The development and use of microbial inoculants for purposes such as disease control and bioremediation is reliant on stability of particular traits in culture, in storage, and upon field application (Terzaghi and O'Hara, 1990). The work described above indicates that many bacteria have evolved strategies for responding to environmental change. Many bacteria are therefore unlikely to express the same phenotypic characteristics on an agar plate, or in broth culture, as they will in the natural environment.

Already there are a number of examples where phenotypic variation has created problems for the biotechnology industry and it is possible that instability of phenotype may be responsible for the failure of some microbial systems to perform as expected once present in the target environment (Lethbridge, 1989). For example, application of rhizobium inoculants to field crops for the purpose of enhancing nitrogen fixation has, in some instances, been less successful than anticipated. Absolute proof that this is caused by phenotypic variation has not been provided, but there are many reports of phenotypic and genotypic instability in *Rhizobium* spp. affecting symbiotic effectiveness (Herridge and Roughley, 1975; Kuykendall and Elkan, 1976; Flores *et al.*, 1988; Sylvester-Bradley *et al.*, 1988; de Lourdes Girard *et al.*, 1991).

A further example is provided by *Xenorhabdus luminescens*, a nematode symbiont which has considerable potential as a biological control agent for noxious insects (Klein, 1990; Gerritsen *et al.*, 1992). When cultured *in vitro, X. luminescens* produces a number of different phenotypic variants which are considered to represent adaptations to particular environmental conditions encountered during the "life cycle" of the bacterium (Gotz *et al.*, 1981). These variants differ in their virulence, and production of avirulent forms during large-scale liquid fermentation is considered responsible for suboptimal-quality nematodes and hampers widespread use of this biological control system (Ehlers *et al.*, 1990).

10.3. Implications for Environmental Release and Risk Assessment

There is currently considerable interest in utilizing genetically engineered bacteria to perform specific tasks in the natural environment. Before such organisms are released it is necessary to consider fully the risks associated with this action. A major question in any risk assessment program concerns mechanisms of survival (Alexander, 1986; Levin *et al.*, 1987). The ability to survive in both target and nontarget habitats depends on the range of niches in which a bacterium can exist. The range of niches will, in turn, be determined by the ability of the phenotype to respond to external stimuli by regulation of gene expression, but will also depend on the capacity of the bacterium for rapid evolutionary change. This capacity, or "adaptive potential" which is highlighted by intraclonal polymorphism, has received little attention and should be addressed before deliberate release into the environment is considered.

11. Conclusions

Survival of bacteria in heterogeneous environments necessitates a significant degree of phenotypic and/or genotypic flexibility (Heslop-Harrison, 1964). In this chapter, attention has been focused on the extent of phenotypic flexibility (and underlying genetic determinants) and a hypothesis developed concerning the significance of intraclonal polymorphism. This hypothesis postulates that phenotypically distinct individuals are generated in response to stress, in a stochastic manner and at a high frequency, and that the resulting diversity facilitates rapid adaptation to environmental change. Further work must now be undertaken both to test the hypothesis and to assess the value of the conceptual model. In particular, it will be necessary to design experiments which address fully the question of whether the frequency of variant production is enhanced by environmental change. The outcome of such experiments may have significant implications for the debate concerning adaptive mutation (Cairns *et al.*, 1988; Hall, 1991; Lenski and Mittler, 1993).

ACKNOWLEDGMENTS. We thank A. K. Lilley, P. Zanotto, K. McCallum, J. Cory, and M. J. Bailey for valuable discussion and we are grateful to authors who provided information from unpublished work. We are especially grateful to R. E. Lenski, J. D. Thompson, N. J. Palleroni, and T.R.G. Gray for critical comments on the manuscript. E. R. Moxon is supported by grants from the Medical Research Council and the Wellcome Trust and I. P. Thompson is supported by the Department of the Environment.

References

Alexander, M., 1986, Ecological concerns relative to genetically engineered microorganisms, in: *Microbial Communities in the Soil* (V. Jensen, A. Kjoller, and L. H. Sorensen, eds.), Elsevier, Amsterdam, pp. 347–354.

Allred, D. R., McGuire, T. C., Palmer, G. H., Leib, S. R., Harkins, T. M., McElwain, T. F., and Barbet, A. F., 1990, Molecular basis for surface antigen size polymorphisms and conservation of a neutralization-sensitive epitope in *Anaplasma marginale, Proc. Natl. Acad. Sci. USA* **87:**3220–3224.

Andrews, J. H., 1991, *Comparative Ecology of Microorganisms and Macroorganisms,* Springer-Verlag, Berlin.

Atlas, R. M., and Bartha, R., 1987, *Microbiology Ecology: Fundamentals and Applications,* 2nd ed., Benjamin–Cummings, Menlo Park, Calif.

Baddour, L. M., Barker, L. P., Christensen, G. D., Parisi, J. T., and Simpson, W. A., 1990, Phenotypic variation of *Staphylococcus epidermis* in infection of transvenous endocardial pacemaker electrodes, *J. Clin. Microbiol.* **28:**676–679.

Bartlett, D. H., Wright, M. E., and Silverman, M., 1988, Variable expression of extracellular polysaccharide in the marine bacterium *Pseudomonas atlantica* is controlled by genome rearrangement, *Proc. Natl. Acad. Sci. USA* **85:**3923–3927.

Beach, D. H., and Klar, A. J. S., 1984, Rearrangements of the transposable mating-type cassettes of fusion yeast, *EMBO J.* **3:**603–610.

Beijerinck, M. W., 1889, Le *Photobacterium luminosum,* bacterie lumineuse de la Mer du Nord, *Arch. Neerl. Sci. Exactes Nat. Haarlem* **23:**401–405.

Bhaskaran, K., and Gorrill, R. H., 1957, A study of antigenic variation in *Vibrio cholerae, J. Gen. Microbiol.* **16:**721-729.

Birkbeck, T. H., and Penn, C. W. (eds.), 1986, *Antigenic Variation in Infectious Disease,* Volume 19, Society for General Microbiology/IRL Press, Oxford.

Blyn, L. B., Braaten, B. A., White-Ziegler, C. A., Rolfson, D. A., and Low, D. A., 1989, Phase-variation of pyelonephritis-associated pili in *Escherichia coli:* Evidence for transcriptional regulation, *EMBO J.* **8:**613–620.

Blyn, L. B., Braaten, B. A., and Low, D. A., 1990, Regulation of *pap* pilin variation by a mechanism involving differential Dam methylation states, *EMBO J.* **9:**4045–4054.

Borst, P., and Greaves, D. R., 1987, Programmed gene rearrangements altering gene expression, *Science* **235:**658–667.

Braaten, B. A., Blyn, L. B., Skinner, B. S., and Low, D. A., 1991, Evidence for a methylation-blocking factor (*mbf*) locus involved in *pap* pilus expression and phase variation in *Escherichia coli, J. Bacteriol.* **173:**1789–1800.

Bradshaw, A. D., 1965, Evolutionary significance of phenotypic plasticity in plants, *Adv. Genet.* **13:**115–155.

Brock, T. D., 1961, *Milestones in Microbiology,* Prentice–Hall, Englewood Cliffs, N.J.

Brophy, L. N., Kroll, S. J., Ferguson, D.J.P., and Moxon, E. R., 1991, Capsulation gene loss and 'rescue' mutations during the Cap$^+$ to Cap$^-$ transition in *Haemophilus influenzae* type b, *J. Gen. Microbiol.* **137:**2571-2576.

Brown, M.R.W., and Williams, P., 1985, The influence of environment on envelope properties affecting survival of bacteria in infections, *Annu. Rev. Microbiol.* **39:**527–556.

Brumbley, S. M., Carney, B. F., and Denny, T. P., 1993, Phenotype conversion in *Pseudomonas solanacearum* due to spontaneous inactivation of PhcA, a putative LysR transcriptional regulator. *J. Bacteriol.* **175:**5477–5487.

Cairns, J., Overbaugh, J., and Miller, S., 1988, The origin of mutants, *Nature* **335:**142–145.

Christensen, G. D., Baddour, L. M., and Simpson, W. A., 1987, Phenotypic variation of *Staphylococcus epidermis* slime production in vitro and in vivo, *Infect. Immun.* **55:**2870–2877.

Claassen, P.A.M., Korstee, G.J.J., Oosterveld-van Vleit, W. M., and van Neerven, A.R.W., 1986, Colonial heterogeneity of *Thiobacillus versutus, J. Bacteriol.* **168:**791–794.

Coetzee, J. N., and Sacks, T. G., 1960, Morphological variants of *Proteus hauseri, J. Gen. Microbiol.* **23:**209–216.

Coote, J. G., 1991, Antigenic switching and pathogenicity: Environmental effects on virulence gene expression in *Bordetella pertussis, J. Gen. Microbiol.* **137**:2493–2503.

Corey, R. J., and Starr, M. P., 1957, Colony types of *Xanthomonas phaseoli, J. Bacteriol.* **74**:137–140.

Costerton, J. W., 1988, Structure and plasticity at various organization levels in the bacterial cell, *Can. J. Microbiol.* **34**:515–521.

Cutri, S. S., Macauley, B. J., and Roberts, W. P., 1984, Characteristics of pathogenic non-fluorescent (smooth) and non-pathogenic fluorescent (rough) forms of *Pseudomonas tolaasii* and *Pseudomonas gingeri, J. Appl. Bacteriol.* **57**:291–298.

Deighton, M., Pearson, S., Capstick, J., Spellman, D., and Borland, R., 1992, Phenotypic variation of *Staphylococcus epidermis* isolated from a patient with native valve endocarditis, *J. Clin. Microbiol.* **30**:2385–2390.

de Lourdes Girard, M., Flores, M., Brom, S., Romero, D., Palacios, R., and Davila, G., 1991, Structural complexity of the symbiotic plasmid of *Rhizobium leguminosarum* bv. *phaseoli, J. Bacteriol.* **173**:2411–2419.

DiRita, V. J., and Mekalanos, J. J., 1989, Genetic regulation of bacterial virulence, *Annu. Rev. Genet.* **23**:455–482.

Dorman, C. J., and Ni Bhriain, N., 1992, Global regulation of gene expression during environmental adaptation: Implication for bacterial pathogens, in: *Molecular Biology of Bacterial Infection,* Volume 49 (C. E. Hormaeche, C. W. Penn, and C. J. Smyth, eds.), Cambridge University Press, London, pp. 193–230.

Durbin, R. D., 1992, Role of toxins for plant-pathogenic pseudomonads, in: *Pseudomonas Molecular Biology and Biotechnology* (E. Galli, S. Silver, and B. Witholt, eds.), American Society for Microbiology, Washington, D.C., pp. 43–55.

Dybvig, K., 1990, Mycoplasmal genetics, *Annu. Rev. Microbiol.* **44**:81–104.

Ehlers, R.-U., Stoesser, S., and Wyss, U., 1990, The influence of the phase variants of *Xenorhabdus* spp. and *Escherichia coli* (Enterobacteriaceae) on the propagation of entomopathogenic nematodes of the genera *Steinernema* and *Heterorhabditis, Rev. Nematol.* **13**:417–427.

Fischetti, V. A., 1991, Streptococcal M protein, *Sci. Am.* **264**:32-39.

Fisher, L. M., 1984, DNA supercoiling and gene expression, *Nature* **307**:686–687.

Flores, M., Gonzalez, V., Pardo, M. A., Leija, A., Martinez, E., Romero, D., Pinero, D., Davila, G., and Palacios, R., 1988, Genomic instability in *Rhizobium phaseoli, J. Bacteriol.* **170**:1191–1196.

Ford, E. B., 1971, *Ecological Genetics,* 3rd ed., Methuen, London.

Gammack, S. M., Paterson, E., Kemp, J. S., Cresser, M. S., and Killham, K., 1992, Factors affecting the motility of microorganisms in soil, in: *Soil Biochemistry,* Volume 7 (G. Stotzky and J.-M. Bolleg, eds.), Dekker, New York, pp. 263–305.

Gerritsen, L.J.M., De Raay, G., and Smits, P. H., 1992, Characterization of form variants of *Xenorhabdus luminescens, Appl. Environ. Microbiol.* **58**:1975–1979.

Gibbs, C. P., Reimann, B.-Y., Schultz, E., Kaufman, A., Haas, R., and Meyer, T. F., 1989, Reassortment of pili genes in *Neisseria gonorrhoeae* occurs by two distinct mechanisms, *Nature* **338**:651-652.

Glasgow, A. C., Hughes, K. T., and Simon, M. I., 1989, Bacterial DNA inversion systems, in: *Mobile DNA* (D. E. Berg and M. M. Howe, eds.), American Society for Microbiology, Washington, D.C., pp. 637–659.

Goor, M., Vantomme, R., Swings, J., Gills, M., Kersters, K., and De Ley, J., 1986, Phenotypic and genotypic diversity of *Pseudomonas tolaasii* and white line reacting organisms isolated from cultivated mushrooms, *J. Gen. Microbiol.* **132**:2249–2264.

Gosti, F., Huang, Y., and Sequeira, L., 1991, Molecular analysis of a gene that affects extracellular polysaccharide production and virulence in *Pseudomonas solanacearum,* in: *Advances in Molecular Genetics of Plant–Microbe Interactions,* Volume 1 (H. Hennecke and D.P.S. Verma, eds.), Kluwer, Dordrecht, pp. 73–77.

Gotz, P., Boman, A., and Brown, H. G., 1981, Interactions between insect immunity and an insect-pathogenic nematode with symbiotic bacteria, *Proc. R. Soc. London Ser. B* **212**:333–350.

Govan, J.R.W., 1989, Alginate and antibiotics, in: *Pseudomonas aeruginosa Infection: Antibiotics and Chemotherapy,* Volume 42 (N. Hoiby, S. S. Pederson, G.H.S. Hand, G. Doring, and I. A. Holder, eds.), Karger, Basel, pp. 88–96.

Grewal, S.I.S., and Rainey, P. B., 1991, Phenotypic variation of *Pseudomonas putida* and *P. tolaasii* affects the chemotactic response to *Agaricus bisporus* mycelial exudate, *J. Gen. Microbiol.* **137**:2761–2768.

Griffiths, M., and Stanier, R. Y., 1956, Some mutational changes in the photosynthetic pigment system in *Rhodopseudomonas spheroides, J. Gen. Microbiol.* **14**:698–706.

Gross, D. C., 1991, Molecular and genetic analysis of toxin production by pathovars of *Pseudomonas syringae, Annu. Rev. Phytopathol.* **29**:247–278.

Gross, D. C., and DeVay, J. E., 1977, Population dynamics and pathogenesis of *Pseudomonas syringae* in maize and cowpea in relation to the in vitro production of syringomycin, *Phytopathology* **67**:475–483.

Guerry, P., Logan, S. M., and Trust, T. J., 1988, Genomic rearrangements associated with antigenic variation in *Campylobacter coli, J. Bacteriol.* **170**:316–319.

Hall, B. G., 1991, Adaptive evolution that requires multiple spontaneous mutations: Mutations involving base substitutions, *Proc. Natl. Acad. Sci. USA* **88**:5882–5886.

Harrison, T. G., Saunders, N. A., Haththotuwa, A., Hallas, G., Birtles, R. J., and Taylor, A. G., 1990, Phenotypic variation amongst genotypically homogenous *Legionella pneumophila* serogroup 1 isolates: Implication for the investigation of outbreaks of Legionnaires' disease, *Epidemiol. Infect.* **104**:181–189.

Henry, B. S., 1933, Dissociation in the genus *Brucella, J. Infect. Dis.* **52**:374–402.

Herridge, D. F., and Roughley, R. S., 1975, Variation in colony characteristics and symbiotic effectiveness of *Rhizobium, J. Appl. Bacteriol.* **38**:19–27.

Heslop-Harrison, J., 1964, Forty years of genecology, *Adv. Ecol. Res.* **2**:159–247.

Higgins, C. F., Dorman, C. J., Stirling, D. A., Waddell, L., Booth, I. R., May, G., and Bremer, E., 1988, A physiological role for DNA supercoiling in the osmotic regulation of gene expression in *S. typhimurium* and *E. coli, Cell* **52**:569-584.

Higgins, C. F., Dorman, C. J., and Ni Bhriain, N., 1990, Environmental influences on DNA supercoiling: A novel mechanism for the regulation of gene expression, in: *The Bacterial Chromosome* (K. Drlica and M. Riley, eds.), American Society for Microbiology, Washington, D.C., pp. 421–432.

Hoffmann, A. A., and Parsons, P. A., 1991, *Evolutionary Genetics and Environmental Stress,* Oxford University Press, London.

Huang, Y., and Sequeira, L., 1990, Identification of a locus that regulates multiple functions in *Pseudomonas solanacearum, J. Bacteriol.* **172**:4728–4731.

Hurlbert, R. E., Xu, J., and Small, C. L., 1989, Colonial and cellular polymorphism in *Xenorhabdus luminescens, Appl. Environ. Microbiol.* **55**:1136–1143.

Jackwood, M. W., Hilt, D. A., and Dunn, P. A., 1991, Observations of colonial phenotypic variation in *Bordetella avium, Avian Dis.* **35**:496–504.

James, J. F., and Swanson, J., 1978, Studies on gonococcus infection. XIII. Occurrence of color/opacity colonial variants in clinical cultures, *Infect. Immun.* **19**:332–340.

Jensen, H. L., 1942, Studies of rhizobia nodulating tropical legumes, *Aust. J. Sci.* **5**:69.

Kaiser, D., 1984, Regulation of multicellular development in *Myxobacteria,* in: *Microbial Development* (R. Losick and L. Shapiro, eds.), Cold Spring Harbor Laboratory, Cold Spring Harbor, N.Y., pp. 197–218.

Kamoun, S., and Kado, C. I., 1990, Phenotypic switching affecting chemotaxis, xanthan production and virulence in *Xanthomonas campestris, Appl. Environ. Microbiol.* **56**:3855-3860.

Kelman, A., and Hruschka, J., 1973, The role of motility and aerotaxis in the selective increase of avirulent bacteria in still broth cultures of *Pseudomonas solanacearum*, *J. Gen. Microbiol.* **76:**177–188.

Keynan, A., and Hastings, J. W., 1961, Biolminescence in *Vibrio harveyi*, *Biol. Bull.* **121:**375.

Kim, S.-R., and Komano, T., 1992, Nucleotide sequence of the R721 shufflon, *J. Bacteriol.* **174:**7053–7058.

King, V., and Clayton, C. L., 1991, Genomic investigation of phenotypic variation in *Campylobacter jejuni* flagellin, *FEMS Microbiol. Lett.* **84:**107–112.

Klein, M. G., 1990, Efficacy against soil-inhabiting insect pests, in: *Entomopathogenic Nematodes in Biological Control* (R. Gaugler and H. K. Kaya, eds.), CRC Press, Boca Raton, Fla., pp. 195–214.

Koch, A. L., 1987, The variability and individuality of the bacterium, in: *Escherichia coli* and *Salmonella typhimurium Cellular and Molecular Biology*, Volume 2 (J. L. Ingraham, K. B. Low, B. Magasanik, S. Moselio, and H. E. Umbarger, eds.), American Society for Microbiology, Washington, D.C., pp. 1606–1614.

Krieg, N. R., and Holt, J. G. (eds.), 1984, *Bergey's Manual of Systematic Bacteriology*, Volume 1, 1st ed., Williams & Wilkins, Baltimore.

Kuykendall, L. D., and Elkan, G. H., 1976, *Rhizobium japonicum* derivatives differing in nitrogen-fixing and carbohydrate utilization, *Appl. Environ. Microbiol.* **32:**511–519.

Lambden, P. R., Heckels, J. E., McBride, H., and Watt, P. J., 1981, The identification and isolation of novel pilus types produced by variants of *Neisseria gonorrhoeae* P9 following selection *in vivo, FEMS Microbiol. Lett.* **10:**339–341.

Lenski, R. E., and Mittler, J. E., 1993, The directed mutation controversy and neo-Darwinism, *Science* **259:**188–194.

Leong, J., 1986, Siderophores: Their biochemistry and possible role in the hbiocontrol of plant pathogens, *Annu. Rev. Phytopathol.* **24:**187–209.

Lethbridge, G., 1989, An industrial view of microbial inoculants for crop plants, in: *Microbial Inoculation of Crop Plants* (R. Campbell and R. M. Macdonald, eds.), Society for General Microbiology/IRL Press, Oxford, pp. 11–28.

Levin, M. A., Seidler, R., Borguin, A. W., Fowle, J. R., III, and Barkay, T., 1987, Developing methods to assess environmental risk, *Bio/Technology* **5:**38.

Levinson, G., and Gutman, G. A., 1987, Slipped-strand mispairing: A major mechanism for DNA sequence evolution, *Mol. Biol. Evol.* **4:**203–221.

Lloyd, D. G., 1984, Variation strategies of plants in heterogeneous environments, *Biol. J. Linn. Soc.* **21:**357–385.

Losick, R., and Youngman, P., 1984, Endospore formation in *Bacillus*, in: *Microbial Development*, (R. Losick, and L. Shapiro, eds.), Cold Spring Harbor Laboratory, New York, pp. 63–88.

Lucas, L. T., and Grogan, R. G., 1969, Pathogenicity and other characteristics of smooth and rough isolates of Pseudomonas lachrymans, *Phytopathol.* **59:**1918–1923.

McBride, H. M., Lambden, P. R., Heckels, J. E., and Watt, P. J., 1981, The role of outer membrane proteins in the survival of *Neisseria gonorrhoeae* P9 within guinea pig subcutaneous chambers, *J. Gen. Microbiol.* **126:**63–67.

McKern, K. M., O'Donnell, I. J., Stewart, D. J., and Clark, B. L., 1985, Primary structure of pilin variation and changes in host cells, *J. Gen. Microbiol.* **55:**409–416.

Marrs, C. F., Ruehl, W. W., Schoolnik, G. K., and Falkow, S., 1988, Pilin gene phase variation of *Moraxella bovis* is due to an inversion of the pilin genes, *J. Bacteriol.* **170:**3032–3039.

Mather, K., 1943, Polygenic inheritance and natural selection, *Biol. Rev.* **18:**32–64.

Maynard-Smith, J., 1990, The evolution of prokaryotes: does sex matter? *Ann. Rev. Ecol. System* **21:**1–12.

Maynard-Smith, J., Dawson, C. G., and Spratt, B. G., 1991, Localized sex in bacteria, *Nature* **349:**29–31.

Meyer, T. F., Gibbs, C. P., and Haas, R., 1990, Variation and control of protein expression in *Neisseria, Annu. Rev. Microbiol.* **44:**451-477.

Moxon, E. R., and Maskell, D., 1992, *Haemophilus influenzae* lipopolysaccharide: The biochemistry and biology of a virulence factor, in: *Molecular Biology of Bacterial Infection,* Volume 49 (C. W. Hormaeche, C. W. Penn, and C. J. Smyth, eds.), Cambridge University Press, London, pp. 75-96.

Moxon, E. R., and Murphy, D., 1978, *Haemophilus influenzae* bacteremia and meningitis resulting from survival of a single organism, *Proc. Natl. Acad. Sci. USA* **75:**1534-1536.

Nealson, K., 1972, Factors controlling the appearance of dark mutants of luminous bacteria, *Biol. Bull.* **143:**471-472.

Olafson, R. W., McCarthy, P. J., Bhatti, A. R., Dooley, J.S.G., Heckels, J. E., and Trust, T. J., 1985, Structural and antigenic analysis of meningococcal pili, *Infect. Immun.* **48:**336-342.

Olivier, J. M., Guillaumes, J., and Martin, D., 1978, Study of bacterial disease of mushroom caps, in: *Proceedings of the Fourth International Conference of Plant Pathogenic Bacteria,* Station de Patologie Vegetale Phytobacteriologie, Angers, pp. 903-916.

Palleroni, N. J., 1984, Pseudomonadaceae, in: *Bergey's Manual of Systematic Bacteriology,* Volume 1, 1st ed. (N. R. Krieg and J. G. Holt, eds.), Williams & Wilkins, Baltimore.

Paruchuri, D. K., and Harshey, R. M., 1987, Flagellar variation in *Serratia marcescens* is associated with color variation, *J. Bacteriol.* **169:**61-65.

Pincus, S. H., Cole, R. L., Wessels, M. R., Corwin, M. D., Kamanga-Sollo, E., Hayes, S. F., Cieplak,

J. W., and Swanson, J., 1992, Group B streptococcal opacity variants, *J. Bacteriol.* **174:**3739-3749.

Plasterk, R. H. A., Simon, M. I., and Barbour, A. G., 1991, Transposition of structural genes to an expression sequence on a linear plasmid causes antigenic variation in the bacterium *Borrelia hermsii, Nature* **318:**257-263.

Quinto, C., de la Vega, H., Flores, M., Fernandez, L., Ballado, T., Soberon, G., and Palacios, R., 1982, Reiteration of nitrogen fixation gene sequences in *Rhizobium phaseoli, Nature* **299:**724-728.

Rainey, P. B., 1989, *The involvement of Pseudomonas putida in the process of basidiome initiation of the cultivated mushroom, Agaricus bisporus,* Ph.D. thesis, University of Canterbury.

Rainey, P. B., 1991, Phenotypic variation of *Pseudomonas putida* and *P. tolaasii* affects attachment to *Agaricus bisporus* mycelium, *J. Gen. Microbiol.* **137:**2769-2779.

Rainey, P. B., Brodey, C. L., and Johnstone, K., 1992, Biology of *Pseudomonas tolaasii,* cause of brown blotch disease of the cultivated mushroom, *Adv. Plant Pathol.* **8:**95-117.

Rainey, P. B., Brodey, C. L., and Johnstone, K., 1993, Identificaiton of a gene cluster encoding three high-molecular-weight prokins, which is required for synthesis of tolaasin by the mushroom pathogen *Pseudomonas tolaasii,* Mol. Microbiol. **8:**643-652.

Rangnekar, V. M., 1988, Variation in the ability of Pseudomonas sp. strain B13 cultures to utilize meta-chlorobenzoate is associated with tandem amplification and deamplification of DNA, *J. Bacteriol.* **171:**1907-1912.

Robertson, B. D., and Meyer, T. F., 1992, Antigenic variation in bacterial pathogens, in: *Molecular Biology of Bacterial Infection,* Volume 49 (C. W. Hormaeche, C. W. Penn, and C. J. Smyth, eds.), Cambridge University Press, London, pp. 61-73.

Rosengarten, R., and Wise, K. S., 1990, Phenotypic switching in mycoplasmas: Phase variation of diverse surface lipoproteins, *Science* **247:**315-318.

Rosengarten, R., and Wise, K., 1991, The Vlp system of *Mycoplasma hyorhinis:* Combinatorial expression of distinct size variant lipoproteins generating high-frequency surface antigenic variation, *J. Bacteriol.* **173:**4782-4793.

Rosqvist, R., Skurnik, M., and Wolf-Watz, H., 1991, Increased virulence of *Yersinia pseudotuberculosis* by two independent mutations, *Nature* **334:**522-525.

Roszak, D. B., and Colwell, R. R., 1987, Survival strategies of bacteria in the natural environment, *Microbiol. Rev.* **51**:365–379.

Sastry, P. A., Pearlstone, J. R., Smillie, L. B., and Paranchych, W., 1983, Amino acid sequence of pilin isolated from *Pseudomonas aeruginosa, FEBS Lett.* **151**:253–256.

Saunders, J. R., 1986, Genetic basis of phase and antigenic variation in bacteria, in: *Antigenic Variation in Infectious Diseases* (T. H. Birkbeck and C. W. Penn, eds.), Society for General Microbiology/IRL Press, Oxford, pp. 57–76.

Saunders, J. R., 1989, The molecular basis of antigenic variation in pathogenic *Neisseria*, in: *Genetics of Bacterial Diversity* (D. A. Hopwood and K. F. Chater, eds.), Academic Press, New York, pp. 268–285.

Schlichting, C. D., 1986, The evolution of phenotypic plasticity in plants, *Annu. Rev. Ecol. Syst.* **17**:667–693.

Schrader, J. A., and Holmes, D. S., 1988, Phenotypic switching of *Thiobacillus ferrooxidans, J. Bacteriol.* **170**:3915–3923.

Schrempf, H., 1983, Reiterated sequences within the genome *Streptomyces,* in: *Proceedings of the Fifth John Innes Symposium* (K. F. Chater, C. A. Kullis, D. A. Hopwood, A.W.B. Johnstone, and H. W. Woolhouse, eds.), Croom Helm, London, pp. 131–142.

Schuhardt, V. T., and Wilkerson, M., 1951, Relapse phenomena in rats infected with single spirochetes (*Borrelia recurrentis* var. *turicate*), *J. Bacteriol.* **62**:215–300.

Seifert, H. S., and So, M., 1988, Genetic mechanisms of bacterial antigenic variation, *Microbiol. Rev.* **52**:327–336.

Seifert, H. S., Ajioka, R. D., Marchal, C., Sparling, P. F., and So, M., 1988, DNA transformation leads to pilin antigenic variation in *Neisseria gonorrhoeae, Nature* **336**:392–395.

Shapiro, J. A., 1986, Control of *Pseudomonas putida* growth on agar surfaces, in: *The Bacteria,* Volume 10 (J. R. Sokatch, ed.), Academic Press, New York, pp. 27–69.

Silverman, M., Martin, M., and Engebrecht, J., 1989, Regulation of luminescence in marine bacteria, in: *Genetics of Bacterial Diversity* (D. A. Hopwood and K. F. Chater, eds.), Academic Press, New York, pp. 71–86.

Simon, M. I., and Silverman, M., 1983, Recombinant regulation of gene expression in bacteria, in: *Gene Function in Prokaryotes* (J. Beckwith, J. Davies, and J. A. Gallant, eds.), Cold Spring Harbor Laboratory, Cold Spring Harbor, N.Y., pp. 211–217.

Smith, R. M., Parisi, J. T., Vidal, L., and Baldwin, J. N., 1977, Nature of the genetic determinant controlling encapsulation in *Staphylococcus aureus, Infect. Immum.* **17**:231–234.

Sneath, P.H.A., 1985, Future of numerical taxonomy, in: *Computer Assisted Bacterial Systematics* (M. Goodfellow, D. Jones, and F. G. Priest, eds.), Society for General Microbiology/Academic Press, London, pp. 415–431.

Snellings, N. J., Johnson, E. M., Kopecko, D. J., Collins, H. H., and Baron, L. S., 1981, Genetic regulation of variable Vi antigenic expression in a strain of *Citrobacter freundii, J. Bacteriol.* **145**:1010–1017.

Sokal, R. R., 1985, The principle of numerical taxonomy: Twenty five years later, in: *Computer-Assisted Bacterial Systematics* (M. Goodfellow, D. Jones, and F. G. Priest, eds.), Society for General Microbiology/Academic Press, London, pp. 1-20.

Stanier, R. Y., Dourdoroff, K., and Adelberg, E. A., 1958, *General Microbiology,* Macmillan & Co., London.

Stanier, R. Y., Palleroni, N. J., and Dourdoroff, K., 1966, The aerobic pseudomonads: A taxonomic study, *J. Gen. Microbiol.* **43**:159–271.

Stebbins, G. L. (ed.), 1950, *Variation and Evolution in Plants,* Columbia University Press, New York.

Stocker, B.A.D., 1949, Measurements of the rate of mutation of flagella antigenic phase in *Salmonella typhimurium, J. Hyg.* **47**:398–413.

Strange, R. E., and Hunter, J. R., 1966, 'Substrate-accelerated death' of nitrogen-limited bacteria, *J. Gen. Microbiol.* **44**:255–262.

Streisinger, G., and Owen, J. E., 1985, Mechanisms of spontaneous and induced frameshift mutation in bacteriophage T4, *Genetics* **109**:633–659.

Sultan, S. E., 1987, Evolutionary implications of phenotypic plasticity in plants, *Evol. Biol.* **21**:127–178.

Swanson, J., 1982, Colony opacity and protein II composition of gonococci, *Infect. Immun.* **37**:359–368.

Swanson, J., 1987, Genetic mechanisms responsible for changes in pilus expression by gonococci, *J. Exp. Med.* **165**:1459–1479.

Swanson, J., and Barrera, O., 1983, Gonococcal pilus subunit size heterogeneity correlates with transition in colony piliation phenotype, not with changes in colony opacity, *J. Exp. Med.* **158**:1459–1472.

Swanson, J., and Koomey, J. M., 1989, Mechanisms for variation of pili and outer membrane protein II in *Neisseria gonorrhoeae*, in: *Mobile DNA* (D. E. Berg and M. M. Howe, eds.), American Society for Microbiology, Washington, D.C., pp. 743–761.

Sylvester-Bradley, R., Thornton, P., and Jones, P., 1988, Colony dimorphism in *Bradyrhizobium* strains, *Appl. Environ. Microbiol.* **54**:1033–1038.

Terzaghi, E., and O'Hara, M., 1990, Microbial plasticity: The relevance to microbial ecology, in: *Advances in Microbial Ecology*, Volume 11 (K. C. Marshall, ed.), Plenum Press, New York, pp. 431–460.

Thompson, J. D., 1991, Phenotypic plasticity as a component of evolutionary change, *Trends Ecol. Evol.* **6**:246–249.

Turner, J.R.G., 1977, Butterfly mimicry: The genetical evolution of adaptation, *Evol. Biol.* **10**:163–206.

Vickerman, M. M., Clewell, D. B., and Jones, G. W., 1991, Ecological implications of glycosyl transferase phase variation in *Streptococcus gordonii*, *Appl. Environ. Microbiol.* **57**:3648–3651.

Warne, S. R., Varley, J. M., Boulnois, G. J., and Norton, M. G., 1990, Identification and characterization of a gene that controls colony morphology and auto-aggregation in *Escherichia coli* K12, *J. Gen. Microbiol.* **137**:455–462.

Weil, E., and Felix, A., 1917, Weitere Untersuchungen uber das Wesen der Fleckfieberag glutination, *Wien. Klin. Wochenschr.* **30**:1509.

Weiser, J. N., Love, J. M., and Moxon, E. R., 1989, The molecular mechanism of phase variation of H. influenzae lipopolysaccharide, *Cell* **59**:657–665.

West-Eberhard, M. J., 1989, Phenotypic plasticity and the origins of diversity, *Annu. Rev. Ecol. Syst.* **20**:249–278.

Willis, D. K., Barta, T. M., and Kinscherf, T. G., 1991, Genetics of toxin production and resistance in phytopathogenic bacteria, *Experientia* **47**:765–771.

Wills, C., 1989, *The Wisdom of the Genes*, Oxford University Press, London.

Wright, S., 1931, Evolution in Mendelian populations, *Genetics* **16**:97–159.

Yates, J. R., Cunningham, R. P., and Holmes, D. S., 1988, IS*T2*: An insertion sequence from *Thiobacillus ferrooxidans*, *Proc. Natl. Acad. Sci. USA* **85**:7284–7287.

Yee, T., and Inouye, M., 1984, Two-dimensional S1 nuclease heteroduplex mapping: Detection of rearrangements in bacterial genomes, *Proc. Natl. Acad. Sci. USA* **81**:2723–2727.

Yogev, D., Rosengarten, R., Watson-McKown, R., and Wise, K. S., 1991, Molecular basis of *Mycoplasma* surface antigenic variation: A novel set of divergent genes undergo spontaneous mutation of periodic coding regions and 5′ regulatory sequences, *EMBO J.* **10**:4069–4079.

7

Decomposition of Shoots of a Salt-Marsh Grass

Methodology and Dynamics of Microbial Assemblages

STEVEN Y. NEWELL

1. Introduction: Methods and Artifacts in Grassland-Decomposition Research

Researchers interested in accurately describing natural microbial participation in the decay of portions of vascular plants must try to avoid altering genuine conditions of decay via their methods (Swift *et al.*, 1979; Boulton and Boon, 1991; Newell, 1994). This is an old refrain (e.g., Park, 1974, on the elusive balance between particle retention and shredder admittance using litterbags), but one that continues to go unheeded (e.g., a paper published in 1992 in a leading aquatic-science journal; methods: green shoots of grass cut, dried, and placed in litterbags on or buried in salt-marsh sediment). "The challenge of ecology immediately reveals the correlated dangers, for it is singularly easy to fall into error through a failure to describe accurately the various parts of the system and to appreciate their possible significance. An error at this stage may lead to the development of inapposite experimental techniques, so that the final synthesis must inevitably fail. A constant temptation besetting the ecologist is that of loose thinking to enable him to gloss over intractable parts of his study" (Griffin, 1972).

For ecologists interested in decomposition in grassland systems (see, e.g., Dickinson, 1983; Andrén and Paustian, 1987; Seastedt, 1988; Hutchinson and King, 1989; Coleman *et al.*, 1990; Lee, 1990; Davis, 1991), systems containing 11% of plant-biomass carbon and 30% of soil organic matter of earth's major temperate and tropical terrestrial ecosystem types (Anderson, 1991), a key life-

STEVEN Y. NEWELL • Marine Institute, University of Georgia, Sapelo Island, Georgia 31327

Advances in Microbial Ecology, Volume 13, edited by J. Gwynfryn Jones. Plenum Press, New York, 1993.

history factor to consider is the presence/absence of leaf and stem abscission (Sexton and Woolhouse, 1984). In grasses, with few exceptions (e.g., bamboo), only the floral parts are abscised; grass shoots maintain a set number of living leaves, with lower senescing leaves being replaced by new ones at the shoot apex (Salim *et al.*, 1988, and references therein). After senescence, leaves begin decay in the canopy, without detachment, so that large crops of standing, decaying leaves are present for much if not all of the year (e.g., Koike *et al.*, 1975; Hussey and Long, 1982; Jordan and Whigham, 1988; Seastedt, 1988; Christian *et al.*, 1990; Lee, 1990; Davis, 1991). Retention of dead stems is an important adaptive strategy for wetland grasses, providing gas channels to rhizomes via aerenchyma (Jordan and Whigham, 1988; Končalová, 1990; Wijte and Gallagher, 1991; Arenovski and Howes, 1992; Armstrong *et al.*, 1992). [Could it be that retention of dead leaves makes high CO_2 and water vapor concentrations (from respiration of internally resident decomposers) available to living portions of shoots (see Hwang and Morris, 1991; Constable *et al.*, 1992)?] Microbes on/in attached leaves and stems decaying in the canopy experience considerably different environmental conditions than do microbes of fallen-litter systems, especially light, persistence or transience of wetness (dew formation, rapidity of evaporation after wetting events), access to soil/sediment inorganic nutrients resulting from subsurface mineralization, proximity to potential microalgal epiphytic partners, shredder-detritivore activity, submergence (especially in coastal and inland wetlands), influence of fermentation products and potential development of anaerobic microzones (especially in wetlands), access to inorganic nutrients in rain, gas/liquid continuity with root/rhizome systems via aerenchymal and hydrophobic leaf-surface channels (e.g., respectively, Morris, 1989; Newell *et al.*, 1991; Holland and Coleman, 1987; Fallon *et al.*, 1985; Suberkropp, 1992a; Newell *et al.*, 1989; Tsutsuki and Ponnamperuma, 1987; Paerl *et al.*, 1990; Armstrong *et al.*, 1992; Raskin and Kende, 1985).

    Decomposition ecologists have often either (1) ignored the literature and field evidence that grasses do not abscise their leaves, or (2) routinely assumed that the standing-dead phase of grass shoots is one in which microbes are negligibly active, for they have often used litterbags (or otherwise moved shoot material directly to sediments) in their studies of decomposition of grass shoots (*present company included:* Benner *et al.*, 1984; Newell *et al.*, 1984). It is now well established that there are assemblages of microbes that are well adapted to the conditions of decay in grass canopies. Seastedt (1985, 1988) found that standing, decaying leaves of prairie grasses could efficiently capture nitrogen (54% retained by microbes), and that standing decay consumed 65% of shoot material produced. Gallagher *et al.* (1984), Newell *et al.* (1985, 1989), and Buth and Voesenek (1987, 1988) found that standing, decaying salt-marsh grasses exhibited microbial respiration rates (to 200 μg CO_2-C/hr per g organic mass of leaf, or higher, at 20–25 ° C) that were on a par with rates for detached litter on soil or sediment surfaces. Buth and Voesenek (1987) and Newell *et al.* (1989) reported high rates of mass loss for standing, decaying leaves of salt-marsh grasses ($k \cong$ -0.01 per day), rates not different from material on the salt-marsh-sediment surface (Newell and Fallon, 1989). Newell *et al.* (1992) have confirmed that microbial (probably fungal/bacterial consortial activity) nitrogen fixation can occur at high rates (to about 30 μmole acetylene reduced/g organic mass of leaf per day) within standing, decaying marsh-grass leaves. Hietz (1992) found that severed shoots of a reed lost organic mass three times slower when hung above the water, but this may have been partially due to the gas/liquid discontinuity of aerenchyma channels to the shoot bases (see also Bruquetas de Zozaya and Neiff, 1991).

Findings of high rates of microbial activity on standing-dead grass shoots would not surprise mycological systematists, who have known for decades that fungi, especially ascomycetes, are well adapted for growth and sexual reproduction in that type of substrate (e.g., Johnson, 1956; Wagner, 1969; Gessner and Kohlmeyer, 1976; Kohlmeyer and Kohlmeyer, 1979; see especially Fig. 24 in Kohlmeyer and Volkmann-Kohlmeyer, 1991: Berlese knew in the 1800s that fungi were substantive secondary producers in decaying cordgrass). There are whole genera of fungi (especially *Phaeosphaeria* Miyake) that are especially adapted for utilizing and are largely confined to the standing-dead-grass system (Leuchtmann, 1984; Shoemaker and Babcock, 1989; Leuchtmann and Newell, 1991). Sadly, it has been rare for decomposition ecologists (those using physical, chemical, biochemical, and radiobiological measurement skills) to form strong functional linkages with mycologists, or for single scientists to develop broad expertise both in decomposition ecology and in mycology (see Rayner, 1992, p. xvii). Strong recognition of fungi (and the other prominent group of mycelial eukaryotic organo-osmotrophs, the oomycotes) as a major subdivision of microbial life forms (Margulis *et al.*, 1990; Hawksworth, 1991), with unique and intriguing capabilities (Cooke and Rayner, 1984; Pirozynski and Hawksworth, 1988; Rayner and Boddy, 1988; Eriksson *et al.*, 1990; Carroll and Wicklow, 1992; Clipson and Jennings, 1992), and the appearance of mycological methods useful to nonspecialists in mycology (e.g., Grigorova and Norris, 1990; Newell and Fallon, 1991; Newell, 1992, 1993, 1994; Norris *et al.*, 1992), are likely to lead to new fusions of mycological and ecological talents and better experimental designs in decomposition research, incorporating recognition of the negative impacts of altering natural environmental conditions (Table I).

2. Smooth Cordgrass: A Popular Research Target

Smooth cordgrass (*Spartina alterniflora* Loisel.) salt marshes exhibit primary productivity rivaling that in any other of earth's ecosystems, and yield large

Table I. Procedural Components of Substrate Pretreatment and Deployment to Be Avoided in Designing Studies of Authentic Decomposition of Grass Shoots[a]

Component	Contraindicated because
Severing from sheath or stem	Most grasses do not abscise leaves or stems, maintaining aerenchymal channels to rhizomes after senescence
Drying, especially oven	Can cause condensation ("browning") of plant chemicals, kill microflora, and lead to spurious leaching
Shredding or grinding	Exposes plant internal structure prematurely; prevents effective penetrative mycelial development
Choice of green substrate	Beginning substrate is unusually high in carbohydrates and protein; interference with timing of microbial colonization
Placement on soil or sediment, or in continuous submergence for intertidal or pond-margin plants	Short-circuits[b] the natural standing decay phase; prematurely exposes substrate to soil/sediment fauna and nutrients

[a]Example sources upon which this table is based (alphabetically listed): Arenovski and Howes (1992); Armstrong *et al.* (1992); Bärlocher (1991); Boulton and Boon (1991); Buchsbaum *et al.* (1991); Fog (1988); Gessner (1992); Ingham (1992); Newell (1991); Newell and Fallon (1989); Salim *et al.* (1988); Salonius (1983).
[b]But note that at higher latitudes, and in agricultural and pastoral situations, this short-circuiting may routinely happen to some portions of shoots via snow/ice deposition and flow, large-grazer trampling, and agricultural harvesting activities (see Andrén and Paustian, 1987; Cranford *et al.*, 1989; Hutchinson and King, 1989).

crops of animals including some of particular commercial value (e.g., blue crabs, peneid shrimp) (Pomeroy and Wiegert, 1981; Boesch and Turner, 1984; Mitsch and Gosselink, 1986; Morris, 1988; Turner and Boesch, 1988; Morris and Haskin, 1990). These facts have attracted many decomposition ecologists to the study of smooth-cordgrass decay. At least 52 papers by more than 100 scientists have been published describing cordgrass-decay phenomena (not including root and rhizome decay; see Benner *et al.*, 1991). Christian (1984) discussed mass-loss results from 11 of these papers, and I list some of these and others in Table II.

The earliest examinations of cordgrass decay took place on Sapelo Island, Georgia (Burkholder and Bornside, 1957). This paper set the tone for much of the subsequent cordgrass-decay work, in that the experimental conditions provided for decay were quite unnatural: whole, green shoots were either (1) cut and placed in 4.5-kg lots in 0.75-m³, permanently submerged, wooden boxes or (2) dried, ground to a powder, suspended in seawater in 250-ml flasks, inoculated with marsh sediment, and incubated on a rotary shaker. Since the natural conditions of standing decay potentially favoring eukaryotic decomposers [especially alternating wet/dry periods; intact substrate (not disintegrated, permitting thorough translocational mycelial pervasion); availability of standing substrate for

Table II. Studies of Decomposition of Shoot Material of Smooth Cordgrass (*Spartina alterniflora*)[a]

| | Substrate treatment and deployment[c] | | | | Microbiological methods[d] | |
Reference[b]	Initial substrate	Predrying	Predeployment disintegration	Environment	Standing crop	Activity
Burkholder 57₁	GR, SH	NO	−	SU[e]	NA	NA
Burkholder 57₂	GR, SH	OV	+	EN	NA	TU
Gosselink 74	YE + BR, SH	OV	+	EN	NI	Δ
Rublee 78₁	GR, SH	AI	−	LI	DB	Δ
Rublee 78₂	GR, SH	FR	+	EN	NA	¹⁴C ↑
Haines 79	BR, SH	OV	+	EN	AT	NF
Lee 80	YE, LE	AI	−	LI	DB, ER	Δ, CO
McKee 82	GR, SH	AI	−	LI, SU	NA	NA
Marinucci 83	GR + YE, SH	AI	+	EN	DB, FU	Δ, CO, AU
Reice 83	BR, LE	NO	−	BU	NA	NA
Tenore 84	BR, LE	OV + FR	+	EN[f]	DB[f]	Δ, CO
Valiela 85	GR + YE, SH	AI	−	LI	NA	NA
Benner 86	GR, SH, EX	OV	+	EN	NA	¹⁴C ↑
Dame 86	GR, SH	AI	−	LI[g]	NA	NA
Twilley 86	GR, SH	NO	−	LI + EN	NA	CO
Fogel 89	GR, SH	NO	+	EN	NA	¹³C
Newell 89	YE, LE	NO	−	NS	DB, FU, AL, ER, IM	Δ, CO, TH, ¹⁴C ↓

(continued)

Table II. cont.

Reference[b]	Substrate treatment and deployment[c]				Microbiological methods[a]	
	Initial substrate	Predrying	Predeployment disintegration	Environment	Standing crop	Activity
Moran 90	GR, SH, EX	OV	+	EN	NA	$^{14}C\uparrow$, DO^{14}C
Buchsbaum 91	GR + YE, SH	AI	−	LI	NI, AM	Δ
Hicks 91	GR & BR, SH	AI	+ & −	EN & LI	GM, AM, DB	Δ

[a]List intended as representative chronological, not comprehensive. See reference lists in Christian (1984), Newell et al. (1985), Valiela et al. (1985), Newell et al. (1989), and Haddad et al. (1992) for further citations.

[b]References: Burkholder and Bornside (1957); Gosselink and Kirby (1974); Rublee et al. (1978); Haines and Hanson (1979); Lee et al. (1980); McKee and Seneca (1982); Marinucci et al. (1983); Reice and Stiven (1983); Tenore et al. (1984); Valiela et al. (1985); Benner et al. (1986); Dame and Kenny (1986); Twilley et al. (1986); Fogel et al. (1989); Newell et al. (1989); Moran and Hodson (1990); Buchsbaum et al. (1990); Buchsbaum et al. (1991); Hicks et al. (1991).

[c]Substrate codes. Initial substrate: BR = brown, standing, dead; EX = lignocellulose extracted and used as substrate; GR = green, living; LE = leaf blades; SH = whole shoots (stems + leaves); YE = yellow-green, senescent. Predrying: AI = air-dried; FR = freeze-dried; NO = no drying; OV = oven-dried (≥ 40°C). Disintegration: − = none; + = substrate disintegrated. Environment for decay: BU = bundles of cut leaves on sediment surface; EN = cut leaves in laboratory enclosures; LI = cut leaves in litterbags on sediment surface; NS = standing, uncut; SU = cut leaves in litterbags, continuously submerged.

[d]Codes for microbiological methods. Standing crop: AL = direct microscopy, algal biovolume; AM = amino acid content; AT = adenosine triphosphate; DB = direct microscopy, bacterial biovolume; ER = ergosterol content (living–fungal mass); GM = glucosamine/muramic-acid content (fungal/bacterial mass); FU = direct microscopy, fungal biovolume; IM = immunoassay; NI = nitrogen content; TU = culture turbidity. Activity: Δ = net change in standing crop; AU = microautoradiography; ^{13}C = stable-isotope content; $^{14}C\uparrow$ = mineralization of plant carbon; $^{14}C\downarrow$ = fixation of CO$_2$; CO = release of CO$_2$ or O$_2$ uptake; DO^{14}C = release of dissolved organic carbon; NF = nitrogen fixation; TH = incorporation of [^{3}H]thymidine in bacterial DNA.

[e]Submerged in wooden crates.

[f]Several-centimeter-deep column of particles, anaerobic (turning black) below the surface. Fungal-biovolume estimates were attempted (Newell et al., 1985), but no fungal material was detected.

[g]A series of deployments, each lasting only 25 days.

ascospore attachment and mycelial entry (without the fungal-lethal temperatures of the drying oven): Visser, 1985; Newell, 1994; and see Table I] were not furnished, it is not surprising that Burkholder and Bornside (1957) pinpointed bacteria as the decomposers of smooth cordgrass. (The word "fungus" is absent from Burkholder and Bornside's 18-page paper.) This conclusion found its way into a famous and valuable model of salt-marsh ecological function (Teal, 1962), and thereby has influenced the thinking of salt-marsh-decomposition ecologists through to the present (see Table II).

One might argue that one aspect of Burkholder and Bornside's (1957) experimental design is not faulty in latitudes higher than 31°N: cutting the shoots and placing them on the sediment or in creeks could simulate natural snow/ice effects (see Bertness, 1984; Cranford *et al.*, 1989; Roman *et al.*, 1990). However, even in cordgrass marshes in Maine (45°N), about two-thirds of the leaves produced by smooth-cordgrass shoots are decayed as standing-dead to the extent that they are lost during the period May–October (Hardisky and Reimold, 1977).

3. Microbial Participation in Cordgrass Decay

Some reviewers of estuarine and salt-marsh ecology have reached one or more of the following conclusions: that little of the nitrogen in decaying cordgrass is in the form of microbial mass; that bacteria are the principal or sole decomposers of cordgrass; and that decaying-cordgrass carbon is mostly lost to respiration, rather than moved through the food web to marsh/estuarine animals (e.g., Mitsch and Gosselink, 1986; Schleyer, 1986; Bowen, 1987; Mann, 1988; Dame, 1989). These incorrect or inaccurate conclusions were based on decomposition research (Table II) incorporating one or more of the artifact-inducing procedures of Table I. It is perhaps not surprising that ground and heated cordgrass (see Tables I and II), not naturally microbially "conditioned" (Bärlocher, 1992), was a relatively poor nutritive support for a deposit feeder (Tenore *et al.*, 1984). Multiple-stable-isotope research with field samples has clearly demonstrated that much of the animal production of salt marshes *is* ultimately derived from cordgrass (Peterson and Howarth, 1987; see also Couch, 1989; Deegan *et al.*, 1990). Animals low in the food web can derive greater than 75% of their carbon from cordgrass (e.g., mummichog minnows, salt-marsh periwinkles), and even high-order predators (blue crabs) can derive about half of their carbon from cordgrass, based on body contents of ^{13}C, ^{34}S, and ^{15}N. These may be underestimates of cordgrass contribution, for fungal decomposers may dilute the ^{34}S signal of decaying cordgrass, by utilizing seawater sulfate (Peterson and Howarth, 1987). C. A. Currin (personal communication) reports that the ^{34}S signal of cordgrass shoots does change between the living stage (range, -10 to $+3$) and the standing-decaying stage ($+12$ to $+14$).

3.1. Fungal Participation

The natural microbial "conditioning" system of intact, decaying cordgrass shoots is dominated by ascomycetous fungi, not by bacteria. May and Odum were the first nonmycologists to point out that fungi were probable major mediators of cordgrass decomposition (May, 1974; Odum *et al.*, 1979, p. 365; see also Hodson *et al.*, 1983, p. 193), but this message did not immediately gain wide acceptance. Although litterbag research since 1980 and work with laboratory microcosms containing dried and ground whole shoots have yielded the result that bacteria were at least equal to fungi with respect to standing crop, and/or that nitrogen of decaying shoot material was not microbial (Table III), this was probably largely a function of artificial conditions of decay (Newell and Fallon, 1989; Newell, 1994). When smooth-cordgrass leaves decay in the natural, attached, standing state, greater than 90% of the microbial standing crop is composed of fungal mass, and much of the nitrogen of the decay system is captured by fungi (Table III). Under these circumstances, fungal percentage of system

Table III. Fungal and Bacterial Standing Crops, Maxima[a], and Fungal Percentage of Total Fungal/Bacterial Crop and of Total Nitrogen at the Time of Maximum Fungal Crop, for Decaying *Spartina alterniflora* Shoot Material

Reference[b]	Fungal crop	Bacterial crop	Fungal % crop	Fungal % N
Lee 80(U)	12	27	31	27
Tenore 84(U)	0	5	0	0
Newell 89(S)[c]	203	6	99+	100
Hicks 91(U)[d]	26	7	93	13
Newell W × NC(S)[c]	106	<1	99+	75
Newell W × NN(S)[c]	188	<1	99+	96

[a]mg microbial organic mass/g organic mass of decaying-shoot system. Conversion factors used: 200 mg organic fungal mass/mg ergosterol; 44 fg organic bacterial mass/cell; 4% N of fungal mass; 10% ash of total mass; 75% free ergosterol of total (Newell and Statzell-Tallman, 1982; Lee and Fuhrman, 1987; Newell, 1994).

[b](U) = shoots cut, dried, and placed in litterbags or ground and placed in microcosms; (S) = shoots decaying in natural, standing position. See Table II for further methods and reference information. Newell W × N entries are unpublished data for control (C) and nitrogen-fertilization (N) treatments in a 1989 wetness × nitrogen field-manipulation experiment (Newell and Arsuffi, unpublished).

[c]Third row, data based on immunoassay (live + dead fungal mass); fifth and sixth rows, ergosterol (probably live only) (Newell, 1992, 1994).

[d]Note that the conversion factor (glucosamine to mass) used was for extramatrical mycelium (18 mg fungal mass/mg GlcN); intramatrical mycelium (naturally most common) may require a higher factor (67 mg organic fungal mass/mg GlcN?: Newell, 1992). Note also that this litterbagged material was originally standing *dead*.

organic mass can rise to some 10 to 20% of total, depending on whether one measures living (membrane-containing) or living-plus-dead (including empty-hyphal) mass (Newell, 1992, 1993, 1994; Table III). Transmission electron micrographs of naturally decaying shoot material revealed extensive fungal occupation of all types of cordgrass tissue (including heavily lignified cell walls), but bacteria were internally present as a minor occupant, and only in the oldest material examined (naked, fallen stems) (Newell *et al.*, 1994).

Enzyme-linked immunosorbent assay and direct observation of ascomata have led to identification of the principal ascomycetous secondary producer in decaying leaves of smooth cordgrass as *Phaeosphaeria spartinicola* Leuchtmann (Gessner, 1977; Newell and Hicks, 1982; Newell *et al.*, 1989; Leuchtmann and Newell, 1991). In some parts of the marsh, a conspicuous competitor for early establishment in dead leaves is *Buergenerula spartinae* Kohlm. & Gessner (Newell and Bärlocher, 1993). There may be a second group of ascomycetes, perhaps especially *Phaeosphaeria halima* (Johnson) Shoemaker & Babcock (see Kohlmeyer and Volkmann-Kohlmeyer, 1991) that follow *P. spartinicola* if leaves are not shredded by invertebrates (Newell and Fallon, 1983), but this is just a hypothesis. On standing, decaying leaf sheaths, *Phaeosphaeria spartinae* (Ellis & Everhart) Shoemaker & Babcock is prominent. On standing, decaying stems, *Passeriniella obiones* (Crouan & Crouan) Hyde & Mouzouras occurs so regularly that it may be equivalent in stem-decay dominance to *P. spartinicola* on leaves [Wagner, 1969 (as *Leptosphaeria discors*); Gessner, 1977 (as *Leptosphaeria obiones*); personal observations].

The amount of fungal mass annually produced in standing, decaying smooth cordgrass in Atlantic south-temperate salt marshes is not trivial. Let us make the following rough assumptions: average annual production of smooth-cordgrass leaf-blade material of 420 g C/m^2 (Pomeroy and Wiegert, 1981; Newell and Arsuffi, unpublished); minimum yield of *P. spartinicola* from smooth-cordgrass leaf decay of 13% of leaf mass [Newell *et al.*, 1989; based on net change in standing crop, which may be quite ($\times 3.5$) conservative: Newell and Fallon, 1991]. Thus, in a 1-m-wide strip of marsh over the approximately 8 km of marsh between barrier islands and the mainland in Georgia, USA, a minimum of 437 kg of fungal organic carbon is synthesized per year. If an equal rate of fungal production applies to leaf sheaths and stems, then the minimum fungal yearly production in the 1-m-wide strip is about one metric ton.

Substantial fungal osmotrophic productivity in standing, decaying cordgrass implies that fungal activity causes potentially important chemical change in cordgrass shoot material before it reaches salt-marsh sediments. Fungal organic mass is added as plant mass is altered and lost. Some of the fungal mass may be nutritively valuable to detritivores (e.g., ergosterol may be an important micronutrient; it is also known as "provitamin D_2"; see Newell *et al.*, 1988) (see "harvest mutualisms" in Carroll, 1992), and some may be very resistant to detritivore or microbial lysis and even be recorded as "lignin" and "lignin-nitrogen" (e.g., Hodson *et al.*, 1984; Wilson *et al.*, 1986; Buchsbaum *et al.*, 1991; Hicks *et al.*, 1991). Bergbauer and Newell (1992) found that lignocellulose of smooth cordgrass was substantially changed by the activity of *P. spartinicola* (see also Newell *et al.*, 1994), and that the fungus caused a loss of cordgrass lignocellulose of 1% per day (21-day incubation), with a fungal yield efficiency of 38% (see also Torzilli and Andrykovitch, 1986, and Fig. 1 of Newell, 1993). Thus, the potentially digestion-resistant plant fibers are partially converted by *P. spartinicola* into potentially detritivore-supportive materials (Bärlocher, 1985; Suberkropp, 1992a).

The "lignin"-bound nitrogen that accumulates in decaying cordgrass proposed as lost to the cordgrass-detrital food web may not be as unavailable as previously suggested (e.g., Buchsbaum *et al.*, 1991; Hicks *et al.*, 1991). The presence of fungal mass can cause inaccurately high estimates of true lignin content in decaying lignocellulosic substrates (e.g., Garcia and Latgé, 1987; Hill and Patriquin, 1990), and could very well be the major source of absolute increases in "lignin" found for cordgrass and other decaying vascular-plant material (e.g., McClaugherty and Berg, 1987; Chauvet, 1988). Perhaps the portion of the "lignin" nitrogen that is actually fungal-wall/melanin nitrogen is available to detritivores adapted for its digestion? Note that melanized fungi are often preferred foods and can serve as sole nutrient sources for fungivores (Shaw, 1992).

Two other key potential fungal contributions to standing, decaying cordgrass are: (1) enzymes that could be captured and used by detritivores; (2) reduction of the antifeedant effects of cordgrass cinnamic acids. The lignocellulolytic enzymes of *P. spartinicola* may be utilizable over extended periods after ingestion of mycelium and immobilization of the enzymes (Bärlocher, 1985; Carroll, 1992). The "detritivores might benefit from selecting substrate supporting fungal growth because it provides fungal enzymes which are more effective than the invertebrate's own enzymes in degrading refractile components of the plant tissue" (Martin, 1984). It has already been established that this type of enzyme acquisition takes place in aquatic detritivores (Suberkropp, 1992a).

Leaves of smooth cordgrass contain high levels of cinnamic acids (to about 4 mg/g organic mass) that probably serve the living plant as antiherbivory defense, but also may deter detritivore feeding and decomposer-microbial activity (Wilson *et al.*, 1986; see Horner *et al.*, 1988). Although Wilson *et al.* (1986) found slow early rates of cinnamic acid loss (e.g., no loss of wall-bound cinnamic acid after 1 month in low-marsh samples) in their litterbag material, naturally positioned, standing-decaying leaves lost 40% of their total cinnamic acids in the first month after senescence (Haddad *et al.*, 1992). Since fungal growth rates are highest during the first few weeks after cordgrass-leaf senescence (e.g., an increase of 700% in living-fungal content between the first and second weeks: Newell and Fallon, 1991), and some fungi, including *P. spartinicola,* are known to metabolize (both degradatively and by polymerization) cinnamic acids (e.g., Rahouti *et al.*, 1989; Reid, 1991; Bergbauer and Newell, 1992), it may be that fungal neutralization of antifeedant effects contributes to the high rates of cordgrass-leaf shredding that have been found for salt-marsh periwinkles (Newell *et al.*, 1989; Kemp *et al.*, 1990; Newell and Bärlocher, 1993), and ameliorates negative effects on decomposer microbes that follow *P. spartinicola*.

3.2 Bacterial Participation

Although bacterial cells accumulate negligibly (relative to fungi) on standing-decaying cordgrass (Table III; maximum of 0.04 mm^3 bacterial volume/cm^2 leaf surface: Newell *et al.*, 1989), it cannot be ruled out that bacteria contribute to lysis of plant material during standing decay. It has recently been recognized that the general pattern of bacterial lytic attack on solid plant substrates is to release enzymes that can pass into the solid material and bring about dissolution (e.g., Moran and Hodson, 1989; Azam *et al.*, 1990). Subsequently, much of the new bacterial production occurs away from the lysing source of dissolved organics, by bacteria suspended in water. The bacteria on standing-decaying leaves of smooth cordgrass exhibit behavior that may fit this pattern: when dry dead leaves are submerged, bacterial specific growth rates on the wet leaves can be 1 per day (Newell *et al.*, 1989; based on rates of incorporation of [^{3}H]thymidine into DNA), but a large percentage of the bacteria present emigrate (passively or actively) (Newell *et al.*, 1985). For example, for leaves at 12 weeks postsenescence (the W × N study of Table III), the number of bacterial cells emigrating during the first hour after submergence was equal to that originally present on the leaves, and subsequent net growth rate on wet leaves was only about 10% of the first-hour emigration rate (Newell and Arsuffi, unpublished). Perhaps the bacterial assemblage on the leaves is at least partially mutualistic with the decomposer ascomycetes in their coincident leaf decay activities (e.g., Rüttiman *et al.*, 1991; Bengtsson, 1992).

One type of bacterium, diazotrophic, is very likely to be mutualistic with cordgrass-decomposing fungi. Nitrogen fixation occurs at high rates on/in standing decaying cordgrass, especially if a fine layer of salt-marsh clay has formed on the dead shoots (to 10^4 μmole acetylene reduced/g organic shoot mass per day: Newell *et al.*, 1992). It is quite possible that *P. spartinicola* forms a nitrogen-fixing partnership with a diazotroph (*Azospirillum* sp. ?), as has been found by Hill and Patriquin (1992) for other melanin-producing fungi on grass litter in warm climates.

Bacteria in salt-marsh sediments have been clearly shown to be important decomposers of smooth-cordgrass shoot material. Benner *et al.* (1984), by chemically exposing cordgrass lignocellulose to sediment bacteria or fungi, showed that sediment bacteria could rapidly mineralize the fine particulate form offered (about 0.5 and 1% per day for lignin and polysaccharide fractions, respectively). Although tunneling bacteria (*Cytophaga?*) were not detected in standing decaying cordgrass (Porter *et al.*, 1989), typical tunneling-bacterial mazes were seen in the particulate lignocellulose of Benner *et al.* (1984) exposed to the sediment bacterial assemblage (unpublished observations; see Eriksson *et al.*, 1990). Benner *et al.* (1988) subsequently showed that conversion of fine-particulate cordgrass lignocellulose to bacterial mass could occur at high efficiency [30%, (bacterial mass/lignocellulose utilized) × 100], and was boosted (to about 45%) by raising ammonium concentrations. Moran and Hodson (1990) found that sediment bacterial assemblages could release substantial quantities of refractory dissolved organic carbon from fine-particulate cordgrass lignocellulose and thereby could potentially be responsible for 44% of the bulk dissolved-organic-carbon standing stock in south-temperate salt marshes. Since much of the standing-dead, cordgrass-shoot material passes to the sediment in small-particulate form (probably at least 35% of original, postsenescent leaf mass in the first 12–20 weeks, and possibly 70% of the eventual total, leaf + fungal system: Newell *et al.*, 1989), with lignocellulose partially exposed by fungal activity, the particulate-lignocellulose work is probably a close physical simulation of natural cordgrass-sediment bacterial decompositional activity. (But, does the absence of fungal mass and enzymes affect the outcome of this type of experiment, using chemically exposed lignocellulose?)

3.3. Algal Involvement

Except perhaps on stems at the air/sediment interface (Fallon *et al.*, 1985; Stowe and Gosselink, 1985), algal mass is very small relative to fungal mass on standing-dead shoots of smooth cordgrass [ratio of maxima for two cohorts of leaves, eukaryotic photoautotrophs:fungus, 0.005:1 (Newell *et al.*, 1989)]. A green microalga, *Pseudendoclonium submarinum* Wille, predominates among the photoautotrophic species on standing-dead cordgrass, and, though present only as a very thin (ca. 5 to 20 μm), scattered veneer, it is virtually always present (Fallon *et al.*, 1985). I have observed this alga forming regular contacts with the ostiolar portions of *P. spartinicola* ascomata, and in electron micrographs (unpublished) of leaf sections, separated from fungal hyphae only by the dead-leaf cuticle. One wonders whether there isn't physiological interplay between these two microbes, since they occur so regularly together, and could easily conceivably form a lichenoid mutualism (Lawrey, 1984; Kohlmeyer and Volkmann-Kohlmeyer, 1988; Hawksworth, 1988; Carroll, 1992; Peveling *et al.*, 1992).

3.4. Shredder Invertebrates

Small animals that comminute decaying vascular-plant material and thereby speed rates of decomposition are perhaps best known from leaf litter in streams

(Cummins *et al.*, 1989; see also Seastedt, 1984; Parkinson, 1988; Schaefer, 1989; Ingham, 1992; Lussenhop, 1992). Fungal "conditioning" of leaves in streams is a prerequisite to shredding activity for many shredder species (Suberkropp, 1992a,b). Since fungal "conditioning" takes place in naturally decaying, standing smooth cordgrass, perhaps it shouldn't be surprising that there is at least one avid shredder of standing-dead cordgrass, namely, the salt-marsh periwinkle, *Littoraria irrorata* (Say) (synonym: *Littorina irrorata*; see Reid, 1989). *L. irrorata* can be the most prominent macroinvertebrate of south-temperate, northwestern Atlantic salt marshes (Daiber, 1982), with densities of over 100 individuals/m^2 marsh (Table IV; see also Odum and Smalley, 1959; Stiven and Hunter, 1976; Newell *et al.*, 1989). The snails spend much of their feeding time on standing decaying cordgrass (90% in June in Louisiana: Alexander, 1979), and snail stomachs and feces contain bits of vascular plant as the primary ingesta, along with fungal hyphae (Alexander, 1979; Bebout, 1988). The snails have the capacity to digest both plant polymers (pectinase, xylanase, cellulase) and fungal polymers (laminarinase, mannanase, glucuronidase; but note that chitinase was not found) (Bärlocher *et al.*, 1989a), and assimilation efficiencies for ingested mycelium (labeled with [^{14}C]glucose) of *P. spartinicola* and *P. obiones* were found to be near 50% (Bebout, 1988). The digestive juices of *L. irrorata* (visceral-hump extracts) caused release of sugars and amino acids both from senescent cordgrass leaves and from mycelium of *P. spartinicola* (more sugars from cordgrass; more amino acids from mycelium). Growth of *P. spartinicola* in senescent cordgrass leaves and in lignocellulose from cordgrass (autoclaved and reinoculated) caused a significant ($p < 0.05$) but not dramatic increase in sugar

Table IV. Densities (Snails/m^2, $\bar{x} \pm 1$ S.D., $n = 10$) of Salt-Marsh Periwinkles[a] **in a Smooth-Cordgrass Marsh at Sapelo Island, Georgia**[b]

Height of shoot canopy		
≤0.5 m	0.5–1.0 m	1.0–1.5 m
412 ± 92	220 ± 59	54 ± 38
(304–616)	(92–304)	(12–128)

[a] All individuals of *Littoraria irrorata* collected within ¼-m^2 sampling areas, July, 1987; range given in parentheses; unpublished data of Thorpe, Arsuffi, and Newell.
[b] At the southwestern corner of the island; 31°N, 81°W; for comparison, densities of living (L) and wholly dead (D) shoots for short, intermediate, and tall areas were, respectively: 155/53 per m^2, L/D; 85/41; 96/68.

release by snails ($+11\%$; whole leaves only), and larger increases (50 to 100%) in amino acid release (Bärlocher *et al.*, 1989b). Thus, it is not yet clear whether the snail/fungal interaction is more of a competition for leaf material, or more of a nutritive benefit to the snail, but recall (see above) that potential benefits to the snail of prior fungal decompositional activity (in addition to provision of microbial organic carbon and nitrogen) include amelioration of antifeedant effects, provision of enzymes, softening of shoot material, provision of nitrogen-fixation capacity, and provision of micronutrients.

Salt-marsh periwinkles are very unevenly distributed in cordgrass marshes (Table IV). In the areas close to creek banks where periwinkles are rare, it is obvious to even the casual observer that leaf shredding takes place much less frequently and intensively than in the portions of the marsh where snails are concentrated. For example, in the spring of 1992 at Sapelo Island, after 2 weeks of extraordinarily warm and wet weather (snails are released from cold dormancy at about 15 ° C: Bingham, 1972), only the portions of the marsh with high snail densities were transformed from dark brown to tan in gross aspect, as a consequence of leaf shredding (removal of fungal melanin) (unpublished observation). By monitoring the flow of ^{15}N from smooth cordgrass to salt-marsh periwinkles, and either excluding or including naturally occurring standing-dead leaves, Kemp *et al.* (1990) established that the snails obtained enough nitrogen, mostly from shredding of dead shoots, to annually replace their standing stock of nitrogen. Since the adult snails involved grew little, one likely explanation of the nitrogen throughput was that output occurred in the form of sexual products. By incubating pieces of standing-decaying cordgrass leaves with or without snails in the laboratory, Newell and Bärlocher (1993) discovered that mid-size (14-mm shell length) snails would shred and ingest 7% of total leaf organic mass per day, and at the same time the snails took 10% per day of the living-fungal mass of the decaying-leaf system. Since the periwinkles clearly have a substantial influence on the rate at which dead shoot material is processed into animal mass, shredded particles, and mineralized matter, the marsh patches in which snails are densely concentrated may not exhibit the successional phases of fungal colonization hypothesized above.

3.5. Microbial Control by Shredders and Other Factors: An Experimental Test

We (Newell and Arsuffi, unpublished) recently conducted a field experiment in which we placed snail enclosures (100 snails in 0.25 m²) in plots of smooth-cordgrass marsh that naturally contained very few snails (< 10 per m²). We tagged senescent leaves (Newell *et al.*, 1989) and measured microbial masses and activities over 84 days (mid-October 1988 to mid-January 1989; see Table III) with and without snails. Perhaps because of low temperatures after the first 4

weeks (< 15 ° C at sampling times), and the fact that we ended our study before
the spring warming, loss of organic mass from leaves was 42% greater between 4
and 8 weeks when snails were present, but was not affected after 8 weeks.
However, in spite of the small mass-loss effect, fungal mass (estimated after
ergosterol assay: Newell, 1992) averaged 52% higher over the period between 4
and 12 weeks when snails were absent, and the percentage of total nitrogen of the
decaying-leaf system that was fungal averaged 1.6-fold higher in the absence of
snails (Table V). Bacterial and algal masses (direct microscopy: Newell et al.,
1986) showed no significant snail effects overall (but algal mass may have been
reduced at 4 weeks: Table V).

Two other manipulations (than ± snails) of the experiment of Table V were:
(1) maintenance of dead-leaf water potential at > −1.5 MPa (see Newell et al.,
1991) by automatic misting and/or (2) fertilization of shoots by injection of
$(NH_4)_2SO_4$ to the root zone periodically for 6 months prior to leaf tagging.
Persistent leaf wetness had an enhancing effect (3.5-fold) on fungal standing crop
only early (≤ 2 weeks postsenescence) in leaf decay; at the 4- to 12-week points,
misted leaves had equivalent fungal standing crops to control, unmanipulated
leaves. Extra nitrogen, however, had a long-term positive effect; at 12 weeks,
fungal standing crop was about twice as great in the fertilized plots as in control
(2.01 versus 1.09 mg organic fungal mass/cm^2 leaf). These findings may mean
that: (1) Spartina–fungal decomposers are well adapted to natural shoot-wetting
regimes (dew, rain, tides) and cannot accumulate more mass with extra water; (2)

**Table V. Microbial Standing Crops (μg Organic Mass
on/under 1 cm^2 Abaxial Leaf Area) for Standing
Decaying Leaves of Spartina alterniflora as Affected by
Snail (Littoraria irrorata) Grazing[a]**

| Leaf age; | Microbial crop | | | Fungal |
snails ±[b]	Fungal	Bacterial	Algal	% N[c]
4 +	462	2.8	4	33
4 −	1024	2.3	14	79
12 +	1000	2.4	20	61
12 −	1360	2.3	10	102

[a]Results of 2-way ANOVA: main effect (± snails), fungal crop ($p < 0.001$);
bacterial ($p = 0.961$); algal ($p = 0.596$); % fungal N ($p < 0.001$); interaction (snails × age), fungal crop ($p = 0.306$); bacterial ($p = 0.497$); algal ($p
= 0.070$); % fungal N ($p = 0.071$).
[b]Age in weeks postsenescence; + = snails present at 400 per m²; − = snails
at <10 per m².
[c]The percentage of total system nitrogen calculated to be fungal nitrogen; see
Table III.

fungi are nitrogen limited during cordgrass-shoot decay (see Newell *et al.*, 1989, and Table V; see also Benner *et al.*, 1988; Morris, 1988; Vitousek and Howarth, 1991). As can be inferred from the data in Table V, the extra nitrogen in fungal mass found for nitrogen-fertilized cordgrass plots accumulates only when periwinkles are absent or rare. If periwinkles have access to the extra fungal nitrogen, they rapidly graze it down to control levels ($\bar{x}$, % N, plus-N treatment, with snails $= 0.5$; without snails $= 0.7$; $p = 0.05$).

During the wetness $\times$ nitrogen experiment of Table V, in addition to effects on fungal standing crop, we measured effects on instantaneous rates of fungal production (Newell and Fallon, 1991; Newell, 1993; accomplished by monitoring flow of [^{14}C]acetate to ergosterol for submerged leaves). The results were consistent with what we found for standing crop. Fungal productivity (as pmole acetate incorporated into ergosterol/μg ergosterol per hr) was greatest with the plus-N treatment ($\bar{x} = 39 \pm 20$ pmol), and least with the plus-water treatment ($\bar{x} = 16 \pm 13$ pmole) ($p < 0.001$). As leaves aged from 2 to 12 weeks postsenescence, fungal productivity fell by a factor of about 2 (2 weeks, $\bar{x} = 33 \pm 19$ pmole; 12 weeks, $\bar{x} = 15 \pm 11$ pmole; $p < 0.05$).

4. Microbes and Cordgrass Decay: Summary

Decomposition of smooth-cordgrass leaves begins immediately after senescence, while leaves are still attached, and ascomycetous fungi dominate the microbial-decomposer crops that accumulate [e.g., ratio of bacterial:microalgal:-fungal crop at 8 weeks postsenescence (December 1988), ca. 1:4:600]. Standing crop of living (membrane-containing) fungal organic mass can rise to $> 10\%$ of total decaying-system mass during standing decay, with specific rates of increase in fungal organic mass of 0.001 to 0.002 per hr during periods of water saturation of leaves. Bacterial participation in shoot decay (primarily on fallen particles, but perhaps also on standing material) probably involves elaboration of lytic enzymes into the solid substrate, and capture of the dissolved products of enzyme action by water-suspended cells. Tunneling bacteria may also be active in cordgrass-particle decay in sediments. Diazotrophic bacteria probably form nitrogen-fixing consortia with decomposer fungi on/in standing-dead shoots. Microalgae may participate as contributors of photosynthetically fixed products to decomposer fungi, based on the regularity of the juxtaposition of these two potential physiological partners. Snails (salt-marsh periwinkles) are the predominant macroinvertebrate shredders of standing, decaying cordgrass leaves. Periwinkles can digest cordgrass-decomposing fungi *and* major plant polymers. It is not yet clear whether snails and fungi are principally antagonistic competitors for dead-cordgrass material, or whether snails benefit from fungal activity, but snails do graze and maintain lower fungal standing crops (e.g., by 30% during 4 to 12 weeks postsenescence, autumn 1988). The net result of the functioning of this decomposer/shredder system, well adapted to activity while shoots are still attached to rhizomes, is probably to retain the major portion of the decaying-shoot material within the marsh ecosystem as it is converted to microbial and animal material or mineralized. This last contention is consistent with evidence flowing from other research angles: there is little or no fallen-litter build-up on the marsh surface, yet neither is there evidence for substantial particulate-carbon outflow from the cordgrass marsh (Chalmers *et al.*, 1985; Morris and Whiting, 1986; Delaune and Lindau, 1987; Morris, 1988; Dame, 1989; Newell, *et al.*, 1989; Dame, *et al.*, 1991; Cifuentes, 1991; Williams *et al.*, 1992) [exception: areas of substantial ice or other scouring action (Bertness, 1984; Schwinghamer *et al.*, 1991)].

5. Selected Intriguing Questions

The results of study of decay of cordgrass in the natural, standing position, performed in Georgia salt marshes, raise several new issues, a selected few of which follow.

- Are fungal standing crops and productivities as high in more northerly parts of the range of smooth cordgrass as they are in Georgia? [I have seen densities of ascomata on standing-dead leaves in Maine and in Ireland (*Spartina anglica* Hubbard) that suggested lower fungal standing crops.]
- How do fungal standing crops and productivities on other standing-dead grasses compare with those of smooth cordgrass?
- Are shredder snails important in more northerly marshes, or in other grassland systems?
- Are there other important (but more cryptic) shredder invertebrates that act upon standing-dead cordgrass (e.g., harpacticoid copepods, amphipods, collembolans; see Phillips, 1979; Boyd, 1981; Covi, 1992)? (I have seen evidence of what appeared to be surface-shredding activity on dead shoots where snails were not present.)
- Most of the information for standing decay is for leaves. Will stems exhibit similar decay phenomena?
- How important is the associative (fungal/bacterial?) nitrogen fixation that occurs on/in standing-dead cordgrass (Newell *et al.*, 1992) to microbial productivity, and how geographically widespread is this N-fixing system? Does the clay film on standing leaves affect fungal processes other than N_2 fixation (see, e.g., Robert and Chenu, 1992)?
- To what extent do cordgrass fungi (and fungi of other grass shoots) depend on wetting of standing-dead leaves by dew (the most common wetting event for cordgrass: Newell *et al.*, 1989)?
- Is there exchange of materials (gases, solutions) between fungal decom-

posers in attached, standing-decaying parts of grass shoots, and living portions of the grass (stems, leaves, rhizomes, roots), or flow of dissolved organics or mineral nutrients from surrounding water to fungal decomposers resident within dead shoots (see Seitzinger *et al.*, 1991; Fry *et al.*, 1992; Turner, 1993)?
* What is the fate of the particles (snail feces, lignocellulosic/fungal bits) that fall away from standing-decaying cordgrass shoots?

ACKNOWLEDGMENTS. Much of my research reviewed herein was supported by the U.S. National Science Foundation, grants OCE-8214899, OCE-8600293, BSR-8604653, and OCE-9115642. This is Contribution No. 729 of the University of Georgia Marine Institute.

References

Alexander, S. K., 1979, Diet of the periwinkle *Littorina irrorata* in a Louisiana salt-marsh, *Gulf Res. Rep.* **6**:293–295.

Anderson, J. M., 1991, The effects of climate change on decomposition processes in grassland and coniferous forests, *Ecol. Appl.* **1**:326–347.

Andrén, O., and Paustian, K., 1987, Barley straw decomposition in the field: A comparison of models, *Ecology* **68**:1190–1200.

Arenovski, A. L., and Howes, B. L., 1992, Lacunal allocation and gas transport capacity in the salt marsh grass *Spartina alterniflora*, *Oecologia* **90**:316–322.

Armstrong, J., Armstrong, W., and Beckett, P. M., 1992, *Phragmites australis:* Venturi- and humidity-induced pressure flows enhance rhizome aeration and rhizosphere oxidation, *New Phytol.* **120**:197–207.

Azam, F., Cho, B. C., Smith, D. C., and Simon, M., 1990, Bacterial cycling of matter in the pelagic zone of aquatic ecosystems, in: *Large Lakes* (M. M. Tilzer and C. Serruya, eds.), Springer, Berlin, pp. 477–488.

Bärlocher, F., 1985, The role of fungi in the nutrition of stream invertebrates, *Bot. J. Linn. Soc.* **91**:83–94.

Bärlocher, F., 1991, Fungal colonization of fresh and dried leaves in the River Teign (Devon, England), *Nova Hedwigia* **52**:349–357.

Bärlocher, F. (ed.), 1992, *The Ecology of Aquatic Hyphomycetes,* Springer, Berlin.

Bärlocher, F., Arsuffi, T. L., and Newell, S. Y., 1989a, Digestive enzymes of the saltmarsh periwinkle *Littorina irrorata* (Mollusca: Gastropoda), *Oecologia* **80**:39–43.

Bärlocher, F., Newell, S. Y., and Arsuffi, T. L., 1989b, Digestion of *Spartina alterniflora* Loisel. material with and without fungal constituents by the periwinkle *Littorina irrorata* Say (Mollusca: Gastropoda), *J. Exp. Mar. Biol. Ecol.* **130**:45–53.

Bebout, B. M., 1988, *The Role of Marine Fungi in the Food Selection and Nutrition of the Salt Marsh Periwinkle* Littorina irrorata *Say (Gastropoda),* Master's thesis, University of North Carolina, Chapel Hill.

Bengtsson, G., 1992, Interactions between fungi, bacteria and beech leaves in a stream microcosm, *Oecologia* **89**:542–549.

Benner, R., Newell, S. Y., Maccubbin, A. E., and Hodson, R. E., 1984, Relative contributions of bacteria and fungi to rates of degradation of lignocellulosic detritus in salt-marsh sediments, *Appl. Environ. Microbiol.* **48**:36–40.

Benner, R., Maccubbin, A. E., and Hodson, R. E., 1986, Temporal relationship between the deposition and microbial degradation of lignocellulosic detritus in a Georgia salt-marsh and the Okefenokee Swamp, *Microb. Ecol.* **12**:291–298.

Benner, R., Lay, J., K'nees, E., and Hodson, R. E., 1988, Carbon conversion efficiency for bacterial growth on lignocellulose: Implications for detritus-based food webs, *Limnol. Oceanogr.* **33**:1514–1526.

Benner, R., Fogel, M. L., and Sprague, E. K., 1991, Diagenesis of belowground biomass of *Spartina alterniflora* in salt-marsh sediments, *Limnol. Oceanogr.* **36**:1358–1374.

Bergbauer, M., and Newell, S. Y., 1992, Contribution to lignocellulose degradation and DOC formation from a salt-marsh macrophyte by the ascomycete *Phaeosphaeria spartinicola*, *FEMS Microbiol. Ecol.* **86**:341–348.

Bertness, M. D., 1984, Ribbed mussels and *Spartina alterniflora* production in a New England salt-marsh, *Ecology* **65**:1794–1807.

Bingham, F. O., 1972, The influence of environmental stimuli on the direction of movement of the supralittoral gastropod *Littorina irrorata, Bull. Mar. Sci.* **22**:309–335.

Boesch, D. F., and Turner, R. E., 1984, Dependence of fishery species on salt marshes: The role of food and refuge, *Estuaries* **7**:460–468.

Boulton, A. J., and Boon, P. I., 1991, A review of methodology used to measure leaf litter decomposition in lotic environments: Time to turn over an old leaf? *Aust. J. Mar. Freshwater Res.* **42**:1–43.

Bowen, S. H., 1987, Composition and nutritional value of detritus, in: *Detritus and Microbial Ecology in Aquaculture* (D. J. W. Moriarty and R. S. V. Pullin, eds.), Int. Ctr. Living Aquatic Res. Mgt., Manila, Philippines, pp. 192–216.

Boyd, P. E., 1981, *Ecology of Three Arenicolous Marine Fungi: I. Their Role in the Diet of the Beachhopper* Orchestia grillus, *and II. The influence of Temperature on the Seasonal and Geographic Distribution of* Asteromyces cruciatus, Sigmoidea marina, *and* Varicosporina ramulosa, Master's thesis, University of North Carolina, Chapel Hill.

Bruquetas de Zozaya, I. Y., and Neiff, J. J., 1991, Decomposition and colonization by invertebrates of *Typha latifolia* L. litter in Chaco cattail swamp (Argentina), *Aquat. Bot.* **40**:185–193.

Buchsbaum, R., Valiela, I., Swain, T., Dzierzeski, M., and Allen, S., 1991, Available and refractory nitrogen in detritus of coastal vascular plants and macroalgae, *Mar. Ecol. Prog. Ser.* **72**:131–143.

Burkholder, P. R., and Bornside, G. H., 1957, Decomposition of marsh grass by aerobic marine bacteria, *Bull. Torrey Bot. Club* **84**:366–383.

Buth, G. J. C., and Voesenek, L. A. C. J., 1987, Decomposition of standing and fallen litter of halophytes in a Dutch salt-marsh, in: *Vegetation between Land and Sea* (A. H. L. Huiskes, C. W. P. M. Blom, and J. Rozema, eds.), Junk, The Hague, pp. 146–162.

Buth, G. J. C., and Voesenek, L. A. C. J., 1988, Respiration of standing and fallen plant litter in a Dutch salt-marsh, in: *Vegetation Structure in Relation to Carbon and Nutrient Economy* (J. T. A. Verhoeven, G. W. Heil, and M. J. A. Werger, eds.), SPB, The Hague, pp. 51–60.

Carroll, G. C., 1992, Fungal mutualism, in: *The Fungal Community* (G. C. Carroll and D. T. Wicklow, eds.), Dekker, New York, pp. 327–354.

Carroll, G. C., and Wicklow, D. T. (eds.), 1992, *The Fungal Community: Its Organization and Role in the Ecosystem,* 2nd ed., Dekker, New York.

Chalmers, A. G., Wiegert, R., and Wolf, P., 1985, Carbon balance in a salt-marsh: Interactions of diffusive export, tidal deposition and rainfall-caused erosion, *Estuarine Coastal Shelf Sci.* **21**:757–771.

Chauvet, E., 1988, Influence of the environment on willow leaf litter decomposition in the alluvial corridor of the Garonne River, *Arch. Hydrobiol.* **112**:371–386.

Christian, R. R., 1984, A life-table approach to decomposition studies, *Ecology* **65**:1693–1697.

Christian, R. R., Bryant, W. L., and Brinson, M. M., 1990, *Juncus roemerianus* production and decomposition along gradients of salinity and hydroperiod, *Mar. Ecol. Prog. Ser.* **68**:137–145.

Cifuentes, L. A., 1991, Spatial and temporal variations in terrestrially derived organic matter from sediments of the Delaware Estuary, *Estuaries* **14**:414–429.

Clipson, N. J. W., and Jennings, D. H., 1992, *Dendryphiella salina* and *Debaryomyces hansenii:* Models for ecophysical adaptation to salinity by fungi that grow in the sea, *Can. J. Bot.* **70**:2097–2105.

Coleman, D. C., Ingham, E. R., Hunt, H. W., Elliot, E. T., Reid, C. P. P., and Moore, J. C., 1990, Seasonal and faunal effects on decomposition in semiarid prairie, meadow and lodgepole pine forest, *Pedobiologia* **34**:207–219.

Constable, J. V. H., Grace, J. B., and Longstreth, D. J., 1992, High carbon dioxide concentrations in aerenchyma of *Typha latifolia*, *Am. J. Bot.* **79**:415–418.

Cooke, R. C., and Rayner, A. D. M., 1984, *Ecology of Saprotrophic Fungi*, Longman, London.

Couch, C. A., 1989, Carbon and nitrogen stable isotopes of meiobenthos and their food resources, *Estuarine Coastal Shelf Sci.* **28**:433–441.

Covi, M. P., 1992, *Intertidal Distribution and Population Dynamics of the Salt Marsh Amphipod Uhlorchestia spartinophila at Sapelo Island, GA*, Master's thesis, University of Georgia, Athens.

Cranford, P. J., Gordon, D. C., and Jarvis, C. M., 1989, Measurement of cordgrass, *Spartina alterniflora*,production in a macrotidal estuary, Bay of Fundy, *Estuaries* **12**:27–34.

Cummins, K. W., Wilzbach, M. A., Gates, D. M., Perry, J. B., and Taliaferro, W. B., 1989, Shredders and riparian vegetation, *BioScience* **39**:24–30.

Daiber, F. C., 1982, *Animals of the Tidal Marsh*, Van Nostrand–Reinhold, Princeton, N.J.

Dame, R. F., 1989, The importance of *Spartina alterniflora* to Atlantic coast estuaries, *Rev. Aquat. Sci.* **1**:639–660.

Dame, R. F., and Kenny, P., 1986, Variability of *Spartina alterniflora* primary production in the euhaline North Inlet estuary, *Mar. Ecol. Prog. Ser.* **32**:71–80.

Dame, R. F., Spurrier, J. D., Williams, T. M., Kjerfve, B., Zingmark, R. G., Wolaver, T. G., Chrzanowski, T. H., McKellar, H. N., and Vernberg, F. J., 1991, Annual material processing by a salt-marsh-estuarine basin in South Carolina, USA, *Mar. Ecol. Prog. Ser.* **72**:153–166.

Davis, S. M., 1991, Growth, decomposition, and nutrient retention of *Cladium jamaicense* Crantz and *Typha domingensis* Pers. in the Florida Everglades, *Aquat. Bot.* **40**:203–224.

Deegan, L. A., Peterson, B. J., and Portier, R., 1990, Stable isotopes and cellulase activity as evidence for detritus as a food source for juvenile Gulf menhaden, *Estuaries* **13**:14–19.

Delaune, R. D., and Lindau, C. W., 1987, $\delta^{13}C$ signature of organic carbon in estuarine bottom sediment as an indicator of carbon export from adjacent marshes, *Biogeochemistry* **4**:225–230.

Dickinson, N. M., 1983, Decomposition of grass litter in a successional grassland, *Pedobiologia* **25**:117–126.

Eriksson, K. E., Blanchette, R. A., and Ander, P., 1990, *Microbial and Enzymatic Degradation of Wood and Wood Components*, Springer, Berlin.

Fallon, R. D., Newell, S. Y., and Groene, L. C., 1985, Phylloplane algae of standing dead *Spartina alterniflora*, *Mar. Biol.* **90**:121–127.

Fog, K., 1988, The effect of added nitrogen on the rate of decomposition of organic matter, *Biol. Rev.* **63**:433–462.

Fogel, M. L., Sprague, E. K., Gize, A. P., and Frey, R. W., 1989, Diagenesis of organic matter in Georgia salt marshes, *Estuarine Coastal Shelf Sci.* **28**:211–230.

Fry, B., Hullar, M., Peterson, B. J., Saupe, S., and Wright, R. T., 1992, DOC production in a salt-marsh estuary, *Arch. Hydrobiol. Beih. Ergebn. Limnol.* **37**:1–8.

Gallagher, J. L., Kibby, H. V., and Skirvin, K. W., 1984, Community respiration of decomposing plants in Oregon estuarine marshes, *Estuarine Coastal Shelf Sci.* **18**:421–431.

Garcia, S., and Latgé, J. P., 1987, A new colorimetric method for dosage of lignin, *Biotechnol. Tech.* **1**:63–68.

Gessner, M. O., 1992, Differences in processing dynamics of fresh and dried litter in a stream ecosystem, *Freshwater Biol.* **26**:387–398.

Gessner, R. V., 1977, Seasonal occurrence and distribution of fungi associated with *Spartina alterniflora* from a Rhode Island estuary, *Mycologia* **69**:477–491.

Gessner, R. V., and Kohlmeyer, J., 1976, Geographical distribution and taxonomy of fungi from salt-marsh *Spartina, Can. J. Bot.* **54**:2023–2037.

Gosselink, J. G., and Kirby, C. J., 1974, Decomposition of salt-marsh grass, *Spartina alterniflora* Loisel., *Limnol. Oceanogr.* **19**:825–832.

Griffin, D. M., 1972, *Ecology of Soil Fungi,* Chapman & Hall, London.

Grigorova, R., and Norris, J. R. (eds.), 1990, *Methods in Microbiology,* Volume 22, Academic Press, New York.

Haddad, R. I., Newell, S. Y., Martens, C. S., and Fallon, R. D., 1992, Early diagenesis of lignin-associated phenolics in the salt-marsh grass *Spartina alterniflora, Geochim. Cosmochim. Acta* **56**:3751–3764.

Haines, E. G., and Hanson, R. B., 1979, Experimental degradation of detritus made from the salt-marsh plants *Spartina alterniflora* Loisel., *Salicornia virginica* L., and *Juncus roemerianus* Scheele, *J. Exp. Mar. Biol. Ecol.* **40**:27–40.

Hardisky, M. A., and Reimold, R. J., 1977, Salt-marsh plant geratology, *Science* **198**:612–614.

Hawksworth, D. L., 1988, Coevolution of fungi with algae and cyanobacteria in lichen symbioses, in: *Coevolution of Fungi with Plants and Animals* (K. A. Pirozynski and D. L. Hawksworth, eds.), Academic Press, New York, pp. 125–148.

Hawksworth, D. L., 1991, The fungal dimension of biodiversity: Magnitude, significance, and conservation, *Mycol. Res.* **95**:641–655.

Hicks, R. E., Lee, C., and Marinucci, A. C., 1991, Loss and recycling of amino acids and protein from smooth cordgrass (*Spartina alterniflora*) litter, *Estuaries* **14**:430–439.

Hietz, P., 1992, Decomposition and nutrient dynamics of reed (*Phragmites australis* (Cav.) Trin. ex Steud.) litter in Lake Neusiedel, Austria, *Aquat. Bot.* **43**:211–230.

Hill, N. M., and Patriquin, D. G., 1990, Evidence for the involvement of *Azospirillum brasilense* and *Helicomyces roseus* in the aerobic nitrogen-fixing/cellulolytic system from sugarcane litter, *Soil Biol. Biochem.* **22**:313–319.

Hill, N. M., and Patriquin, D. G., 1992, Interactions between fungi and nitrogen-fixing bacteria during decomposition, in: *The Fungal Community* (G. C. Carroll and D. T. Wicklow, eds.), Dekker, New York, pp. 783–796.

Hodson, R. E., Benner, R., and Maccubbin, A. E., 1983, Transformations and fate of lignocellulosic detritus in marine environments, *Biodeterioration* **5**:185–195.

Hodson, R. E., Christian, R. R., and Maccubbin, A. E., 1984, Lignocellulose and lignin in the salt-marsh grass *Spartina alterniflora:* Initial concentrations and short-term, post-depositional changes in detrital matter, *Mar. Biol.* **81**:1–7.

Holland, E. A., and Coleman, D. C., 1987, Litter placement effects on microbial and organic matter dynamics in an agroecosystem, *Ecology* **68**:425–433.

Horner, J. D., Gosz, J. R., and Cates, R. G., 1988, The role of carbon-based plant secondary metabolites in decomposition in terrestrial ecosystems, *Am. Nat.* **132**:869–883.

Hussey, A., and Long, S. P., 1982, Seasonal changes in weight of above-ground and below-ground vegetation and dead plant material in a salt-marsh at Colne Point, Essex, *J. Ecol.* **70**:757–771.

Hutchinson, K. J., and King, K. L., 1989, Volume and activity of microorganisms in litter from native and sown temperate pasture species, *Aust. J. Ecol.* **14:**157–167.

Hwang, Y. H., and Morris, J. T., 1991, Evidence for hygrometric pressurization in the internal gas space of *Spartina alterniflora, Plant Physiol.* **96:**166–171.

Ingham, R. E., 1992, Interactions between invertebrates and fungi: Effects on nutrient availability, in: *The Fungal Community* (G. C. Carroll and D. T. Wicklow, eds.), Dekker, New York, pp. 669–690.

Johnson, T. W., 1956, Marine fungi. I. *Leptosphaeria* and *Pleospora, Mycologia* **48:**495–505.

Jordan, T. E., and Whigham, D. F., 1988, The importance of standing dead shoots of the narrow leaved cattail, *Typha angustifolia* L., *Aquat. Bot.* **29:**319–328.

Kemp, P. F., Newell, S. Y., and Hopkinson, C. S., 1990, Importance of grazing on the salt-marsh grass *Spartina alterniflora* to nitrogen turnover in a macrofaunal consumer, *Littorina irrorata*, and to decomposition of standing-dead *Spartina, Mar. Biol.* **104:**311–319.

Kohlmeyer, J., and Kohlmeyer, E., 1979, *Marine Mycology: The Higher Fungi,* Academic Press, New York.

Kohlmeyer, J., and Volkmann-Kohlmeyer, B., 1988, *Halographis* (Opegraphales), a new endolithic lichenoid from corals and snails, *Can. J. Bot.* **66:**1138–1141.

Kohlmeyer, J., and Volkmann-Kohlmeyer, B., 1991, Illustrated key to the filamentous higher marine fungi, *Bot. Mar.* **34:**1–61.

Koike, K., Shôji, S., and Yoshida, S., 1975, Seasonal and yearly change of biomass and litter, in: *Ecological Studies in Japanese Grasslands* (M. Numata, ed.), University of Tokyo Press, Tokyo, pp. 141–147.

Končalová, H., 1990, Anatomical adaptations to waterlogging in roots of wetland graminoids: Limitations and drawbacks, *Aquat. Bot.* **38:**127–134.

Lawrey, J. D., 1984, *Biology of Lichenized Fungi,* Praeger, New York.

Lee, C., Howarth, R. W., and Howes, B. L., 1980, Sterols in decomposing *Spartina alterniflora* and the use of ergosterol in estimating the contribution of fungi to detrital nitrogen, *Limnol. Oceanogr.* **25:**290–303.

Lee, S., and Fuhrman, J. A., 1987, Relationships between biovolume and biomass of naturally derived marine bacterioplankton, *Appl. Environ. Microbiol.* **53:**1298–1303.

Lee, S. Y., 1990, Net aerial primary productivity, litter production and decomposition of the reed *Phragmites communis* in a nature reserve in Hong Kong: Management implications, *Mar. Ecol. Prog. Ser.* **66:**161–173.

Leuchtmann, A., 1984, Über *Phaeosphaeria* Miyake und andere bitunicate Ascomyceten mit mehrfach querseptierten Ascosporen, *Sydowia Ann. Mycol.* **37:**75–198.

Leuchtmann, A., and Newell, S. Y., 1991, *Phaeosphaeria spartinicola*, a new species on *Spartina, Mycotaxon* **41:**1–7.

Lussenhop, J., 1992, Mechanisms of microarthropod–microbial interactions in soil, *Adv. Ecol. Res.* **23:**1–33.

McClaugherty, C., and Berg, B., 1987, Cellulose, lignin and nitrogen concentrations as rate regulating factors in late stages of forest litter decomposition, *Pedobiologia* **30:**101–112.

McKee, K. L., and Seneca, E. D., 1982, The influence of morphology in determining the decomposition of two saltmarsh macrophytes, *Estuaries* **5:**302–309.

Mann, K. H., 1988, Production and use of detritus in various freshwater, estuarine, and coastal marine systems, *Limnol. Oceanogr.* **33:**910–930.

Margulis, L., Corliss, J. O., Melkonian, M., and Chapman, D. J. (eds.), 1990, *Handbook of Protoctista,* Jones & Bartlett, Boston.

Marinucci, A. C., Hobbie, J. E., and Helfrich, J. V. K., 1983, Effect of litter nitrogen on decomposition and microbial biomass in *Spartina alterniflora, Microb. Ecol.* **9:**27–40.

Martin, M. M., 1984, The role of ingested enzymes in the digestive processes of insects, in:

Invertebrate–Microbial Interactions (J. M. Anderson, A. D. M. Rayner, and D. W. H. Walton, eds.), Cambridge University Press, London, pp. 155–172.

May, M. S., 1974, Probable agents for the formation of detritus from the halophyte, *Spartina alterniflora,* in: *Ecology of Halophytes* (R. J. Reimold and W. H. Queen, eds.) Academic, New York, pp. 429–440.

Mitsch, W. J., and Gosselink, J. G., 1986, *Wetlands,* Van Nostrand–Reinhold, Princeton, N.J.

Moran, M. A., and Hodson, R. E., 1989, Bacterial secondary production on vascular plant detritus: Relationships to detritus composition and degradation rate, *Appl. Environ. Microbiol.* **55:**2178–2189.

Moran, M. A., and Hodson, R. E., 1990, Contributions of degrading *Spartina alterniflora* lignocellulose to the dissolved organic carbon pool of a salt-marsh, *Mar. Ecol. Prog. Ser.* **62:**161–168.

Morris, J. T., 1988, Pathways and controls of the carbon cycle in salt marshes, in: *The Ecology and Management of Wetlands* (D. D. Hook, ed.), Croom Helm, London, pp. 497–510.

Morris, J. T., 1989, Modelling light distribution within the canopy of the marsh grass *Spartina alterniflora* as a function of canopy biomass and solar angle, *Agric. For. Meteorol.* **46:**349–361.

Morris, J. T., and Haskin, B., 1990, A 5-yr record of aerial primary production and stand characteristics of *Spartina alterniflora, Ecology* **71:**2209–2217.

Morris, J. T., and Whiting, G. J., 1986, Emission of gaseous carbon dioxide from salt-marsh sediments and its relation to other carbon losses, *Estuaries* **9:**9–19.

Newell, S. Y., 1992, Estimating fungal biomass and productivity in decomposing litter, in: *The Fungal Community* (G. C. Carroll and D. T. Wicklow, eds.), Dekker, New York, pp. 521–561.

Newell, S. Y., 1993, Membrane-containing fungal mass and fungal specific growth rate in natural samples, in: *Handbook of Methods in Aquatic Microbial Ecology* (P. F. Kemp, B. F. Sherr, E. B. Sherr, and J. J. Cole, eds.), Lewis, Boca Raton, Fla., pp. 579–586.

Newell, S. Y., 1994, Methods for determining biomass and productivity of mycelial marine fungi, in: *The Isolation and Study of Marine Fungi* (E. B. G. Jones, ed.), Wiley, New York (in press).

Newell, S. Y., and Bärlocher, F., 1993, Removal of fungal and total organic matter from decaying cordgrass leaves by shredder snails, *J. Exp. Mar. Biol. Ecol.* (in press).

Newell, S. Y., and Fallon, R. D., 1983, Study of fungal biomass dynamics within dead leaves of cordgrass: Progress and potential, in: *Proceedings of the International Symposium on Aquatic Macrophytes,* Catholic University, Nijmegen, Netherlands, pp. 150–160.

Newell, S. Y., and Fallon, R. D., 1989, Litterbags, leaf tags, and decay of nonabscised intertidal leaves, *Can. J. Bot.* **67:**2324–2327.

Newell, S. Y., and Fallon, R. D., 1991, Toward a method for measuring instantaneous fungal growth rates in field samples, *Ecology* **72:**1547–1559.

Newell, S. Y., and Hicks, R. E., 1982, Direct-count estimates of fungal and bacterial biovolume in dead leaves of smooth cordgrass (*Spartina alterniflora* Loisel.), *Estuaries* **5:**246–260.

Newell, S. Y., and Statzell-Tallman, A., 1982, Factors for conversion of fungal biovolume values to biomass, carbon, and nitrogen: Variation with mycelial ages, growth conditions, and strains of fungi from a salt-marsh, *Oikos* **39:**261–268.

Newell, S. Y., Fell, J. W., Statzell-Tallman, A., Miller, C., and Cefalu, R., 1984, Carbon and nitrogen dynamics in decomposing leaves of three coastal marine vascular plants of the subtropics, *Aquat. Bot.* **19:**183–192.

Newell, S. Y., Fallon, R. D., Cal Rodriguez, R. M., and Groene, L. C., 1985, Influence of rain, tidal wetting and relative humidity on release of carbon dioxide by standing-dead saltmarsh plants, *Oecologia* **68:**73–79.

Newell, S. Y., Fallon, R. D., and Tabor, P. S., 1986, Direct microscopy of natural assemblages, in: *Bacteria in Nature,* Volume 2 (J. S. Poindexter and E. R. Leadbetter, eds.), Plenum Press, New York, pp. 1–48.

Newell, S. Y., Arsuffi, T. L., and Fallon, R. D., 1988, Fundamental procedures for determining ergosterol content of decaying plant material by liquid chromatography, *Appl. Environ. Microbiol.* **54**:1876–1879.

Newell, S. Y., Fallon, R. D., and Miller, J. D., 1989, Decomposition and microbial dynamics for standing, naturally positioned leaves of the salt-marsh grass *Spartina alterniflora, Mar. Biol.* **101**:471–481.

Newell, S. Y., Arsuffi, T. L., Kemp, P. F., and Scott, L. A., 1991, Water potential of standing-dead shoots of an intertidal grass, *Oecologia* **85**:321–326.

Newell, S. Y., Hopkinson, C. S., and Scott, L. A., 1992, Patterns of nitrogenase activity (acetylene reduction) associated with standing, decaying shoots of *Spartina alterniflora, Estuarine Coastal Shelf Sci.* **35**:127–140.

Newell, S. Y., Porter, D., and Lingle, W. L., 1994, Lignocellulolysis by ascomycetes (Fungi) of a saltmarsh grass (smooth cordgrass), *Microsc. Res. Techn.* (in press).

Norris, J. R., Read, D. J., and Varma, A. K. (eds.), 1992, *Methods in Microbiology,* Volume 24, *Techniques for the Study of Mycorrhiza,* Academic Press, New York.

Odum, E. P., and Smalley, A. E., 1959, Comparison of population energy flow of a herbivorous and a deposit-feeding invertebrate in a salt-marsh ecosystem, *Proc. Natl. Acad. Sci. USA* **45**:617–622.

Odum, W. E., Kirk, P. W., and Zieman, J. C., 1979, Non-protein nitrogen compounds associated with particles of vascular plant detritus. *Oikos* **32**:363–367.

Paerl, H. W., Rudek, J., and Mallin, M. A., 1990, Stimulation of phytoplankton production in coastal waters by natural rainfall inputs: Nutritional and trophic implications, *Mar. Biol.* **107**:247–254.

Park, D., 1974, On the use of the litterbag method for studying degradation in aquatic habitats, *Int. Biodeterior. Bull.* **10**:45–48.

Parkinson, D., 1988, Linkages between resource availability, microorganisms and soil resources, *Agric. Ecosyst. Environ.* **24**:21–32.

Peterson, B. J., and Howarth, R. W., 1987, Sulfur, carbon, and nitrogen isotopes used to trace organic matter flow in the salt-marsh estuaries of Sapelo Island, Georgia, *Limnol. Oceanogr.* **32**:1195–1213.

Peveling, E., Burg, H., and Tenberge, K. B., 1992, Epiphytic algae and fungi on spruce needles, *Symbiosis* **12**:173–187.

Phillips, N. W., 1979, The relative importance of bacterial and fungal biomass and *Spartina* organic matter in the nutrition of two species of salt-marsh amphipods, *Biol. Bull.* **157**:389.

Pirozynski, K. A., and Hawksworth, D. L. (eds.), 1988, *Coevolution of Fungi with Plants and Animals,* Academic Press, New York.

Pomeroy, L. R., and Wiegert, R. W. (eds.), 1981, *The Ecology of a Salt Marsh,* Springer, Berlin.

Porter, D., Newell, S. Y., and Lingle, W. L., 1989, Tunneling bacteria in decaying leaves of a seagrass, *Aquat. Bot.* **35**:397–403.

Rahouti, M., Seigle-Murandi, F., Steiman, R., and Eriksson, K. E., 1989, Metabolism of ferulic acid by *Paecilomyces variotii* and *Pestalotia palmarum, Appl. Environ. Microbiol.* **55**:2391–2398.

Raskin, I., and Kende, H., 1985, Mechanisms of aeration in rice, *Science* **228**:327–329.

Rayner, A. D. M., 1992, Introduction, in: *The Fungal Community* (G. C. Carroll and D. T. Wicklow, eds.), Dekker, New York, pp. xvii–xxiv.

Rayner, A. D. M., and Boddy, L., 1988, *Fungal Decomposition of Wood,* Wiley, New York.

Reice, S. R., and Stiven, A. E., 1983, Environmental patchiness, litter decomposition and associated faunal patterns in a *Spartina alterniflora* marsh, *Estuarine Coastal Shelf Sci.* **16**:559–571.

Reid, D. G., 1989, The comparative morphology, phylogeny and evolution of the gastropod family Littorinidae, *Philos. Trans. R. Soc. London* **324**:1–110.

Reid, I. D., 1991, Intermediates and products of synthetic lignin (dehydrogenative polymerizate) degradation by *Phlebia tremellosa*, *Appl. Environ. Microbiol.* **57**:2834–2840.

Robert, M., and Chenu, C., 1992, Interactions between soil minerals and microorganisms, *Soil Biochem.* **7**:307–404.

Roman, C. T., Able, K. W., Lazarri, M. A., and Heck, K. L., 1990, Primary productivity of angiosperm and macroalgae dominated habitats in a New England salt-marsh: A comparative analysis, *Estuarine Coastal Shelf Sci.* **30**:35–45.

Rublee, P., Cammen, L., and Hobbie, J., 1978, Bacteria in a North Carolina salt-marsh: Standing crop and importance in the decomposition of *Spartina alterniflora, Publ. Univ. N.C. Sea Grant* **UNC-SG-78-11.**

Rüttiman, C., Vicuña, R., Mozuch, M.D., and Kirk, T. K., 1991, Limited bacterial mineralization of fungal degradation intermediates from synthetic lignin, *Appl. Environ. Microbiol.* **57**:3652–3655.

Salim, K. A., Carter, P. L., Shaw, S., and Smith, C. A., 1988, Leaf abscission zones in *Molinia caerulea* (L.) Moench, the purple moor grass, *Ann. Bot.* **62**:429–434.

Salonius, P. O., 1983, Effects of air drying on the respiration of forest soil microbial populations, *Soil Biol. Biochem.* **15**:199–203.

Schaefer, M., 1989, Secondary production and decomposition, in: *Temperate Deciduous Forests* (E. Röhrig and B. Ulrich, eds.), Elsevier, Amsterdam, pp. 175–218.

Schleyer, M. H., 1986, Decomposition in estuarine ecosystems, *J. Limnol. Soc. S. Afr.* **12**:90–98.

Schwinghamer, P., Kepkay, P. E., and Foda, A., 1991, Oxygen flux and community biomass structure associated with benthic photosynthesis and detritus decomposition, *J. Exp. Mar. Biol. Ecol.* **147**:9–35.

Seastedt, T. R., 1984, The role of microarthropods in decomposition and mineralization processes, *Annu. Rev. Entomol.* **29**:25–46.

Seastedt, T. R., 1985, Canopy interception of nitrogen in bulk precipitation by annually burned and unburned tallgrass prairie, *Oecologia* **66**:88–92.

Seastedt, T. R., 1988, Mass, nitrogen, and phosphorus dynamics in foliage and root detritus of tallgrass prairie, *Ecology* **69**:59–65.

Seitzinger, S. P., Gardner, W.S., and Spratt, A. K., 1991, The effect of salinity on ammonium sorption in aquatic sediments: Implications for benthic nutrient recycling, *Estuaries* **14**:167–174.

Sexton, R., and Woolhouse, H. W., 1984, Senescence and abscission, in: *Advanced Plant Physiology* (M. B. Wilkins, ed.), Pitman, London, pp. 469–497.

Shaw, P. J. A., 1992, Fungi, fungivores, and fungal food webs, in: *The Fungal Community* (G. C. Carroll and D. T. Wicklow, eds.), Dekker, New York, pp. 295–310.

Shoemaker, R. A., and Babcock, C. E., 1989, *Phaeosphaeria, Can. J. Bot.* **67**:1500–1599.

Stiven, A. E., and Hunter, J. T., 1976, Growth and mortality of *Littorina irrorata* Say in three North Carolina marshes, *Chesapeake Sci.* **17**:168–176.

Stowe, W. C., and Gosselink, J. G., 1985, Metabolic activity of the epiphytic community associated with *Spartina alterniflora, Gulf Res. Rep.* **8**:21–26.

Suberkropp, K., 1992a, Interactions with invertebrates, in: *The Ecology of Aquatic Hyphomycetes* (F. Bärlocher, ed.), Springer, Berlin, pp. 118–134.

Suberkropp, K., 1992b, Aquatic hyphomycete communities, in: *The Fungal Community* (G. C. Carroll and D. T. Wicklow, eds.), Dekker, New York, pp. 729–747.

Swift, M. J., Heal, O. W., and Anderson J. M., 1979, *Decomposition in Terrestrial Ecosystems*, University of California Press, Berkeley.

Teal, J. M., 1962, Energy flow in a salt-marsh ecosystem of Georgia, *Ecology* **43**:614–624.

Tenore, K. R., Hanson, R. B., McClain, J., Maccubbin, A. E., and Hodson, R. E., 1984, Changes in composition and nutritional value to a benthic deposit feeder of decomposing detritus pools, *Bull. Mar. Sci.* **35:**299–311.

Torzilli, A. P., and Andrykovitch, G., 1986, Degradation of *Spartina* lignocellulose by individual and mixed cultures of salt-marsh fungi, *Can. J. Bot.* **64:**2211–2215.

Tsutsuki, K., and Ponnamperuma, F. N., 1987, Behavior of anaerobic decomposition products in submerged soils, *Soil Sci. Plant Nutr.* **33:**13–33.

Turner, R. E., 1993, Carbon, nitrogen, and phosphorus leaching rates from *Spartina alterniflora* Loisel salt marshes, *Mar. Ecol. Prog. Ser.* **92:**135–140.

Turner, R. E., and Boesch, D. F., 1988, Aquatic animal production and wetland relationships: Insights gleaned following wetland loss or gain, in: *The Ecology and Management of Wetlands* (D. D. Hook, ed.), Croom Helm, London, pp. 25–39.

Twilley, R. R., Ejdung, G., Romare, P., and Kemp, W. M., 1986, A comparative study of decomposition, oxygen consumption and nutrient release for selected aquatic plants occurring in an estuarine environment, *Oikos* **47:**190–198.

Valiela, I., Teal, J. M., Allen, S.D., Van Etten, R., Goehringer, D., and Volkmann, S., 1985, Decomposition in salt-marsh ecosystems: The phases and major factors affecting disappearance of above-ground organic matter. *J. Exp. Mar. Biol. Ecol.* **89:**29–54.

Visser, S., 1985, Role of soil invertebrates in determining the composition of soil microbial communities, in: *Ecological Interactions in Soil* (D. Atkinson, D. J. Read, and M. B. Usher, eds.), Blackwell, Oxford, pp. 297–317.

Vitousek, P. M., and Howarth, R. W., 1991, Nitrogen limitation on land and in the sea: How can it occur? *Biogeochemistry* **13:**87–115.

Wagner, D. T., 1969, Ecological studies on *Leptosphaeria discors,* a graminicolous fungus of salt marshes, *Nova Hedwigia* **18:**383–396.

Wijte, A. H. B. M., and Gallagher, J. L., 1991, The importance of dead and young live shoots of *Spartina alterniflora* (Poaceae) in a mid-latitude salt-marsh for overwintering and recoverability of underground reserves, *Bot. Gaz.* **152:**509–513.

Williams, T. M., Wolaver, T. G., Dame, R. F., and Spurrier, J. D., 1992, The Bly Creek ecosystem study—Organic carbon transport within a euhaline salt-marsh basin, North Inlet, South Carolina, *J. Exp. Mar. Biol. Ecol.* **163:**125–139.

Wilson, J. O., Buchsbaum, R., Valiela, I., and Swain, T., 1986, Decomposition in salt-marsh ecosystems: Phenolic dynamics during decay of litter of *Spartina alterniflora, Mar. Ecol. Prog. Ser.* **29:**177–187.

8

Dynamics of Autotrophic Picoplankton in Marine and Freshwater Ecosystems

THOMAS WEISSE

1. Introduction

1.1. Historical Perspective and Scope of This Review

Small unicellular algae in the size range of picoplankton (0.2–2.0 μm; Sieburth *et al.*, 1978) are ubiquitous components of pelagic ecosystems. They contribute substantially to both phytoplankton biomass and production in marine and freshwater ecosystems. In the early 1950s, Rhode found up to 11,600 cells/ml of minute green algae (size 1–2 μm or less) in oligotrophic subarctic Lake Katterjaure (Rhode, 1955). Abundances of those "μ-algae" ranging from 1000 to 10,000 per ml were also common in the winter plankton of other lakes around Abisko, Sweden (Rhode, 1955).

Although the existence of picoplanktonic algae, therefore, has been known for a long time, the autotrophic picoplankton has received increasing attention only within the past decade. The advent of new techniques, namely epifluorescence microscopy and flow cytometry, for the enumeration of suspended minute cells enabled researchers to quantify picocyanobacteria and the smallest eukaryotic algae which had been overlooked in previous studies. The application of flow cytometry even led to the recent detection of extremely abundant (10^4–10^5 cells/ml) "very small red fluorescing bodies" (Li and Wood, 1988) and "green photosynthetic bacteria" (Neveux *et al.*, 1989) in the ocean. These cells have been identified as prochlorophytes (Chisholm *et al.*, 1988; see Section 1.2). Prochlorophytes are, because of rapid fading of their weak autofluorescence,

THOMAS WEISSE • Limnological Institute of Constance, D-78434 Constance, Germany. Present address: Fisheries and Oceans Canada, West Vancouver Laboratory, West Vancouver, British Columbia, V7V 1N6 Canada.

Advances in Microbial Ecology, Volume 13, edited by J. Gwynfryn Jones. Plenum Press, New York, 1993.

difficult to visualize under the epifluorescence microscope (Chisholm *et al.*, 1988; Li and Wood, 1988).

Many aspects of the taxonomy, physiology, and ecology of autotrophic picoplankton have been the subject of competent reviews recently (Glover, 1985; Fogg, 1986; Stockner and Antia, 1986; Stockner, 1988), and two special volumes have been published on marine (Platt and Li, 1986) and freshwater (Stockner, 1991a) picoplankton. Comparatively little is known, however, of the population dynamics of autotrophic picoplankton (APP) in their natural environments.

The variability of APP numbers, biomass, production, and losses in space and time have only been studied on relatively broad scales. It is the scope of this review to summarize the available information on short- and long-term dynamics of APP across aquatic ecosystems and to identify areas where more research is needed. I will concentrate on the information obtained from natural, "wild," populations. Results from laboratory observations on physiological mechanisms and metabolic pathways will be included where they help to interpret the dynamic behavior of natural populations.

1.2. Taxonomic Composition of Marine and Limnic Picoplankton

The APP consists of prokaryotic coccoid cyanobacteria and prochlorophytes, and of the smallest eukaryotic algae of similar size and shape. Among cyanobacteria, phycoerythrin-rich (PE) strains can be differentiated from phycocyanin-rich (PC) strains. A currently unresolved problem is the distinction between loose aggregates of unicellular picocyanobacteria of the *Synechococcus* type and truly colony-forming species such as *Microcystis* (Stockner, 1991b; Stockner and Shortreed, 1991). The sheath that surrounds cell colonies is often invisible under the epifluorescence microscope or may be broken apart by filtration. A functional discrimination between free-living and colonial cyanobacteria is therefore arbitrary. In most of the studies summarized in this review, colonial cyanobacteria were not included because they are commonly counted by inverted microscopy, independently from picocyanobacteria which are enumerated using epifluorescence microscopy. Until a proper distinction between the free-living and colonial cyanobacteria can be made in routine investigations using more sophisticated techniques, it is wise to follow Stockner's (1991b) advice to enumerate individual, loosely aggregated, and colonial cells in different categories. For unknown reasons, colonial cyanobacteria are more prominent in fresh than in salt water (Stockner, 1991b).

A major taxonomic difference between marine and freshwater picoplankton appears to be the lack of prochlorophytes in lakes. In the ocean, the small coccoid prochlorophyte species *Prochlorococcus marinus* (Chisholm *et al.*, 1992) is a ubiquitous component of picophytoplankton in the euphotic zone. The abundance of prochlorophytes is best documented in the North Atlantic Ocean including the Sargasso Sea where cell numbers may exceed 10^5 cells/ml and outnumber those of picocyanobacteria (Chisholm *et al.*, 1988; Li and Wood, 1988; Neveux *et al.*, 1989; Olson *et al.*, 1990a; Veldhuis and Kraay, 1990). Picoplanktonic prochlorophytes have also been reported from the euphotic zone of the Pacific (Chisholm *et al.*, 1988) and the Mediterranean Sea (Vaulot *et al.*, 1990; Li *et al.*, 1992). The presence of "redshifted" divinyl-like chlorophyll a (Chisholm *et al.*, 1988; Veldhuis and Kraay, 1990) which has been identified as chlorophyll a_2 with cultured *Prochlorococcus marinus* (Goericke and Repeta, 1992) indicates that prochlorophytes are also prominent in the Banda Sea, Indonesia (Gieskes *et al.*, 1988). A filamentous prochlorophyte species, *Prochlorothrix hollandica* (Burger-Wiersma *et al.*, 1989), has been found in the plankton of eutrophic Dutch lakes (Burger-Wiersma *et al.*, 1986; Van Liere *et al.*, 1989). With light microscopy, this colonial species cannot be distinguished from *Oscillatoria limnetica* (Van Liere *et al.*, 1989). Functionally, *P. hollandica* does not belong to the picoplankton. Stockner and Shortreed (1991) found small (0.5–1.0 μm), PC-rich cyanobacteria codominant with unicellular and colonial PE-rich cyanobacteria of the *Synechococcus* type in a small oligotrophic lake on Queen Charlotte Islands, British Columbia. These authors speculate that those cells might belong to the *Prochlorophyta*. However, unless ultrastructural evidence from electron microscopy and/or identification of the pigment composition which is unique in prochlorophytes (Chisholm *et al.*, 1988, 1992; Veldhuis and Kraay, 1990; Goericke and Repeta, 1992) is provided, it appears more likely that those cells are "ordinary" PC-rich cyanobacteria which are known from many lakes (Stockner and Antia, 1986). In the Laurentian Great Lakes Huron and Michigan, oligotrophic "mini-oceans" where the occurrence of picoplanktonic prochlorophytes might be more likely than in more eutrophic small lakes, numerous red-fluorescing cells have been found (Fahnenstiel *et al.*, 1991b). Autofluorescence characteristics and ultrastructure derived from transmission electron microscopy revealed that they were *Chlorella*-like eukaryotic cells. Yet, since much more effort has been devoted to the detection of prochlorophytes in the ocean than in lakes, it is probably too early to conclude that prochlorophytes are completely absent from freshwater picoplankton.

The eukaryotic picoplankton are composed of members from different algal classes (for reviews consult Fogg, 1986; Platt and Li, 1986; Stockner and Antia, 1986; Stockner, 1991b). Some small marine eukaryote taxa such as Prasinophyceae and Eustigmatophyceae are unknown from freshwater picoplankton (Stockner, 1988).

1.3. The Species Problem

It is largely unknown to what extent results obtained with cultured material may be applied to the natural habitats. Conversely, in the case of cyanobacteria, many characters traditionally employed to discriminate not only between species but even between genera of natural populations were either not expressed in axenic cultures or varied with culture conditions (Rippka, 1988). There is currently no key available for the identification of proper picoplankton species (but see Rippka et al., 1979; Griffiths, 1984; Rippka, 1988; and the diverse taxonomic literature for small eukaryotic algae). Since the majority of APP "forms" are prokaryotes that lack cell organelles and internal structures useful for identification, a morphological distinction between different species or strains of APP is based on only very few characters and appears fruitless. Distinctions made on phenotypic features and the DNA base composition characterized three different types among the genus Synechococcus and two among Synechocystis (Stanier et al., 1986; Rippka, 1988). Using numerical taxonomy, Griffiths (1984) differentiated six strains among the genus Synechocystis and five among Synechococcus. The wide range of the guanine plus cytosine content of their DNA indicates the need to subdivide these genera (Stanier et al., 1986). An attempt has been made to split the genus Synechococcus into four genera (Rippka and Cohen-Bazire, 1983), but its final classification awaits further evidence (Rippka, 1988). In an ultrastructural study of PE-rich cyanobacterial populations from the North Atlantic, Johnson and Sieburth (1979) found characteristic differences in the cell size and arrangements of the thylakoid membranes. The natural populations were classified into three ultrastructural types. Using immunofluorescence, Campbell and Carpenter (1987) could further confirm earlier results (Glover et al., 1986a) indicating that PE-rich oceanic cyanobacteria from the Northwest Atlantic and Northeast Pacific contain more than one strain (serogroup) which exhibit considerable DNA polymorphism (Wood and Townsend, 1990). Recent investigations into the gene sequence of natural marine populations further indicate that the prokaryotic PE picocyanobacteria and prochlorophytes, which dominate among the oceanic APP, are a heterogeneous assemblage. Analysis of 16 S ribosomal RNA genes of picoplankton from the Sargasso Sea revealed high genetic diversity among closely related cyanobacteria, and suggested the existence of at least three novel lineages (Giovannoni et al., 1990; Britschgi and Giovannoni, 1991). Accordingly, the cultured picoplankton strains may represent only a very small fraction of the natural populations (Ward et al., 1990; Olsen, 1990). At present it appears safe to conclude that even the morphologically uniform PE-rich cyanobacteria consist of more than one species as speculated a decade ago (Platt et al., 1983). Evidence has accumulated that the diversity of freshwater picocyanobacteria and eukaryotic picoplankton is also greater than previously assumed (reviewed by Stockner, 1991b).

It is clear that more sophisticated techniques such as immunofluorescence (Campbell et al., 1983; Campbell and Carpenter, 1987), flow cytometry (Olson et al., 1985, 1990a,b; Chisholm et al., 1988; Veldhuis and Kraay, 1990; Vaulot et al., 1989, 1990; and others), image analysis (Psenner, 1990), transmission electron microscopy (e.g., Johnson and Sieburth, 1979, 1982; Leppard *et al.*, 1987; Andreoli *et al.*, 1989; Fahnenstiel *et al.*, 1991a), and gene sequencing (Giovannoni *et al.*, 1990; Olsen, 1990; Ward *et al.*, 1990; Britschgi and Giovannoni, 1991; and others) are needed to investigate the taxonomic composition and seasonal succession of APP more adequately. The reader should bear in mind that any generalizations made in the following text on the regional and seasonal occurrence of APP and their population dynamics suffer from the currently insufficient taxonomic resolution of the picoplankton assemblage.

2. Population Dynamics of Autotrophic Picoplankton— Seasonal Variation

2.1. Variation in Picoplankton Cell Numbers

The seasonal variation of APP is well documented for several lakes and some coastal marine areas (Tables I and II). Although there are some remarkable exceptions (e.g., Olson *et al.*, 1990a; Weisse and Kenter, 1991), most studies performed in temperate areas found highest picoplankton abundance in summer when water temperature reaches its annual maximum and low values during the cold season.

If not stated otherwise, colonial cyanobacteria are not included in the data given in Tables I and II. In most oligotrophic and mesoeutrophic environments, PE-rich cyanobacteria of the *Synechococcus* type dominate numerically and in terms of biomass (Stockner, 1988). Recent investigations using flow cytometry revealed, however, that subsurface concentrations of prochlorophytes may exceed those of *Synechococcus* spp. in oceanic waters while biomass of the smaller prochlorophytes is usually lower than cyanobacterial biomass (Chisholm *et al.*, 1988; Olson *et al.*, 1990a; Vaulot *et al.*, 1990). During summer, peaks of *Synechococcus* were commonly found closer to the surface than the maximum concentrations of prochlorophytes which were related to the deep chlorophyll maximum (Chisholm *et al.*, 1988; Li and Wood, 1988; Olson *et al.*, 1990a). In winter, both picoplankton types may cooccur in near-surface waters (Olson *et al.*, 1990a; Vaulot *et al.*, 1990). The displacement in their vertical distribution during summer was explained by their different pigment composition. The major pigments of prochlorophytes absorb light most efficiently at the wavelengths in the blue light range (460–480 nm) which dominate in the light spectrum at the bottom of the euphotic zone in oceanic areas (Chisholm *et al.*, 1988; Olson *et al.*, 1990a). In this respect, prochlorophytes resemble eukaryotic picoplankton (Glover *et al.*, 1986b). PC-rich cyanobacteria have been reported to prevail occasionally in lakes in abundances comparable to those of PE-rich cyanobacteria (Stockner and Shortreed, 1991; Maeda *et al.*, 1992), but their usual concen-

Table I. Seasonal Variation of Autotrophic Picoplankton Numbers in the Epilimnion of Freshwater Lakes and Reservoirs

Location	Trophic state[a]	APP$_{min}$ (10^4/ml)	APP$_{max}$ (10^4/ml)	Type[b]	Sampling interval	Sampling period	Reference
Temperate lakes							
Danish							
L. Bureso	MO	<0.1	32	P,E			
L. Esrum	ME	<0.1	14	P,E			
L. Bastrup	E	<0.1	>70	E,P	2–3 weeks	Feb 1989–March 1990	Søndergaard (1991)
L. Fureso	E	<0.1	21	P,E			
L. Frederiksborg Sl.	E	<0.1	22	E,P			
L. Arreso	H	<0.1	16	E,P^{col}			
L. Gribso	D	<0.1	15	E			
Lake Belau, Germany	E	0.01	159	P,E	1–4 weeks	March 1991–Oct 1992	S. Barkmann (unpublished)
N. English							
Wastwater	O	0.80	82.1	P			
Thirlmere	O	0.10	19.1	P			
Ennerdale Water	O	1.62	130	P			
Ullswater	MO	0.01	24.6	P	Monthly	Jan–Dec	Hawley and Whitton (1991)
Derwentwater	MO	0.07	26.5	P			
Coniston Water	MO	0.02	45.0	P			
Bassenthwaite Lake	M	0.07	7.92	P			
Estwaite Water	M	0.009	0.34	P			
Malham Tarn	ME	0.012	3.26	P,E			
Cassop Pond	ME	0.012	1.65	P,E			
Llyn Padarn, Wales	M	0.016	11	P	Biweekly	2 years	Kennaway and Edwards (1989)
Hungarian							
Lake Balaton,							
Siofok Basin	M	3	110	P	2–6 weeks	Jan–Dec	Vörös et al. (1991)
Keszthely B.	H	10	210	P^{col},E			

Marcali Reservoir	H	130	340	Pcol,E			
L. Constance	ME	<0.01	87.6	P,E	1–4 weeks	5 years	Weisse and Kenter (1991 and unpublished data)
L. Huron	O	0.017	1.93	E	2 weeks to > 3 months	2 years	Fahnenstiel et al. (1991b)
L. Michigan	O	0.1	1.69	E	17 times in 4 years	All seasons	Fahnenstiel et al. (1991)
L. Ontario	ME	<0.01	74.6	P	2–5 weeks	Apr–Dec	Caron et al. (1985)
Five Ontario lakes	O–M	<0.1	<10–37	P	Biweekly	May–Sept (1–3 cycles)	Pick and Agbeti (1991)
Little Round Lake, Ontario	O	?	500	P,E	11 times	May 1981–May 1982	Craig (1984, 1987)
Eight B.C. lakes	O	<0.5	ca. 18	Pcol,E	2 weeks–1 month	Apr–Oct	Stockner and Shortreed (1991)
L. Biwa, N. Basin	M	<?	29	P	1–4 weeks	June–Dec 1985	Nagata (1986, 1988)
		<0.7	230	P		July 1989–Nov 1990	Maeda et al. (1992)
Six lakes in New Zealand, South Isl.	O–E	<0.01	27	P,E	1 per season	Oct–July	Burns and Stockner (1991)
Subarctic lakes							
Three B.C. and Yukon lakes	O	?	15.5	Pcol,E	Monthly	June–Sept	Stockner and Shortreed (1991)
Subtropical lakes							
L. Kinneret	E	<0.01	80	P,E	2–4 weeks	2 years	Malinsky-Rushansky and Berman (1991)

[a]Trophic state: O, oligotrophic; MO, mesooligotrophic; M, mesotrophic; ME, mesoeutrophic; E, eutrophic; H, hypertrophic; D, dystrophic.
[b]Type: E, eukaryotes; P, prokaryotes; Pcol, colonial prokaryotes.

Table II. Seasonal Variation of Autotrophic Picoplankton Numbers in Epilimnetic Marine and Brackish Environments

Location	Trophic state[a]	APP$_{min}$ (10^4/ml)	APP$_{max}$ (10^4/ml)	Type[b]	Sampling interval	Sampling period	Reference
NW Atlantic, coastal		<0.01	>10	Syn.	Daily to biweekly	7 entire years	Waterbury et al. (1986)
Irish Sea, coastal	E	0.10	15.0	P	Weekly	2 years	El Hag and Fogg (1986)
Irish Sea, offshore	ME	0.17	8.1	P	1–2 weeks	2 years	
NE Pacific, coastal	ME	0.1	7	P	Monthly	16 months	Krempin and Sullivan (1981)
NW Atlantic, off Bermuda	O	<0.1	12	P	11 occasions	14 months	Olson et al. (1990a)
Baltic Sea[c], northern	O	?	ca. 170	P,E	1–2 times per week	All seasons	Kuosa (1988, 1991b)
Baltic Sea[c], southern, coastal	E	<2	58	P[d],E[d]	1–2 times per month	April–Oct	Jochem (1988, 1990)
Pozzatini valley[c], Venetia (Italy)	?	0.15	2.5	P,E	1–2 weeks	May–Nov	Andreoli et al. (1989)
Lagoon of S. Gilla[c], Sardinia (Italy)		<0.2	1.0	P,E	Biweekly	Nov–Sept	Andreoli et al. (1989)

[a]Trophic state: O, oligotrophic; ME, mesoeutrophic; E, eutrophic.
[b]Type: E, eukaryotes; P, prokaryotes; P$_{col}$, colonial prokaryotes; Pr, Prochlorophytes; Syn., Synechococcus spp.
[c]Brackish waters.
[d]Size fraction <3 μm.

trations are distinctly lower (Stockner and Antia, 1986). Likewise, near-surface numbers of eukaryotic autotrophic picoplankton (EAP) are commonly two to three orders of magnitude lower than those of PE-rich cyanobacteria. Eukaryotes are, however, the dominant autotrophic picoplankters in the epilimnion of eutrophic and dystrophic lakes (Craig, 1987; Søndergaard, 1990, 1991; Stockner and Shortreed, 1991) and may also dominate at the bottom of the euphotic zone in the ocean (Murphy and Haugen, 1985; Chisholm *et al.*, 1988).

Because of differences in the sampling frequency and unknown factors related to size and morphometry of the sampling locations (such as allochthonous input of nutrients and organic matter), it is difficult to draw any clear-cut conclusions from the results presented in Tables I and II. Total picoplankton numbers range from $< 10^2$ to $> 10^6$ cells/ml in natural habitats. If lakes smaller than 5 km^2 surface area (most of the English and Danish lakes mentioned in Table I as well as Little Round Lake) are omitted, it appears that total picoplankton abundance increases along a gradient leading from oligotrophic to eutrophic–hypertrophic environments. A decline of picoplankton concentrations at the border between eutrophic and hypertrophic waters as suggested by Stockner (1991b) is not obvious.

There is some indication that the relative seasonal variation in lakes is related to their trophic state: it is low to moderate in both oligotrophic and eutrophic–hypertrophic systems and highest in mesotrophic–eutrophic lakes. In the latter, APP abundance may change seasonally by almost four orders of magnitude, thus spanning the entire range of variation known from the cross-system comparison. Again, this trend is blurred if the smallest lakes (< 5 km^2 surface area) are included. It seems therefore likely that in small and shallow lakes, factors unrelated to macronutrients have a more pronounced impact on picoplankton abundance than in large lakes.

Except for high picoplankton cell numbers recorded in the brackish Baltic Sea, abundance of marine picoplankton tends to be lower than that of freshwater picoplankton at comparable trophic state. In two brackish environments of the Mediterranean Sea, Andreoli *et al.* (1989) found substantially lower APP concentrations than Jochem (1988, 1990) and Kuosa (1988, 1991b) in different parts of the Baltic. The reason for the high APP abundance in the Baltic is not known. Results from lake fertilization (Stockner, 1987; Shortreed and Stockner, 1990; Stockner and Shortreed, 1988), experimental enclosures (Wehr, 1991), and empirical evidence suggest that APP abundance in lakes is more often limited by nitrogen than by phosphorus (discussed by Stockner, 1991b). In chemostat cultures of the limnic *Synechococcus linearis* the critical N/P supply ratio, above which nitrogen limitation switches to phosphorus limitation, was much higher (24 by weight) than those found for other algae (Healey, 1985). Healey concluded that "*S. linearis* would tend to be N-limited in environments where many other algae would be P-limited." Similarly, Suttle (1987; quoted by Pick and

Lean, 1987) using experimental manipulations of chemostats inoculated with natural freshwater phytoplankton obtained dominance of *Synechococcus* sp. at a high N/P supply ratio of 20 (by weight). At lower N/P ratios (2 and 7), diatoms and *Scenedesmus* dominated. More experimental evidence is needed to reveal whether the generally lower picoplankton abundance in marine as compared with freshwater ecosystems is mainly caused by N limitation.

2.2. Seasonal Variation of Picocyanobacteria in Fresh, Marine, and Brackish Waters: Examples from Temperate Regions

I will illustrate the annual cycle of picocyanobacteria in the different aquatic environments using one well-studied example from each type in temperate regions. In Lake Constance, picoplankton have been studied for several years (Fig. 1). In this prealpine lake, the APP is composed mainly of coccoid cyanobacteria of the *Synechococcus* type (Weisse, 1988). Although considerable inter-

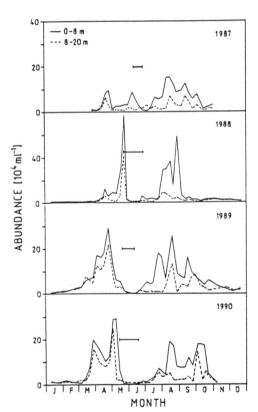

Figure 1. Annual cycles of autotrophic picoplankton in Lake Constance. Solid line denotes average cell number in 0–8 m, dashed line in 8–20 m depth. Bars indicate the duration of the clear-water phase. (Weisse and Kenter, 1991; reproduced with permission.)

annual variation in epilimnetic picoplankton cell numbers is evident (Weisse and Schweizer, 1991), the major features of the annual cycle repeat every year. We can identify five seasonal phases: winter minimum, spring peak, clear-water low, summer to late-summer peaks, and a small autumn peak. The latter is variable and does not occur in every year. Temperature and stratification of the water column trigger the onset of the spring bloom and the autumnal decline. From April through October, however, temperature is less important, and the population dynamics of APP is determined by a close coupling between growth and grazing losses (Weisse, 1988). With the exception of the clear-water phase when excessive metazooplankton grazing causes all microplankton components including APP to decline (Lampert and Schober, 1978; Güde, 1989; Müller et al., 1991; Weisse, 1991a), protozoa such as ciliates and heterotrophic nanoflagellates are the primary consumers of the picoplankton production. It is important to note that in near-surface waters (0–8 m) the annual minimum is reached during the clear-water phase when water temperature is relatively high (15–20°C). In winter, when surface water temperature in the deep parts of the lake usually ranges from 0.5 to 5°C, APP are present in low numbers (0.5–1.5 × 10⁴ cells/ml).

Among lakes, the pronounced spring peak seems to be a unique characteristic of APP in Lake Constance. Smaller spring peaks have also been recorded in various other lakes (Nagata, 1990; Kennaway and Edwards, 1989; Hawley and Whitton, 1991; Stockner and Shortreed, 1991), but the occurrence of the annual maximum abundance during spring has not been found elsewhere in freshwater. The decline of the spring peak is not caused by overgrazing, but appears to be related to deteriorating weather conditions and short-term destabilization of the water column stratification, nutrient limitation, or a combination of both (Weisse et al., 1990).

A similar seasonal pattern as in Lake Constance is known from Woods Hole Harbor (Fig. 2), where the annual cycle of marine APP (*Synechococcus* spp.) has been studied in detail for many years (Waterbury et al., 1986). In the coastal northwest Atlantic, the spring peaks also exceeded the summer maxima in several of the observed years. Weather conditions apparently have a strong impact on the onset of the spring bloom. In Woods Hole Harbor, a surface water temperature of 6°C signals the onset of the spring bloom and the decline of *Synechococcus* in the fall (Waterbury et al., 1986). As in Lake Constance, cell concentrations are variable in summer, and smaller peaks occur at irregular intervals. In contrast to the former, a clear-water phase does not occur, and the annual minimum of APP cell numbers in Woods Hole Harbor is recorded in late winter. Similar seasonal patterns as in Woods Hole Harbor were found at five offshore stations on the continental shelf and slope of Cape Cod, Massachusetts (Waterbury et al., 1986).

In the brackish waters of the Baltic Sea off Tvärminne, Finland, the seasonal variation of prokaryotic and eukaryotic picoplankton has been recorded for one

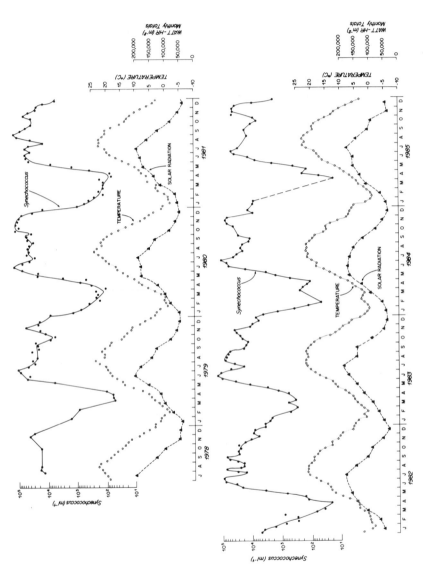

Figure 2. Annual cycles of *Synechococcus* spp. in Woods Hole Harbor, 1978–1985. Surface cell numbers of *Synechococcus* are compared to surface water temperature and to monthly totals of solar radiation. (Waterbury *et al.*, 1986; reproduced with permission.)

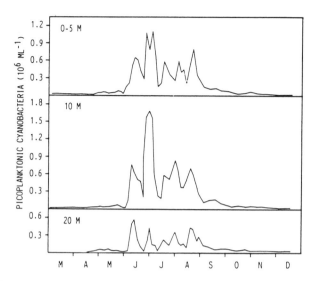

Figure 3. Seasonal abundance of picocyanobacteria off Tvärminne, Baltic Sea. (Kuosa, 1991b; reproduced with permission.)

annual cycle (Kuosa, 1991b; Figs. 3 and 4). Salinity at the sampling station is variable with a mean value of about 6°/oo. Water temperature varies from sub-zero to about 16°C, and this oligotrophic area is ice covered for several months. In near-surface waters (0–10 m), the abundance of picocyanobacteria increased sharply during the decline of the phytoplankton spring bloom, when nutrients were exhausted and water temperature raised from about 6 to 10°C (Kuosa, 1991b). It is obvious from Fig. 3 that the first cyanobacterial peak declined before a second increase yielded the annual maximum observed in July. The late summer decline coincided with the destabilization of the water column and thus enhanced mixing (Kuosa, 1991b).

The seasonal succession of picocyanobacteria in different aquatic habitats from various regions is an area where more detailed research is needed before we can identify possible trends in relation to latitude. Using the few parameters hitherto available for the characterization of natural picocyanobacterial popula-tions in routine investigations, members of the genus *Synechococcus* appear fairly uniform worldwide. It is unknown, however, whether the different cya-nobacterial peaks which are obvious in many environments during the course of the year are composed of one species or whether several species follow each other because of seasonal succession *sensu stricto*. In Lake Constance, only minor differences in the carotenoid pigment composition and average cell size and shape of the dominant picocyanobacteria were found between the spring and

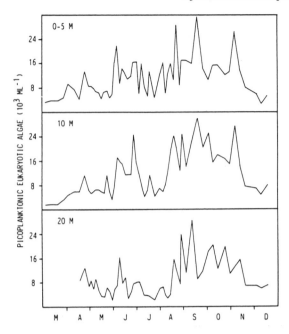

Figure 4. Seasonal abundance of eukaryotic picoplankton off Tvärminne, Baltic Sea. (Kuosa, 1991b; reproduced with permission.)

summer peaks (Weisse and Kenter, 1991). Yet, seven different picocyanobacterial clones have been isolated from Lake Constance which were classified into three different categories according to their pigment composition, carotenoids, and phycobiliproteins (Ernst, 1991; Ernst et al., 1992). During the exceptional picoplankton blooms observed in Lake Biwa in 1989 and 1990, Maeda et al. (1992) noted a succession of two differently colored PE-rich and one PC-rich *Synechococcous* strain. Three dominant strains were isolated and characterized using transmission electron microscopy and emission/absorbance spectra. Based on some pertinent features of their cultures, the authors concluded that the clones represent three dominant, bloom-forming *Synechococcous* species. To my knowledge, this is the only case where a true seasonal succession among picocyanobacteria has been documented.

Evidence has accumulated that temperature, which has been advanced as the primary factor controlling the occurrence of APP in marine (Murphy and Haugen, 1985; El Hag and Fogg, 1986) and freshwater (Caron et al., 1985) systems, alone does not explain the seasonal cycles of picocyanobacteria. In 11 temperate and subarctic lakes in western Canada, Stockner and Shortreed (1991) found a poor correspondence between epilimnetic temperature and APP abundance. At a station off Bermuda, Olson et al. (1990a) even noted an inverse relationship between temperature and the seasonal abundance of *Synechococcus* while prochlorophytes peaked in summer at maximum surface water temperatures. This study is, as far as I know, the only one where the seasonal distributions of *Synechococcus* and prochlorophytes have been determined together. The relative seasonal variation of prochlorophyte cell numbers was low (threefold) if they were integrated over the upper 200 m of the water column. Yet, cell numbers varied by more than two orders of magnitude at discrete depths in the epilimnion with peak values usually occurring close to the nitracline. Olson *et al.* (1990a) concluded that the regulation of the seasonal and vertical distribution of prochlorophytes and *Synechococcus* spp. are clearly different. Winter presence of prochlorophytes with surface abundances ranging from 10^3 to 5×10^4 cells/ml is also known from the Mediterranean Sea (Vaulot *et al.,* 1990).

We may, therefore, conclude that although picoplankton cell numbers are often positively correlated with temperature on a broad seasonal scale, parameters other than temperature have a strong impact on the population dynamics of APP (Kennaway and Edwards, 1989). Nutrients influence both the absolute abundance and the relative importance of picoplankton to total phytoplankton biomass (Stockner and Antia, 1986; Stockner, 1991b). Nutrients further have a significant impact on the taxonomic composition of the picoplankton assemblage (see Section 4). Physiological adaptations in relation to light are less important for the control of seasonal cycles, because APP peaks occur under a wide range of light regimes in various environments. The light response is more important in regulating the vertical distribution of picoplankton cell numbers (Glover *et al.,* 1986b, 1987, and references therein). At the present state of knowledge it appears plausible that, whenever large seasonal fluctuations of picocyanobacterial numbers occur in stratified waters, they are primarily caused by the coupling and uncoupling between growth and loss processes (Weisse, 1988). Temporary release from grazing will enhance seasonal fluctuations. The increasing significance of grazing suggests a shift from bottom-up control via nutrients in oligotrophic toward top-down control via grazing in more eutrophic environments.

The potential impact of virus attack for the seasonal dynamics of APP requires further research. Viruses might control picoplankton populations at certain periods of the year (Suttle *et al.,* 1990, 1991; Klut and Stockner, 1990; Proctor and Fuhrman, 1990). Finally, as outlined above, we cannot rule out that an unknown part of the seasonal variation is in fact related to seasonal succession of various species with different ecological niches.

2.3. Seasonal Variation of Eukaryotic Picoplankton (EAP)

EAP have received far less attention in most ecological studies than picocyanobacteria, probably because EAP cell numbers are usually distinctly lower than cyanobacterial numbers and more difficult to visualize under the epifluorescence microscope (Fahnenstiel *et al.*, 1991a). It is important to note that, although the abundance is lower, EAP biomass may reach similar levels as picocyanobacterial biomass because EAP cells are commonly somewhat larger than prokaryotes (Pick and Agbeti, 1991).

The seasonal cycle of EAP differed markedly from that of picocyanobacteria in the Tvärminne area (Fig. 4). Eukaryotic picoplankton was already abundant during the cold water period preceding the spring bloom of larger phytoplankton. Maximum cell numbers occurred in autumn during the period of deep mixing. During the rest of the year, the EAP showed little clear-cut variation (Kuosa, 1991b). Cell numbers of EAP varied by one order of magnitude (10^3 to 10^4 cells/ml) over the course of the year, a small seasonal variation compared with that of picocyanobacteria. Similar cell numbers of EAP have been found in the western Baltic (Jochem, 1990), at a neritic station of the North Atlantic (Murphy and Haugen, 1985), and in Lakes Huron and Michigan (Fahnenstiel *et al.*, 1991b). The latter investigation reported the same seasonal distribution of EAP as found by Kuosa (1991b) in the Baltic. In lakes Huron and Michigan, EAP cell numbers also peaked during spring isothermal mixing/early thermal stratification, when surface water temperatures were between 3 and 9°C (Figs. 5 and 6 in Fahnenstiel *et al.*, 1991b). Dominance of EAP biomass over picocyanobacterial biomass during isothermal conditions was also confirmed by Pick and Agbeti (1991). In their investigation conducted in temperate Ontario lakes, EAP prevailed in spring or early summer, when water temperature ranged from 5 to 10°C.

The pattern of the seasonal distribution of prokaryotic and eukaryotic autotrophic picoplankton becomes more complex considering the investigation conducted by Søndergaard (1990, 1991) in seven Danish lakes. In four (hyper)eutrophic lakes (see Table I) where EAP numbers exceeded those of cyanobacteria, EAP maxima occurred in summer. In dystrophic Lake Gribsø, which was unique in this study because of the complete absence of picocyanobacteria, EAP peaked in late spring. In the two less eutrophic lakes Esrum and Buresø, where picocyanobacteria dominated among the APP, EAP peaks occurred in early spring before picocyanobacteria reached their highest numbers. This latter pattern is virtually identical with those reported from the Baltic Sea (Kuosa, 1991b) and from the Laurentian Great Lakes (Fahnenstiel *et al.*, 1991b). Søndergaard (1991) mentioned that the EAP cells were probably *Chlorella*-like green algae, but unfortunately no attempt was made to identify the EAP species. In lakes Huron and Michigan, transmission electron microscopy and the emission spectrum also characterized the dominant EAP as chlorophytes of the *Chlorella* type (Fahnenstiel *et al.*, 1991b). Similarly, Stockner and Shortreed (1991) described the red-fluorescing, chloroplast-bearing cells which dominated in dystrophic coastal lakes in British Columbia as *Chlorella*-like eukaryotes. As in most of the other investigations, seasonal variability of EAP was relatively low.

In conclusion, it appears that in oligotrophic to mesoeutrophic waters, eukaryotic picoplankton occur in lower numbers, their seasonal cycle is less pronounced and controlled by different factors than that of picocyanobacteria. When cooccurring with cyanobacteria, EAP tend to peak earlier in the year at lower water temperatures. The maxima of EAP seem to be related positively to nutrient supply by vertical mixing. Along a gradient of increasing nutrient concentrations and decreasing pH, EAP cell numbers increase and progressively replace unicellular picocyanobacteria.

3. Short-Term Variation and Diel Periodicity

3.1. Apparent Growth Rates *in Situ*

From the foregoing discussion it is obvious that the earlier contention that APP numbers are relatively constant at 10^4 cells/ml (Fogg, 1986) needs to be discarded. It is clear now that the abundance of APP is more variable than that of bacteria which fluctuate by only two orders of magnitude (10^5–10^7 cells/ml) in natural waters.

During periods of exponential population increase, pronounced day-to-day variations of picoplankton cell numbers occur at a fixed sampling station. Under such conditions, when losses are minimal, the apparent growth rate which can be calculated from changes in cellular abundance at the sampling location may approach the gross growth rate (when losses are zero). It is important to note that the calculated apparent growth rate is sensitive to the sampling interval. It can only be assessed with some accuracy if the sampling frequency is on the order of the picoplankton doubling time. This effect is obvious considering growth rates of APP populations in Lake Constance (Table III). If rates were calculated based on the routine weekly sampling, maximum apparent growth in spring was relatively constant (0.12–0.15 per day). In 1988 and 1991, when we sampled daily or even twice per day, we obtained distinctly higher growth rates, up to 0.38 per day, because APP peaks were short-termed occurring on temporal scales of several days. The latter estimate is in good agreement with measured gross growth rates in Lake Constance in spring (Weisse, 1988; Weisse *et al.*, 1990). In Woods Hole Harbor, maximum apparent growth rates of *Synechococcus* vary from 0.12 to 0.23 per day during spring (Waterbury *et al.*, 1986). In June, at higher temperatures of about 15°C, maximum growth rates up to 0.58 per day were recorded (Waterbury *et al.*, 1986). Similarly, highest apparent growth rates measured in Lake Constance in summer (July/August) were 0.59 per day (Weisse, unpublished results). The latter values correspond to a doubling time of 1.2 days. In Jack's Lake, Ontario, maximum net increase reaches 0.14–0.18 per

Table III. Maximum Rates of Net Population Increase μ of Autotrophic Picoplankton in Lake Constance (0–8 m Average) during Spring[a]

Year	μ (per day)	n	Period	Sampling interval
1987	0.13	3	6–21 April	Weekly
1988	0.15	3	5–19 April	Weekly
	0.23	5	12–14 April	Twice per day
	0.21	5	15–17 April	Twice per day
	0.38	3	18–19 April	Twice per day
1989	0.12	3	21 March–4 April	Weekly
1990	0.15	4	6–27 March	Weekly
1991	0.14	3	5–17 April	Weekly
	0.33	3	12–14 April	Daily
1992	0.12	3	14–28 April	Weekly

[a]Rates were calculated only for those periods when population increase at the sampling location was continuous for at least three sampling occasions (n = number of sampling occasions; T. Weisse, original).

day in July (Pick and Agbeti, 1991; Pick and Berube, 1992). Slightly lower values, about 0.13 per day, were measured in Lake Ontario from June through August when picoplankton numbers increased from 1×10^3 to 4×10^6 cells/ml (Caron et al., 1985). For reasons stated above, we must consider those estimates as minimum values for the respective net growth rates in situ.

Considerable short-term population increases of APP have also been reported from offshore oligotrophic marine sites. Glover et al. (1988a,b) monitored a Synechococcus bloom in the Sargasso Sea. Cell numbers increased by 50% over 48 hr, equivalent to an apparent growth rate of 0.2 per day. At one station in the central Red Sea, the average APP cell numbers in the euphotic zone trebled within 2 days corresponding to a net increase of 0.52 per day (Gradinger et al., 1992). Off Bermuda, Olson et al. (1990a) monitored a "bloom" of prochlorophytes occurring in March. The net increase of prochlorophyte cell numbers corresponded to growth rates of 0.38 per day.

3.2. Gross Growth Rates and Grazing Loss Rates

From the high apparent growth rates recorded in various aquatic ecosystems during periods of exponential population increase, it is clear that picocyanobacteria grow rapidly in situ when environmental conditions are favorable. The potential of rapid growth even under low-light conditions has been demonstrated for Synechococcus spp. in laboratory cultures (Table IV). The results presented were chosen because they indicate that (1) Synechococcus is able to grow rapidly at low-light intensities and (2) growth may saturate at relatively low-light intensities, but (3) some strains exhibit continuous growth at high irradiances. The high gross and relatively low apparent growth rates commonly found in natural picoplankton populations during most of the year (see Tables III, V and VI) imply control by loss processes. Attempts have been made to measure gross growth and grazing loss rates using various techniques. I found six freshwater (Table V) and eight marine (Table VI) studies where growth and grazing loss rates of APP have been assessed. Grazing loss rates were similar or somewhat lower than measured growth rates, suggesting that both processes are largely balanced. It should be noted that losses include biological processes other than grazing which normally cannot be separated properly from grazing in short-term experiments. Virus-induced cell lysis (Suttle et al., 1990; Klut and Stockner, 1990; Proctor and Fuhrman, 1990, 1991), fungal parasitism, or autolysis of senescent cells may also efficiently reduce APP numbers. The surplus of picoplankton growth over biological losses may be removed physically from epilimnetic waters by washout or sedimentation of aggregated cells. Active, strongly autofluorescent cyanobacteria resembling Synechococcus have been reported associated with phytodetritus at a depth of 4500 m in the northeastern Atlantic (Lochte and Turley, 1988). We do not know, however, whether sedimen-

**Table IV. Growth Rates of Exponentially Increasing Cultures
of Picocyanobacteria[a]**

Synechococcus species	Origin[b]	Growth rate (per day)	I_{exp} ($\mu E/m^2$ per sec)	I_{sat}	Reference
DC-2	M	1.7	45	110	Morris and Glover (1981)
Syn	M	2.8	55	130	
WH7803	M	1.23	40	—	Waterbury et al. (1986)
	M	1.87	200 to >400	>2000	Kana and Gilbert (1987)
	M	0.65	150	—	Gilbert and Ray
WH8018	M	0.60	150	—	(1990)
4 WH strains	M	0.10–0.47[c]	6	—	Campbell and Car-
		0.25–0.99[c]	21	—	penter (1986a)
		0.44–1.02[c]	55	—	
BO 8801	F	0.5–0.9	8 to 965[d]	100 to >320	Schweizer (1993)
S. linearis	F	0.30–1.44	12–144	ca. 100	Healey (1985)

[a]I_{exp} denotes experimental light intensity, I_{sat} saturating light intensity where growth was maximal.
[b]F, freshwater cultures; M, marine cultures.
[c]Temperature ranging from 15 to 25°C.
[d]Temperature ranging from 5 to 25°C.

Table V. Growth Rates and Grazing Loss Rates of Natural Autotrophic Picoplankton in Freshwater Ecosystems

Location	Trophic state	Size fraction[b]	Growth rate (per day)	Methods[c]	C conversion factor	Grazing loss (per day)	Methods	Season	Ref.
L. Superior	O	P	0.8–1.5 (2)[d]	SGR	121 fg/μm³	—	—	—	Fahnenstiel et al. (1986)
L. Michigan	O	Syn.	0.11–0.67 (19)	SGR/SDT/FDC/SMI/ICA	121 fg/μm³	0.09–0.50 (9)	SMI/SDT/RLC	Apr–Nov	Fahnenstiel et al. (1991a,c)
L. Huron	O	Syn.	0.13–0.93 (20)	SGR/SDT/FDC/SMI/ICA	121 fg/μm³	0.11–0.69 (6)	SMI/SDT/RLC	Apr–Nov	Fahnenstiel et al. (1991a,c)
L. Huron	O	P	0.10–2.14 (7) 0.10–0.94 (6)	SMI	—	0.43–2.42 (7)	SMI	Aug/Sept	Weisse (1991b and unpublished)
L. Erie	M/E	P	0.31–1.32 (2)	SMI	—	0.91–1.03 (2)	SMI	Aug/Sept	Weisse (1991b and unpublished)
L. Ontario	M/E	P	0.29–0.47 (3)	SF	—	—	—	—	Weisse (unpublished)
Jack's L., Ontario	M	P	0.60–0.76 (3)	SDT	—	0.33–0.77 (3)	SDT	May–July	Pick and Agbeti (1991)
			1.33–1.66 (2)	FDC	—	—	—	June/Aug	Pick and Berube (1992)
L. Constance	M/E	P	0.14–1.22 (24)	SDT	—	0.05–1.27 (24)	SDT	March–Oct	Weisse (1988), Weisse et al. (1990)
L. Belau	E	P	0.22–0.91 (3)	FDC	—	—	—	May–July	S. Barkmann (personal communication)

[a]Trophic state: O, oligotrophic; M, mesotrophic; E, eutrophic.
[b]Size fraction: P, prokaryotes (cyanobacteria); Syn., Synechococcus spp.
[c]Methods: FDC, frequency of dividing cells; ICA, increase of cellular abundance; RLC, radioactively labeled cells; SDT, seawater dilution technique; SF, selective filtration; SGR, specific growth rate; SMI, selective metabolic inhibitors.
[d]Numbers in parentheses are number of experiments.

Table VI. Growth Rates and Grazing Loss Rates of Natural Autotrophic Picoplankton in Various Marine Environments

Location	Trophic state	Size fraction[b]	Growth rate (per day)	Methods[c]	C conversion factor	Grazing loss (per day)	Method	Temp./season	Reference
NE Atlantic	O	<1 μm	min 0.15 (1[d])[e]	SGR	Measured POC	—		July	Platt et al. (1983)
NE Atlantic, coastal & upwelling	O/M	<1 μm	0.9–8.9 (5)	SGR/TAR	121 fg C/μm³	—		June	Douglas (1984)
NW Atlantic	O	Syn. Syn.	0.52–0.84 (4) 0.54–0.86 (4)	SDT FDC		0–0.83 (3) 0.33–0.79 (4)	SDT SMI	July/Aug	Campbell and Carpenter (1986a)
NW Atlantic[f]	O	Syn.	0.42–0.86 (17)	FDC		—		Feb/Mar + July/Aug	Campbell and Carpenter (1986b)
NW Atlantic, coastal	ME	Syn.	0–1.56 (16)	FDC				All seasons	Carpenter and Campbell (1988)
NW Atlantic	O	<3 μm/Syn.	0.6–2.2 (14) 0.50–1.21 (17)	SGR/TAR	121 fg C/μm³	0.62 (avg)	NGR	18–24°C/Apr	Iturriaga and Marra (1988)
NW Atlantic, Sargasso Sea	O	Syn.	1.9–2.0 (1)	ICA/SGR		1.2 (1)	NGR	Apr/May	Waterbury et al. (1986)
NW Atlantic, coastal	O	Syn.	1.0–1.9 (2)	ICA/SGR		0.3 (2)	NGR	July/Sept	Waterbury et al. (1986)
Equatorial Atlantic	O	<1 μm	0.11–3.83 (5)	SGR	22.5 × Chl. a			Apr	Herbland and Le Bouteiller (1981)
NE Pacific, coastal	O	<5 μm	0.7–1.1 (2)	SGR	294 fg C/cell			16°C/Sept	Putt and Prezelin (1985)
NW Pacific	O	<1 μm	1.2–2.5 (4)	SF/FDC		1.9–2.4 (2)	SF	22–23°C/Nov	Kudoh et al. (1990)

(continued)

Table VI. (*Continued*)

Location	Trophic state[a]	Size fraction[b]	Growth rate (per day)	Methods[c]	C conversion factor	Grazing loss (per day)	Method	Temp./season	Reference
NE Pacific, coastal	O	<1 μm	0–0.75 (6)	SGR	200 fg C/μm³			Febr	Vernet et al. (1990)
N Pacific	O	<3 μm	0.89–1.70 (6)	SF				25°C	Bienfang and Takahashi (1983)
	O	P	1.42–1.98 (2)	SDT		0.14–0.39 (2)	SDT	Sept	Landry et al. (1984)
	O	Tot	0.66–2.0 (6)	Var	150 fg C/cell			27°C	Laws et al. (1984)
NW Pacific	O	P	1.3–2.3 (8)	SGR	121 fg C/μm³	0.2–0.4 (6)	RLC	?	Iturriaga and Mitchell (1986)
SW Pacific	O	<2 μm, Syn.	0–1.2 (19)	SF					Furnas (1991)
NW Indian Ocean	O/M	P	0.53–1.03 (3)	SDT		0.37–1.24 (3)	SDT	Sept/Oct	Burkill et al. (1993)
Baltic Sea	O/M	P	0–0.53 (9)	SF				Apr–Aug	Kuosa (1991b)

[a]Trophic state: O, oligotrophic; M, mesotrophic; ME, mesoeutrophic.
[b]Size fraction: P, prokaryotes (cyanobacteria); Syn., Synechococcus spp.; Tot, total phytoplankton (unfiltered).
[c]Methods: FDC, frequency of dividing cells; ICA, increase of cellular abundance; NGR, net growth rate; RLC, radioactively labeled cells; SDT, seawater dilution technique; SF, selective filtration; SGR, specific growth rate; SMI, selective metabolic inhibitors; TAR, track autoradiography.
[d]Average of several stations.
[e]Numbers in parentheses are number of experiments.
[f]Including Sargasso Sea stations and one station from the Caribbean Sea.

tation of aggregated cells attached to marine or lake "snow" particles is of general importance removing part of the picoplankton production from the euphotic zone. Sedimentation of unicellular picoplankton is negligible because these minute cells do hardly sink (Takahashi and Bienfang, 1983; Raven, 1986). Among losses, grazing is, therefore, currently considered the most important parameter.

When comparing Tables V and VI it is apparent that growth rates in marine waters tend to be higher than those measured in lakes. Growth rates exceeding one doubling per day (equivalent to $\mu > 0.693$ per day) have been unambiguously reported from offshore oligotrophic seas, irrespective of the uncertainty involved relating to the different methods applied. Yet, some reservation is needed when comparing growth rates across systems. When specific growth rates (SGR) are estimated from a comparison of size-fractionated primary production or track autoradiography, respectively, and picoplankton cell numbers, the latter need to be converted into units of carbon biomass. The resulting growth rate is very sensitive to the conversion factor applied. Several of those oceanic studies which found the highest values most likely overestimated population growth rates because cell carbon was underestimated based on inappropriately low conversion factors ($C = 121–150$ fg/μm^3 or $C = 22.5 \times$ chlorophyll a, respectively). Recent results suggest that the volume-specific carbon conversion factor is close to 200 fg C/μm^3 (Kana and Glibert, 1987; Vernet et al., 1990; Sondergaard, 1991; Weisse and Kenter, 1991). Similarly, a C:chlorophyll a factor of 22.5 is at the lower end of values reported in the literature which vary between 22 and 130 (Schweizer, 1993). I consider, therefore, those SGR where size-fractionated primary production has been related to cell carbon estimated from low conversion factors unrealistically high. If we remove this bias by recalculating growth rates using a conversion factor of 200 fg C/μm^3, results from 15 of the 18 marine experimental series are below 2.0 per day. If we further assume that the growth rate reported by Herbland and Le Bouteiller (1981) for the equatorial Atlantic is overestimated because of the low C:chlorophyll a ratio applied, there remain only two studies (Douglas, 1984; Kudoh et al., 1990) which measured growth rates exceeding 2.0 per day. The same argument should apply to the limnic growth rates obtained by Fahnenstiel et al. (1986, 1991a,c) in lakes Huron and Michigan. In their investigation, average SGR were even higher than growth rates calculated from selective metabolic inhibitors (SMI) and dilution experiments (SDT; Fahnenstiel et al., 1991a). It is likely that the conversion factor between biovolume and cell carbon of picoplankton varies in relation to environmental conditions, cell size, and taxonomic position. Yet, the carbon conversion factor has not been assessed for natural populations under various conditions.

In summary, it appears presumptuous to conclude that growth rates of APP in marine waters are higher than in lakes. Similarly, at present we cannot decide whether growth rates of natural picoplankton populations are related to the trophic state of their environment. It is clear, however, that the high growth rates measured in oligotrophic ecosystems approach those obtained for exponentially growing *Synechococcus* in laboratory cultures under similar light and temperature conditions (Table IV).

3.3. Picoplankton Grazers

Numerous plankton organisms of various taxonomic position have been identified as picoplankton feeders (for review see Stockner and Antia, 1986). Only a few studies, however, have tried to quantify the consumption of picoplankton production specifically in the natural environment.

Most investigators assume that bacterivorous heterotrophic nanoflagellates (HNF) in the size range from 2 to 20 μm are also the primary picoplankton predators. Phagotrophic phytoflagellates are considered temporarily important picoplankton feeders both in lakes (Bird and Kalff, 1986, 1987; Sanders *et al.*, 1989) and in the ocean (Estep *et al.*, 1986). The taxonomic composition and ecological significance of phagotrophic phytoflagellates have been reviewed recently (Porter, 1988; Boraas *et al.*, 1988; Sanders and Porter, 1988; Sanders, 1991). Laval (1971) reported direct consumption of chroococcoid cyanobacteria by the choanoflagellate *Salpingoeca pelagica*. Meanwhile, chroococcoid cyanobacteria have been observed in food vacuoles of HNF in lakes (Caron *et al.*, 1985; Boraas *et al.*,1985; Fahnenstiel *et al.*, 1986; Nagata, 1988; Weisse, 1988) and marine areas (Laval, 1971; Perkins *et al.*, 1981; Johnson *et al.*, 1982; Landry *et al.*, 1984; Iturriaga and Mitchell, 1986; Kuosa, 1991a; Chavez *et al.*, 1990). In Lake Biwa, the percentage of HNF containing chroococcoid cyanobacteria in their food vacuoles varied seasonally between < 1% and up to 52% (Nagata, 1988). The percentage was correlated positively with cyanobacterial abundance and negatively with water temperature. In most cases, one HNF contained one cyanobacterium in its food vacuole. In Lake Ontario, up to 15% of HNF were found with ingested chroococcoid cyanobacteria when cyanobacterial cell numbers exceeded 10^5 per ml (Caron *et al.*, 1985). Similar findings have been reported from marine studies. In the equatorial Pacific, a mean of 21% of the choanoflagellates enumerated had APP in their vacuoles (Chavez *et al.*, 1990). Evidence that HNF can thrive on a picoplankton diet was also provided by laboratory work. The helioflagellate *Actinomonas* sp. was maintained in a nonaxenic culture of marine *Synechococcus* for over 1 year (Johnson *et al.*, 1982). In a recent review of the nutritional mode of HNF, Sanders (1991) classified four species as cyanobacterivorous and another one (*Noctiluca*) as probably cyanobacterivorous.

Despite this wealth of qualitative information, it is largely unknown whether the majority of HNF complement their bacterial diet by ingestion of picoplankton, whose biomass is usually lower than bacterial biomass, or if some HNF actively select for or against APP. Caron *et al.* (1991) investigated the feeding of *Paraphysomonas* sp. and two ciliates on three strains of *Synechococcus* and two heterotrophic bacteria in laboratory experiments. Of the three protozoa, only an unidentified scuticociliate selected against *Synechococcus* when a mixed diet of bacteria and cyanobacteria was offered as food. When cyanobacteria were the sole food, growth efficiency and cell yield of the protozoa were substantially lower than when bacteria were present. The poor growth efficiencies of protozoa were explained by incomplete digestion of *Synechococcus*. Caron *et al.* (1991) complemented their laboratory studies with some field experiments using natural picoplankton populations in Woods Hole Harbor. Unlike the ingestion rates, clearance rates of the protozoa were similar for bacterial and cyanobacterial prey. The authors concluded that protozoa usually do not select for or against natural *Synechococcus*. A similar conjecture was made by Hagström *et al.* (1988) concerning results from a chemostat experiment with bacteria and *Synechococcus*.

Verity and Villareal (1986) compared the relative food value of two *Synechococcus* clones with ten clones of dinoflagellates and flagellates and ten diatom clones for two *Tintinnopsis* species. In contrast to all other food items, both tintinnid species exhibited 100% mortality when fed cyanobacteria. Similar to Caron *et al.* (1991), Verity and Villareal (1986) addressed this effect to nutritional inadequacy such as indigestibility of *Synechococcus*.

It is presently unknown to what extent marine filter feeders (bivalves, bryozoans, invertebrate larvae) and mucous net feeders (appendicularians, pteropods, *Noctiluca*) which are able to ingest bacteria use APP as food sources (Stockner and Antia, 1986; Stockner, 1988). Two gastropod larvae, *Crepidula aculeata* and *Littoraria scabra*, could thrive on a picoplankton diet (Bell, 1991). Bell concluded that "in oligotrophic oceans, a considerable portion of larval nutrition is derived from picoplankton." Numerous picoplankton cells found in a strictly carnivorous chaetognath have been interpreted as evidence for rapid trophic transfer from cyanobacteria to higher levels of the pelagic food web (Iturriaga and Mitchell, 1986).

Field studies that measured community grazing loss rates of APP (Tables V and VI) provided indirect evidence that nanoplankton were the major picoplankton consumers in most natural environments. Using a size-fractionation technique and assuming that small HNF were the sole APP grazers, Kuosa (1991a) calculated that an average flagellate would eat up to 200 cyanobacteria per day. Besides HNF (including small dinoflagellates), small ciliates, namely oligotrichs, prostomids, and scuticociliates, are also prominent in this size class. The potential grazing impact of ciliates on picoplankton has been demonstrated in various environments (e.g., Sherr *et al.*,1991a,b). Ciliate feeding rates on natural APP have not yet been quantified. The same holds for the picoplankton consumption by metazooplankton. Some species of rotifers, e.g., *Keratella co-chlearis*, have been observed with consumed APP (Caron *et al.*, 1985; Mac-Isaac, in Stockner and Shortreed, 1989). Burns and Stockner (1991) found some rotifers with ingested APP in New Zealand lakes, while *Keratella* did not contain picoplankton in their guts. Indirect evidence suggests that rotifers may act as significant picoplankton feeders when rotifers are abundant (Stockner, 1988; Sanders *et al.*, 1989; Weisse and Schweizer, 1991). In his review on rotifer feeding, Sterner (1989) concluded that "picoplankton have a refuge from grazing by some species of rotifers, but not from others."

Picocyanobacteria have also been documented in the guts of several cladoceran genera, *Eubosmina* (MacIsaac, in Stockner and Antia, 1986), *Ceriodaphnia* and *Bosmina* (Burns and Stockner, 1991). In Lake Oglethorpe, Georgia, *Daphnia* and *Ceriodaphnia* ingested microspheres of cyanobacterial size (0.57 μm; Sanders *et al.*, 1989). The ability to feed on picoplankton-sized particles among cladocera depends on the distances between the setulae on the feeding appendages. There are several cladoceran species which were classified as highly efficient picoplankton feeders (Geller and Müller, 1981; Gophen and Geller, 1984; Brendelberger, 1985; for review consult Sterner, 1989). It appears likely that bacterioplankton and APP may be grazed more heavily by crustaceans during periods when larger prey are reduced, as during clear-water periods (Sanders *et al.*, 1989; Weisse and Kenter, 1991). In limnocorral experiments conducted in the hypertrophic part of Lake Balaton, cladocerans drastically reduced biomass of colonial and unicellular cyanobacteria (Vörös *et al.*, 1991). Copepods generally prefer larger food than picoplankton (reviewed by Sterner, 1989). Experiments performed with natural plankton communities from an Ontario lake further suggest that mesozooplankton usually prefer nanoplankton when offered together with picoplankton food (Mazumder *et al.*, 1990).

A general problem that is not considered in common short-term grazing experiments is the viability of the cells ingested. It is possible that APP cells remain intact inside their grazers during the gut or food vacuole passage. If so, APP may even benefit from the enhanced nutrient supply in passage (Stockner, 1991b).

In summary, we have not climbed much higher to reach a new summit of our knowledge (Stockner, 1991b) on the fate of picoplankton production over the past decade. The earlier contention that "further research is necessary to quantify the significance of algal picoplankton use by a variety of metazoans (and proto-zoans) in lakes and oceans" (Stockner and Antia, 1986) is still valid. It is important to measure not only ingestion rates in short-term experiments, but to assess the nutritive value of cyanobacteria relative to heterotrophic bacteria and small eukaryotic algae. Recent findings suggest that large species-specific differences in the use of APP are likely even among HNF. In seasonally varying ecosystems such as mesoeutrophic temperate lakes or coastal areas, the fate of APP production should be investigated during the different seasonal stages of the planktonic system. Because of logistic constraints, we face the paradoxical situation that our knowledge on picoplankton feeders is especially sparse in oligotrophic offshore areas where the APP is the dominant phytoplankton size class in terms of biomass and production (Stockner and Antia, 1986).

3.4. Diel Cycles of Cell Division and Photosynthesis

When samples are taken repeatedly at a fixed location over the course of the day, it is difficult to separate fluctuations in picoplankton abundance resulting from diurnal changes between growth and loss rates from small-scale patchiness (Davis *et al.*, 1985). Short-term variations in picoplankton cell numbers may originate from diel cycles of cell division. Diel rhythms in the frequency of dividing cells (FDC) have been proven for marine (Waterbury *et al.*, 1986; Campbell and Carpenter, 1986a; Prezelin *et al.*, 1987; Carpenter and Campbell, 1988) and freshwater picocyanobacteria (Fahnenstiel *et al.*, 1991c; Pick and Berube, 1992; Schweizer, 1993). Most of these studies found highest percentages of dividing cells in the second half of the light period (Table VII). It appears clear now that at least *Synechococcus* spp., like many diatoms and in contrast to most other phytoplankton, predominantly divide during the light period (Armbrust *et al.*,1989). Yet, there are obvious exceptions to this rule. Prezelin *et al.* (1987) reported that in the Northwest Atlantic FDC was greatest at midnight. The FDC appears to be related to the meteorological conditions and the time of the year. It is higher on a sunny day than on a cloudy or stormy day (Waterbury *et al.*, 1986; Campbell and Carpenter, 1986a) and higher in summer than in winter when some populations seem to be almost dormant (Waterbury *et al.*, 1986; Carpenter and Campbell, 1988; Schweizer, 1993). In the latter case, no diel maxima in the percentage of FDC were found. The maximum of dividing cells was close to 30% in most studies, indicating rapid population gross growth (Table VII). Considerably lower values were reported from the North American Great Lakes (Fahnenstiel *et al.*, 1991c), from the Mediterranean Sea (Hagström *et al.*, 1988), and from one investigation in the Sargasso Sea (Prezelin *et al.*, 1987). Distinctly higher values have been found in the Northwest Pacific (Kudoh *et al.*, 1990) and in Lake Constance (Schweizer, 1993). In the latter and in several of the other studies, a significant fraction of cells were apparently arrested in the division state at night. If this is the case, two of the assumptions inherent in the FDC approach to determine *in situ* gross growth rates of natural populations, namely constant and identical duration of cell division in all cells (McDuff and Chisholm, 1982), are violated.

There is evidence from laboratory cultures that marine *Synechococcus* spp.

Table VII. Frequency of Dividing Cells of Limnic and Marine Picocyanobacteria

Location	Trophic state[a]	FDC (%)	Time of FDC maximum	Reference
Jack's Lake, Ontario	M	12–27	Noon–early afternoon	Pick and Berube (1992)
L. Huron and L. Michigan	O	2–10	Midday–evening	Fahnenstiel et al. (1991b)
Cultures from L. Huron	—	2–30	5–12 hr after beginning of light period	Fahnenstiel et al. (1991b)
Lake Constance	ME	30–65	Afternoon–evening	Schweizer (1993)
Lake Belau	E	3–19	Midday–evening or night	S. Barkmann (personal communication)
Lab. cultures	—	10–35	4 hr before end of light period	Waterbury et al. (1986)
Marine environments				
NW Atlantic	O	2–23	Just after sunset, if occurring	Campbell and Carpenter (1986b)
	O	5–15	Midnight	Prezelin et al. (1987)
	O	0–38	Late afternoon–early evening	Li and Dickie (1991)
NW Atlantic, Long Island Sound	ME	0–32	Midday, if occurring	Carpenter and Campbell (1988)
NW Atlantic, coastal	O	2–32	Midday–evening	Waterbury et al. (1986)
Sargasso Sea	O	0–14	3 hr before dusk	Waterbury et al. (1986)
Mediterranean Sea	O	2–10	Dawn and dusk	Hagström et al. (1988)
NW Pacific	O	5–42	Dusk	Kudoh et al. (1990)
Marine lab. cultures	—	2–23	8–18 hr after beginning of light period	Campbell and Carpenter (1986b)

[a]Trophic state: M, mesotrophic; O, oligotrophic; ME, mesoeutrophic; E, eutrophic.

display two gaps in DNA synthesis, at the beginning and at the end of the cell cycle, and that the duration of these gaps is light-dependent (Armbrust et al., 1989). This would explain the proportion of dividing cells at night when those cells remain in the doublet stage and are no longer dividing. If this proportion is low (< 5% of the population), the effect on the calculated gross growth rates should be tolerable (McDuff and Chisholm, 1982). The duration of cell division, t_d, has rarely been determined in situ. Most investigators assumed a constant t_d of 3 to 4 hr derived from exponentially growing laboratory cultures (Campbell and Carpenter, 1986b; Carpenter and Campbell, 1988; Fahnenstiel et al., 1991b; Pick and Berube, 1991). Yet, t_d is dependent on temperature and growth rate, and constancy of t_d is therefore given only at growth rates exceeding 0.3 to 0.4 per day (Campbell and Carpenter, 1986b; Fahnenstiel *et al.*, 1991b). Laboratory studies with cultured *Synechococcus* provided some evidence for a true circadian rhythm of cell division (Sweeney and Borgese, 1989), while another investigation did not support the existence of an endogenous rhythm of cell division (Pick and Berube, 1992).

Estimates of *in situ* gross growth rates derived from FDC analysis are on the same order as those obtained with other techniques (see Tables V and VI).

Diel rhythms have also been shown for photosynthesis of natural picoplankton populations in the ocean and in inland lakes (Putt and Prezelin, 1985; Prezelin *et al.*, 1986; Schweizer and Heusel, 1992; and others). Since growth and production rates of APP seem to be discontinuous over the day, one might expect that grazing loss is also periodic. This appears to be plausible because the cell volume of those cells which are about to divide is larger than the average cell volume of nondividing cells and grazing by protozoa is size-selective (Andersson *et al.*, 1986; Gonzalez *et al.*, 1990; Chrzanowski and Simek, 1990). Diel feeding rhythms are known for heterotrophic nanoflagellates, the major potential consumers of picoplankton biomass (Hagström *et al.*, 1988; Weisse, 1989; Wikner *et al.*, 1990). The possible periodicity of grazing loss rates in relation to the diel cell cycle of picocyanobacteria needs to be further investigated with natural picoplankton populations.

3.5. Impact of Physical Forcing on Short-Term Dynamics of Picoplankton

Little is known of the impact of physical factors on the short-term dynamics of picoplankton numbers. Storms may have negative or positive effects because destratification and enhanced turbulence may decrease near-surface cell numbers and lower the average light intensity to which the cells are exposed. Positive effects may originate from an improved nutrient supply because of enhanced mixing or a perturbation of the picoplankton grazers (Waterbury *et al.*, 1986). Nitrate intrusions in the nanomolar range were followed by a *Synechococcus* "bloom" in the Sargasso Sea (Glover *et al.*, 1988a,b). Yet models have shown that more intense mixing generally favors larger phytoplankton at the expense of picophytoplankton (Cushing, 1989; Taylor and Joint, 1990). This effect can be demonstrated in upwelling ecosystems. Models developed by Moloney and Field (1991a–c) for the Benguela upwelling region and by Kumar *et al.* (1991) for an upwelling area off the west coast of South Island, New Zealand, identified ambient nutrient concentration which was supplied by physical mixing (upwelling) as the most important factor determining the size structure of the phytoplankton community. Model outcome predicted that shifts in the average size of the phytoplankton community occur within several days which is consistent with empirical results (e.g., Hall and Vincent, 1990).

Oceanic fronts may create picoplankton patches although the overall effect of mixing fronts on the occurrence of picoplankton was found to be low (El Hag and Fogg, 1986). In lakes, it has been suggested that displacement by seiches may change the vertical profile and average picoplankton numbers at a given sampling location (Gaedke and Schimmele, 1991) but empirical evidence is still lacking. Differential displacement of APP populations by local upwelling or downwelling and by internal waves may have a pronounced effect on the picoplankton distribution in a given area and create mesoscale (tens to hundreds of meters) patches. Picoplankton patchiness has been little studied thus far. In a quasisynoptic investigation of the APP distribution across Lake Constance, Weisse and Kenter (1991) found a threefold horizontal variation of APP cell numbers and biomass during a period of calm and sunny weather and, hence, stable stratification of the water column. Nutrient concentrations were low at all 11 stations investigated. A similar relative variation of APP cell numbers was found in a lakewide investigation across oligotrophic Lake Huron (Weisse and Munawar, 1989). In both investigations the distance between stations ranged from less than 1 up to more than 10 km. Considerable spatial variation of APP cell numbers on scales exceeding 10 km has also been documented for several oceanic regions (e.g., Murphy and Haugen, 1985; Iturriaga and Marra, 1988; Chavez et al., 1990; Prezelin and Glover, 1991; Gradinger et al., 1992). Small-scale variability of APP in the microbial important range from submicrons to meters has not yet been studied (Porter et al., 1988).

4. Prokaryotic and Eukaryotic Picoplankton in Relation to the Trophic State: A Hypothesis to Explain the Dominance of Prokaryotes in Oligotrophic Waters

Although, as I have outlined above, the APP abundance in larger water bodies appears to increase with increasing water trophy, the relative contribution of picoplankton biomass and production decreases along a gradient leading to eutrophy (Fogg, 1986; Porter et al., 1988). Picoplankton dominates the total phytoplankton biomass and production in oligotrophic lakes (Stockner, 1988, 1991b; Burns and Stockner, 1991; Sondergaard, 1990, 1991; Hawley and Whitton, 1991; Petersen, 1991) and in the central oligotrophic parts of the oceans (summarized by Fogg, 1986; Stockner and Antia, 1986; Stockner, 1988). Although attempts have been made to explain this apparent phenomenon, the reasons for the picoplankton dominance are still debatable. In the following I will outline a hypothesis which might explain why picoplankton is most significant under nutrient-limited conditions.

Cell size is the most obvious difference between picoplankton and larger algae. The physiological consequences of small size have been extensively discussed by Raven (1986). A major effect of scaling is that the surface-to-volume ratio increases with decreasing cell size. Because several physiological functions are directly related to this ratio, some authors assume that their favorable surface-to-volume ratio sufficiently explains the predominance of picoplankton in oligotrophic waters (e.g., Fenchel, 1988; Sondergaard, 1990; Thingstad and Sakshaug, 1990). A more comprehensive conceptual framework that described the increasing importance of both autotrophic and heterotrophic picoplankton, i.e., bacteria, with decreasing nutrient status has been developed by Porter et al. (1988). These authors proposed to divide the summed bacterial and autotrophic picoplankton production by the combined total autotrophic and heterotrophic production and denoted the quotient "measure of microbial strength" (MOMS). According to Porter et al. (1988), the cause for the preponderance of picoplankton in oligotrophic waters is efficient sequestering of DOM and nutrients by picoplankton, coupled with minimal sedimentation loss and subsequent consumption of the produced material by epilimnetic consumers. Second, heterotrophic and autotrophic picoplankton appear to be more strongly regulated by temperature than nano- and microplankton. The latter argument would explain why picoplankton tend to dominate in seasonally varying dimictic lakes during summer (Porter et al., 1988). Yet, in warm-monomictic mesoeutrophic Lake Constance, similar peaks of autotrophic picoplankton were found in spring and late summer, irrespective of the difference in water temperature (Weisse, 1988; Weisse and Kenter, 1991). Spring peaks were also recorded from other mesotrophic or eutrophic lakes (Kennaway and Edwards, 1989; Pick and Agbeti, 1991) and from marine areas (Waterbury et al., 1986). Since the nutritional mode of bacteria and autotrophic picoplankton are different, I will largely exclude bacteria from the following discussion and focus on the autotrophic picoplankton.

All picoplanktonic algae differ from larger phytoplankton in two respects. First, small cells have the selective advantage of reduced sinking velocities according to Stokes law. Second, although some physiological functions are negatively related to decreasing cell size, picoplankton cells overall have an advantage over larger cells with respect to uptake of dissolved nutrients at low bulk concentrations (Raven, 1986; Fenchel, 1988). Therefore, picoplankton should be favored relative to larger phytoplankton when the allochthonous supply with matter (nutrients) is scarce. This situation is typical for oligotrophic waters where the production is largely based on regenerated nutrients, and rapid cycling of matter is driving the whole system (Dugdale and Goering, 1967; Eppley and Peterson, 1979). Any output mechanism such as settling out of the euphotic zone would ultimately lead to a rapid exhaustion of substrates and thus impoverish the system.

The MOMS concept might explain why picoplankton have a selective advantage over larger plankton under oligotrophic conditions. It does, however, not consider differences which are apparent *among* the autotrophic picoplankton in relation to the nutrient status. Recent investigations revealed that (1) relative to eukaryotes, picocyanobacteria and prochlorophytes play a more prominent role at the least productive stations within one relatively homogeneous marine area (Glover, 1985; Glover et al., 1986a; Hall and Vincent, 1990; Hall, 1991; Vaulot et al., 1990) and in the more oligotrophic of nearby lakes (Stockner and Short-reed, 1989; Søndergaard, 1990, 1991), (2) chroococcoid cyanobacteria outnumber eukaryotic picoalgae in near-surface waters while eukaryotes can numerically dominate at the bottom of the euphotic zone (Murphy and Haugen, 1985; Glover et al., 1988b), and (3) in seasonally varying areas, the percentage of prokaryotic APP increases from spring through summer when nutrient concentrations decrease and the systems switches from "new" production to "regenerated" production (Porter et al., 1988; Jochem, 1988; Søndergaard, 1990; Kuosa, 1991b).

Hypotheses that explain some of these apparently different distributional trends between prokaryotic and eukaryotic picoplankton have been advanced. Thus, the different vertical distribution might be caused by specific light adaptations relating to differences in the pigment composition of cyanobacteria and eukaryotic algae (Fogg, 1986; Glover et al., 1986b). The predominance of cyanobacteria in oceanic surface waters can, however, not be explained by specific light adaptations, since at saturating irradiances Synechococcus and eukaryotic picoalgae have comparable growth rates (Glover et al., 1987). Murphy and Haugen (1985) found a marked trend toward higher relative abundances of eukaryotes with increasing latitude in the North Atlantic and addressed this effect mainly to temperature. As the authors stated, it is also possible that a gradient in some nutrient was more limiting to the cyanobacteria than to the eukaryotes. It has been demonstrated that marine Synechococcus may use some of their PE pigment as a nitrogen reserve (Wyman et al., 1985; Glover et al., 1988a, and references therein). This, as well as the potential to fix atmospheric dinitrogen (Mitsui et al., 1986) or to use organic nitrogen compounds such as amino acids (Paerl, 1991), could explain the predominance of Synechococcus-like cyanobacteria in the nitrogen-depleted central parts of the oceans. It does, however, not explain why a similar trend is also apparent in phosphorus-limited lakes (Stockner and Shortreed, 1989; Søndergaard, 1990, 1991). Furthermore, it is surprising that, at least as far as we currently know, there is no clear taxonomic trend among eukaryotic picoplankton in their distribution relative to nutrient or light availability. Therefore, specific ecophysiological differences such as light/dark adaptation or different nutrient kinetics would not explain the observed global distinctions in the distribution of prokaryotic and eukaryotic picoplankton.

Prokaryotic picoplankton is selectively favored in the most oligotrophic retentive systems relative both to larger algae and to eukaryotic picoplankton, irrespective of the kind of the limiting nutrient. Therefore, some unspecific relationship to nutrients appears to be the most reliable cause that explains all of the above-mentioned trends in the relative significance of prokaryotic and eukaryotic picoplankton. I believe that these differences are related to the internal organization of the respective cells.

A basic feature of cyanobacteria and prochlorophytes is their simple prokaryotic organization. Neither cyanobacteria nor prochlorophytes possess internal cell structures such as nuclei, mitochondria, or ribosomes characteristic of eukaryotes. According to the higher information contained in their genome, the minimal DNA content of a eukaryotic cell of 0.5 μm diameter amounts to 5.9% of its cell mass compared with 1.6% of a prokaryotic cell of the same size (Raven, 1986). The different level of structural organization has important physiological consequences. Compared with prokaryotes, eukaryotes must devote a larger fraction of their internal metabolism to maintenance processes. For instance, in contrast to prokaryotes, eukaryotes possess internal membranes. Accordingly the fraction of the carbon assimilated that is needed for the construction and maintenance of membranes is almost twice as high in a small eukaryote than in a similar-sized prokaryote (Raven, 1986). Because of the lower costs for maintenance metabolism it could be anticipated that a prokaryotic cell has a lower specific metabolism than a eukaryotic cell at a given size (Williams, 1981). Invariably coupled with the higher specific metabolism is the substrate demand. Consequently, to produce the same amount of eukaryotic biomass should require distinctly more energy and matter, i.e., nutrients, than to produce prokaryotic biomass of similar-sized organisms. I conclude, therefore, that, combined with the nonsinking of picoplankton, prokaryotes predominate in oligotrophic oceans because they use the scarce matter (nutrients) more efficiently than eukaryotes. The basic difference of the concept outlined here and the MOMS hypothesis is that it is not primarily cell size but rather the simple internal level of organization that is responsible for the evolutionary success of picoplankton under oligotrophic conditions. The relationship to the MOMS concept (Porter *et al.*, 1988) is illustrated in Fig. 5. For the survival of a productive system, the optimal strategy in oligotrophic waters would be to produce small, fast-growing, simply organized, round cells with high surface-to-volume ratios. Apparently, both heterotrophic bacteria and autotrophic picoplankton come close to this idealization. Under eutrophic conditions, when there is an ample supply with nutrients, eukaryotes outcompete prokaryotes because of their efficient nutrient-uptake systems (Raven, 1986; Fenchel, 1988). From an evolutionary point of view, we may envision the ancient prokaryotic picoplankton which have probably been in existence for over 2 billion years (Stockner and Porter, 1988) as part of the original microbial food web (Azam *et al.*, 1983) which is still present in all oceans (Lenz, 1992). The classical food web which is based on larger eukaryotic algae developed later in environments where nutrient concentrations became higher and environmental conditions favored the diversification of major phytoplankton groups and a large array of their metazoan consumers.

The revised concept I suggest can be tested experimentally. The growth

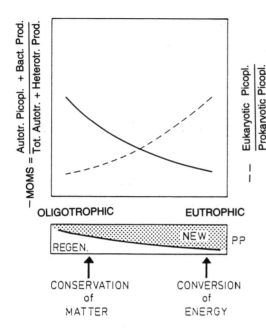

Figure 5. The measure of microbial strength (MOMS) concept (upper panel, modified after Porter et al., 1988) in the system context. Prokaryotic picoplankton production dominates in oligotrophic systems where total primary production (PP) is largely based on regenerated nutrients and in which, therefore, organisms have been selected for the conservation of matter (lower panel). In eutrophic systems, in contrast, larger eukaryotic organisms prevail which efficiently use the ample substrate supply converting physical energy into energy-rich organic substrates. Under these conditions, the relative significance of eukaryotic algae among the picoplankton is also higher. (Modified after Weisse, 1991b.)

yield of several prokaryotic and eukaryotic picoplankton-sized species should be tested in competition experiments under various nutrient and light regimes. If my hypothesis is correct, prokaryotes would win under nutrient limiting conditions while eukaryotes would be the superior competitors when the nutrient supply is higher. Light may modify but should not change the general outcome of such experiments.

5. Concluding Remarks

Investigations on the dynamics of APP in freshwater and marine environments have been concentrated on PE-rich unicellular cyanobacteria which prevail in oligotrophic to mesotrophic waters. In the lower trophic range, picoplankton abundance is primarily controlled by the availability of nutrients. Picoplankton abundance in the ocean appears to be somewhat lower than in lakes of comparable trophic state. It should be further investigated whether nitrogen is the primary macronutrient limiting picoplankton abundance. Nutrients are also important for the contribution of picoplankton biomass relative to total phytoplankton biomass and for the taxonomic composition among picoplankton. Low nutrient concentrations generally favor prokaryotic picoplankton whereas eukaryotic picoplankton become increasingly important with higher nutrient load. Low pH values also selectively favor eukaryotes at the expense of prokaryotic picoplankton.

Based mainly on traditional techniques, some differences in the taxonomic composition of picoplankton between marine and freshwater environments became obvious. Prochlorophytes have not been recorded from lake picoplankton. The dynamics of the ubiquitous unicellular cyanobacteria show, however, no pronounced differences in relation to salinity.

Experimental results demonstrated that *in situ* growth rates may approach maximum growth rates measured with cultured material under optimal laboratory conditions. Apparent growth rates, however, are usually distinctly lower *in situ* because growth is balanced by losses to a large extent.

Among loss processes, grazing is currently considered the most important one. Protozoa, namely heterotrophic flagellates and ciliates, and small metazoa such as rotifers have been identified as the primary picoplankton grazers. Picoplankton grazing by metazoans becomes more important at higher trophic levels. Certain species of freshwater cladocerans efficiently reduce picoplankton biomass, especially at times when larger food is scarce. As a consequence of the high grazing pressure, picoplankton peaks occur in mesotrophic and eutrophic environments only when grazing is reduced. It is a task for future studies to quantify species-specific grazing rates and to assess the nutritive value of APP relative to bacteria and larger phytoplankton.

Virus-induced cell lysis of picoplankton has been reported from various regions but its significance for the control of APP abundance and production is poorly understood.

Large seasonal fluctuations of picoplankton abundance are common in mesotrophic and eutrophic waters. Picoplankton cell numbers are higher during the growing season than in winter. The timing of APP peaks is variable depending on strain and location. It is a major drawback for the analysis of factors controlling the seasonal dynamics that the genotypic and phenotypic variability of prokaryote picoplankton are largely unknown. Temperature triggers the onset of picoplankton blooms in some environments but does not appear to be a primary factor for the population dynamics in other environments, at least during the growing season.

Short-term dynamics of picoplankton abundance and production have been studied only little. Daily primary production studies and investigations using the frequency of dividing cells (FDC) technique revealed distinct diurnal rhythms. Highest FDC values were commonly reported from the afternoon or early evening, but exceptions to this rule apparently exist. It remains unknown whether size-selective grazing is coupled with the picoplankton cell cycle.

Future studies should concentrate on picoplankton population dynamics *sensu stricto* and progressively replace bulk measurements by rate measurements on a per cell basis.

It may be disappointing for the reader that I have been unable to disclose any more dramatic differences in the dynamics of marine and freshwater picoplankton and their respective control mechanisms. I anticipate, however, that the current view of the APP being composed of only a few functional guilds (unicellular versus colonial picoplankton, prokaryotic versus eukaryotic picoplankton) will progressively change when more biological information on the individual picoplankton species is provided. The biological variability within a given picoplankton population has to be assessed before we can draw clear-cut generalizations on the factors controlling picoplankton dynamics across systems.

ACKNOWLEDGMENTS. I thank M. Søndergaard for constructive comments on an earlier version of this manuscript. S. Barkman and A. Schweizer provided unpublished data. Financial support by the Deutsche Forschungsgemeinschaft within the Special Collaborative Program "Cycling of Matter in Lake Constance" is gratefully acknowledged.

References

Andersson, A., Larsson, U., and Hagström, A., 1986, Size-selective grazing by a microflagellate on pelagic bacteria, *Mar. Ecol. Prog. Ser.* **33**:51–57.
Andreoli, C., Rascio, N., Dalla Vecchia, F., and Talarico, L., 1989, An ultrastructural research on natural populations of picoplankton from two brackish water environments in Italy, *J. Plankton Res.* **11**:1067–1074.
Armbrust, E. V., Bowen, J. D., Olson, R. J., and Chisholm, S.W., 1989, Effect of light on the cell cycle of a marine Synechococcus strain, *Appl. Environ. Microbiol.* **55**:425–432.
Azam, F., Fenchel, T., Field, J. G., Gray, J. S., Meyer-Reil, L. A., and Thingstad, F., 1983, The ecological role of water-column microbes in the sea, *Mar. Ecol. Prog. Ser.* **10**:257–263.
Bell, J. L., 1991, Patches and picoplankton—Effects on larval life spans of gastropod larvae, *Am. Zool.* **31**:6A.
Bienfang, P. K., and Takahashi, M., 1983, Ultraplankton growth rates in a subtropical ecosystem, *Mar. Biol.* **76**:213–218.
Bird, D. J., and Kalff, J., 1986, Bacterial grazing by planktonic lake algae, *Science* **231**:493–495.
Bird, D. J., and Kalff, J., 1987, Algal phagotrophy: Regulating factors and importance relative to photosynthesis in *Dinobryon* (Chrysophyceae), *Limnol. Oceanogr.* **32**:277–284.
Boraas, M. E., Remsen, C. C., and Seale, D. D., 1985, Phagotrophic flagellate populations in Lake Michigan: Use of image analysis to determine numbers and size distribution, *Eos* **66**:1299.
Boraas, M. E., Estep, K. W., Johnson, P. W., and Sieburth, J. M., 1988, Phagotrophic phototrophs: The ecological significance of mixotrophy, *J. Protozool.* **35**:249–252.
Brendelberger, H., 1985, Filter mesh-size and retention efficiency for small particles: Comparative studies with Cladocera, *Arch. Hydrobiol. Beih. Ergebn, Limnol.* **21**:135–146.
Britschgi, T. B., and Giovannoni, S. J., 1991, Phylogenetic analysis of a natural marine bacterioplankton population by rRNA gene cloning and sequencing, *App. Environ. Microbiol.* **57**:1707–1713.
Burger-Wiersma, T., Veenhuis, M., Korthals, H. J., Van de Wiel, C. C. M., and Mur, L. R., 1986, A new prokaryote containing chlorophylls a and b, *Nature* **320**:262–264.
Burger-Wiersma, T., Stal, L. J., and Mur, L. R., 1989, *Prochlorothrix hollandica* gen. nov., sp. nov.: A filamentous oxygenic photoautotrophic procaryote containing chlorophylls *a* and *b:* Assign-

ment to *Prochlorotrichaceae* fam. nov. and order *Prochlorales* Florenzano, Balloni and Materassi 1986, with emendation of the ordinal description, *Int. J. Syst. Bacteriol.* **39**:250–257.

Burkill, P. H., Leakey, R. J. G., Owens, N. J. P., and Mantoura, R. F. C., 1993, *Synechococcus* and its importance to the microbial foodweb of the northwest Indian Ocean, *Deep-Sea Res.:* Part II, **40**:773–782.

Burns, C. W., and Stockner, J. G., 1991, Picoplankton in six New Zealand lakes: Abundance in relation to season and trophic state, *Int. Rev. Gesamten Hydrobiol.* **76**:523–536.

Campbell, L., and Carpenter, E. J., 1986a, Diel patterns of cell division in marine *Synechococcus* spp. (Cyanobacteria): Use of the frequency of dividing cells technique to measure growth rate, *Mar. Ecol. Prog. Ser.* **32**:139–148.

Campbell, L., and Carpenter, E. J., 1986b, Estimating the grazing pressure of heterotrophic nanoplankton on *Synechococcus* spp. using the sea water dilution technique and selective metabolic inhibitors, *Mar. Ecol. Prog. Ser.* **33**:121–129.

Campbell, L., and Carpenter, E. J., 1987, Characterization of phycoerythrin-containing *Synechococcus* spp. populations by immunofluorescence, *J. Plankton Res.* **9**:1167–1181.

Campbell, L., Carpenter, E. J., and Iacono, V. J., 1983, Identification and enumeration of marine chroococcoid cyanobacteria by immunofluorescence, *App. Environ. Microbiol.* **46**:553–559.

Caron, D. A., Pick, F. R., and Lean, D. R. S., 1985, Chroococcoid cyanobacteria in Lake Ontario: Vertical and seasonal distributions during 1982, *J. Phycol.* **21**:171–175.

Caron, D. A., Lin Lim, E., Miceli, G., Waterbury, J. B., and Valois, F. W., 1991, Grazing and utilization of chroococcoid cyanobacteria and heterotrophic bacteria by protozoa in laboratory cultures and a coastal plankton community, *Mar. Ecol. Prog. Ser.* **76**:205–217.

Carpenter, E. J., and Campbell, L., 1988, Diel patterns of cell division and growth rates of *Synechococcus* spp. in Long Island Sound, *Mar. Ecol. Prog. Ser.* **47**:179–183.

Chavez, F. P., Buck, K. R., and Barber, R. T., 1990, Phytoplankton taxa in relation to primary production in the equatorial Pacific, *Deep-Sea Res.* **37**:1733–1752.

Chisholm, S. W., Olson, R. J., Zettler, E. R., Goericke, R., Waterbury, J. B., and Welschmeyer, N. A., 1988, A novel free-living prochlorophyte abundant in the oceanic euphotic zone, *Nature* **334**:340–343.

Chisholm, S. W., and others, 1992, *Prochlorococcus marinus* nov. gen. nov. sp.: An oxytrophic procaryote containing divinyl-chlorophyll *b*, *Arch. Microbiol.* **157**:297–300.

Chrzanowski, T. H., and Simek, K., 1990, Prey-size selection by freshwater flagellated protozoa, *Limnol. Oceanogr.* **35**:1429–1436.

Craig, S. R., 1984, Productivity of algal picoplankton in a small meromictic lake, *Verh. Int. Verein. Limnol.* **22**:351–354.

Craig, S. R., 1987, The distribution and contribution of picoplankton to deep photosynthetic layers in some meromictic lakes, *Acta Acad. Abo.* **47**:55–81.

Cushing, D. H., 1989, A difference in structure between ecosystems in strongly stratified waters and in those that are only weakly stratified, *J. Plankton Res.* **11**:1–15.

Davis, P. G., Caron, D. A., Johnson, P. W., and Sieburth, J. M., 1985, Phototrophic and apochlorotic components of picoplankton and nanoplankton in the North Atlantic: Geographic, vertical, seasonal and diel distributions, *Mar. Ecol. Prog. Ser.* **21**:15–26.

Douglas, D. J., 1984, Microautoradiography-based enumeration of photosynthetic picoplankton with estimates of carbon-specific growth rates, *Mar. Ecol. Prog. Ser.* **14**:223–228.

Dugdale, R. C., and Goering, J. J., 1967, Uptake of new and regenerated forms of nitrogen in primary productivity, *Limnol. Oceanogr.* **12**:196–206.

El Hag, A. G. D., and Fogg, G. E., 1986, The distribution of coccoid blue-green algae (cyanobacteria) in the Menai Straits and the Irish Sea, *Br. Phycol. J.* **21**:45–54.

Eppley, R. W., and Peterson, B. J., 1979, Particulate organic matter flux and planktonic new production in the deep ocean, *Nature* **282**:677–680.

Ernst, A., 1991, Cyanobacterial picoplankton from Lake Constance: I. Isolation by fluorescence characteristics, *J. Plankton Res.* **13:**1307–1312.

Ernst, A., Sandmann, G., Postius, C., Brass, S., Kenter, U., and Böger, P., 1992, Cyanobacterial picoplankton from Lake Constance. II. Classification of isolates by cell morphology and pigment composition, *Bot. Acta* **105:**161–167.

Estep, K. W., Davis, P. G., Keller, M. D., and Sieburth, J. M., 1986, How important are oceanic algal nanoflagellates in bacterivory? *Limnol. Oceanogr.* **31:**646–650.

Fahnenstiel, G. L., Sicko-Goad, L., Scavia, D., and Stoermer, E. F., 1986, Importance of picoplankton in Lake Superior, *Can. J. Fish. Aquat. Sci.* **43:**235–240.

Fahnenstiel, G. L., Carrick, H. J., and Iturriaga, R., 1991a, Physiological characteristics and food-web dynamics of *Synechococcus* in Lakes Huron and Michigan, *Limnol. Oceanogr.* **36:**219–234.

Fahnenstiel, G. L., Carrick, H. J., Rogers, C. E., and Sicko-Goad, L., 1991b, Red fluorescing phototrophic picoplankton in the Laurentian Great Lakes: What are they and what are they doing? *Int. Rev. Gesamten Hydrobiol.* **76:**603–616.

Fahnenstiel, G. L., Patton, T. R., Carrick, H. J., and McCormick, M. J., 1991c, Diel division cycle and growth rates of *Synechococcus* in Lakes Huron and Michigan, *Int. Rev. Gesamten Hydrobiol.* **76:**657–664.

Fenchel, T., 1988, Marine Plankton food chains, *Annu. Rev. Ecol. Syst.* **19:**19–38.

Fogg, G. E., 1986, Picoplankton, *Proc. R. Soc. London Ser. B* **228:**1–30.

Furnas, M. J., 1991, Net in situ-growth rates of phytoplankton in an oligotrophic, tropical shelf ecosystem, *Limnol. Oceanogr.* **36:**13–29.

Gaedke, U., and Schimmele, M., 1991, Internal seiches in Lake Constance: Influence on plankton abundance at a fixed sampling site, *J. Plankton Res.* **13:**743–754.

Geller, W., and Müller, H., 1981, The Filtration apparatus of cladocera: Filter mesh-sizes and their implications of food selectivity, *Oecologia* **49:**316–321.

Gieskes, W. W. C., Kraay, G. W., Nontji, A., Setiapermana, D., and Sutomo, 1988, Monsoonal alternation of a mixed and a layered structure in the phytoplankton of the euphotic zone of the Banda Sea (Indonesia): A mathematical analysis of algal pigment fingerprints, *Neth. J. Sea Res.* **22:**123–137.

Giovannoni, S. J., Britschgi, T. B., Moyer, C. L., and Field, K. G., 1990, Genetic diversity in Sargasso Sea bacterioplankton, *Nature* **345:**60–63.

Glibert, P. M., and Ray, R. T., 1990, Different patterns of growth and nitrogen uptake in two clones of marine *Synechococcus, Mar. Biol.* **107:**273–280.

Glover, H. E., 1985, The physiology and ecology of the marine cyanobacterial genus *Synechococcus*, in: *Advances in Aquatic Microbiology* (H. W. Jannasch and P. J. L. Williams, eds.), Academic Press, New York, pp. 49–107.

Glover, H. E., Campbell, L., and Prezelin, B. B., 1986a, Contribution of *Synechococcus* to size-fractioned primary productivity in three water masses in the Northwest Atlantic Ocean, *Mar. Biol.* **91:**193–203.

Glover, H. E., Keller, M. D., and Guillard, R. L., 1986b, Light quality and oceanic ultraphytoplankters, *Nature* **319:**142–143.

Glover, H. E., Keller, M. D., and Spinrad, R. W., 1987, The effects of light quality and intensity on photosynthesis and growth of marine eukaryotic and prokaryotic phytoplankton clones, *J. Exp. Mar. Biol. Ecol.* **105:**137–159.

Glover, H. E., Prezelin, B. B., Campbell, L., Wyman, M., and Garside, C., 1988a, Observations on a nitrate-dependent *Synechococcus* bloom in surface Sargasso Sea water, *Nature* **331:**161–163.

Glover, H. E., Prezelin, B. B., Campbell, L., and Wyman, M., 1988b, Pico- and ultraplankton Sargasso Sea communities: Variability and comparative distributions of *Synechococcus* spp. and algae, *Mar. Ecol. Prog. Ser.* **49:**127–139.

Goericke, R., and Repeta, D. J., 1992, The pigments of *Prochlorococcus marinus:* The presence of divinyl chlorophyll *a* and *b* in a marine procaryote, *Limnol. Oceanogr.* **37:**425–433.

Gonzalez, J. M., Sherr, E. B., and Sherr, B. F., 1990, Size-selective grazing on bacteria by natural assemblages of estuarine flagellates and ciliates, *Appl. Environ. Microbiol.* **56:**583–589.

Gophen, M., and Geller, W., 1984, Filter mesh size and food particle uptake by *Daphnia, Oecologia* **64:**408–412.

Gradinger, R., Weisse, T., and Pillen, T., 1992, Significance of picocyanobacteria in the Red Sea and the Gulf of Aden, *Bot. Mar.* **35:**245–250.

Griffiths, A. J., 1984, A descriptive numericlature for isolates of cyanobacteria, *Br. Phycol. J.* **19:**233–238.

Güde, H., 1989, The role of grazing on bacteria in plankton succession, in: *Plankton Ecology* (U. Sommer, ed.), Springer, Berlin, pp. 337–364.

Hagström, A., Azam, F., Andersson, A., Wikner, J., and Rassoulzadegan, F., 1988, Microbial loop in an oligotrophic pelagic marine ecosystem: Possible roles of cyanobacteria and nanoflagellates in the organic fluxes, *Mar. Ecol. Prog. Ser.* **49:**171–178.

Hall, J. A., 1991, Long-term preservation of picophytoplankton for counting by fluorescence microscopy, *Br. Phycol. J.* **26:**169–174.

Hall, J. A., and Vincent, W. F., 1990, Vertical and horizontal structure in the picoplankton communities of a coastal upwelling system, *Mar. Biol.* **106:**465–471.

Hawley, G. R. W., and Whitton, B. A., 1991, Seasonal changes in chlorophyll-containing picoplankton populations of ten lakes in northern England, *Int. Rev. Gesamten Hydrobiol.* **76:**545–554.

Healey, F. P., 1985, Interacting effects of light and nutrient limitation on the growth rate of *Synechococcus linearis* (Cyanophyceae), *J. Phycol.* **21:**134–146.

Herbland, A., and Le Bouteiller, A., 1981, The size distribution of phytoplankton and particulate organic matter in the equatorial Atlantic Ocean: Importance of ultraseston and consequences, *J. Plankton Res.* **3:**659–673.

Iturriaga, R., and Marra, J., 1988, Temporal and spatial variability of chroococcoid cyanobacteria *Synechococcus* spp. specific growth rates and their contribution to primary production in the Sargasso Sea, *Mar. Ecol. Prog. Ser.* **44:**175–181.

Iturriaga, R., and Mitchell, B. G., 1986, Chroococcoid cyanobacteria: A significant component in the food web dynamics of the open ocean, *Mar. Ecol. Prog. Ser.* **28:**291–297.

Jochem, F., 1988, On the distribution and importance of picocyanobacteria in a boreal inshore area (Kiel Bight, western Baltic), *J. Plankton Res.* **10:**1009–1022.

Jochem, F., 1990, Zur Struktur und Dynamik autotropher Ultraplankton-Gemeinschaften in marinen Warmwasser-Ökosystemen, *Ber. Inst. Meeresk. Kiel* **195:**1–220.

Johnson, P. W., and Sieburth, J. M., 1979, Chroococcoid cyanobacteria in the sea: A ubiquitous and diverse phototrophic biomass, *Limnol. Oceanogr.* **24:**928–935.

Johnson, P. W., and Sieburth, J. M., 1982, In-situ morphology and occurrence of eucaryotic phototrophs of bacterial size in the picoplankton of estuarine and oceanic waters, *J. Phycol.* **18:**318–327.

Johnson, P. W., Huai-Shu, X., and Sieburth, J. M., 1982, The utilization of chroococcoid cyanobacteria by marine protozooplankters but not by calanoid copepods, *Ann. Orst. Inst. Oceanogr. Paris* **58:**297–308.

Kana, T. M., and Glibert, P. M., 1987, Effect of irradiances up to 2000 µE m^{-2} s^{-1} on marine *Synechococcus* WH7803—I. Growth, pigmentation, and cell composition, *Deep-Sea Res.* **34:**479–495.

Kennaway, G. M. A., and Edwards, G., 1989, Seasonal and vertical distribution of picoplankton in Llyn Padarn, Gwynedd, *Br. Phycol. J.* **24:**375–384.

Klut, M. E., and Stockner, J. G., 1990, Virus-like particles in an ultraoligotrophic lake on Vancouver Island, British Columbia, *Can. J. Fish. Aquat. Sci.* **47:**725–730.

Krempin, D. W., and Sullivan, C. W., 1981, The seasonal abundance, vertical distribution, and relative microbial biomass of chroococcoid cyanobacteria at a station in southern California coastal waters, *Can. J. Microbiol.* **27**:1341–1344.

Kudoh, S., Kanada, J., and Takahashi, M., 1990, Specific growth rates and grazing mortality of chroococcoid cyanobacteria *Synechococcus* spp. in pelagic surface waters in the sea, *J. Exp. Mar. Biol. Ecol.* **142**:201–212.

Kumar, S. K., Vincent, W. F., Austin, P. C., and Wake, G. C., 1991, Picoplankton and marine food chain dynamics in a variable mixed-layer: A reaction-diffusion model, *Ecol. Modelling* **57**:193–219.

Kuosa, H., 1988, Occurrence of autotrophic picoplankton along an open sea–inner archipelago gradient in the Gulf of Finland, Baltic Sea, *Ophelia* **28**:85–93.

Kuosa, H., 1991a, Protozoan grazing on picophytoplankton and nanophytoplankton in the northern Baltic Sea: Direct evidence from epifluorescence microscopy, *Arch. Hydrobiol.* **119**:257–266.

Kuosa, H., 1991b, Picoplanktonic algae in the northern Baltic Sea: Seasonal dynamics and flagellate grazing, *Mar. Ecol. Prog. Ser.* **73**:269–276.

Lampert, W., and Schober, U., 1978, Das regelmäßige Auftreten von Frühjahrsalgen-Maximum and "Klarwasserstadium" im Bodensee als Folge von klimatischen Bedingungen und Wechselwirkugen zwischen Phyto- und Zooplankton, *Arch. Hydrobiol.* **82**:364–386.

Landry, M. R., Haas, L. W., and Fagerness, V. L., 1984, Dynamics of microbial plankton communities: Experiments in Kaneohe Bay, Hawaii, *Mar. Ecol. Prog. Ser.* **16**:127–133.

Laval, M., 1971, Ultrastructure et mode de nutrition du choanoflagelle *Salpingoeca pelagica* sp. nov. Comparison avec les choanocytes des sporangiares, *Protistologica* **7**:325–336.

Laws, E. A., Redalje, D. G., Haas, L. W., Bienfang, P. K., Eppley, R. W., Harrison, W. G., Karl, D. M., and Marra, J., 1984, High phytoplankton growth rates in oligotrophic Hawaiian coastal waters, *Limnol. Oceanogr.* **29**:1161–1169.

Lenz, J., 1992, Microbial loop, microbial food web and classical food chain: Their significance in pelagic marine ecosystems, *Arch. Hydrobiol.* **37**:265–278.

Leppard, G. G., Urciuoli, D., and Pick, F. R., 1987, Characterization of cyanobacterial picoplankton in Lake Ontario by transmission electron microscopy, *Can. J. Fish. Aquat. Sci.* **44**:2173–2177.

Li, W. K. W., and Dickie, P. M., 1991, Relationship between the number of dividing and nondividing cells of cyanobacteria in North Atlantic picoplankton, *J. Phycol.* **27**:559–565.

Li, W. K. W., and Wood, A. M., 1988, Vertical distribution of North Atlantic ultraphytoplankton: Analysis by flow cytometry and epifluorescence microscopy, *Deep-Sea Res.* **35**:1615–1638.

Li, W. K. W., Lewis, M. R., and Lister, A., 1992, Flow cytometric detection of prochlorophytes and cyanobacteria in the Gulf of Policastro, Italy, *Arch. Hydrobiol.* **124**:309–316.

Lochte, K., and Turley, C. M., 1988, Bacteria and cyanobacteria associated with phytodetritus in the deep sea, *Nature* **333**:67–69.

McDuff, R. E., and Chisholm, S. W., 1982, The calculation of in situ growth rates of phytoplankton populations from fractions of cells undergoing mitosis: A clarification, *Limnol. Oceanogr.* **27**:783–788.

Maeda, H., Kawai, A., and Tilzer, M. M., 1992, The water bloom of cyanobacterial picoplankton in Lake Biwa, Japan, *Hydrobiologia* **248**:93–103.

Malinsky-Rushansky, N., and Berman, T., 1991, Picocyanobacteria and bacteria in Lake Kinneret, *Int. Rev. Gesamten Hydrobiol* **76**:555–564.

Mazumder, A., McQueen, D. J., Taylor, W. D., Lean, D. R. S., and Dickman, M. D., 1990, Microzooplankton and mesozooplankton grazing on natural picoplankton and nanoplankton in contrasting plankton communities produced by planktovore manipulation and fertilization, *Arch. Hydrobiol.* **118**:257–282.

Mitsui, A., Kumazawa, S., Takahashi, A., Ikemoto, H., Cao, S., and Arai, T., 1986, Strategy by which nitrogen-fixing unicellular cyanobacteria grow photoautotrophically, *Nature* **323**:720–722.

Moloney, C. L., and Field, J. G., 1991a, The size-based dynamics of plankton food webs. I. A simulation model of carbon and nitrogen flow, *J. Plankton Res.* **13**:1003–1038.

Moloney, C. L., and Field, J. G., 1991b, The size-based dynamics of plankton food webs. II. Simulation of three contrasting southern Benguela food webs, *J. Plankton Res.* **13**:1039–1092.

Moloney, C. L., and Field, J. G., 1991c, Modelling carbon and nitrogen flows in a microbial plankton community, in: *Protozoa and Their Role in Marine Processes* (P. C. Reid, C. M. Turley, and P. H. Burkill, eds.), NATO ASI Series, Volume G 25, Springer, Berlin, pp. 443–474.

Morris, I., and Glover, H. E., 1981, Physiology of photosynthesis by marine coccoid cyanobacteria—Some ecological implications, *Limnol. Oceanogr.* **26**:957–961.

Müller, H., Schöne, A., Pinto-Coelho, R. M., Schweizer, A., and Weisse, T., 1991, Seasonal succession of ciliates in Lake Constance, *Microb. Ecol.* **21**:119–138.

Murphy, L. S., and Haugen, E. M., 1985, The distribution and abundance of phototrophic ultra-plankton in the North Atlantic, *Limnol. Oceanogr.* **30**:47–58.

Nagata, T., 1986, The seasonal abundance and vertical distribution of the < 3-μm phytoplankton in the North Basin of Lake Biwa, *Ecol. Res.* **1**:207–221.

Nagata, T., 1988, The microflagellate–picoplankton food linkage in the water column of Lake Biwa, *Limnol. Oceanogr.* **33**:504–517.

Nagata, T., 1990, Contribution of picoplankton to the grazer food chain of Lake Biwa, in: *Large Lakes—Ecological Structure and Function* (M. M. Tilzer and C. Serruya, eds.), Springer, Berlin, pp. 526–539.

Neveux, J., Vaulot, D., Courties, C., and Fukai, E., 1989, Green photosynthetic bacteria associated with the deep chlorophyll maximum in the Sargasso Sea, *C. R. Acad. Sci* **308**:9–14.

Olsen, G. J., 1990, Variation among the masses, *Nature* **345**:20–21.

Olson, R. J., Vaulot, D., and Chisholm, S. W., 1985, Marine phytoplankton distributions measured using shipboard flow cytometry, *Deep-Sea Res.* **32**:1273–1280.

Olson, R. J., Chisholm, S. W., Zettler, E. R., Altabet, M. A., and Dusenberry, J. A., 1990a, Spatial and temporal distributions of prochlorophyte picoplankton in the North Atlantic Ocean, *Deep-Sea Res.* **37**:1033–1051.

Olson, R. J., Chisholm, S. W., Zettler, E. R., and Armbrust, E. V., 1990b, Pigments, size, and distribution of *Synechococcus* in the North Atlantic and Pacific oceans, *Limnol. Oceanogr.* **35**:45–58.

Paerl, H. W., 1991, Ecophysiological and trophic implications of light-stimulated amino acid utilization in marine picoplankton, *Appl. Environ. Microbiol.* **57**:473–479.

Perkins, F. O., Haas, L. W., Philipps, D. E., and Webb, K. L., 1981, Ultrastructure of a marine *Synechococcus* possessing spinae, *Can. J. Microbiol.* **27**:318–329.

Petersen, R., 1991, Carbon-14 uptake by picoplankton and total phytoplankton in eight New Zealand lakes, *Int. Rev. Gesamten Hydrobiol.* **76**:631–641.

Pick, F. R., and Agbeti, M., 1991, The seasonal dynamics and composition of photosynthetic picoplankton communities in temperate lakes in Ontario, Canada, *Int. Rev. Gesamten Hydrobiol.* **76**:565–580.

Pick, F. R., and Berube, C., 1992, Diel cycles in the frequency of dividing cells of freshwater picocyanobacteria, *J. Plankton Res.* **14**:1193–1198.

Pick, F. R., and Lean, D. R. S., 1987, The role of macronutrients (C,N,P) in controlling cyanobac-terial dominance in temperate lakes, N.Z. *J. Mar. Freshwater Res.* **21**:425–434.

Platt, T., and Li, W. K. W. (eds.), 1986, Photosynthetic picoplankton, *Can. Bull, Fish. Aquat. Sci.* **214**.

Platt, T., Subba Rao, D. V., and Irwin, B., 1983, Photosynthesis of picoplankton in the oligotrophic ocean, *Nature* **301**:702–704.

Porter, K. G., 1988, Phagotrophic phytoflagellates in microbial food webs, *Hydrobiologia* **159**:89–97.

Porter, K. G., Paerl, H., Hodson, R., Pace, M., Priscu, J., Riemann, B., Scavia, D., and Stockner, J., 1988, Microbial interactions in lake foodwebs, in: *Complex Interactions in Lake Communities* (S. R. Carpenter, ed.), Springer, Berlin, pp. 234–255.

Prezelin, B. B., and Glover, H. E., 1991, Variability in time/space estimates of phytoplankton, biomass and productivity in the Sargasso Sea (North Atlantic Ocean), *J. Plankton Res.* **13**(Suppl.):S45–S68.

Prezelin, B. B., Putt, M., and Glover, H. E., 1986, Diurnal patterns in photosynthetic capacity and depth-dependent photosynthesis–irradiance relationships in *Synechococcus* spp. and larger phytoplankton in three water masses in the northwest Atlantic Ocean, *Mar. Biol.* **91**:205–217.

Prezelin, B. B., Glover, H. E., and Campbell, L., 1987, Effects of light intensity and nutrient availability on diel patterns of cell metabolism and growth in populations of *Synechococcus* spp., *Mar. Biol.* **95**:469–480.

Proctor, L. M., and Fuhrman, J. A., 1990, Viral mortality of marine bacteria and cyanobacteria, *Nature* **343**:60–62.

Proctor, L. M., and Fuhrman, J. A., 1991, Roles of viral infection in organic particle flux, *Mar. Ecol. Prog. Ser.* **69**:133–142.

Psenner, R., 1990, From image analysis to chemical analysis of bacteria: A long-term study? *Limnol. Oceanogr.* **35**:234–237.

Putt, M., and Prezelin, B. B., 1985, Observations of diel patterns of photosynthesis in cyanobacteria and nanoplankton in the Santa Barbara Channel during 'el Nino,' *J. Plankton Res.* **7**:779–790.

Raven, J. A., 1986, Physiological consequences of extremely small size for autotrophic organisms in the sea, *Can. Bull. Fish. Aquat. Sci.* **214**:1–70.

Rhode, W., 1955, Productivity: Can plankton production proceed during winter darkness in subarctic lakes? *Verh. Int. Ver. Limnol.* **12**:117–122.

Rippka, R., 1988, Recognition and identification of cyanobacteria, *Methods Enzymol.* **167**:28–67.

Rippka, R., and Cohen-Bazire, G., 1983, The Cyanobacteriales: A legitimate order based on the type strain *Cyanobacterium stanieri*? *Ann. Microbiol. (Inst. Pasteur)* **134B**:21–36.

Rippka, R., Deruelles, J., Waterbury, J. B., Herdman, M., and Stanier, R. Y., 1979, Generic assignments, strain histories, and properties of pure cultures of cyanobacteria, *J. Gen. Microbiol.* **111**:1–61.

Sanders, R. W., 1991, Trophic strategies among heterotrophic flagellates, *Syst. Assoc. Spec. Vol.* **45**:21–38.

Sanders, R. W., and Porter, K. G., 1988, Phagotrophic phytoflagellates, *Adv. Microb. Ecol.* **10**:167–192.

Sanders, R. W., Porter, K. G., Bennett, S. J., and DeBiase, A. E., 1989, Seasonal patterns of bacterivory by flagellates, ciliates, rotifers, and cladocerans in a freshwater plankton community, *Limnol. Oceanogr.* **34**:673–687.

Schweizer, A., 1993, Die Ökologie des autotrophen Picoplanktons im Bodensee, Ph.D. thesis, University of Konstanz.

Schweizer, A., and Heusel, R., 1992, Picoplankton photosynthesis and diurnal variations in photosynthesis–irradiance relationship in a eutrophic and meso-oligotrophic lake, *Hydrobiologia* **238**:131–138.

Sherr, E. B., Sherr, B. F., Berman, T., and Hadas, O., 1991a, High abundance of picoplankton-ingesting ciliates during late fall in Lake Kinneret, Israel, *J. Plankton Res.* **13**:789–799.

Sherr, E. B., Sherr, B. F., and McDaniel, J., 1991b, Clearance rates of less-than-6 μm fluorescently labeled algae (FLA) by estuarine protozoa—Potential grazing impact of flagellates and ciliates, *Mar. Ecol. Prog. Ser.* **69**:81–92.

Shortreed, K. S., and Stockner, J. G., 1990, Effect of nutrient additions on lower trophic levels of an oligotrophic lake with a seasonal deep chlorophyll maximum, *Can J. Fish. Aquat. Sci.* **47**:262–273.

Sieburth, J. M., Smetacek, V., and Lenz, J., 1978, Pelagic ecosystem structure: Heterotrophic compartments of the plankton and their relationship to plankton size fractions, *Limnol. Oceanogr.* **23**:1256–1263.

Søndergaard, M., 1990, Picophytoplankton in Danish lakes, *Verh. Int. Ver. Limnol.* **24**:609–612.

Søndergaard, M., 1991, Phototrophic picoplankton in temperate lakes: Seasonal abundance and importance along a trophic gradient, *Int. Rev. Gesamten Hydrobiol.* **76**:505–522.

Stanier, R. Y., Ingraham, J. I., Wheelis, M. L., and Painter, P. R., 1986, *The Microbial World*, 5th ed., Prentice–Hall, Englewood Cliffs, N.J.

Sterner, R. W., 1989, The role of grazers in phytoplankton succession, in: *Plankton Ecology* (U. Sommer, ed.), Springer, Berlin, pp. 337–364.

Stockner, J. G., 1987, Lake fertilization: The enrichment cycle and lake sockeye (*Oncorhynchus nerka*) production, *Can. Spec. Publ. Fish. Aquat. Sci.* **96**:198–215.

Stockner, J. G., 1988, Phototrophic picoplankton: An overview from marine and freshwater ecosystems. *Limnol. Oceanogr.* **33**:765–775.

Stockner, J. G. (ed.), 1991a, Autotrophic picoplankton in freshwater ecosystems, *Int. Rev. Gesamten Hydrobiol.* **76**(4), special issue.

Stockner, J. G., 1991b, Autotrophic picoplankton in freshwater ecosystems: The view from the summit, *Int. Rev. Gesamten Hydrobiol.* **76**:483–492.

Stockner, J. G., and Antia, N. J., 1986, Algal picoplankton from marine and freshwater ecosystems: A multidisciplinary perspective, *Can. J. Fish. Aquat. Sci.* **43**:2472–2503.

Stockner, J. G., and Porter, K. G., 1988, Microbial food webs in freshwater planktonic ecosystems, in: *Complex Interactions in Lake Communities* (S. R. Carpenter, ed.), Springer, Berlin, pp. 69–83.

Stockner, J. G., and Shortreed, K. S., 1988, Response of Anabaena and Synechococcus to manipulation of nitrogen:phosphorus ratios in a lake fertilization experiment, *Limnol. Oceanogr.* **33**:1348–1361.

Stockner, J. G., and Shortreed, K. S., 1989, Algal picoplankton production and contribution to food webs in oligotrophic British Columbia lakes, *Hydrobiologia* **173**:151–166.

Stockner, J. G., and Shortreed, K. S., 1991, Autotrophic picoplankton: Community composition, abundance and distribution across a gradient of oligotrophic British Columbia and Yukon Territory lakes, *Int. Rev. Gesamten Hydrobiol.* **76**:581–601.

Suttle, C. A., 1987, Effects of nutrient patchiness and N:P supply ratios on the ecology and physiology of freshwater phytoplankton, Ph.D. thesis, University of British Columbia.

Suttle, C. A., Chan, A. M., and Cottrell, M. T., 1990, Infection of phytoplankton by viruses and reduction of primary productivity, *Nature* **347**:467–469.

Suttle, C. A., Chan, A. M., and Cottrell, M. T., 1991, Use of ultrafiltration to isolate viruses from seawater which are the pathogens of marine phytoplankton, *Appl. Environ. Microbiol.* **57**:721–726.

Sweeney, B. M., and Borgese, M. B., 1989, A circadian rhythm in cell division in a prokaryote, the cyanobacterium *Synechococcus* WH7803, *J. Phycol.* **25**:183–186.

Takahashi, M., and Bienfang, P. K., 1983, Size structure of phytoplankton biomass and photosynthesis in subtropical and tropical Hawaiian waters, *Mar. Biol.* **76**:203–211.

Taylor, A. H., and Joint, I., 1990, A steady-state analysis of the 'microbial loop' in stratified systems, *Mar. Ecol. Prog. Ser.* **59**:1–17.

Thingstad, F., and Sakshaug, E., 1990, Control of phytoplankton growth in nutrient recycling ecosystems. Theory and terminology, *Mar. Ecol. Prog. Ser.* **63**:261–272.

Van Liere, L., Breebaart, L., and Dullemont, Y. J., 1989, Determining the relative number of prochlorophytes in lake phytoplankton using epifluorescence microscopy, *Br. Phycol. J.* **24**:391–394.

Vaulot, D., Courties, C., and Partensky, F., 1989, A simple method to preserve oceanic phytoplankton for flow cytometric analyses, *Cytometry* **10**:629–635.

Vaulot, D., Partensky, F., Neveux, J., Mantoura, R. F. C., and Llewellyn, C. A., 1990, Winter presence of prochlorophytes in surface waters of the northwestern Mediterranean Sea, *Limnol. Oceanogr.* **35**:1156–1164.

Veldhuis, M. J. W., and Kraay, G. W., 1990, Vertical distribution and pigment composition of a picoplanktonic prochlorophyte in the subtropical North Atlantic: A combined study of HPLC-analysis of pigments and flow cytometry, *Mar. Ecol. Prog. Ser.* **68**:121–127.

Verity, P. G., and Villareal, T. A., 1986, The relative food value of diatoms, dinoflagellates, flagellates, and cyanobacteria for tintinnid ciliates, *Arch. Protistenkd.* **131**:71–84.

Vernet, M. Mitchell, B. G., and Holm-Hansen, O., 1990, Adaptation of *Synechococcus* in situ determined by variability in intracellular phycoerythrin-543 at a coastal station off the Southern California coast, USA, *Mar. Ecol. Prog. Ser.* **63**:9–16.

Vörös, L., Gulyas, P., and Nemeth, J., 1991, Occurrence, dynamics and production of picoplankton in Hungarian shallow lakes, *Int. Rev. Gesamten Hydrobiol.* **76**:617–629.

Ward, D. M., Weller, R., and Bateson, M. M., 1990, 16S rRNA sequences reveal numerous uncultured microorganisms in a natural community, *Nature* **345**:63–65.

Waterbury, J. B., Watson, S. W., Valois, F. W., and Franks, D. G., 1986, Biological and ecological characterization of the marine unicellular cyanobacterium *Synechococcus*, *Can. Bull. Fish. Aquat. Sci.* **214**:71–120.

Wehr, J. D., 1991, Nutrient and grazer-mediated effects on picoplankton and size structure in phytoplankton communities, *Int. Rev. Gesamten Hydrobiol.* **76**:643–656.

Weisse, T., 1988, Dynamics of autotrophic picoplankton in Lake Constance, *J. Plankton Res.* **10**:1179–1188.

Weisse, T., 1989, The microbial loop in the Red Sea: Dynamics of pelagic bacteria and heterotrophic nanoflagellates, *Mar. Ecol. Prog. Ser.* **55**:241–250.

Weisse, T., 1991a, The annual cycle of hetertrophic freshwater nanoflagellates: Role of bottom-up versus top-down control, *J. Plankton Res.* **13**:167–185.

Weisse, T., 1991b, The microbial food web and its sensitivity to eutrophication and contaminant enrichment: A cross-system overview, *Int. Rev. Gesamten Hydrobiol.* **76**:327–338.

Weisse, T., and Kenter, U., 1991, Ecological characteristics of autotrophic picoplankton in a pre-alpine lake, *Int. Rev. Gesamten Hydrobiol.* **76**:493–504.

Weisse, T., and Munawar, M., 1989, Evaluation of the microbial loop in the North American Great Lakes, *Can. Tech. Rep. Fish. Aquat. Sci.* **1709**:1–30.

Weisse, T., and Schweizer, A., 1991, Seasonal and interannual variation of autotrophic picoplankton in a large prealpine lake (Lake Constance), *Verh. Int. Ver. Limnol.* **24**:821–825.

Weisse, T., Müller, H., Pinto-Coelho, R. M., Schweizer, A., Springmann, D., and Baldringer, G., 1990, Response of the microbial loop to the phytoplankton spring bloom in a large prealpine lake, *Limnol. Oceanogr.* **35**:781–794.

Wikner, J., Rassoulzadegan, F., and Hagström, A., 1990, Periodic bacterivore activity balances bacterial growth in the marine environment, *Limnol. Oceanogr.* **35**:313–324.

Williams, P. J. L., 1981, Incorporation of microheterotrophic processes into the classical paradigm of the planktonic food web, *Kiel. Meeresforsch. Sonderh.* **5**:11–28.

Wood, A. M., and Townsend, D., 1990, DNA polymorphism within the WH7803 serogroup of marine *Synechococcus* spp. (cyanobacteria), *J. Phycol.* **26**:576–585.

Wyman, M., Gregory, R. P. F., and Carr, N. G., 1985, Novel role for phycoerythrin in a marine cyanobacterium, *Synechococcus* strain DC-2, *Science* **230**:818–820.

9

Fact or Fiction—Bacterial Growth Rates and Production as Determined by [*methyl*-³H]-Thymidine?

RICHARD D. ROBARTS and TAMAR ZOHARY

1. Introduction

Bacteria play key roles in the functioning of natural aquatic systems: they are major decomposers of organic matter and are important in energy and nutrient cycling and transformations. While their importance in the water column and sediments of inland and marine systems is widely acknowledged, there is also growing evidence to their importance in vast regions of the terrestrial subsurface (Ghiorse and Wilson, 1988).

For almost a century, bacteria have been known to form part of the plankton of inland and marine aquatic ecosystems. As noted by Hobbie (1988), research in the first 90 years focused on the numbers of organisms and on the species that grew in the laboratory on artificial media (the species approach). Only in recent years have new techniques and instruments led to the "process approach," revealing the total numbers, activity and growth rates of planktonic bacteria in nature (Hobbie, 1988).

Methodological shortcomings probably present the greatest impediment to our understanding of bacterial ecology and the factors influencing their growth rates and production in ecosystems. The development of reliable methods to measure biomass and specific growth rates of microbial assemblages is still considered to be the most fundamental objective of experimental microbial ecology (Karl, 1980).

RICHARD D. ROBARTS • National Hydrology Research Institute, Environment Canada, Saskatoon, Saskatchewan S7N 3H5, Canada.   **TAMAR ZOHARY** • The Yigal Allon Kinneret Laboratory, Tiberias 14102, Israel.

Advances in Microbial Ecology, Volume 13, edited by J. Gwynfryn Jones. Plenum Press, New York, 1993.

The use of [^{14}C]glucose by Parsons and Strickland (1962) and subsequent development of a method to determine rates of bacterial uptake, respiration, and turnover of organic compounds at natural substrate concentrations (Wright and Hobbie, 1965; Hobbie and Crawford, 1969) provided much data on the decomposition and flow of organic carbon through food webs in a wide range of natural systems. Since bacteria degrade a large number of organic substrates, the method was modified to use labeled sugars, amino acids, organic acids, lignocellulose, and other dissolved and particulate substrates (Robarts, 1986). These early studies demonstrated that bacteria were actively metabolizing organic matter but did not provide quantitative estimates of growth rates and production.

While the growth of autotrophic bacteria that fix carbon dioxide for their primary source of carbon can potentially be measured using $^{14}CO_2$, until recently there has not been a reliable method to determine the growth of natural assemblages of heterotrophic bacteria that utilize organic substrates for a carbon source (Moriarty, 1986). The three most common methods in use are: the incorporation of [^{3}H]adenine into RNA and DNA by prokaryotes and unicellular algae to give total microbial production (Karl, 1982), the incorporation of [*methyl*-^{3}H]thymidine ([^{3}H]-TdR) into bacterial DNA (Moriarty, 1986), and the incorporation of [^{3}H]leucine into bacterial protein (Kirchman *et al.*, 1985, 1986). According to Riemann and Bell (1990), all three methods give complementary results, although there is controversy that the [^{3}H]adenine method actually measures total microbial production (Fuhrman *et al.*, 1986a,b; Karl and Winn, 1986). Of the two nucleic acid precursor methods, there are theoretical and procedural advantages in using [^{3}H]-TdR (Fuhrman and Azam, 1980; Moriarty, 1986). Despite being subject to criticism and controversy (e.g., Moriarty, 1986; Riemann and Bell, 1990; Brittain and Karl, 1990; see below), the [^{3}H]-TdR method has been used more frequently over the past 10 years than any other method to determine bacterial production (Ducklow and Carlson, 1992).

A number of reviews have examined and compared various methods to measure bacterial growth and activity (Van Es and Meyer-Reil, 1982; Azam and Fuhrman, 1984; Staley and Konopka, 1985; Moriarty, 1986; Reimann and Bell, 1990). However, an in-depth examination of recent advances and growing understanding of the thymidine method has not been made since Moriarty's (1986) review. A lot of information has been published in the intervening years but our understanding of the method when used with natural bacterial assemblages is still poor and the method remains controversial. In this review, we collate and examine new (post-1986) information on the thymidine method against a background of earlier studies, highlighting the theoretical principles, practical complexities, and controversial issues associated with the procedure. Ultimately, we assess the validity of the method and the question of whether our rapidly expanding knowledge of bacterial ecology as determined using labeled thymidine is fact or fiction.

2. Theoretical Basis for the Use of Thymidine

Growth in bacteria is marked by cell division and an increase in numbers and biomass of cells. Synthesis of new cell components such as peptidoglycan (walls), membranes, protein, RNA, and DNA must occur before cells divide. Measurement of the rate of DNA synthesis is related to cell division; once DNA synthesis has begun it proceeds to completion, culminating in cell division (Lark, 1969; O'Donovan, 1978; Moriarty, 1986). DNA synthesis does not occur in nongrowing cells (Brock, 1971). This means that bacterial growth rate can be measured from the rate of DNA synthesis (Moriarty, 1984) or, potentially, from the rate at which DNA becomes labeled with an exogenously supplied labeled precursor to DNA, such as [³H]-TdR.

Deoxythymidine (henceforth called thymidine) is the deoxyribonucleoside of the pyrimidine base thymine, in which the deoxyribose is conjugated to the base (thymine-2-deoxyribose, TdR) (Fig. 1). Thymidine is a unique nucleoside as the major function of its nucleotides in cells is participation in DNA synthesis. It also participates as dTDP-rhamnose in the biosynthesis of lipopolysaccharide carbohydrate (Gabriel, 1987). Thymine is specifically incorporated into DNA but exogenous sources cannot be incorporated into DNA without the simultaneous addition of a deoxyribonucleoside (AdR, GdR, IdR) to provide deoxyribose-1-phosphate required for the thymidine phosphorylase reaction (O'Donovan, 1978).

A basic assumption of the [³H]-TdR assay is that added [³H]-TdR is taken up by growing bacterial cells. Since nongrowing cells do not synthesize DNA, DNA and other macromolecules should not be significantly labeled above background with [³H]-TdR (Moriarty, 1986). Most of what little is known about pyrimidine nucleoside transport in bacteria comes from the studies of Munch-Petersen and Mygind (1983). As pointed out by Moriarty (1986), in *E. coli* thymidine is transported into the cell intact by an energy-dependent process. Moriarty noted that at least two different transport mechanisms were described by Munch-Peterson and Mygind (1983).

A fundamental knowledge of thymidine metabolism is essential for anyone who wishes to label DNA (O'Donovan, 1978). While the [³H]-TdR assay appears relatively simple, it is based on complex biochemistry [for a detailed review see O'Donovan and Neuhard (1970); additional information can be found in O'Donovan (1978), Moriarty (1986), and Kornberg and Baker (1992)]. Without this fundamental knowledge, users risk serious methodological errors (Kornberg and Baker, 1992), and, as this review will show, many have fallen afoul of these.

There are two principal pathways of nucleotide biosynthesis (Fig. 2) which are fundamental to the understanding and use of [³H]-TdR in measuring bacterial

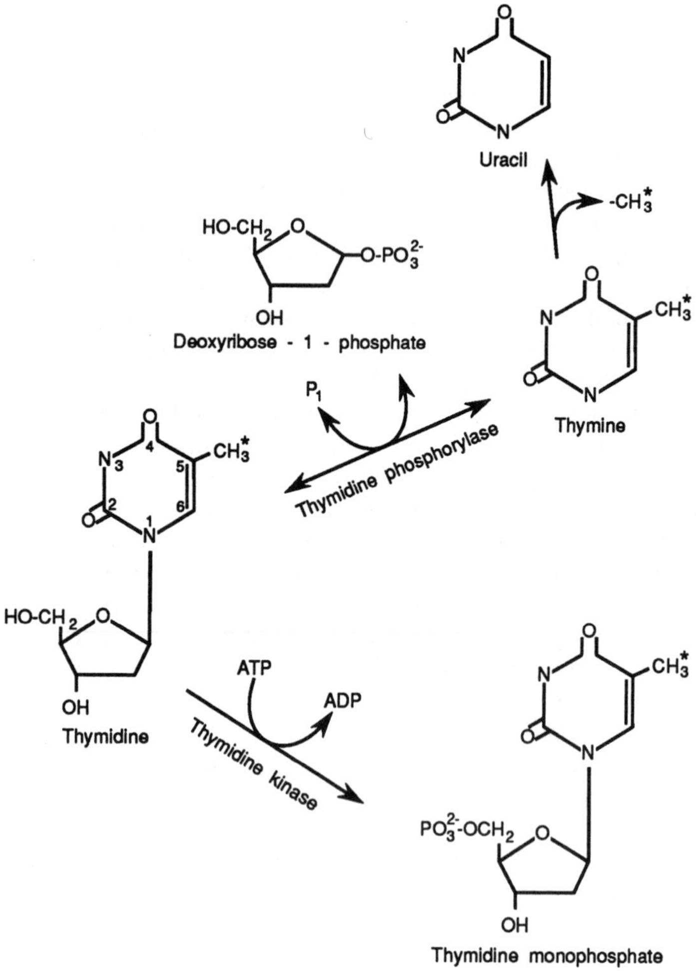

Figure 1. Reactions and structures of some compounds involving [*methyl*-^{3}H]thymidine ([^{3}H]-TdR). Location of label is indicated by an asterisk. (Modified from Moriarty, 1986.)

growth rates in natural assemblages. In the *de novo* pathway, internal cellular components (ribose phosphate, certain amino acids, CO_2, NH_3) are combined in successive reactions to synthesize nucleotides (Kornberg and Baker, 1992). Nucleotides formed by this pathway do not pass through a stage or pool containing free purine bases (adenine, guanine), pyrimidine bases (cytosine, uracil, thymine), or the corresponding nucleosides. With the salvage pathway, free bases and nucleosides arising from breakdown of excess nucleotides or nucleic acids

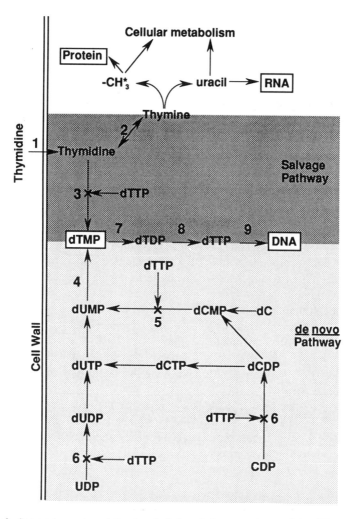

Figure 2. Some salvage, degradative (nonshaded), and *de novo* pathways of thymidine nucleotide metabolism in bacterial cells. The CH₃ group lost from thymine contains the ³H label, indicated by an asterisk. This is generally assumed to be the major pathway to account for nonspecific labeling but, in fact, may not be important as generally thought (see p. 376). *De novo* synthesis of dTMP from UDP is a minor pathway, accounting for only 20% of dTMP formation, compared with 80% of dTMP synthesis from CDP (O'Donovan, 1978). Sites where feedback inhibition occurs by dTTP are marked with an X. dTMP, dTDP, and dTTP are thymidine mono-, di-, and triphosphates, respectively; dUMP, dUDP, and dUTP are mono-, di-, and triphosphates of deoxyuridine; dC is deoxycytidine; dCMP, dCDP, and dCTP are mono-, di-, and triphosphates of deoxycytidine. Enzymes: 1, active transport mechanism; 2, thymidine phosphorylase; 3, thymidine kinase; 4, thymidylate synthetase; 5, deoxycytidylate deaminase; 6, ribonucleoside reductase; 7, dTMP kinase; 8, nucleoside diphosphate kinase; 9, DNA polymerase. (Modified from Moriarty, 1986, and Kornberg and Baker, 1992.)

are converted back to nucleotide triphosphates (Fig. 2). When present, the *de novo* routes of purine and pyrimidine nucleotide synthesis are virtually the same in all cells whereas the salvage routes are far more diverse in nature and distribution and knowledge of the enzymes involved is fragmentary (Kornberg and Baker, 1992). The [³H]-TdR assay is based on exogenously supplied thymidine (nucleoside) being incorporated into DNA via the salvage pathway (Fig. 2). Kornberg and Baker have stressed that the design and interpretation of labeling experiments must consider the details of salvage metabolism.

Once [³H]-TdR has been transported into the cell, it must be converted to dTMP (thymidine monophosphate or thymidylate) by the key salvage pathway enzyme, thymidine kinase. Thymidylate is subsequently converted to dTDP (thymidine diphosphate) by highly specific dTMP kinase and to dTTP (thymidine triphosphate) by nonspecific nucleoside diphosphate kinase in order to label DNA (Figs. 1 and 2). Therefore, only microorganisms that possess a transport system for thymidine, as well as thymidine kinase, are able to take up [³H]-TdR and incorporate it into DNA. A basic assumption of the [³H]-TdR assay is that most growing heterotrophic bacterial populations contain organisms with a thymidine transport system and thymidine kinase (see Section 4.3).

Although thymidine is readily incorporated into bacterial cells, incorporation stops after a short period because of its rapid breakdown in the cell to thymine by inducible thymidine phosphorylase (Figs. 1 and 2; O'Donovan, 1978). Thus, the [³H]-TdR assay for natural bacterial populations is a pulse labeling assay of short duration (minutes) after which the labeled DNA must be extracted and purified.

The thymidine used in ecological studies has the hydrogen of the methyl group labeled. Catabolism of thymidine to thymine and the further degradation of thymine can result in loss of the labeled methyl group. Label may be incorporated into protein or used in other cellular metabolic processes (Fig. 2). This nonspecific labeling of macromolecules other than DNA may be extensive but the mechanism(s) by which this is achieved is largely unknown. Very few microorganisms, with the major exception of fungi, are known to demethylate thymine so that the importance of this proposed pathway (Fig. 2) for nonspecific labeling is unknown (Vogels and van der Drift, 1976; G. A. O'Donovan, personal communication). As nonspecific labeling can be extensive with natural populations, it is essential that labeled DNA be extracted from cells and purified. Following the degradation of thymine, there are no direct routes for the label to be incorporated into RNA or DNA but greatly diluted label will be found in these and all cellular compounds if the methyl group enters the general pool of metabolites (Moriarty, 1986).

Dilution of the rate of DNA labeling by [³H]-TdR can occur in several ways: (1) through the action of thymidylate synthetase where dTMP is generated from dUMP (deoxyuridine monophosphate) (*de novo* pathway, Fig. 2) and mixed with dTMP formed by thymidine kinase from [³H]-TdR (salvage pathway, Fig. 2). The specific activity of dTTP must be known to calculate the rate of DNA synthesis from [³H]-TdR incorporation. (2) There are also interactions between nucleosides during uptake by the cell and competition between thymidine and uridine during transport has been reported (Moriarty, 1986). The extent of DNA labeling by [³H]-TdR could therefore be influenced by the presence of other nucleosides in the environment external to the cell. This has been observed for sediment bacteria (Moriarty, 1986) but seems to be the only such case. However, Moriarty concluded that the major dilution of [³H]-TdR is likely to occur at the synthesis of dTMP where the *de novo* and salvage pathways converge (Fig. 2).

It is obvious that it is essential that the *de novo* pathway be blocked while labeling bacterial DNA with [³H]-TdR and only the salvage pathway is operational, otherwise major underestimations of DNA synthesis may be observed. Thymidine triphosphate is an important regulator of pyrimidine nucleotide biosynthesis and an increase in the dTTP pool size will slow or turn off the supply of dTMP by *de novo* synthesis (Fig. 2; Moriarty, 1986). If sufficient [³H]-TdR is added to natural samples, it is generally assumed (see Moriarty, 1986) that *de novo* synthesis can be inhibited and isotope dilution (both internal and external) be prevented (see Section 4.2). However, Beacham *et al.* (1971) and others (see O'Donovan, 1978) have found that increasing the concentration of exogenously supplied thymidine decreases the dTTP pool indicating that thymidine inhibits a step in its own conversion to dTTP. For maximum incorporation of label, the *lowest possible* concentration of [³H]-TdR should be used (O'Donovan, 1978) but it is possible that such a concentration may not be high enough to completely inhibit *de novo* synthesis.

Moriarty (1986) has argued that the specific activity of dTTP will be equivalent to that of the [³H]-TdR added so that only measurement of labeled DNA will be needed. This resolves the technical problem with natural samples of having to separate bacteria from other microorganisms to measure the specific activity of bacterial dTTP.

3. Historical Development of the [³H]-TdR Assay for Bacterial Growth Estimates in Natural Systems

Heterotrophic bacterial populations in natural environments are generally heterogeneous both in terms of species and metabolic capabilities and states, and usually coexist with other microorganisms. According to Azam and Fuhrman (1984), any suitable method for measuring bacterial production must have the following prerequisites: (1) the method must be specific for bacteria; (2) it must be applicable for a variety of growth states, not just balanced growth; (3) experimental manipulation of samples must be minimal in order to prevent significant changes in growth rate; and (4) the method should have demonstrable reliability, precision, and sensitivity. In theory, the measurement of [*methyl*-^{3}H]thymidine incorporation is the method which best satisfies these criteria.

The [^{3}H]-TdR assay for bacterial growth rate determination basically involves the pulse labeling of cells in sediment, soil, or water samples. [^{3}H]-TdR is added at concentrations high enough (see p. 377 and Section 4.2) to block dilution by external and internal (*de novo* synthesis) sources. Samples are incubated for a set period, usually less than 1 hr, and the labeled DNA and other macromolecules are recovered from water samples either as an ice-cold TCA (trichloroacetic acid) precipitate or labeled DNA is extracted and purified. More complicated procedures are required for soil and sediment samples but these are based on the same principle. Growth and production rates are then calculated by means of established conversion factors.

Although a number of procedures exist for the extraction of DNA from bacterial cells (Hutchison and Munro, 1961), microbial ecologists working with natural populations have until recently used modifications of the methods of either Schmidt and Thannhauser (1945) or Schneider (1945). The Schmidt–Thannhauser method uses cold acid to extract macromolecules, alkaline hydrolysis to separate RNA from DNA, and cold acid to precipitate DNA. Schneider's method differs in that it uses hot acid to extract nucleic acids from cells.

Hutchison and Munro (1961) concluded that there was irrefutable evidence that the Schneider extraction procedure can result in both incomplete extraction of DNA (e.g., Roodyn and Mandel, 1960) and destruction of deoxyribose leading to underestimates of DNA concentration. Furthermore, Servais *et al.* (1987) have demonstrated that extracted and purified labeled DNA is incompletely hydrolyzed in hot 5% TCA, leading to underestimates of the rate of DNA synthesis. Yet, some microbial ecologists continue to use this procedure, even for bacterioplankton samples (e.g., Findlay *et al.*, 1991) where collection of labeled DNA could be effectively done using cellulose nitrate membrane filters. It is for these reasons that it is unfortunate that Wetzel and Likens (1991) in their textbook recommended the use of hot acid extraction of [^{3}H]-TdR-labeled macromolecules.

The Schmidt–Thannhauser method also has weaknesses. Roodyn and Mandel (1960) noted that their study, and several others, showed "RNA" in this procedure was contaminated with protein breakdown products. DNA is not completely dissolved out of the cells of some bacteria, such as *Bacillus cereus,* with alkali (Roodyn and Mandel, 1960). DNA is also very labile to acid and easily fragments on subsequent treatment with alkali; these fragments appear in the RNA fraction (Moriarty, 1986). Hutchison and Munro (1961) have noted that there is evidence to show that RNA hydrolysis is often incomplete with this procedure which would also bias estimates of the amount of DNA labeled.

Many aquatic ecologists using [^{3}H]-TdR have reversed the initial steps of the Schmidt–Thannhauser method when attempting to isolate labeled DNA and applied alkali first and then acid. This modification, intended to increase the amount of labeled DNA extracted, is generally referred to as the acid–base hydrolysis method. Others have dropped the alkali step altogether, precipitated the labeled macromolecules in cold TCA, and assumed DNA comprised a fixed proportion of the precipitate. This procedure is referred to as the cold TCA precipitate method.

The concept of using [³H]-TdR to measure bacterial growth rates has been adapted by microbial ecologists working in a diversity of environments. Procedures for recovering macromolecules labeled by [³H]-TdR have been developed for water, sediment, and soil populations as well as for epiphytic and epilithic populations. In the following sections we review the historical development of these procedures.

3.1. Water Samples

To our knowledge, Brock (1967) was the first to use the incorporation of [³H]-TdR into DNA as a measure of heterotrophic bacterial production in natural environments. He used [³H]-TdR in conjunction with autoradiography to calculate the growth rate of the marine epiphyte *Leucothrix mucor*. Later a relationship between the incorporation rate of [³H]-TdR into TCA-insoluble macromolecules by bacterial cultures and growth rate was established by Kunicka-Goldfinger (1976).

Hollibaugh *et al.* (1980) labeled natural assemblages of marine bacteria with [³H]-TdR to determine the grazing rates of microzooplankton. Separation of labeled DNA, RNA, and proteins was done using acid–base hydrolysis procedures: the radioactivity in all three macromolecules was determined by placing an aliquot of water with labeled bacteria in an equal volume of ice-cold 10% TCA and extracting for 3 min at 0°C. Ice-cold 5% TCA makes the cells permeable to small molecules without hydrolyzing macromolecules. The precipitated labeled macromolecules were collected on HA Millipore filters (mixed cellulose acetate and cellulose nitrate). A second aliquot was used to determine labeled DNA and protein by hydrolyzing RNA in 0.5 N NaOH at 60°C for 30 min, precipitating the labeled DNA and protein in TCA at 0°C, and collecting these on membrane filters. Labeled protein was determined by hydrolyzing both DNA and RNA in 5% TCA at 100°C for 30 min. The solution was then chilled and the precipitated protein was collected on a membrane filter. Label appearing in DNA and RNA was found by subtraction. Hollibaugh *et al.* found that uptake and incorporation of [³H]-TdR was linear for 1 hr, 37% of the label taken up appeared in macromolecules and that of this amount, 82% appeared in the DNA fraction.

Fuhrman and Azam (1980) incubated coastal bacterioplankton samples (in conjunction with the study of Hollibaugh *et al.*, 1980) with [³H]-TdR to estimate bacterial production. After incubation periods of a few minutes to a few hours, subsamples were chilled on ice for 1 min before an equal volume of ice-cold 10% TCA was added. After 5 min on ice, the mixture was filtered through an HA Millipore filter and rinsed twice with ice-cold 5% TCA. Antarctic marine samples were incubated with [³H]-TdR for up to 36 hr. Subsamples were removed and filtered through membrane filters and washed twice with ice-cold 5% TCA. After this, the funnel was removed and the filter edge was washed twice with ice-cold 5% TCA and twice with ice-cold 95% ethanol.

In a subsequent paper, Fuhrman and Azam (1982) modified the cold TCA precipitation procedure by adding a carrier solution of 50 μg calf thymus DNA + 50 μg bovine serum albumin in 50 μl of 0.1 N NH₄OH to aid precipitation of labeled macromolecules. In order to separate labeled DNA, RNA, and proteins, they used protocols that were modified slightly from those of Hollibaugh *et al.* (1980).

Karl (1982) terminated bacterial incorporation of [³H]-TdR either by adding an equal volume of ice-cold 10% TCA or by filtering labeled cells onto Whatman GF/F filters and then extracting them with ice-cold 5% TCA. In addition, he added 1 mg of nonlabeled RNA, DNA, and protein to each sample prior to collecting the precipitate to catalyze the precipitation and aid the quantitative separation and recoveries of the labeled macromolecules. Karl reported that this step increased the recovery of labeled DNA, RNA, and proteins by as much as 38%.

Fuhrman and Azam's (1980, 1982) papers were instrumental in the enhancement of studies on bacterial production in aquatic environments. However, they also had the effect of lulling microbial ecologists into believing that it was now an easy process to obtain accurate measures of bacterial production—add a small amount of [³H]-TdR, incubate for a few minutes, extract in ice-cold TCA, collect the material on membrane filters, and convert to cells produced (see Section 4.5), was the general recipe being proselytized. Fuhrman and Azam (1980), however, noted that [³H]-TdR incorporation as measured in cold TCA-insoluble material is not necessarily a direct measure of DNA synthesis or production. They made the following assumptions to convert their [³H]-TdR incorporation rates to production estimates:

1. Bacteria were the only microorganisms which incorporated [³H]-TdR added at nanomolar concentrations.
2. All growing bacteria utilized [³H]-TdR.
3. Labeled DNA comprised 80% of the total labeled macromolecules in the cold TCA precipitate, as determined by Hollibaugh *et al.* (1980).
4. The specific activity of added [³H]-TdR was unaffected by ambient thymidine.

5. Total bacterial DNA contained 25 mole% thymidylic acid residues, a mean value taken from the literature and which remains an acceptable estimate today (G. A. O'Donovan, personal communication).
6. The amount of DNA per cell ranged from 7.47×10^{-16} to 4.82×10^{-15} g, the range of genome size which had been reported for nonphotosynthetic prokaryotes.

The combination of these assumptions yielded a conversion factor of 2.0×10^{17} to 1.3×10^{18} cells produced per mole of [^{3}H]-TdR incorporated (see also Section 4.5).

Extraction and Purification of Labeled DNA

The amount of [^{3}H]-TdR incorporated into DNA must be determined for correct conversion to production rates, although this is disputed by Riemann (1984) and Riemann and Bell (1990). In studies of bacterial production in water samples following Fuhrman and Azam, most users of the [^{3}H]-TdR method employed the simple cold TCA precipitate procedure and assumed a constant proportion of DNA based on either a literature value or one that they initially derived using acid–base hydrolysis. However, the acid–base hydrolysis procedure did not extract and purify labeled DNA but only estimated it by subtracting the amounts of label appearing in the "protein" precipitate from that in the "DNA + protein" precipitate. Several workers have derived methods to extract and purify labeled DNA.

In order to separate labeled DNA, RNA, and proteins, Karl (1982) first washed samples three times with 5% TCA and twice with 95% ethanol before evaporating them *in vacuo*. The TCA-insoluble material was then hydrolyzed in 1 N NaOH for 1 hr at 37°C. The solution was acidified and centrifuged and the resulting pellet, containing labeled DNA and protein (the supernatant contained RNA), was washed twice with 5% TCA and twice with 95% ethanol (all at 4°C). The pellet was then dried *in vacuo* and extracted in hot (100°C) 5% TCA for 30 min to hydrolyze the DNA. The supernatant was assayed for labeled DNA content while the pellet was extracted in NaOH at 37°C for 18 hr, centrifuged, and the supernatant collected for assaying of labeled protein content.

Karl's (1982) use of the Schmidt–Thannhauser method has been criticized by Moriarty (1986) because of its inherent weaknesses, as noted above, which Moriarty claims partially account for the extensive nonspecific labeling, i.e., the labeling of macromolecules other than DNA, reported by Karl.

Witzel and Graf (1984) proposed adsorbing labeled DNA onto a hydroxylapatite column, after grinding labeled cells collected on filters with sea sand at low temperatures, and subsequent elution with phosphate buffer. This method, as noted by Servais *et al.* (1987), is tedious and impractical for large series of samples. More importantly, RNA and DNA are not quantitatively separated and grinding cells in alumina or glass powder yields a DNA of lower molecular weight than the DNA released by enzyme or detergent lysis (Burnison and Nuttley, 1990).

Servais et al. (1987) developed a method in which a water sample was split into two fractions after the cells had been labeled with [³H]-TdR. Labeled bacteria in the one sample were lysed with detergent and then incubated with DNase to selectively hydrolyze DNA. The macromolecules in both the DNase-treated and untreated samples were precipitated in cold TCA. The amount of labeled DNA was determined from the difference in radioactivity between the treated and untreated samples. Our experience using nucleases with wild populations is that the results are highly variable (Wicks and Robarts, unpublished data). Constant adjustments to the amount of DNase, the incubation conditions, and the amount of sample used necessitated the use of large numbers of replicates.

Wicks and Robarts (1987) used NaOH followed by ice-cold TCA to lyse bacterial cells and precipitate labeled DNA and other macromolecules. The precipitate was collected on cellulose nitrate filters (0.2-μm pore size), washed with 5 ml of 50% (w/v) phenol–chloroform to remove labeled proteins (Maniatis et al., 1982) and 5 ml of ice-cold 80% ethanol to remove labeled lipids (Robarts and Wicks, 1989). Results of DNase digestion experiments indicated that the precipitate contained only labeled DNA. The method is simple and adaptable to field use as the labeled DNA can be preserved with NaOH for at least 24 hr without significant losses (Wicks and Robarts, 1987).

Burnison and Nuttley (1990) modified Witzel and Graf's (1984) hydroxylapatite chromatography method to reliably separate labeled DNA from other labeled macromolecules without the use of acid–base hydrolysis or volatile organic solvents. Labeled cells were lysed with lysozyme, freeze-thaw and sonication procedures. The cellular contents were suspended in sodium phosphate buffer with urea and then added to small glass columns containing hydroxylapatite. This method seems to effectively separate labeled DNA from other labeled macromolecules, recovers > 93% of DNA, has low control values, and variance between replicates for both control and live values is low. Because the method does not use harsh bases, acids, or organic solvents, Burnison and Nuttley (1990) believe the procedure is readily adaptable to field use, although it is also relatively complex and time-consuming.

Burnison and Nuttley (1990) have criticized Wicks and Robarts's (1987) method not only because it requires strong acid, base, and volatile organic solutions, but also because of the relatively low level of DNA recovery (average 75%) and high and variable sample and control values. However, Burnison and Nuttley's data are independent confirmation of two important points: (1) that the labeled material from the Wicks and Robarts method is only labeled DNA and (2) that the recovery values estimated by Wicks and Robarts are correct. Torréton and Bouvy (1991) have found that for bacterioplankton from a tropical lagoon, phenol–chloroform did not completely remove all labeled protein resulting in a small contamination of the DNA fraction with what they described as an otherwise efficient extraction procedure.

The high background values with the Wicks and Robarts (1987) procedure are caused by the adsorption of unincorporated [3H]-TdR to dissolved organic matter and to cellulose nitrate filters. These filters also bind DNA and were chosen for that reason. However, our experience in a wide range of natural systems is that while the values are high they are relatively constant for a given [3H]-TdR concentration and that this has been the experience of other researchers (R. T. Bell, personal communication). It is also our experience that careful application of the method would produce variability between replicate samples of < 10% and frequently ≤5.

In our recent work in the ultraoligotrophic Eastern Mediterranean Sea we have modified the Wicks and Robarts (1987) method (Fig. 3). By using a larger volume of water, the amount of incorporated label to be measured is increased relative to controls. The procedure also reduces the possibility of label carryover which in oligotrophic samples could be crucial to sensitivity and variability. In order to reduce the adsorption of unincorporated label to the membrane filters, we soak filters in sterile sample water containing cold TdR. In our tests in the Eastern Mediterranean this significantly reduced the control value (Table I) and similar results have been found in other aquatic environments (R. T. Bell, personal communication).

From our experience with the use of [3H]-TdR in Canadian prairie saline lakes, which contain high concentrations of DOC (> 25 mg C/liter^{-1}), we found that control values can be reduced from 20,000–100,000 dpm to 100–400 dpm on 47-mm-diameter cellulose nitrate membrane filters by adding 500 μl of formaldehyde to water samples (10 ml) for 5 min prior to the addition of NaOH when using the Wicks and Robarts (1987) DNA extraction procedure (Waiser and Robarts, unpublished data). Alongi (1988) reported that the addition of formaldehyde saturated with cold thymidine to mangrove sediment samples decreased label adsorption to sediment clay and tannins. High and variable control values are a methodological problem which can be resolved to increase the sensitivity and reliability of the [3H]-TdR assay.

3.2. Sediment and Soil Samples

It is more difficult to measure bacterial rates of DNA synthesis in sediments than in water because [3H]-TdR adsorbs to humic acids and inorganic components of sediments such as clays and hydrous oxides and DNA is difficult to extract (Moriarty and Pollard, 1990). [3H]-TdR has been used infrequently to obtain soil bacterial population growth and production rates. In addition, bacteria

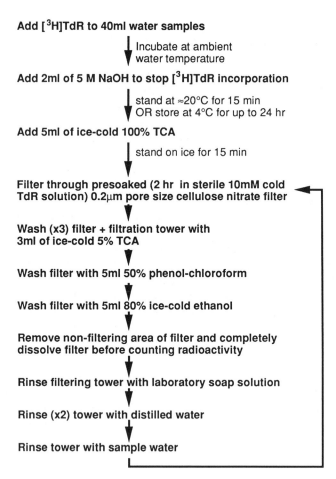

Figure 3. Protocol for [³H]-TdR labeling of bacterial DNA and its extraction and purification from cells in oligotrophic waters. The protocol is a modification of the method of Wicks and Robarts (1987). [³H]-TdR is added at a final concentration of 20 nM, or as determined by isotope dilution experiments (see Section 4.2), using high-specific-activity thymidine (i.e., 70–90 Ci/nmole). Reagents: 100% TCA = 100 g TCA made up to 100 ml water; 50% phenol–chloroform = 50 g phenol made up to 100 ml with chloroform; 80% ethanol = 80 ml ethanol plus 20 ml water. Filters can be dissolved in ethyl acetate (0.7 ml) or appropriate scintillation fluor (e.g., Canberra Packard's Filter Count). Vortex the solution to ensure the filter dissolves completely.

in sediments live in marked gradients of oxygen and nutrients and when these are disturbed changes in growth rate may occur. In order to create the minimal amount of disturbance, Findlay *et al.* (1985) recommend that labeled solutions be injected into sediment cores. This creates concentration gradients which can influence the measured rate of incorporation, e.g., at the point farthest from the

**Table I. The Effect of Presoaking Cellulose
Nitrate Membrane Filters in Cold Thymidine
($\sim$10 mM for $\sim$2 hr) on the Amount of [^{3}H]-TdR
(dpm) Adsorbed to Filters in Control Samples Killed
at Time Zero with 5 N NaOH[a]**

Filters presoaked in:	Mean	S.D.	No. of cases
Sterile seawater	1147	417	46
Sterile seawater + 10 mM thymidine	152	97	69

[a]Data obtained with water samples from the Eastern Mediterranean Sea.

site of injection the concentration of [^{3}H]-TdR may not be great enough to inhibit *de novo* synthesis (see Section 4.2).

Moriarty and Pollard (1990) recommend that [^{3}H]-TdR be mixed with sediment to ensure even distribution at a high enough concentration to prevent isotope dilution. While a change in the rate of DNA synthesis will probably occur, there is a lag period between the disturbance and the change (Moriarty, 1986; Moriarty and Pollard, 1990). Moriarty and Pollard tested three means of measuring bacterial production in sediments and concluded that small sediment cores mixed into a small amount of filtered, overlying water created the least amount of disturbance. They also noted that disturbance effects could be greatest for anaerobic sediments and that time course studies should be undertaken to determine the best incubation time for specific sediments.

Thomas *et al.* (1974) measured bacterial growth in soils by flooding small samples with [^{3}H]-TdR. They extracted the labeled DNA using hot 5% TCA and precipitated it as copper nucleate. DNA is not effectively extracted in hot acid, a procedural error repeated by later researchers, leading to underestimates of the rate of DNA labeling (Hutchison and Munro, 1961; Munro and Fleck, 1966; Servais *et al.*, 1987; Moriarty and Pollard, 1990).

Tobin and Anthony (1978) used [^{3}H]-TdR as a measure of microbial activity in Lake Erie sediments. Unlike Thomas *et al.*, Tobin and Anthony did not use hot acid extraction to recover labeled DNA but instead terminated their incubations with NaOH which was used to hydrolyze RNA and solubilize DNA. They used a series of acid washes (5% ice-cold TCA) followed by centrifugation to purify labeled DNA. Enzymatic and chromatographic techniques indicated that > 93% of recovered label appeared in DNA.

Moriarty and Pollard (1981) took cores from a seagrass bed and slurried them with [^{3}H]-TdR. Extraction of labeled DNA was done using modifications of Tobin and Anthony's (1978) procedure. Incubation was terminated by addition of 0.6 M NaOH and the mixture was heated at 100°C for 4 hr, centrifuged, and the supernatants dialyzed overnight against running water. Acid was added to the supernatant which was cooled on ice to precipitate labeled macromolecules (assumed to be DNA based on Tobin and Anthony's data) which were collected on glass fiber filters. Labeled DNA was then hydrolyzed in hot 5% TCA for liquid scintillation counting. However, Servais *et al.* (1987) have shown that this type of treatment does not completely hydrolyze DNA after 2 hr which could mean that the rate of DNA synthesis was underestimated. Indeed, Moriarty (1984) notes that DNA recovery varied from 40 to 70% and was generally 55 ± 5%.

Findlay *et al.* (1984) proposed an acid–base hydrolysis procedure which they described as a more efficient method to recover labeled DNA from sediments. Sediments were first washed with cold 5% TCA to remove unincorporated [^{3}H]-TdR. They found that the extraction of DNA with 0.6 N NaOH at 37°C yielded poor recoveries and a large proportion of DNA was degraded. Instead, extraction with 0.3 N NaOH + 25 mM EDTA + 0.1% SDS at 25°C for 12 hr gave maximal recovery and a yield of 75% which was contrary to Bell and Ahlgren's (1987) results showing extraction was maximal (84 ± 7% S.D.) with 0.6 N NaOH at a temperature of 100°C for 1 hr. Findlay *et al.* then centrifuged the mixture, chilled the supernatant to 0°C, neutralized it with HCl, added TCA to a final concentration of 5%, added carrier DNA to aid precipitation, and then centrifuged. DNA was hydrolyzed in hot 5% TCA, but other researchers (e.g., Tibbles *et al.*, 1992) using Findlay and colleagues' method have instead collected the DNA on membrane filters to eliminate the problem of incomplete DNA hydrolysis (see Section 4.1). Recovery efficiencies for DNA from both a high organic sediment and sandy sediment were about 75% (Findlay *et al.*, 1984) but no chromatographic or enzymatic data were provided to demonstrate the purity of the labeled product referred to as DNA. Findlay *et al.* also applied a similar extraction scheme to water column bacteria which had been collected on polycarbonate filters, the major difference being that the extraction time in NaOH was only 15 min.

A major problem in using [^{3}H]-TdR with sediments is removing all of the unincorporated label. Findlay *et al.* (1984) found that their procedure did not remove all of the label adsorbed to sediment. It is for this reason that Moriarty and Pollard (1981) used dialysis in their extraction procedure. To this end, Pollard (1987) designed a dialysis membrane and diffusion system which allows the dialysis of a large number of samples over the 16 hr required to remove the unincorporated label. This technique is particularly useful in marine sediments composed of coralline sandy material where acid reacts with $CaCO_3$ (Pollard and Kogure, 1993).

Thorn and Ventullo (1988) measured bacterial growth rates in subsurface soils from several sites in the United States. Thorn and Ventullo used modifications of the methods of Moriarty and Pollard (1981) and Findlay *et al.* (1984). With both methods they collected the labeled DNA on cellulose nitrate filters rather than hydrolyze it. They found that the harsher extraction conditions with

Moriarty and Pollard's method gave a DNA recovery of $<$ 1 to 18% while the Findlay *et al.* method recovered 62 to 77% of labeled DNA. DNA extraction efficiencies differed markedly between sediment types with silt-clay sediments generally giving lower efficiencies than sandy sediments, which was contrary to the results of Fallon *et al.* (1983). In addition, Thorn and Ventullo also found that the addition of carrier DNA and unlabeled thymidine was necessary for optimal macromolecule recovery: the carrier DNA promotes precipitation of low concentrations of macromolecules in TCA while cold thymidine minimizes control values by reducing nonspecific binding of [^{3}H]-TdR.

Christensen *et al.* (1989) estimated growth rates of a species they identified as *Pseudomonas* (which do not contain thymidine kinase and are therefore incapable of incorporating [^{3}H]-TdR, see Section 4.3.1) in the rhizosphere of sugar beet roots by subtracting [^{3}H]-TdR incorporation in soil with roots from that in soil without roots. They used the acid–base procedure of Riemann (1984), with modifications from the method of Findlay *et al.* (1984), but found that labeled DNA was not extracted efficiently using 1 N NaOH at 60°C without first homogenizing the soil.

Bååth and Johansson (1990) used [^{3}H] TdR to measure bacterial growth rates on the rhizoplane of rape seedlings grown in sand. They extracted DNA using the method of Findlay *et al.* (1984) with some modifications. They were able to recover 81% of [^{14}C]-DNA from these soils.

Bååth and Johansson (1990) found that axenic rape seedling roots incorporated [^{3}H]-TdR into DNA, but always less than roots with bacteria. They noted that this plant incorporation would be especially important in the root tip region where DNA synthesis takes place. If roots are present in an environment, care should be exercised in interpreting bacterial [^{3}H]-TdR incorporation data.

Bååth (1990) measured bacterial growth rates in a sandy loam soil and a forest humus using [^{3}H]-TdR and the acid–base hydrolysis procedure of Findlay *et al.* (1984). Bååth recommended that bacterial ecologists using [^{3}H]-TdR in soils should use acid–base hydrolysis to purify DNA because of extensive nonspecific labeling of protein.

Bååth (1990) also noted that [^{3}H]-TdR incorporation data for the humus were more uncertain than for the sandy loam soil because (1) the recovery of [^{14}C]-DNA was 58% from the humus and 75% from the soil and (2) statistical variation was higher because of high zero-time control values, probably caused by nonspecific binding of [^{3}H]-TdR to organic matter. This nonspecific binding appeared to be correlated with the amount of organic matter in a sample. Although attempts to lower zero-time controls by adding large amounts of unlabeled thymidine with formaldehyde were unsuccessful, Bååth found that the addition of small amounts of humus reduced control values. Bååth concluded that the [^{3}H]-TdR technique appears most reliable for soil with low organic matter content.

Albrechtsen and Winding (1992) used [³H]-TdR to measure bacterial growth rates in glaciofluvial sediments. [³H]-TdR was added to sediment slurries at a concentration of 202 nM (isotope dilution was not estimated) and samples were incubated for 16 hr at 10°C. The rate of DNA labeling was linear over this time period. Labeled DNA was extracted using the method of Thorn and Ventullo (1988) except that instead of collecting the DNA on membrane filters they hydrolyzed it in hot TCA. This procedure, together with the lack of correction for isotope dilution (see Section 4.2), probably resulted in their underestimating the rate of DNA labeling and bacterial production (see Section 3.1).

3.3 Epilithic and Epiphytic Bacteria

Labeled thymidine has been used to measure bacterial production in attached marine algal–bacterial consortia (Murray *et al.*, 1986, 1987), in Antarctic cyanobacterial mats (Vincent and Howard-Williams, 1989), and in epiphytic bacteria on *Spartina alterniflora* (Fallon and Newell, 1986) and epilithic consortia on rocks in streams (Stock and Ward, 1989; Hudson *et al.*, 1990). Production in these studies was determined either from the label in cold TCA precipitates using modifications of the Fuhrman and Azam (1980) method (Murray *et al.*, 1986, 1987; Vincent and Howard-Williams, 1989) or from the rate of DNA labeling (Fallon and Newell, 1986) as determined by the acid–base hydrolysis procedures used by Fuhrman and Azam (1982). Stock and Ward (1989) and Hudson *et al.* (1990) used modifications of the Findlay *et al.* (1984) method to extract labeled DNA. Hudson *et al.* collected labeled DNA on cellulose nitrate filters instead of hydrolyzing it. However, even with this change they reported lower DNA recoveries ($\bar{x} = 58 \pm 11\%$) than those reported for sediments or waters.

Although Murray *et al.* (1987) reported that physical disruption of attached bacteria produced [³H]-TdR incorporation rates four to five times higher than populations that had not been disrupted, Hudson *et al.* found that breaking rocks into small fragments did not affect the rate of DNA labeling by epilithic bacteria.

3.4. Conclusion

A remarkably wide range of modifications of the acid–base hydrolysis procedure have been adopted and as a result comparisons between different studies are difficult and should be undertaken with caution. There is an urgency for microbial ecologists to adopt a single methodology for planktonic and for sediment/soil bacterial populations.

4. Factors Affecting Growth Rate and Production Estimates

A number of factors, apart from the problems described above in recovering the label from bacterial cells, can affect estimates of bacterial growth rate and production when using [^{3}H]-TdR with natural microbial consortia. These rates may be underestimated because of the labeling of macromolecules other than DNA (nonspecific labeling), dilution of the label by other sources, and the presence of bacteria not able to take up and incorporate [^{3}H]-TdR. On the other hand, bacterial production and growth rates may be overestimated if organisms other than bacteria take up significant amounts of [^{3}H]-TdR. We examine each of these factors and assess their impact on the validity of using [^{3}H]-TdR to determine bacterial production and growth rates.

4.1. Nonspecific Labeling

Hollibaugh *et al.* (1980) found that the incorporation of [^{3}H]-TdR into macromolecules was linear for 1 hr and that 82% of the label was present in the DNA fraction. After 6 hr only 28% of [^{3}H]-TdR was found in the DNA fraction. In addition, Hollibaugh *et al.* found that bacteria released both volatile and nonvolatile ^{3}H-labeled substances during the first hour of incubation and that these were taken up by bacteria.

In a follow-up study, Fuhrman and Azam (1982) noted that measuring [^{3}H]-TdR in only cold TCA precipitates sacrifices some precision for the sake of convenience and quick results. They referred to their earlier work (cited in Fuhrman and Azam, 1980, as unpublished data) which indicated that 80–95% of the TCA precipitate was labeled DNA. Subsequent experiments indicated that the average percentage of labeled DNA in the cold TCA precipitate was 84% with one sample having a value of $\sim$ 65%.

On the basis of Fuhrman and Azam's (1982) work, most bacterial ecologists assumed that the bulk of the label in cold TCA precipitates was DNA and in their calculations used a constant percentage. Others, however, attempted to use acid–base hydrolysis to separate out the label appearing in DNA, RNA, and proteins (see Sections 3.1–3.3)—the possibility of other labeled macromolecules appearing in the cold TCA precipitate was generally ignored. This mistaken interpretation of Fuhrman and Azam's paper also disregarded information in Schmidt and Thannhauser (1945), Schneider (1945), and studies of bacterial biosynthesis such as Roberts *et al.* (1963). Also ignored was the biochemical basis of the thymidine method (Fig. 2), which purposely employs labeled-methyl thymidine in short, pulse experiments to minimize the labeling of other macromolecules, especially RNA.

In reviewing the literature, Brittain and Karl (1990) found that the distribution of tritium in acid-insoluble materials ranged from 0 to 90% in DNA, 20 to

79% in RNA, and 20 to 100% in protein for marine systems; from 0 to 103% in DNA, 1 to 72% in RNA, and 0 to 49% in protein for freshwater systems; and in marine sediments the distribution was 0 to 35% in DNA, 34 to 67% in RNA, and 20 to 59% in protein. Some studies have reported that this distribution varies over diel cycles; e.g., Riemann *et al.* (1982) found the percentage labeling of DNA to be 18 to 38% and Jeffrey *et al.* (1990) measured a range of about 20 to 80%. However, few studies have used enzymatic and/or chromatographic techniques to confirm nonspecific labeling thereby ignoring the many potential problems in separating macromolecules with acid–base hydrolysis (see Hutchison and Munro, 1961; Section 3).

Witzel and Graf (1984) reported the presence of ^3H from [^3H]-TdR in DNA, RNA, and other macromolecules on the basis of hydroxylapatite chromatography. However, as already noted, this method did not quantitatively separate RNA and DNA (Burnison and Nuttley, 1990). Riemann (1984) used DNase and RNase to determine the macromolecular composition of the precipitates from acid–base hydrolysis procedures and found that the [^3H]-RNA fraction was < 7%.

Using acid–base hydrolysis procedures, Robarts *et al.* (1986) carried out time course experiments to determine the distribution of ^3H from [^3H]-TdR in macromolecules of bacteria from a hypertrophic reservoir (Fig. 4). No consistent pattern with time was found, with the percentage ^3H in DNA ranging from 0 to 39.1% while the RNA fraction contained up to 98.1% and the protein fraction up to 80.6%. These data were similar to seasonal patterns obtained from the same reservoir (Fig. 4). The immediate question then became whether these macromolecular labeling patterns were real or an artifact of the acid–base hydrolysis procedures. In contrast to the inconsistent DNA labeling pattern by [^3H]-TdR using acid–base hydrolysis, the modified method by Wicks and Robarts (1987) produces linear labeling for extended periods in a wide variety of environments (Fig. 5; see also Wicks and Robarts, 1987; Bell and Riemann, 1989).

Robarts *et al.* (1986) used enzymatic and chromatographic techniques to analyze precipitates from acid–base hydrolysis procedures and concluded that these procedures are not adequate for quantifying labeled DNA in the presence of other labeled macromolecules, a conclusion also made by Torréton and Bouvy (1991). In cold TCA precipitates, Robarts *et al.* found no RNA, 24% DNA, 6% protein, 37% ethanol-soluble products (assumed to be lipids), 11% $KHCO_3$-soluble products, and 22% of the label remained unaccounted. These data confirmed earlier studies by others (e.g., Roodyn and Mandel, 1960; Roberts *et al.*, 1963) that macromolecules other than DNA can be labeled by [^3H]-TdR and with short incubation times and nanomolar concentrations of [^3H]-TdR RNA is not significantly labeled as predicted by Moriarty (1986). The fraction called RNA by bacterial ecologists using the acid–base hydrolysis procedure was probably labeled lipids and other macromolecules.

Recently several studies have indicated RNA labeled with [^3H]-TdR using

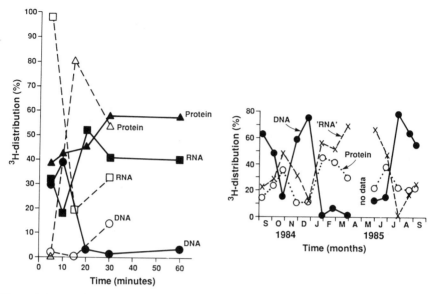

Figure 4. Time course (left panel) and seasonal (right panel) incorporation of [³H]-TdR into macromolecules of bacteria from an African reservoir as determined by acid–base hydrolysis. Broken lines in the left panel are for a May water sample and solid lines are for an October sample. (Data from Robarts *et al.*, 1986; right panel modified from Robarts *et al.*, 1986.)

Figure 5. Time course of [³H]-TdR incorporation into DNA of bacteria from two Canadian saline lakes [Humboldt (hypereutrophic) and Redberry (oligotrophic)] and the Eastern Mediterranean Sea (ultraoligotrophic) as determined by the method of Wicks and Robarts (1987). Data sources: Canadian lakes (Robarts, unpublished data); Eastern Mediterranean Sea (Zohary and Robarts, 1992).

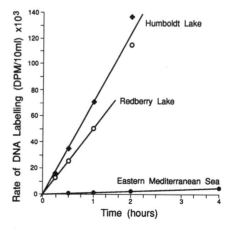

acid–base hydrolysis but have not offered either enzymatic or chromatographic evidence to support these claims (e.g., Novitsky, 1986; Bloem *et al.*, 1988; Carmen *et al.*, 1988; Hollibaugh, 1988; Jeffrey and Paul, 1988a; Paul *et al.*, 1990). Carmen *et al.* worked with sediments that, after labeling the bacteria, they washed with TCA and ethanol and then dried. At least two methodological errors may have caused the observed labeling of "RNA" and/or led to underestimation of the concentration of labeled DNA. First, drying the sediment can lead to the breakdown of DNA by enzymatic processes (Hutchison and Munro, 1961) and second, the hot acid extraction they used does not completely hydrolyze DNA (Roodyn and Mandel, 1960; Servais *et al.*, 1987). Moriarty and Pollard (1990) commented that they had previously worked on the same sediments as Carmen *et al.* and found that the rate of DNA labeling was three orders of magnitude higher.

Servais *et al.* (1987) reported that 15–28% of [^{3}H]-TdR incorporated by bacteria in three water samples appeared in RNA, as determined by RNase treatment, while Brittain and Karl (1990) found that labeling of RNA was greater in marine sediments (> 50%) than in surface marine waters (~ 20%) but at depth this increased to 60–86%. Protein labeling also occurred in both water and sediment samples, often at a rate greater than that for DNA. This nonspecific labeling occurred within 10 min of the label being taken up by the cells indicating to Brittain and Karl that the labeling of RNA and protein is not caused by recycling during extended incubation periods.

Jeffrey and Paul (1988a) examined the effect of 5-fluoro-2'-deoxyuridine (FdUrd), a powerful and irreversible inhibitor of thymidylate synthetase that catalyzes the methylation of dUMP to dTMP (Fig. 2), on the incorporation of [^{3}H]-TdR by bacterioplankton in a variety of fresh and salt waters. FdUrd completely prevented nonspecific labeling of protein and "RNA" at low [^{3}H]-TdR concentrations but at high concentrations it had little effect. Jeffrey and Paul also found that dihydrofolate reductase inhibitors, amethopterin and trimethoprim, had no effect on macromolecular labeling patterns. They concluded that dihydrofolate reductase and thymidylate synthetase were not involved in nonspecific labeling by [^{3}H]-TdR.

Jeffrey and Paul (1988a) proposed that a likely pathway for nonspecific labeling involved the conversation of [^{3}H]-TdR to thymine via the thymidine phosphorylase reaction (Figs. 1 and 2). Further degradation of thymine to uracil involves stepwise dehydrogenation and decarboxylation reactions by thymine 7-hydroxylase and uracil-5-carboxylic acid decarboxylase. According to Jeffrey and Paul, these reactions could account for ^{3}H from the methyl group entering into a series of catabolic or anabolic pathways and possibly account for the production of ^{3}H$_2$O found by Karl (1982), Hollibaugh (1988), and Brittain and Karl (1990).

Brittain and Karl (1990) confirmed the labeling of RNA with high-performance liquid chromatographic (HPLC) separation of piperidine hydrolysates followed by measurement of isolated monophosphates. The main labeled monomers isolated for water samples were CMP and AMP while in sediment samples, GMP and UMP were also labeled. This pattern of monomer labeling of RNA indicated that the base portion of the nucleotide and not the ribose sugar moiety was labeled (Brittain and Karl, 1990).

In addition to finding protein and RNA labeling by [3H]-TdR, Brittain and Karl (1990) also found labeled volatile and nonvolatile degradation products which were rapidly released from cells at rates faster than the rate of [3H]-TdR incorporation into stable macromolecules. According to Brittain and Karl, the standard degradation pathway for [3H]-TdR (Fig. 2) coupled with utilization of Krebs cycle intermediates for biosynthesis of amino acids, purines, and pyrimidines could account for their observed nonspecific labeling of bacteria in water and sediment samples.

In contrast to Brittain and Karl's (1990) observations, Torréton and Bouvy (1991) found that [3H]-TdR was not incorporated into RNA as determined enzymatically although acid–base hydrolysis indicated significant ($\sim$ 21–61%) RNA labeling.

Ducklow $et\ al.$ (1992) followd [3H]-TdR incorporation into both cold-TCA-insoluble macromolecules and DNA [Wicks and Robarts (1987) method] in open ocean samples incubated over 40 hr. Precipitates from both methods were washed with ethanol. They noted that the ratio of [3H]-TdR in DNA to that in cold TCA remained unchanged at $\sim$ 90% throughout the incubation.

Robarts and Wicks (1989) examined the variability of the labeled ethanol-soluble products (ethanol fraction) they had identified earlier (Robarts $et\ al.$, 1986; see p. 390). In 12 freshwater and marine systems they found that up to 87% of ^{3}H was removed from cold TCA precipitates by ethanol. Similar results were obtained for both hot NaOH and hot TCA procedures. Reverse-phase HPLC showed that the labeled molecules in the ethanol were 78–88% [3H]-TdR. Robarts and Wicks found that the rate of labeling of this ethanol fraction was correlated with the rate of total macromolecular labeling (cold TCA precipitate) and less strongly with the rate of DNA labeling. In experiments in which cells were labeled with either [3H]-TdR or $^{32}PO_4^{3-}$ they showed that above a total macromolecular labeling rate of $\sim$ 1 pmole/liter per hr, bacterial cells bind [3H]-TdR, but do not incorporate it, to phospholipids in the cell envelope.

Roodyn and Mandel (1960), Hollibaugh (1988), Torréton and Bouvy (1991), and Hollibaugh and Wong (1992) have all reported that [3H]-TdR labels bacterial lipids while Gabriel (1987) demonstrated its involvement in the biosynthesis of lipopolysaccharide carbohydrate. Hollibaugh and Wong measured the variation in the ethanol fraction (average 32%) for bacterial populations from San Francisco Bay and used correlation analysis to determine the environmental factors affecting this variation. They found no single factor that was dominantly correlated to the amount of [³H]-TdR removed by ethanol but that the percentage (relative to the cold TCA precipitate) removal was correlated with bacterial abundance. Hollibaugh and Wong concluded that (1) the labeling of lipids is a property of the sample and not an artifact of extraction or incubation techniques and (2) the labeling of lipids is not related to the growth rate of bacteria, yet it introduces a significant and variable bias into growth rate estimates based on [³H]-TdR incorporation.

Cho and Azam (1988) noted that bacteria in deeper waters generally show a lower percentage of [³H]-TdR incorporation into DNA than those in surface waters which may be a response to nutrient limitation. They tested this hypothesis using seawater cultures and measured the rate of DNA and protein labeling using acid–base hydrolysis. The distribution of ³H in protein increased from 3.8% on day 1 to 74% by day 9. They considered that this represented nitrogen starvation and found that addition of nitrogen rapidly caused a reversal of this label distribution. This confirmation of nonspecific labeling in relation to metabolic status of cells must be viewed cautiously.

Other researchers have also hypothesized that bacteria may use [³H]-TdR as a carbon source rather than as a DNA precursor (Servais et al., 1987; Robarts and Wicks, 1989; Brittain and Karl, 1990; Hollibaugh and Wong, 1992). Robarts and Wicks suggested that the adsorption of [³H]-TdR onto lipids in bacteria may represent a storage strategy for later use in cellular maintenance, nitrogen metabolism, or other cellular processes. However, W. S. Gardner (personal communication) found that bacteria in Lake Michigan water did not normally use [³H]-TdR as a carbon source but that they could adapt to it when exposed to high levels (micromolar) for about 3 days.

Another process to possibly account for nonspecific labeling is extracellular release of labeled products and their reincorporation during incubation with [³H]-TdR. Although this labeling pathway was discounted by Brittain and Karl (1990), Paul et al. (1987) found that dissolved DNA (D-DNA) was produced by actively growing bacteria in marine waters and removed through the metabolic activities of heterotrophic bacteria. Paul et al. (1988) developed a model of DNA utilization by estuarine bacterial populations: DNA is rapidly bound to the cell surface and hydrolyzed by cell-associated and extracellular nonspecific nucleases; DNA hydrolysis products are transported into the cell and are rapidly salvaged into nucleic acids with little accumulation into intracellular nucleotide pools. In a Florida reservoir, Paul et al. (1990) found that labeled dissolved DNA, RNA, and protein were produced from [³H]-TdR (as determined by acid–base hydrolysis). This labeled macromolecular production represented 3.1% of cellular incorporation of [³H]-TdR while production of D-DNA was 2.3% of cellular [³H]-TdR incorporation. Paul et al. (1990) also showed that while actively growing populations of phytoplankton and bacterioplankton produced dissolved RNA and protein, only active bacterioplankton produced measurable quantities of dissolved DNA. Results similar to those of Paul and his colleagues have been reported by Karl and Bailiff (1989).

In conclusion, it is clear that nonspecific labeling of bacterial macromolecules in addition to DNA is ubiquitous. Labeling by [^{3}H]-TdR of lipids and proteins appears to be generally accepted. Wicks and Robarts (1987) used phenol–chloroform and ethanol rinses of cold TCA precipitates to remove these labeled products. Labeling of RNA remains controversial. Relatively few microorganisms are known to be able to degrade pyrimidines along a pathway involving the reduction of either uracil or thymine (Vogels and van der Drift, 1976; see Figs. 1 and 2) as proposed, for example, by Jeffrey and Paul (1988a) and Brittain and Karl (1990). If this is generally true for natural populations, it is imperative that other biochemical pathways(s) be investigated which could lead to improvements in the [^{3}H]-TdR assay and to an understanding of why nonspecific labeling is so prevalent in some systems but not in others. Brittain and Karl have noted that data on nonspecific labeling have been contradictory, resulting, at least partially, from the lack of a uniform method for extraction and purification of individual macromolecules.

The [^{3}H]-TdR assay is a pulse-labeling assay intended for short incubations to target the labeling of DNA. Extended incubation time, especially in waters > 20°C, increases the possibility of nonspecific labeling of other macromolecules. It is for this reason that the method of Servais *et al.* (1985) to measure bacterial mortality by the loss of labeled DNA from cells incubated with [^{3}H]-TdR for 5–20 hr is not recommended. This problem would be compounded by the use of standard acid–base hydrolysis procedures as employed by them.

4.2. Isotope Dilution

Isotope dilution can occur from both intracellular and extracellular sources. Intracellular isotope dilution may be caused by *de novo* synthesis of pyrimidines in bacteria. Thymidylate synthetase catalyzes the conversion of dUMP to dTMP (Fig. 2). dTMP synthesized by this pathway dilutes labeled dTMP formed from exogenous [^{3}H]-TdR (Pollard and Moriarty, 1984; see Section 2). Extracellular isotope dilution may be caused by ambient concentrations of thymidine or compounds that compete for the same enzymes as [^{3}H]-TdR during salvage of exogenous nucleosides (Jeffrey and Paul, 1988a).

In Fuhrman and Azam's (1980) experiments with coastal bacterioplankton, rates of [^{3}H]-TdR incorporation were only slightly increased above the rate at 5 nM by five- or tenfold increases in [^{3}H]-TdR concentrations. Fuhrman and Azam concluded that isotope dilution was insignificant.

Fuhrman and Azam (1982) readdressed the problem of isotope dilution in two ways. First, they found that the rate of [^{3}H]-TdR incorporation into DNA (mitomycin C-sensitive material) at 5 nM varied from 83 to 99% of the rate measured at 25 nM. Second, they used parallel experiments of DNA labeling by [³H]-TdR and orthophosphate (³²P and ³³P). The fraction of cold TCA-insoluble incorporation inhibited by mitomycin C was taken to be mainly DNA as determined by acid–base hydrolysis. They then compared the number of moles of phosphorus incorporated into DNA to four times the number of moles of [³H]-TdR incorporated into DNA based on the following assumptions: that the specific activity of [³H]-TdR and its derivatives was unaffected by isotope dilution and that DNA is one-fourth thymidylate residues. These assumptions, and the fact that acid–base hydrolysis cannot be used to accurately separate labeled DNA from other labeled macromolecules (Robarts *et al.*, 1986), may have accounted for the conclusion that the [³H]-TdR assay underestimated DNA synthesis by a factor of 2.7 to 7.1 compared with the rate obtained with phosphorus. Moriarty (1984) pointed out that [³H]-TdR labels DNA only and not RNA (but see above) while ³²P would label both nucleic acids and, in addition, mitomycin C may block RNA and DNA synthesis.

Moriarty (1986) has cogently reviewed how to determine if isotope dilution was significant in bacterial growth rate measurements using [³H]-TdR with natural populations. He pointed out that it is not possible to measure the specific activity of any nucleotide at the site of DNA synthesis simply by extracting the nucleotides and measuring it directly. However, according to Moriarty, the specific activity of precursors (labeled thymine in dTTP) at the site of DNA synthesis can be estimated using an isotope dilution analysis as done by Moriarty and Pollard (1981), but which has been criticized on a number of points (see Karl, 1982). Karl stated that the only way to accurately assess combined effects of extracellular and intracellular dilution of the specific activity of [³H]-TdR is through direct measurement of the specific radioactivity of the immediate nucleotide triphosphate precursor pool. Moriarty (1986) argued that the isotope dilution method measures the dilution of [³H]-TdR in dTTP by all sources of thymine in DNA. An essential condition for this is that DNA polymerase be the rate-limiting step for [³H]-TdR incorporation which, if the concentration of [³H]-TdR is high enough, should satisfy this condition in bacteria with normal regulatory mechanisms (Pollard and Moriarty, 1984; Moriarty, 1986). Moriarty noted, however, that oligotrophic bacteria may not regulate DNA synthesis in the normal way so that dilution could still occur. Hollibaugh (1988) has cautioned against the application of a technique that was originally developed for uniform cell populations (e.g., Forsdyke, 1971) to heterogeneous populations of natural systems.

One isotope dilution method is a serial dilution procedure that involves adding a constant amount of [³H]-TdR to a series of samples with increasing amounts of unlabeled thymidine. The samples are incubated, the labeled DNA is extracted, and the reciprocal of radioactivity is plotted against thymidine concentration (Fig. 6). The plotted thymidine concentration is either only the cold

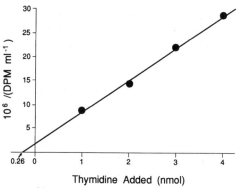

Figure 6. Isotope dilution plot of [³H]-TdR incorporation into DNA for bacteria in Lake Kinneret (Israel) sediments. Data were generated using the methods of Findlay *et al.* (1984) and Pollard and Moriarty (1984); a constant amount (0.09 nmole) of [³H]-TdR was added to a 100-μl sediment slurry with increasing amounts of cold thymidine. Cold thymidine concentration is plotted against the reciprocal of radioactivity incorporated. Negative x-intercept is 0.26 nmole indicating the effective thymidine pool size and isotope dilution, with a degree of participation in DNA synthesis of 36%. Data source: Hadas, Pinkas, and Zohary (unpublished data).

thymidine (e.g., Findlay *et al.*, 1984; Bell, 1986) or the total of hot and cold thymidine (e.g., Pollard and Moriarty, 1984). If the plotted line passes through the origin, no isotope dilution occurred. However, a negative intercept on the x-axis indicates the amount of isotope dilution relating to other sources of thymidine. The negative intercept on the x-axis in plots using total thymidine represents dilution by extracellular and intracellular nonlabeled thymidine while in plots using only cold thymidine it represents the sum of the nonlabeled intracellular and extracellular thymine plus the concentration of added labeled thymidine. Caution must therefore be used when comparing different studies of isotope dilution: the degree of participation (DP) of [³H]-TdR in DNA labeling is calculated as concentration of [³H]-TdR/x-intercept for plots using cold thymidine while in calculations using labeled and unlabeled thymidine, DP = concentration of [³H]-TdR/(x-intercept + concentration of [³H]-TdR). This isotope dilution method has been validated by Pollard and Moriarty (1984) using cultures of a marine bacterium growing in a chemostat.

Curiously, in all of the papers we reviewed the negative x-intercept (dilution pool) in isotope dilution experiments was determined from linearized data (see Fig. 6) yet Forsdyke (1971) emphasized that he used this format *only* for rapid visual analysis of experimental results. As he pointed out, this treatment is subject to errors from using reciprocals to linearize data and he calculated dilution using a nonlinear regression model as has been recommended by Li (1983) for parameter estimation in studies of bacterial uptake of organic substrates. Kaplan *et al.* (1992) were able to calculate three linear functions in an isotope dilution plot spanning concentrations of 0.031 to 53 μM total thymidine for stream bed sediments. These functions gave estimates of isotope dilution ranging from 0.08 to 28.84 μM. Similar results were obtained with stream water cultures. Even so, Kaplan *et al.* concluded that their data validated the use of the reciprocal plot technique for estimating isotopic dilution.

Forsdyke's (1971) nonlinear model is $x = 1/(\theta_1 + \theta_2 \cdot y')$, where $\theta_1 = p/n$ and p is the dilution pool size (in dilution units) and n is the slope; $\theta_2 = 1/n$; x is the amount of [³H]-TdR incorporated into DNA (dpm) and y' is the added cold thymidine in dilution units (concentration of [³H]-TdR/concentration of cold thymidine (y)). y can be substituted for y' (Pollard and Moriarty, 1984). Forsdyke's equation can be simplified to $y = p + n/x$ and be solved by a nonlinear curve-fitting program. For the example data in Fig. 6, $p = 0.25$ nmole and DP = 37% which are only small changes from the linearized data. However, in experiments where data variance is large (e.g., the data for Fig. 6a in Findlay *et al.*, 1991), the more mathematically robust nonlinear solution will differ significantly from the linear solution (see Li, 1983).

The apparent reticence of microbial ecologists to use the nonlinear model may partially account for the discrepancies found between estimates of [³H]-TdR dilution calculated using Forsdyke's method and other methodologies in studies reviewed below and the large isotope dilution corrections employed by some investigators (e.g., Findlay *et al.*, 1991).

A second approach for determining if isotope dilution is occurring is to add increasing amounts of [³H]-TdR at a constant specific activity to a series of samples (Moriarty, 1986), as essentially was done by Fuhrman and Azam (1980). *De novo* synthesis is assumed (see p. 377) to be inhibited at the concentration at which the rate of incorporation does not increase (Fig. 7). In some experiments the rate of [³H]-TdR incorporation decreases above a particular [³H]-TdR concentration (e.g., Robarts *et al.*, 1986) probably because thymidine inhibits its own conversion to dTTP (see Beacham *et al.*, 1971). Pollard and Moriarty (1984) noted this method works only when there is no endogenous or exogenous pools of thymidine and a double-reciprocal plot is required to show dilution. Bell

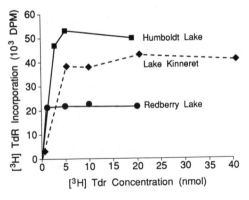

Figure 7. The rate of [³H]-TdR incorporation into DNA versus [³H]-TdR concentration for bacteria in samples from Humboldt and Redberry lakes (see Fig. 5; Robarts, unpublished data) and from Lake Kinneret, Israel (T. Berman, unpublished data). Plots indicate isotope dilution should not have occurred when [³H]-TdR concentrations ≥ 2 nM for Redberry Lake and ≥ 5 nM for Humboldt Lake and Lake Kinneret were used to measure bacterial rates of DNA synthesis.

(1986) and Chróst *et al.* (1988) compared this approach with that used by Moriarty and Pollard (1981) and found that both indicated similar optimal concentrations of [^{3}H]-TdR for maximal degree of participation in DNA synthesis.

Jeffrey and Paul (1988a) examined the problem of isotope dilution by using Moriarty and Pollard's (1981) protocol and by amending a second set of samples with FdUrd. They assumed that the first method gave total isotope dilution while the second would give intracellular dilution as FdUrd should inhibit endogenous synthesis of thymidine nucleotides and increase the DP of exogenous [^{3}H]-TdR (Rosenbaum-Oliver and Zamenhof, 1972). Extracellular dilution was calculated by subtraction.

Jeffrey and Paul's (1988a) experiments for fresh, estuarine, and marine waters indicated that extracellular dilution was significant (4.1–8.4 nM) in two out of ten bacterioplankton samples. Intracellular isotope dilution was determined to be negligible in two cases (0.43 and 0.47 nM) but was 1.9 nM in another sample. While high isotope dilution was possible, Jeffrey and Paul thought it was not common. In a wide variety of environments, ranging from oligotrophic to eutrophic and freshwater to marine, they found total isotope dilution to be < 2 nM.

Jeffrey and Paul's (1988a) data contrast sharply with those of Chrzanowski (1988) who found that the rate of DNA labeling (also based on standard acid–base hydrolysis) could be underestimated by as much as 109% in a shallow, mesotrophic reservoir. The DP values varied both spatially and temporally and appeared to be affected by water temperature. In winter DP was generally > 80% whereas in summer it was typically < 60% so that accounting for isotope dilution in the colder months did little to alter incorporation estimates. These data supported Chrzanowski's assumption that if bacterial growth rates are rapid and the demand for thymidine cannot be met by salvage pathways alone, then the discrepancy between isotopic-dilution-corrected uptake and uptake rates not corrected for isotopic dilution would increase. However, Chrzanowski's observations are at variance with earlier studies such as that by Rosenbaum-Oliver and Zamenhof (1972) with *E. coli*. They found that slowing cell growth by lowering temperature caused DP to decrease. In the logarithmic phase, Rosenbaum-Oliver and Zamenhof found DP to be higher than in the beginning of the stationary phase and concluded that exogenous [^{3}H]-TdR is more convenient for DNA synthesis during faster cell growth.

Similar spatial and temporal changes in DP as measured by Chrzanowski, as well as diel variations, have been measured by Chróst *et al.* (1988). While these data indicated that instantaneous rates of DNA labeling could be significantly underestimated if isotope dilution by *de novo* synthesis of precursors was not accounted for, Chrzanowski noted that this does little to change seasonal patterns of uptake.

Chrzanowski's (1988) data were for a 1-year period; in subsequent years, in which he used the DNA extraction technique of Wicks and Robarts (1987), he found that isotope dilution did not lead to serious underestimates of DNA labeling by [³H]-TdR (T. H. Chrzanowski, personal communication), similar to the conclusion of Jeffrey and Paul (1988a).

In a subsequent study, Jeffrey and Paul (1988b) compared the rate of DNA synthesis estimated from [³H]-TdR incorporation with fluorometrically determined changes in DNA content of an exponentially growing bacterial isolate and naturally occurring bacterial populations. Even after allowing for isotope dilution, nonspecific macromolecular labeling, and efficiency of DNA recovery, they found that the rate of [³H]-TdR incorporation consistently underestimated the amount of DNA synthesized by six- to eightfold. Jeffrey and Paul concluded that although the relationship of [³H]-TdR incorporation to DNA synthesis appeared consistent, there were significant sources of thymine bases incorporated into DNA which could not be accounted for by isotope dilution assays. Such results, as Jeffrey and Paul (1988b) pointed out, agreed with those of Fuhrman and Azam (1982; see above) and also with more recent studies of Bloem et al. (1989), Painting et al. (1989), and Ellenbroek and Cappenberg (1991). We agree with Jeffrey and Paul's (1988b) concluding statement that there is much to learn about the enzymatic pathways associated with thymidine incorporation in natural bacterial populations, but part of the underestimates they calculated could be related to the fact that they used acid–base hydrolysis procedures which can significantly distort the measured rate of DNA labeling by [³H]-TdR (see above).

Moriarty and Pollard (1990) noted that from their experience it is necessary to add about three orders of magnitude more [³H]-TdR to sediments than to water in order to obtain maximal rates of incorporation. This is because of the adsorption of [³H]-TdR onto various sediment materials.

Findlay et al. (1984) found significant isotope dilution in water and sediment samples from a blackwater river. They measured effective pool sizes of 0 to 66 nmole TdR per 2 cm³ of sediment and from 0 to 6 nmole TdR per 20 ml water, giving dilution correction factors of 1 to 120 in sediments and 1 to 9.8 in water samples. The degree of participation of [³H]-TdR in sediments from a hypereutrophic lake varied between 20 and 30% (Bell and Ahlgren, 1987). A fourfold increase in [³H]-TdR concentration only raised DP to 80%. Bell and Ahlgren concluded that since isotope dilution had to be checked in each experiment, it was most economical to use the lower [³H]-TdR concentration. This is also generally true for maximal incorporation of [³H]-TdR as the lowest concentration of thymidine possible should be used (O'Donovan, 1978).

Tibbles et al. (1992) reported that [³H]-TdR had to be added to water samples from a saltmarsh lagoon at concentrations > 9.3 nM, while to sediment samples concentrations > 0.7 nmole/g DW (dry weight) were required to prevent isotope dilution. They also found that isotope dilution varied seasonally and that the changes in sediment isotope dilution generally followed those in the overlying water.

Isotope dilution on the rhizoplane of rape seedlings grown in sand was found to decrease with the age of the plant, ranging from zero on 26-day-old plants to about 1.2 nM on 5-day-old plants (Bååth and Johansson, 1990). With soil bacterial populations, Bååth (1990) found isotope dilution to range from 0.1 to 0.47 nM per 0.25–1.0 g wet weight of soil. He found no significant difference in the degree of isotope dilution between a sandy loam soil and humus and concluded that in order to achieve a DP of 90%, at least 4 nM [^{3}H]-TdR had to be added to soil samples.

Moriarty and Pollard (1990) found in seagrass sediments a relationship between the amount of [^{3}H]-TdR incorporated into DNA and the amount of sediment used. Isotope dilution occurred in 0.8 g of sediment but not with 0.2 g. The amount of label appearing in DNA increased linearly up to a sediment weight of ~0.4 g, which Moriarty and Pollard concluded was the maximum weight of sediment that could be used without incurring isotope dilution. They also noted that for other sediments with higher clay contents, as little as 20 mg of sediment was optimum. Although this procedure may resolve the problem of exogenous isotope dilution, it may not account for intracellular dilution as noted for bacterioplankton samples by Jeffrey and Paul (1988b).

In epilithic stream microbial consortia, Hudson et al. (1990) found that the effective pool sizes of thymidine were substantial (63–440 nM) and varied between sites and at the same site on different dates. In parallel studies they estimated the effective thymidine pool size to be 15–65 nM in water and 226–7103 nM in sediments.

Another potential cause of isotope dilution is associated with sterilization of [^{3}H]-TdR solutions. Wetzel and Likens (1991) recommend autoclaving [^{3}H]-TdR solutions but we (Wicks and Robarts, unpublished data) and others (T. H. Chrzanowski, personal communication) have found from HPLC analyses that heat treatment of [^{3}H]-TdR leads to the rapid formation of thymine. In such solutions thymine forms an unpredictable proportion of the total label and can exceed 50%. We recommend storage of [^{3}H]-TdR in 3% ethanol at 4°C, which also minimizes autodegradation.

In conclusion, data from a wide range of natural habitats indicate that isotope dilution can be a significant factor requiring attention when using [^{3}H]-TdR to measure bacterial growth rates and production. The degree of isotope dilution appears to be greatest in sediments, largely as a result of [^{3}H]-TdR adsorbing to sediment materials, and researchers working in these habitats should try to estimate the effective pool size using isotope dilution plots. With bacterioplankton, most have generally concluded that isotope dilution can be prevented with the use of [^{3}H]-TdR concentrations usually between 10 and 20 nM, although as little as 5 nM may be sufficient in oligotrophic systems. However, there is now evidence (e.g., Jeffrey and Paul, 1988b) to indicate that our present means of calculating isotope dilution and/or the concentration of [³H]-TdR required to block *de novo* synthesis does not take into acount intracellular dilution. This problem urgently requires research to determine how general and significant this may be in different systems.

4.3. Specificity of [³H]-TdR for Growing Heterotrophic Bacteria

A method for measuring growth rates of heterotrophic bacteria has to be specific. Theoretically with the [³H]-TdR method all actively growing heterotrophic bacteria should incorporate [³H]-TdR into DNA while other microorganisms and nongrowing heterotrophic bacteria should not. This is not always the case (see Moriarty, 1984, 1986; Cho and Azam, 1988; Riemann and Bell, 1990). In this section we examine mainly newer studies addressing this issue which were not cited in these earlier reviews.

4.3.1. Aerobic Heterotrophic Bacteria

Güde (1984) tested the ability of four bacterial isolates to utilize [³H]-TdR. An isolate of *Pseudomonas* sp. did not take up [³H]-TdR at concentrations up to 500 nM, while isolates of *Chromobacterium* sp., *Cytophaga* sp., and an unidentified bacterium were all able to take up [³H]-TdR with saturation maxima ranging from 50 to 200 nM.

Pollard and Moriarty (1984) found that two of several species of marine pseudomonads they tested were unable to take up [³H]-TdR. *Pseudomonas putida* was not able to use exogenous sources of thymidine (Wicks and Robarts, unpublished data). According to Carlson *et al.* (1985), *Pseudomonas* spp. generally lack thymidine phosphorylase and thymidine kinase activities (see Fig. 2). Saito *et al.* (1985) found that most *Pseudomonas* species they studied lacked thymidine kinase activity. They noted that the distribution of thymidine kinase activity among various bacteria showed some correlation with a phylogenetic tree based on 5 S rRNA sequences in which bacteria with 5 S rRNA of the 118N type did not have thymidine kinase activity. However, in addition to Pollard and Moriarty (1984), others have also reported [³H]-TdR incorporation by a number of *Pseudomonas* species (Carlson *et al.*, 1985; Saito *et al.*, 1985; Davis, 1989; Jeffrey and Paul, 1990).

Davis (1989) examined the uptake and incorporation of thymidine by 34 marine bacterial isolates (*Vibrio* sp., *Pseudomonas* sp., *Cytophaga* sp., *Flavobacterim* sp.). Thymidine was supplied either as [³H]-TdR at a final concentration of 19 nM or as [2-¹⁴C]thymidine at a concentration of 9.1 μM. Four strains from the genera *Vibrio, Pseudomonas,* and *Flavobacterium* were unable to incorporate thymidine at either concentration while two isolates from the genera

Pseudomonas and *Cytophaga* were able to incorporate thymidine at the higher concentration but not at the lower one (Davis, 1989).

Davis's (1989) results with *Vibrio* are similar to those of Saito *et al.* (1985) who found that two strains of *Vibrio parahaemolyticus*, as well as *V. fluvalis*, did not show thymidine kinase activity. Johnstone and Jones (1989) found that *V. anguillarum* could take up [³H]-TdR and incorporate it into macromolecules while no significant incorporation was measured in strain N8.

Jeffrey and Paul (1990) examined 41 bacterial isolates, including a *Vibrio* sp., *V. alginolyticus, Pseudomonas atlantica, P. stutzeri, P. aeruginosa,* and four strains of *E. coli,* for thymidine uptake (total cell-associated radioactivity), thymidine incorporation (cold TCA precipitates), and thymidine kinase activity. They found that 37 of the isolates were capable of [³H]-TdR incorporation while the 4 organisms that did not incorporate [³H]-TdR also transported [³H]-TdR poorly and lacked thymidine kinase activity. Attempts by Jeffrey and Paul to detect thymidine kinase genes in the isolates by molecular probing were unsuccessful.

Contrary to the data in the above studies which demonstrated that various *Pseudomonas* species could incorporate [³H]-TdR, all *Pseudomonas* species lack thymidine kinase and are incapable of incorporating [³H]-TdR into DNA (G. A. O'Donovan, personal communication). A recent study (Beck, Linscott, and O'Donovan, unpublished data) examined all available *Pseudomonas* species for the presence of thymidine kinase and did not find it. Whereas formerly named *Pseudomonas* species such as *P. acidovorans, P. maltophilia,* and *P. avreofaciens* previously have been shown to contain thymidine kinase and thus incorporate [³H]-TdR specifically into DNA, these species have recently been reclassified as *Comamonas acidovorans, Xanthomonas maltophilia,* and *Sphingomonas avreofaciens,* respectively (G. A. O'Donovan, personal communication). Thus, as it now stands, the genus *Pseudomonas* lacks thymidine kinase.

A *Vibrio* sp., which could not incorporate [³H]-TdR, was transformed by Jeffrey and Paul (1990) using a plasmid that contained an *E. coli* thymidine kinase gene to determine if the inability to incorporate [³H]-TdR was related to the absence of the enzyme. Earlier work by Carlson *et al.* (1985) indicated that this approach resulted in several *Pseudomonas* spp. and a thymidine kinase mutant of *Salmonella typhimurium* incorporating [³H]-TdR. Jeffrey and Paul, however, found that their transformed cells could not transport or incorporate [³H]-TdR even though high levels of thymidine kinase activity in the transformants were detected. Jeffrey and Paul concluded that the inability of some marine bacteria to incorporate [³H]-TdR may not only be related to the lack of thymidine kinase but also to the absence of thymidine transport systems.

Douglas *et al.* (1987) used microautoradiography to enumerate marine bacteria capable of utilizing labeled glutamate and [³H]-TdR. The percentage (relative to a total acridine orange count) of cells able to take up [^{3}H]-TdR ranged between 5.9 and 18.5% while the proportion of bacteria able to use glutamate varied from 23.2 to 97%. Douglas *et al.* (1987) concluded that in some environments thymidine-based estimates of bacterial production may be representative of only a subpopulation of the total active bacteria.

The results of Douglas *et al.* (1987) supported earlier work by, for example, Ramsay (1974) and Novitsky (1983a,b) but were contrary to the data of Fuhrman and Azam (1982) whose experiments indicated that virtually all active heterotrophic bacteria in their samples could use exogenous thymidine.

The uptake patterns over depth of glucose, glutamate, and [^{3}H]-TdR by bacterioplankton measured by Novitsky (1983a) in a marine system were similar and glutamate ($\leq$35%) was taken up by a slightly greater percentage of the population than thymidine ($\leq$21%) whereas glucose ($\leq$16%) was taken up by the smallest percentage of the population. Similarly, Novitsky (1983b) found that the percentage of the bacterial population at the sediment–water interface that could take up glutamate did not exceed 10.5% while the percentage of the population taking up [^{3}H]-TdR did not exceed 9.5%. In an Antarctic marine system, Bird and Karl (1991) found that although bacterial incorporation of labeled glutamate varied 170-fold and [^{3}H]-TdR incorporation by only 2-fold, both substrates indicated similar seasonal patterns of the bacterioplankton. The overall relationship between glutamate and [^{3}H]-TdR incorporation was significant but not strong ($r^2 = 0.64$, $n = \sim 250$) (Bird and Karl, 1991).

The difference between the rate of [^{3}H]-TdR incorporation and the number of cells incorporating [^{3}H]-TdR compared with other organic compounds in the above studies may have been the result of cells being metabolically active but not actively growing and hence not synthesizing nucleic acids, or because they lacked thymidine kinase and/or [^{3}H]-TdR transport systems as suggested by Jeffrey and Paul (1990). Furthermore, when comparing autoradiographic results from different radioisotopes, as in the above studies, it is important to try to have equal DPM per cell for each isotope (Fuhrman and Azam, 1982; H. Ducklow, personal communication). The absolute uptake rates, i.e., the uptake rate per cell, can differ markedly if the specific activities of the isotopes are different. Since making a reduced silver grain is a threshold process, slow-growing cells can possibly be positive for one substrate but not for another even though both isotopes are being taken up (H. Ducklow, personal communication). For example, Ducklow (personal communication) has calculated from Douglas *et al.'s* (1987) data that glutamate had a much higher DPM per cell than [^{3}H]-TdR which makes questionable the conclusions that were drawn.

In brackish waters around Sapelo Island, Georgia, Pedrós-Alió and Newell (1989) found high bacterial cell numbers and rates of [^{3}H]-TdR incorporation. Despite this they found, using microautoradiography, that the percentage of cells labeled with [^{3}H]-TdR ranged from 1 to 69% ($\bar{x} = 16\%$). In laboratory cultures of bacteria from these waters, up to 57% of the cells were labeled by [³H]-TdR even during exponential growth.

Pedrós-Alió and Newell (1989) considered a number of possible explanations for the low number of cells in their samples capable of incorporating [³H]-TdR: inhibition of [³H]-TdR incorporation by a contaminant, the presence of dead or dormant cells, cells that were metabolically active but not synthesizing DNA, cells lacked [³H]-TdR transport systems, and cells took up [³H]-TdR and used it for growth processes but took up so little that the autoradiograms were not exposed. They deduced that the most likely explanation was that a large number of the cells that were actively growing and replicating lacked [³H]-TdR transport systems. Pedrós-Alió and Newell (1989) concluded that the underlying assumption of the [³H]-TdR method that all active [sic] heterotrophic bacteria take up [³H]-TdR must be questioned if not rejected.

Mården et al. (1988) measured the incorporation of [³H]-TdR into macromolecules by marine bacterial isolates when undergoing a starvation survival response. They found high rates of [³H]-TdR incorporation during the initial phase of starvation and two strains had a net increase in DNA content during the first hours of starvation. The rate of [³H]-TdR incorporation decreased with time of starvation, corresponding to a decrease in the percentage of the population that incorporated [³H]-TdR (determined by autoradiography–epifluorescence technique). However, even after 24 and 48 hr of starvation, some [³H]-TdR incorporation into DNA still occurred. Estimates of biomass production by natural bacterial populations based on [³H]-TdR incorporation assume that only actively growing cells incorporate the label. The data of Mården et al. indicating that nongrowing cells in different states of starvation incorporate [³H]-TdR, therefore, have potential implications for the interpretation of [³H]-TdR-based growth rate estimates. Other researchers have also reported significant [³H]-TdR incorporation in nongrowing marine and freshwater bacteria (e.g., Bloem et al., 1988; Davis, 1989).

In contrast to these results, data from a recent study of four marine *Vibrio* species in batch culture indicated that as the cultures approached zero growth in stationary phase, [³H]-TdR incorporation also approached zero (Fig. 8).

4.3.2. Anaerobic Bacteria

The limited data available for bacteria in anaerobic environments suggest that not all anaerobic bacteria are capable of incorporating [³H]-TdR or that anaerobic bacteria take up less exogenous thymidine per mole of DNA produced than do aerobes and that a smaller percentage of [³H]-TdR taken up is incorporated into DNA compared with other macromolecules (Gilmour et al., 1990).

In the anaerobic region of the mixolimnion of a meromictic lake, Zehr et al. (1987) found significant [³H]-TdR incorporation by the bacterial population.

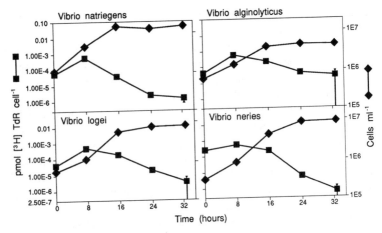

Figure 8. The incorporation of [³H]-TdR into DNA of marine *Vibrio* during the time course of cell growth in batch cultures (Snyder, Robarts, and Caldwell, unpublished data). Vertical bars represent ± 1 S.D. of the mean of replicate measurements when these exceed the size of the data symbols. Note that [³H]-TdR incorporation declines with increasing time in stationary phase, tracking changes in cell growth.

They also reported that isolates from the anaerobic monimolimnion were able to incorporate label into macromolecules precipitable in cold TCA. Similarly, McDonough *et al.* (1986) and Robarts and Wicks (1990) found that bacterial populations in anaerobic hypolimnia of lakes are capable of incorporating [³H]-TdR into macromolecules and DNA. McDonough *et al.* demonstrated that at least some obligate anaerobes were capable of incorporating [³H]-TdR; aeration of anaerobic water samples resulted in substantially inhibited [³H]-TdR incorporation. Austin and Findlay (1989) found that anaerobic bacteria in the sediments of the Hudson River estuary were capable of incorporating [³H]-TdR. Anaerobic bacteria in tropical mangrove sediments incorporate [³H]-TdR (Alongi, 1988). Frequently in such studies, however, the rate of [³H]-TdR incorporation is significantly higher in aerobic than in anaerobic samples with similar bacterial standing crops (e.g., McDonough *et al.*, 1986; Sanders and Porter, 1986; Zehr *et al.*, 1987).

Pollard and Moriarty (1984) measured [³H]-TdR incorporation by mixed cultures of anaerobic bacteria from a sea grass bed. There was good correlation between the rate of [³H]-TdR incorporation and growth rate determined by direct microscopy. Pollard and Moriarty concluded that [³H]-TdR is probably used by many common anaerobic bacteria but noted that those with specialized nutrient requirements, such as sulfate-reducing bacteria (SRB), probably do not take up [³H]-TdR. They also found that acetate-utilizing sulfate reducers did not take up [³H]-TdR and incorporate it into DNA.

Gilmour et al. (1990) tested Pollard and Moriarty's (1984) hypothesis that SRBs cannot take up exogenous [³H]-TdR. They incubated ten bacterial isolates from the sediments of Chesapeake Bay plus a pure culture of *Desulfovibrio desulfuricans aestuarii* in SO_4^{2-}-reducing media with from 1 to 100 nM [³H]-TdR. Gilmour and colleagues' experiments indicated that usually [³H]-Tdr uptake was only a few times greater than in formaldehyde-killed controls, even after overnight incubations with dense cultures of log-phase cells. *E. coli*, which they used as a positive control, accumulated [³H]-TdR about 10^4 times faster than the SRBs. Similar observations have been obtained by others using pure cultures of SRBs and *E. coli* (Wicks and Robarts, unpublished data). Recently, Winding (1992) reported that *Desulfovibrio vulgaris* G11 did not incorporate [³H]-TdR into macromolecules extractable in hot TCA.

When Gilmour et al. added molybdate, an inhibitor of SO_4^{2-} reduction, to anoxic sediments, amino acid uptake was significantly inhibited but [³H]-TdR incorporation did not decrease. Gilmour et al. concluded that SRBs take up exogenous [³H]-TdR at lower rates than aerobic bacteria and possibly at lower rates than other anaerobes. They cautioned that [³H]-TdR incorporation in anaerobic environments may grossly underestimate bacterial production depending on the amount of sulfate-reducing activity in a sample and suggested that the capability for [³H]-TdR incorporation by methanogens and acetogens should also be checked before the technique is applied to anoxic freshwater systems.

Winding (1992) tested the ability of axenic cultures of fermentative (*Clostridium formicoaceticum, C. cellobioparum, Acetobacterium woodii*) and methanogenic (*Methanococcus vannielii, Methanospirillum hungatei, Methanobacterium formicicum*) bacteria to incorporate [³H]-TdR into hot TCA-soluble macromolecules. [³H]-TdR was added at a final concentration of 100 nM and cells were exposed to the label for 3 or 24 hr. Winding (1992) found that all of the fermentative bacteria, but only *M. formicicum* of the methanogens, were cable of incorporating [³H]-TdR. She concluded that bacterial growth rates estimated from rates of [³H]-TdR incorporation in anaerobic environments would mainly represent fermentative bacteria.

4.3.3. Other Specialized Bacterial Groups

Johnstone and Jones (1989) tested five chemolithotrophic bacteria for their ability to incorporate [³H]-TdR: *Nitrosomonas cryotolerans* and *Nitrosococcus oceanus*, marine ammonium-oxidizing bacteria; *Nitrobacter* sp., a marine nitrite-oxidizing bacterium; *Methylocystis parvus* and *Methylosinus trichosporium*, freshwater methane-oxidizing bacteria. None of these were able to incorporate [³H]-TdR, which Johnstone and Jones concluded was related to the absence of transport mechanisms for exogenous thymidine. Johnstone and Jones based their conclusion on the following observations: cells (*N. cryotolerans*) exposed to [³H]-TdR for 3 hr and washed with seawater did not contain label, concentrations of up to 50 nM [^{3}H]-TdR were not taken up by *N. cryotolerans* after 3 hr incubation, and cells (*Nitrobacter* sp.) exposed to 5 nM [^{3}H]-TdR for 24 hr did not incorporate label into TCA-precipitable macromolecules.

Contrary to the observations of Johnstone and Jones (1989), Kraffzik and Conrad (1991) found that [^{3}H]-TdR was incorporated by pure cultures of 16 chemolithotrophic and methanotrophic bacteria, including *M. trichosporium* tested by Johnstone and Jones. [^{3}H]-TdR incorporation by Kraffzik and Conrad's cultures also occurred in the absence of an exogenous energy substrate but was increased by addition of CO or H$_2$. Kraffzik and Conrad found that addition of CH$_4$ increased [^{3}H]-TdR incorporation by *M. trichosporium* only if cells had been starved. In contrast to these results using cultures, they found bacterioplankton of Lake Constance (Germany) did not increase [^{3}H]-TdR incorporation when water samples were amended with H$_2$ or CH$_4$ but occasionally increased incorporation with CO additions. Kraffzik and Conrad concluded that reduced gases were apparently poor substrates for the growth of bacterioplankton in Lake Constance.

Thymidine incorporation into halophilic archaeobacteria and eubacteria in solar saltern ponds of different salinities was measured by Oren (1990). [^{3}H]-TdR incorporation rates reached 148 pmole/liter per hr and even at salt concentrations of 400 g/liter relatively high rates were measured. By adding taurocholate, which causes lysis of halobacteria without affecting eubacteria, Oren found that at salt concentrations > 250 g/liter, all of the [^{3}H]-TdR incorporation was attributable to halobacteria.

4.3.4. Cyanobacteria

Cyanobacteria, which are autotrophic prokaryotes, do not incorporate [^{3}H]-TdR (e.g., Fuhrman and Azam, 1982; Bern, 1985; Lovell and Konopka, 1985; Robarts and Wicks, 1989), at least not at the concentrations normally used in bacterioplankton studies (but see work by Rivkin with eukaryotic algae in Section 4.3.6).

4.3.5. Fungi

Fungi are generally agreed not to contain thymidine kinase, largely based on the work of Grivell and Jackson (1968) and are, therefore, unable to incorporate exogenous [^{3}H]-TdR into DNA. More recently, Findlay *et al.* (1984) tested log-phase axenic cultures of three fungi (*Pythium aphanidermata, Rhizopus stolonifer, Alternaria alternata*) for [^{3}H]-TdR uptake. After labeling, fungi were collected by centrifugation and washed five times with 5% formaldehyde. Findlay *et al.* found that only *R. stolonifer* incorporated label into intact mycelium. None of the fungi tested incorporated [^{3}H]-TdR into DNA. Similarly, Fallon and

Newell (1986) found that two axenic cultures of fungi (*Phaeosphaeria typharum*, *Buergenerula spartinae*) incorporated [³H]-TdR into protein but not into DNA. Bååth (1990) produced bacterium-free cultures of 15 soil fungi and tested their ability to incorporate [³H]-TdR into DNA. He found that none of the fungi incorporated [³H]-TdR.

4.3.6. Eukaryotic Phytoplankton

Using microautoradiography, Fuhrman and Azam (1982) found that [³H]-TdR labeled only nonphotosynthetic bacteria in incubations < 6 hr while in 12-hr incubations < 1% of the label was associated with pennate diatoms and small flagellates. Similar results have been reported by Fuhrman *et al.* (1986a). In addition, they compared the rate of [³H]-TdR incorporation and [¹⁴C]bicarbonate incorporation in water samples with and without the addition of cycloheximide, a eukaryote-specific inhibitor. The inhibitor substantially (62%) reduced bicarbonate assimilation but not [³H]-TdR incorporation (12%). These data indicated that photosynthetic eukaryotes were not significantly incorporating [³H]-TdR. Bern (1985) and Pollard and Moriarty (1984) reported no [³H]-TdR incorporation by pure cultures of autotrophic eukaryotes.

Rivkin (1986) has noted that for most eukaryotic algae the cell division cycle consists of four sequential intervals. Two temporal gaps generally separate periods of DNA synthesis from cell division and new DNA is formed by semi-conservative replication. According to Rivkin, exogenously supplied [³H]-TdR could be taken up and phosphorylated to dTMP by thymidine kinase and with subsequent phosphorylation to dTTP. As noted by Rivkin, [³H]-TdR would only be incorporated into DNA during the period of DNA synthesis. On this basis, and using high concentrations of [³H]-TdR (75–150 nM) and long incubation periods (12–24 hr), Rivkin and co-workers developed a method to measure cell division rates of eukaryotic algae (e.g., Rivkin, 1986; Rivkin and Voytek, 1986). However, as noted by Rivkin (1986), it is unlikely that the conditions used to calculate algal growth rates using [³H]-TdR preclude using the label to measure bacterial production which is done using short incubation times and low concentrations of [³H]-TdR except in sediments and soils.

4.4. Cellular DNA Content

The DNA content of bacteria must be accurately known in order to convert the rate of DNA synthesis into the number of bacteria produced. In their earlier paper, Fuhrman and Azam (1980) used a mean of literature values (range 7.47×10^{-16} to 4.82×10^{-15} g/cell) to achieve this. In their later paper (Fuhrman and Azam, 1982) they measured the DNA concentration and bacterial numbers in the 0.2- to 0.6-μm size fraction of natural seawater. The mean value calculated from eight experiments was 2.6×10^{-15} g/cell. They felt that this could be an overestimate relating to the possible presence of extracellular DNA. A number of recent studies have shown that dissolved DNA (D-DNA) is a ubiquitous component (0.56 to 88 μg/liter) of the dissolved organic matter of all oceanic, neritic, estuarine, and freshwater habitats (Karl and Bailiff, 1989).

Fuhrman and Azam (1982) also derived a DNA per cell concentration by incubating seawater, which had been filtered through a 3-μm pore size filter, and measuring the rate of incorporation of [^{3}H]-TdR and ^{32}P into DNA (acid–base hydrolysis method) in the presence and absence of mitomycin C, an antibiotic that prevents cell division. The calculated value was 2.4 fg DNA/cell, in remarkable agreement with the mean of their direct estimates.

Paul and Carlson (1984) estimated that the DNA content per bacterial cell ranged from 5.8 to 14.4 fg/cell ($\bar{x} = 9.8$ fg/cell). These values were higher than had been measured in other studies in which most values were between 2 and 5 fg/cell (Cho and Azam, 1988) leading Paul and Carlson to speculate that their high values could have been caused by the presence of large bacteria and/or microeukaryotes, use of Hoechst 33258 stain, or contamination by detrital DNA. In later studies, Paul et al. (1985) recorded a value of 5.7 fg/cell and Jeffrey and Paul (1988b) estimated values of 5.3 to 14.0 fg/cell.

In a recent investigation of the macromolecular composition of marine bacterioplankton, Simon and Azam (1989) noted that small bacteria are very "dry," e.g., 0.026 μm^3 cells had 46% (v/v) water while 0.4 μm^3 cells consisted of 82% water, comparable to cultured E. coli. In addition, their calculations indicated that as bacteria become smaller their dry weight becomes rich in DNA, e.g., 13% of dry weight in 0.026 μm^3 cells versus 5% in 0.4 μm^3 cells. Simon and Azam list bacterial cell DNA contents ranging from 2.5 fg/cell for 0.026 μm^3 cells to 5.0 fg/cell for 0.4 μm^3 cells.

Ellenbroek and Cappenberg (1991), using the Hoechst 33258 method, concluded that the high DNA values measured by Paul and Carlson (1984) were not inherent in the method. The DNA content of freshwater bacteria, grown in steady-state continuous cultures with generation times of 0.25 to 3.7 days, varied little with most values being between 3.7 and 4.9 fg/cell. They recorded one value of 6.9 fg/cell at the shortest generation time but it deviated significantly from other values. Discarding this value yielded a mean DNA content of 4.05 $\pm$ 0.38 fg/cell and a coefficient of variation of 9.4%.

The DNA content per cell increases with growth rate in bacterial cultures (Coveney and Wetzel, 1988), while in starved V. cholerae cells, Hood et al. (1986) observed that the DNA content decreased gradually for at least 30 days by which time 75% of the total DNA had disappeared. With pure cultures of bacteria, DNA contents > 5 fg/cell are sometimes reported (Ellenbroek and Cappenberg, 1991). Ellenbroek and Cappenberg pointed out that when these bacteria are cultured at high growth rates, multiple genome copies occur resulting in high

DNA contents which are irrelevant for calculations involving natural populations where growth rates are likely to be much lower.

On the basis of the limited data available, it appears that a DNA content > 2 but < 5 fg/cell is probably typical for most marine and freshwater bacteria. Clearly more data are required.

An equally contentious issue is the C:DNA ratio (Karl and Winn, 1986; Fuhrman *et al.*, 1986b), which is required to convert cells produced to carbon units, but also for which there are few data. As noted by Psenner (1990), the measurement of bacterial carbon remains a problem but this information is essential for studies on bacterial production and investigations of the interactions between bacteria, autotrophs, and grazers.

4.5. Conversion Factors

We have reviewed the development of the $[^3H]$-TdR assay to assess bacterial growth and production rates in natural systems and examined our current knowledge on a number of methodological issues that can affect the rates measured. The final, and highly controversial, issue is the conversion factor used to convert the rate of $[^3H]$-TdR incorporation to number of cells produced per unit volume and time, i.e., to bacterial growth rate and production units, parameters essential for intersystem comparisons and for intrasystem carbon flow considerations. This conversion can be done using either theoretical or empirical factors. Empirical conversion factors have only been derived for water samples and not for sediment samples (Kemp, 1990) and microbial ecologists use either a theoretical value for sediment bacterial populations or employ a factor obtained for planktonic populations.

Fuhrman and Azam (1980) calculated that the theoretical conversion factor ranged from 2.0×10^{17} to 1.3×10^{18} cells/mole $[^3H]$-TdR incorporated into DNA (see Section 3.1 for assumptions used). They found that production estimates from $[^3H]$-TdR incorporation using these values agreed well with production measured by cell counts except in diluted samples where $[^3H]$-TdR-based production was lower than actual cell production. According to Fuhrman and Azam, a likely explanation for this difference was that the conversion factor was too conservative because of a change in dissolved organic carbon concentration in the filtrates.

Fuhrman and Azam (1982) used cellular DNA contents they measured to recalculate the conversion factor to be 1.7 and 2.4×10^{18} for a nearshore and offshore station, respectively. Empirically derived estimates of the conversion factor using $[^3H]$-TdR incorporation versus cells produced gave factors of 1.3–1.4×10^{18} cells produced per mole of $[^3H]$-TdR incorporated.

Empirically derived conversion factors are produced from water samples that are diluted 1 in 10: water is filter-sterilized using 0.2-μm pore size filters and to this is added water that has been filtered through 1- or 3-μm pore size filters to remove grazer populations. Dilution is necessary as bacterial numbers do not usually increase rapidly in whole samples (Christian et al., 1982; Kirchman et al., 1982). Changes in bacterial number or bacterial volume and [³H]-TdR incorporation rates with time are then monitored.

Ducklow et al. (1992) have reviewed the methods used to calculate empirically derived conversion factors and examined their advantages and disadvantages. The methods are: the derivative method first proposed by Kirchman et al. (1982), the modified derivative method of Ducklow and Hill (1985), the integrative method (Fuhrman and Azam, 1980; Riemann et al., 1987; Coveney and Wetzel, 1988), and the cumulative method (Bjørnsen and Kuparinen, 1991). The mathematical formulations for these methods are given by Ducklow et al. (1992) and their derivations can be found in the references noted above. Below we present the advantages and disadvantages of each method as given by Ducklow et al..

1. *Derivative method:* assumes that cell number and rate of [³H]-TdR incorporation increase in tandem, that the time course of [³H]-TdR incorporation rates gives an estimate of μ, the specific growth rate, and that σ (the slope of [³H]-TdR incorporation) equals μ, the slope of cell increase. This is not always true as σ has been observed to be $>$ μ (Ducklow and Hill, 1985; Ducklow et al., 1992) and the method should not be used unless it can be demonstrated that σ = μ.

2. *Modified derivative method:* μ is estimated as the slope of the regression between increasing cell numbers over time. The conversion factor is calculated using either the initial values of [³H]-TdR incorporation and cell numbers or the y-intercepts of the regression equations of cell numbers and [³H]-TdR incorporation over time. Maximum weight is given to cell numbers, which Ducklow et al. (1992) believe provide the best indicator of growth processes.

3. *Integrative method:* is based on the total number of cells produced and total amount of [³H]-TdR incorporated over time. Cell production is estimated either as the difference between the initial and final cell counts (Riemann et al., 1987) or from the integration of cells produced over successive intervals (Coveney and Wetzel, 1988). Total [³H]-TdR incorporation is obtained by integrating the rate of [³H]-TdR incorporation over time. Ducklow et al. found that conversion factors generated from this method were lower than those from the modified derivative method because the [³H]-TdR incorporation rates, which are in the denominator of the integrative method equation, increased more rapidly than cell numbers. The ratio of total cell numbers to total [³H]-TdR incorporated decreases with time so that the conversion factor also decreases as incubation time increases. This raises the problem of what is the best incubation interval and Ducklow et al. indicated that it might be possible to extend the incubation until an asymptotic conversion value has been found but that these values may not be true for the ambient populations sampled.

4. *Cumulative method:* is similar to the integrative method but differs in using the slope of the regression of cell abundance on cumulative [³H]-TdR incorporation and produces a time-weighted ratio of cells produced to [³H]-TdR incorporated. While Bjørnsen and Kuparinen (1991) have stated that the advantage of this method is that it takes into account all of the data, Ducklow *et al.* have pointed out that like the integrative method, it too is sensitive to lack of coupling between [³H]-TdR incorporation and cell numbers in incubated samples. They noted, however, that an advantage of the method is that the appropriate length of incubation can be determined from the regression parameters and concluded that probably the shortest incubation period from which a significant regression could be obtained would be best.

Ducklow *et al.* (1992) concluded that the modified derivative method gives the most reliable method for calculating the conversion factor because it is insensitive to uncoupled rates of [³H]-TdR incorporation and cell production. They also noted that this uncoupling over time scales of a day or more may indicate unbalanced growth by bacterial populations, an adaptation to variable environmental conditions, and results in conversion factors that are either higher (derivative method) or lower (integrative and cumulative methods) than would be measured with populations in balanced growth. When growth is balanced, all models should give essentially the same conversion factor and under such conditions Ducklow *et al.* agree with Bjørnsen and Kuparinen (1991) that the cumulative model makes optimal use of the data. The modified derivative method gave a mean conversion factor of $2.65 \pm 0.73 \times 10^{18}$ cells/mole [³H]-TdR incorporated into DNA for open ocean samples (Ducklow *et al.*, 1992).

Ducklow and Carlson (1992) reviewed the conversion factors derived for a wide range of marine systems and found they ranged from a low of 1×10^{17} to a high of 60×10^{18} cells produced/mole [³H]-TdR incorporated and calculated a median value of 2×10^{18} cells produced/mole [³H]-TdR incorporated. Not all of the studies included in the survey extracted and purified labeled DNA. In a similar survey of conversion factors from freshwater and marine systems, Bell (1990) found that the values ranged from about 0.5 to 30×10^{18} cells/mole [³H]-TdR incorporated, but this range did not include values > 20 when the [³H]-TdR concentration used was only 5–10 nM. Bell noted that a conversion factor is not realistic unless the concentration of [³H]-TdR used maximizes the degree of participation of [³H]-TdR in DNA synthesis. His hypothesis was supported by a review of the literature which indicated that when the [³H]-TdR concentration used was > 10 nM, conversion factors usually approached the theoretical factor of $\sim 1 \times 10^{18}$ cells/mole. A similar conclusion was also reached by Chróst *et al.* (1988) and Smits and Riemann (1988). In studies where conversion factors are not empirically derived, Bell recommends the use of a value between 1 and 2×10^{18} cells/mole. He also noted that it is possible to make estimates of bacterial production directly from rates of [³H]-TdR incorporation using recent information on C per cell and DNA per cell (Simon and Azam, 1989; also see references in Section 4.4) thereby eliminating the need for empirical conversion factors.

In their study of empirical conversion factors for coastal marine bacteria, based on labeled macromolecules in cold TCA precipitates, Riemann *et al.* (1987) found the average value to be 1.1×10^{18} cells/mole [^{3}H]-TdR incorporated (S.E. $= 0.05 \times 10^{18}$, $n = 63$). They also observed no significant change in the conversion factor with different media, temperature, or cell generation time.

Smits and Riemann (1988) calculated conversion factors for freshwater bacteria grown in diluted batch cultures. They found bacterial generation time had a significant effect on the derived factor based on label appearing in cold TCA precipitates: the average value was 2.15×10^{18} cells/mole when the generation time was > 20 hr but with generation times < 20 hr the average value was 11.8×10^{18} cells/mole. They also found that conversion factors were higher at 20°C than at 10 or 15°C but that changes in the medium had no effect. Smits and Riemann concluded that the rate of [^{3}H]-TdR incorporation into DNA is probably limited by uptake at faster generation times and that freshwater bacterioplankton cell production is underestimated when a conversion factor of 2.15×10^{18} cells/mole is used. However, Bloem *et al.* (1989) found that the conversion factor was relatively constant in continuous freshwater bacterial cultures with specific growth rates of 0.007 to 0.116 per hr, similar to results of Bjørnsen and Kuparinen (1991), and Ellenbroek and Cappenberg (1991) who suggested that the conversion of [^{3}H]-TdR to labeled dTMP by thymidine kinase may have been the reason why empirically determined (0.25 to 1.31×10^{18} cells/mole) and theoretical (0.26 to 0.34×10^{18} cells/mole based on measured DNA content) conversion factors differed. For four species of marine *Vibrio* grown in continuous culture at generation times of 5 to 100 hr, significant differences (up to 50%) in the conversion factor between species were observed (Snyder, Robarts, and Caldwell, unpublished data), a point alluded to by Painting *et al.* (1989), but not caused by culture conditions within species (Fig. 9).

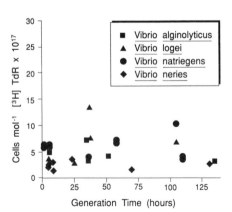

Figure 9. The relationship between conversion factors and growth rate at [^{3}H]-TdR saturation for four species of marine *Vibrio* (Snyder, Robarts, and Caldwell, unpublished data). Note the independence of conversion factors with growth rate.

Coveney and Wetzel (1988) prescreened, diluted, and amended water samples from an oligotrophic lake with organic and inorganic nutrients. They found that prescreening samples resulted in increased conversion factors estimated per cell and as per cell volume while the addition of inorganic phosphorus led to lower factors as [³H]-TdR incorporation was stimulated more than growth. The addition of organic substrates, such as glucose and amino acids, generally did not result in higher conversion factors. Coveney and Wetzel also observed that dilution of samples caused an increase in cell number-based conversion factors but not in volume-based conversion factors. Further analysis of their data indicated that much of the variation in cell number-based conversion factors was related to changes in mean cell volume of the bacteria. Similarly, we have found that biovolume-based conversion factors for [³H]-TdR incorporation into DNA were less variable, both between growth rates within species and between species for all growth rates, than cell number-based conversion factors for four *Vibrio* species (Snyder, Robarts, and Caldwell, unpublished data).

In a novel approach to the question of conversion factors, Cole *et al.* (1989) used a detailed organic carbon budget of an oligotrophic lake as an ecosystem-level calibration of bacterial processes. Their budget constrained the conversion factor to between 1 and 6 $\times$ 10¹⁸ cells/mole [³H]-TdR incorporated and indicated that if the conversion factor was > 10 $\times$ 10¹⁸ cells/mole, bacterial respiration alone would exceed the total input of carbon to the system.

In conclusion, while the question of conversion factors remains highly controversial and the published numbers are wide-ranging, we agree with Bell (1990) that values between 1 and 2 $\times$ 10¹⁸ cells/mole are most realistic. However, we stress the point, also made by Bell, that it is now possible to make estimates of bacterial production directly from [³H]-TdR incorporation using recent information on C per cell and DNA per cell which eliminates the need for empirical conversion factors obtained from bacterioplankton growing in either altered "natural" samples or culture conditions. This development is particularly pertinent for sediment and soil microbial ecologists who have not yet determined empirical conversion factors. We suspect that bacterial growth rates and production calculated in this way cannot be any more biased, and quite possibly less biased, than from using such artificial methods or from arbitrarily choosing a conversion factor from the literature.

5. Conclusions

Microbial ecologists have searched long and hard for a universal substrate to measure bacterial growth rates and production in natural systems. Tritiated thymidine has been considered by many to be that universal substrate.

Although O'Donovan (1978) has noted that "a fundamental knowledge of thymidine metabolism (Section 2) is required of anyone who routinely labels

DNA for any purpose," one of the main conclusions arising from the present review is that probably this is frequently not the case. The [³H]-TdR assay is frequently incorrectly executed and, as a result, much of the published data on bacterial production and growth rates in natural systems may be unnecessarily biased toward either an overestimate or an underestimate depending on the methodological errors made. The extent of the bias, or if it is even significant, is unknown. However, the bias introduced by these methodological errors may be relatively minor compared with that imposed by factors inherent in natural systems (e.g., different species, metabolic requirements, and physiological states) which we have no control over and, indeed, about which we have very little knowledge.

Fuhrman and Azam's 1982 paper, although not the original paper on the use of [³H]-TdR in ecological studies, stimulated an exponential increase in published studies not only on bacterial production and its fate in a wide range of environments, but on the role of heterotrophic bacteria in the environment generally. Thymidine has been used to assess the relationship between heterotrophic bacteria and autotrophs, their importance as food resources for flagellates and micro- and macrozooplankton, and their significance to carbon and energy cycles in inland and marine waters. [³H]-TdR has also been used as an assay tool in toxicity studies (e.g., Riemann and Lingaard-Jørgensen, 1990) and to determine bacterial mortality by viruses (e.g., Heldal and Bratbak, 1991). This has led to new concepts of the role of heterotrophic bacteria in ecosystems and is based on a method that is still controversial in terms of what it actually measures.

On theoretical grounds (see Section 2), [³H]-TdR appeared to be the tool microbial ecologists were seeking. At low (nanomolar) concentrations, [³H]-TdR labels DNA of only bacteria. However, macromolecules other than DNA may also be labeled, significant intracellular isotope dilution (and extracellular dilution, especially in sediment/soil samples) may occur, and not all bacteria, notably species of *Pseudomonas,* can incorporate [³H]-TdR into DNA. The significance of the latter is not known since our knowledge of bacterial species in natural populations, and the variance and succession of species within populations, is only rudimentary (Lee and Fuhrman, 1991). As Lee and Fuhrman have noted, although microbial ecologists are aware that dominant species probably differ between environments over time, bacterial populations are usually treated as a single group. Consequently, even when the [³H]-TdR assay is correctly executed, errors in estimates of growth and production rates may still occur.

Much of the controversy with the method stems from the lack of a single protocol for use with planktonic populations and one for sediments/soils. In this regard, the recent call to initiate a course of action to standardize these protocols by G. Jost (Institut für Ostseeforschung) and H. Ducklow (Horn Point Environmental Lab), stemming from the workshop on Microbial Ecology of Pelagic Environments held in Helsingor, Denmark, we believe is a step in the right direction. Too many researchers do not use, or misuse, the valid methods available to extract and purify labeled DNA. Lack of support for this point of view in recent reviews (e.g., Riemann and Bell, 1990; Bell, 1993) only ensures that the problems will not be resolved.

Another problem area is the extrapolation of [^{3}H]-TdR data obtained in laboratory cultures to the real world. We support the use of cultures to answer specific questions which may not otherwise be approachable but invoking such results as proof that [^{3}H]-TdR incorporation does not accurately measure, or does measure, bacterial growth of heterogeneous natural populations needs to be done cautiously. Similarly, the derivation of empirical conversion factors from manipulated populations seems to us to be questionable. The enormous spread in such factors, as recently found by Ducklow and Carlson (1992) among others, is not surprising. Knowledge of the DNA and carbon contents of natural bacteria is progressing to the point where such empirical conversion factors will not be required, as suggested by Bell (1990).

We have not compared the [^{3}H]-TdR assay with other current methods of measuring bacterial growth rates as this has been done in several reviews and many studies (see Riemann and Bell, 1990). Riemann and Bell concluded that when these methods are used properly, they are complementary. Such comparisons are meaningless, since all of the methods are controversial. Moriarty (1986) has successfully argued that the [^{3}H]-TdR assay has theoretical strengths over other assays currently in use.

Should the operational problems with the [^{3}H]-TdR method warrant its rejection? The data on bacterial growth rates and production using [^{3}H]-TdR in a wide range of habitats are considerable and have led to new insights into the role of heterotrophic bacteria in surface and subsurface waters. We do not recommend that the method be discarded at this time since much of the controversy surrounding it may be due to faulty application. We must standardize accurate and dependable protocols for the [^{3}H]-TdR assay and see that they are properly used by microbial ecologists. Only then will we be able to decide if the [^{3}H]-TdR assay should be rejected.

To test the assumptions of the [^{3}H]-TdR assay we need data for natural populations using independent and reliable methods. One possibility is the thymidine analog, bromodeoxyuridine combined with a monoclonal antibody detection assay (Cawood and Savage, 1983). This method is promising but the small cell size and total biomass of natural populations will probably make it feasible only if the cells are visualized with a flow cytometer capable of analyzing such small particles or if samples are concentrated on blots (Santavy, Snyder, Robarts and Caldwell, unpublished data).

It may be that there is a better method than the [^{3}H]-TdR assay to measure bacterial growth rate and production in natural systems. Realistically, however, there is probably no single, simple, and reliable method. What we must do then is develop a suite of methods that together allow us to analyze bacterial growth and production *in situ*.

ACKNOWLEDGMENTS. A number of people generously permitted us to use unpublished data, made available manuscripts that were either submitted or in press, or drew our attention to published papers that we were unaware of: Russell Bell, Tom Berman, Thomas Chrzanowski, Hugh Ducklow, Wayne Gardner, Ora Hadas, Tim Hollibaugh, David Karl, Paul Kemp, Gerry O'Donovan, Peter Pollard, Debbie Santavy, Dick Snyder, Marley Waiser, Richard Wicks. We thank Hugh Ducklow, Gerry O'Donovan, Dick Snyder, and Warwick Vincent for critically reading various drafts of the manuscript. R.D.R. acknowledges David Moriarty, who prensented the challenge, and Richard Wicks, who provided the skills, which together led us to participate in the development of the [³H]-TdR assay.

References

Albrechtsen, H.-J., and Winding, A., 1992, Microbial biomass and activity in subsurface sediments from Vejen, Denmark, *Microb. Ecol.* **23:**303–317.

Alongi, D. M., 1988, Bacterial productivity and microbial biomass in tropical mangrove sediments, *Microb. Ecol.* **15:**59–79.

Austin, H. K., and Findlay, S. E. G., 1989, Benthic bacterial biomass and production in the Hudson River estuary, *Microb. Ecol.* **18:**105–116.

Azam, F., and Fuhrman, J. A. 1984, Measurement of bacterioplankton growth in the sea and its regulation by environmental conditions, in: *Heterotrophic Activity in the Sea* (J. E. Hobbie and P.J. L. Williams, eds.), Plenum Press, New York, pp. 179–196.

Bååth, E., 1990, Thymidine incorporation into soil bacteria, *Soil Biol. Biochem.* **22:**803–810.

Bååth, E., and Johansson, T., 1990, Measurement of bacterial growth rates on the rhizoplane using ³H-thymidine incorporation into DNA, *Plant Soil* **126:**133–139.

Beacham, I. R., Beacham, K., Zaritsky, A., and Pritchard, R. H., 1971, Intracellular thymidine triphosphate concentrations in wild type and in thymine requiring mutants of *Escherichia coli* 15 and K12, *J. Mol. Biol.* **60:**75–86.

Bell, R. T., 1986, Further verification of the isotope dilution approach for estimating the degree of participation of [³H]thymidine in DNA synthesis in studies of aquatic bacterial production, *Appl. Environ. Microbiol.* **52:**1212–1214.

Bell, R. T., 1990, An explanation for the variability in the conversion factor deriving bacterial cell production from incorporation of [³H]-thymidine, *Limnol. Oceanogr.* **35:**910–915.

Bell, R. T., 1993, Estimating growth and productivity of heterotrophic bacterioplankton via incorporation of tritiated thymidine, in: *Current Methods in Aquatic Microbial Ecology* (P. Kemp, B. Sherr, E. Sherr, and J. J. Cole, eds.), Lewis Publ., Chelsea, Mich. (in press).

Bell, R. T., and Ahlgren, I., 1987, Thymidine incorporation and microbial respiration in the surface sediment of a hypereutrophic lake, *Limnol. Oceanogr.* **32:**476–482.

Bell, R. T., and Riemann, B., 1989, Adenine incorporation into DNA as a measure of microbial production in freshwaters, *Limnol. Oceanogr.* **34:**435–444.

Bern, L., 1985, Autoradiographic studies of [*methyl*-³H]thymidine incorporation in a cyanobacterium (*Microcystis wesenbergii*)–bacterium association and in selected algae and bacteria, *Appl. Environ. Microbiol.* **49:**232–233.

Bird, D. F., and Karl, D. M., 1991, Spatial patterns of glutamate and thymidine assimilation in

Bransfield Strait, Antarctica during and following the austral spring bloom, *Deep-Sea Res.* **38**:1057–1075.

Bjørnsen, P. K., and Kuparinen, J., 1991, Determination of bacterioplankton biomass, net production and growth efficiency in the Southern Ocean, *Mar Ecol. Prog. Ser.* **71**:185–194.

Bloem, J., Starink, M., Bär-Gilissen, M.-J. B., and Cappenberg, T. E., 1988, Protozoan grazing, bacterial activity, and mineralization in two-stage continuous cultures, *Appl. Environ. Microbiol.* **54**:3113–3121.

Bloem, J., Ellenbroek, F. M., Bär-Gilissen, M.-J. B., and Cappenberg, T. E., 1989, Protozoan grazing and bacterial production in stratified Lake Vechten estimated with fluorescently labeled bacteria and by thymidine incorporation, *Appl. Environ. Microbiol.* **55**:1787–1795.

Brittain, A. M., and Karl, D. M., 1990, Catabolism of tritiated thymidine by aquatic microbial communities and incorporation of tritium into RNA and protein, *Appl. Environ. Microbiol.* **56**:1245–1254.

Brock, T. D., 1967, Bacterial growth rate in the sea: Direct analysis by thymidine autoradiography, *Science* **155**:81–83.

Brock, T. D., 1971, Microbial growth rates in nature, *Bacteriol. Rev.* **35**:39–58.

Burnison, B. K., and Nuttley, D. J., 1990, Purification of DNA for bacterial productivity estimates, *Appl. Environ. Microbiol.* **56**:362–365.

Carlson, C. A., Stewart, G. J., and Ingraham, J. L., 1985, Thymidine salvage in *Pseudomonas stutzeri* and *Pseudomonas aeruginosa* provided by heterologous expression of *Escherichia coli* thymidine kinase gene, *J. Bacteriol.* **163**:291–295.

Carmen, K. R., Dobbs, F. C., and Guckert, J. B., 1988, Consequences of thymidine catabolism for estimates of bacterial production: An example for a coastal marine sediment, *Limnol. Oceanogr.* **33**:1595–1606.

Cawood, A. H. H., and Savage, J. R. K., 1983, A comparison of the use of bromodeoxyuridine and [³H]thymidine in studies of the cell cycle, *Cell Tissue Kinet.* **16**:51–57.

Cho, B. C., and Azam, F., 1988, Heterotrophic bacterioplankton production measurement by the tritiated thymidine incorporation method, *Ergebn. Limnol.* **31**:153–162.

Christensen, H., Funck-Jensen, D., and Kjøller, A., 1989, Growth rate of rhizosphere bacteria measured directly by the tritiated thymidine incorporation technique, *Soil Biol. Biochem.* **21**:113–117.

Christian, R. R., Hanson, B. B., and Newell, S. Y., 1982, Comparison of methods for measurement of bacterial growth rates in mixed batch cultures, *Appl. Environ. Microbiol.* **43**:1160–1165.

Chróst, R., Overbeck, J., and Wcislo, R., 1988, Evaluation of the [³H]thymidine method for estimating bacterial growth rates and production in lake water: Re-examination and methodological comments, *Acta Microbiol. Pol.* **37**:95–112.

Chrzanowski, T. H., 1988, Consequences of accounting for isotopic dilution in thymidine incorporation assays, *Appl. Environ. Microbiol.* **54**:1868–1870.

Cole, J. J., Caraco, N. F., Strayer, D. L., Ochs, C., and Nolan, S., 1989, A detailed organic carbon budget as an ecosystem-level calibration of bacterial respiration in an oligotrophic lake during summer, *Limnol. Oceanogr.* **34**:286–296.

Coveney, M. F., and Wetzel, R. G., 1988, Experimental evaluation of conversion factors for the [³H]thymidine incorporation assay of bacterial secondary productivity, *Appl. Environ. Microbiol.* **54**:2018–2026.

Davis, C. L., 1989, Uptake and incorporation of thymidine by bacterial isolates from an upwelling environment, *Appl. Environ. Microbiol.* **55**:1267–1272.

Douglas, D. J., Novitsky, J. A., and Fournier, R. O., 1987, Microautoradiography-based enumeration of bacteria with estimates of thymidine-specific growth and production rates, *Mar. Ecol. Prog. Ser.* **36**:91–99.

Ducklow, H. W., and Carlson, C. A. 1992, Oceanic bacterial production, *Adv. Microb. Ecol.* **12**:113–181.

Ducklow, H. W., and Hill, S. M., 1985, Tritiated thymidine incorporation and the growth of heterotrophic bacteria in warm core rings, *Limnol. Oceanogr.* **30**:260–272.

Ducklow, H. W., Kirchman, D. L., and Quinby, H. L., 1992, Determination of bacterioplankton growth rates during the North Atlantic spring phytoplankton bloom: Cell growth and macromolecular synthesis in seawater cultures, *Microb. Ecol.* **24**:125–144.

Ellenbroek, F. M., and Cappenberg, T. E., 1991, DNA synthesis and tritiated thymidine incorporation by heterotrophic freshwater bacteria in continuous culture, *Appl. Environ. Microbiol.* **57**:1675–1682.

Fallon, R. D., and Newell, S. Y., 1986, Thymidine incorporation by the microbial community of standing dead *Spartina alterniflora*, *Appl. Environ. Microbiol.* **52**:1206–1208.

Fallon, R. D., Newell, S. Y., and Hopkinson, C. S., 1983, Bacterial production in marine sediments: Will cell specific measures agree with whole system metabolism? *Mar. Ecol. Prog. Ser.* **11**:119–127.

Findlay, R. H., Pollard, P. C, Moriarty, D. J. W., and White, D. C., 1985, Quantitative determination of microbial activity and community nutritional status in estuarine sediments: Evidence for a disturbance artifact, *Can. J. Microbiol.* **31**:493–498.

Findlay, S. E. G., Meyer, J. L., and Edwards, R. T., 1984, Measuring bacterial production via rate of incorporation of [³H]thymidine into DNA, *J. Microbiol. Methods* **2**:57–72.

Findlay, S. E. G., Pace, M. L., Lints, D., Cole, J. J., Caraco, N. F., and Peierls, B., 1991, Weak coupling of bacterial and algal production in a heterotrophic ecosystem: The Hudson River estuary, *Limnol. Oceanogr.* **36**:286–278.

Forsdyke, D. R., 1971, Application of the isotope dilution principle to the analysis of factors affecting the incorporation of [³H]uridine and [³H]cytidine into cultured lymphocytes, *Biochem. J.* **125**:721–732.

Fuhrman, J. A., and Azam, F., 1980, Bacterioplankton secondary production estimates for coastal waters of British Columbia, Antarctica and California, *Appl. Environ. Microbiol.* **39**:1085–1095.

Fuhrman, J. A., and Azam, F., 1982, Thymidine incorporation as a measure of heterotrophic bacterioplankton production in marine surface water: Evaluation and field results, *Mar. Biol.* **66**:109–120.

Fuhrman, J. A., Ducklow, H. W., Kirchman, D. L., Hudak, J., McManus, G. B., and Kramer, J., 1986a, Does adenine incorporation into nucleic acids measure total microbial production? *Limnol. Oceanogr.* **31**:627–636.

Fuhrman, J. A,. Ducklow, H. W., Kirchman, D. L., and McManus, G. B., 1986b, Adenine and total microbial production: A reply, *Limnol. Oceanogr.* **31**:1395–1400.

Gabriel, O., 1987, Biosynthesis of sugar residues for glycogen, peptidoglycan, lipopolysaccharide, and related systems, in: *Escherichia coli and Salmonella typhimurium* (F. C. Neuhard, J. L. Ingraham, K. B. Low, B. Magasanik, M. Schaechter, and H. E. Umbargar, eds.), Volume 1, American Society for Microbiology, Washington, D.C., pp. 504–511.

Ghiorse, W. C., and Wilson, J. T., 1988, Microbial ecology of the terrestrial subsurface, *Adv. Appl. Microbiol.* **33**:107–172.

Gilmour, C. C., Leavitt, M. E., and Shiaris, M. P., 1990, Evidence against incorporation of exogenous thymidine by sulfate-reducing bacteria, *Limnol. Oceanogr.* **35**:1401–1409.

Grivell, A., and Jackson, J., 1968, Thymidine kinase: Evidence for its absence from *Neurospora crassa* and some other microorganisms, and the relevance of this to specific labelling of deoxyribonucleic acid, *J. Gen. Microbiol.* **54**:307–317.

Güde, H., 1984, Test for validity of different radioisotope activity measurements by microbial pure and mixed cultures, *Ergebn. Limnol.* **19**:257–266.

Heldal, M., and Bratbak, G., 1991, Production and decay of viruses in aquatic environments, *Mar. Ecol. Prog. Ser.* **72**:205–212.

Hobbie, J. E., 1988, A comparison of the ecology of planktonic bacteria in fresh and salt water, *Limnol. Oceanogr.* **33**:750–764.

Hobbie, J. E., and Crawford, C. C., 1969, Respiration corrections for bacterial uptake of dissolved organic compounds in natural waters, *Limnol. Oceanogr.* **14**:528–532.

Hollibaugh, J. T., 1988, Limitations of the [³H]thymidine method for estimating bacterial productivity due to thymidine metabolism, *Mar. Ecol. Prog. Ser.* **43**:19–30.

Hollibaugh, J. T., and Wong, P. S., 1992, Ethanol extractable substrate pools and the incorporation and metabolism of thymidine, L-leucine and other low molecular weight substrates by bacterioplankton, *Can. J. Microbiol.* **38**:605–613.

Hollibaugh, J. T., Fuhrman, J. A., and Azam, F., 1980, Radioactive labeling of natural assemblages of bacterioplankton for use in trophic studies, *Limnol. Oceanogr.* **25**:172–181.

Hood, M. A., Guckert, J. B., White, D. C., and Deck, F., 1986, Effect of nutrient deprivation on lipid, carbohydrate, DNA, RNA, and protein levels in *Vibrio cholerae*, *Appl. Environ. Microbiol.* **52**:788–793.

Hudson, J. J., Roff, J. C., and Burnison, B. K., 1990, Measuring epilithic bacterial production in streams, *Can. J. Fish. Aquat. Sci.* **47**:1813–1820.

Hutchinson, W. C., and Munro, H. N., 1961, The determination of nucleic acids in biological materials, *Analyst* **86**:768–813.

Jeffrey, W. H., and Paul, J. H., 1988a, Effect of 5-fluoro-2'-deoxyuridine on [³H]thymidine incorporation by bacterioplankton in the waters of southwest Florida, *Appl. Environ. Microbiol.* **54**:331–336.

Jeffrey, W. H., and Paul, J. H., 1988b, Underestimation of DNA synthesis by [³H]thymidine incorporation in marine bacteria, *Appl. Environ. Microbiol.* **54**:3165–3168.

Jeffrey, W. H., and Paul, J. H., 1990, Thymidine uptake, thymidine incorporation, and thymidine kinase activity in marine bacterium isolates, *Appl. Environ. Microbiol.* **56**:1367–1372.

Jeffrey, W. H., Paul, J. H., Cazares, L. H., DeFlaun, M. F., and David, A. W., 1990, Correlation of nonspecific macromolecular labeling with environmental parameters during [³H]thymidine incorporation in the waters of southwest Florida, *Microb. Ecol.* **20**:21–35.

Johnstone, B. H., and Jones, R. D., 1989, A study on the lack of [methyl-³H]thymidine and uptake and incorporation by chemolithotrophic bacteria, *Microb. Ecol.* **18**:73–77.

Kaplan, L. A., Bott, T. L., and Bielicki, J. K., 1992, Assessment of [³H]thymidine incorporation into DNA as a method to determine bacterial productivity in stream bed sediments, *Appl. Environ. Microbiol.* **58**:3614–3621.

Karl, D. M., 1980, Cellular nucleotide measurements and applications in microbial ecology, *Microbiol. Rev.* **44**:739–796.

Karl, D. M., 1982, Selected nucleic acid precursors in studies of aquatic microbial ecology, *Appl. Environ. Microbiol.* **44**:891–902.

Karl, D. M., and Bailiff, M. D., 1989, The measurement and distribution of dissolved nucleic acids in aquatic environments, *Limnol. Oceanogr.* **34**:543–558.

Karl, D. M., and Winn, C. D., 1986, Does adenine incorporation into nucleic acids measure total microbial production?: A response to comments by Fuhrman et al., *Limnol. Oceanogr.* **31**:1384–1394.

Kemp, P. F., 1990, The fate of benthic bacterial production, *Rev. Aquat. Sci.* **2**:109–124.

Kirchman, D. L., Ducklow, H. W., and Mitchell, R., 1982, Estimates of bacterial growth from changes in uptake rates and biomass, *Appl. Environ. Microbiol.* **44**:1296–1307.

Kirchman, D. L., K'Nees, E., and Hodson, R., 1985, Leucine incorporation and its potential as a measure of protein synthesis by bacteria in natural aquatic systems, *Appl. Environ. Microbiol.* **49**:599–607.

Kirchman, D. L., Newell, S. Y., and Hodson, R. E., 1986, Incorporation versus biosynthesis of leucine: Implication for measuring rates of protein synthesis and biomass production by bacteria in marine systems, *Mar. Ecol. Prog. Ser.* **32**:47–59.

Kornberg, A., and Baker, T. A., 1992, *DNA Replication,* 2nd ed., Freeman, San Francisco.

Kraffzik, B., and Conrad, R., 1991, Thymidine incorporation into lake water bacterioplankton and pure cultures of chemolithotrophic (CO, H_2) and methanotrophic bacteria, *FEMS Microbiol. Ecol.* **23**:7–14.

Kunicka-Goldfinger, W., 1976, Determination of growth of aquatic bacteria by measurements of incorporation of tritiated thymidine, *Acta Microbiol. Pol.* **25**:279–286.

Lark, K. G., 1969, Initiation and control of DNA synthesis, *Annu. Rev. Biochem.* **38**:569–604.

Lee, S., and Fuhrman, J. A., 1991, Spatial and temporal variation of natural bacterioplankton assemblages studied by total genomic DNA cross-hybridization, *Limnol. Oceanogr.* **36**:1277–1287.

Li, W. K. W., 1983, Consideration of errors in estimating kinetic parameters based on Michaelis–Menten formalism in microbial ecology, *Limnol. Oceanogr.* **28**:185–190.

Lovell, C. R., and Konopka, A., 1985, Primary and bacterial production in two dimictic Indiana lakes, *Appl. Environ. Microbiol.* **49**:485–491.

McDonough, R. J., Sanders, R. W., Porter, K. G., and Kirchman, D. L., 1986, Depth distribution of bacterial production in a stratified lake with an anoxic hypolimnion, *Appl. Environ. Microbiol.* **52**:992–1000.

Maniatis, T., Fritsch, E. F., and Sambrook, J., 1982, *Molecular Cloning, A Laboratory Manual,* Cold Spring Harbor Laboratory, Cold Spring Harbor, N.Y.

Mården, P., Hermansson, M., and Kjelleberg, S., 1988, Incorporation of tritiated thymidine by marine bacterial isolates when undergoing a starvation survival response, *Arch. Microbiol.* **149**:427–432.

Moriarty, D. J. W., 1984, Measurement of bacterial growth rates in some marine systems using the incorporation of tritiated thymidine into DNA, in: *Heterotrophic Activity in the Sea* (J. E. Hobbie and P.J. L. Williams, eds.), Plenum Press, New York, pp. 217–231.

Moriarty, D. J. W., 1986, Measurement of bacterial growth rates in aquatic systems from rates of nucleic acid synthesis, *Adv. Microb. Ecol.* **9**:246–292.

Moriarty, D. J. W., and Pollard, P. C., 1981, DNA synthesis as a measure of bacterial productivity in seagrass sediments, *Mar. Ecol. Prog. Ser.* **5**:151–156.

Moriarty, D. J. W., and Pollard, P. C., 1990, Effects of radioactive labelling of macromolecules, disturbance of bacteria and adsorption of thymidine to sediment on the determination of bacterial growth rates in sediments with tritiated thymidine, *J. Microbiol. Methods* **11**:127–139.

Munch-Petersen, A., and Mygind, B., 1983, Transport of nucleic acid precursors, in: *Metabolism of Nucleotides, Nucleosides and Nucleobases in Microorganisms* (A. Munch-Petersen, ed.), Academic Press, New York, pp. 259–305.

Munro, H. N., and Fleck, A., 1966, The determination of nucleic acids, in: *Methods of Biochemical Analysis* (D. Glick, ed.), Interscience, New York, pp. 113–176.

Murray, R. E., Cooksey, K. E., and Priscu, J. C, 1986, Stimulation of bacterial DNA synthesis by algal exudates in attached algal–bacterial consortia, *Appl. Environ. Microbiol.* **52**:1177–1182.

Murray, R. E., Cooksey, K. E., and Priscu, J. C., 1987, Influence of physical disruption on growth of attached bacteria, *Appl. Environ. Microbiol.* **53**:2997–2999.

Novitsky, J. A., 1983a, Heterotrophic activity throughout a vertical profile of seawater and sediment in Halifax Harbour, Canada, *Appl. Environ. Microbiol.* **45**:1753–1760.

Novitsky, J. A., 1983b, Microbial activity at the sediment–water interface in Halifax Harbour, Canada, *Appl. Environ. Microbiol.* **45**:1761–1766.

Novitsky, J. A., 1986, Degradation of dead microbial biomass in a marine sediment, *Appl. Environ. Microbiol.* **52**:504–509.

O'Donovan, G. A., 1978, Thymidine metabolism in bacteria (and "How, or how not, to label DNA"), in: *DNA Synthesis: Present and Future* (I. Molineux and M. Kohiyama, eds.), Plenum Press, New York, pp. 219–253.

O'Donovan, G. A., and Neuhard, J., 1970, Pyrimidine metabolism in microorganisms, *Bacteriol. Rev.* **34**:278–343.

Oren, A., 1990, Thymidine incorporation in saltern ponds of different salinities: Estimation of in situ growth rates of halophilic archaeobacteria and eubacteria, *Microb. Ecol.* **19**:43–51.

Painting, S. J., Lucas, M. I., and Muir, D. G., 1989, Fluctuations in heterotrophic bacterial community structure, activity and production in response to development and decay of phytoplankton in a microcosm, *Mar. Ecol. Prog. Ser.* **53**:129–141.

Parsons, T. R., and Strickland, J. D. H., 1962, On the production of particulate organic carbon by heterotrophic processes in sea water, *Deep Sea Res.* **8**:211–222.

Paul, J. H., and Carlson, D. J., 1984, Genetic material in the marine environment: Implication for bacterial DNA, *Limnol. Oceanogr.* **29**:1091–1097.

Paul, J. H., Jeffrey, W. H., and DeFlaun, M. F., 1985, Particulate DNA in subtropical oceanic and estuarine planktonic environments, *Mar. Biol.* **90**:95–101.

Paul, J. H., Jeffrey, W. H., and DeFlaun, M. F., 1987, Dynamics of extracellular DNA in the marine environment, *Appl. Environ. Microbiol.* **53**:170–179.

Paul, J. H., Jeffrey, W. H., and DeFlaun, M. F., 1988, Mechanisms of DNA utilization by estaurine microbial populations, *Appl. Environ. Microbiol.* **54**:1682–1688.

Paul, J. H., Jeffrey, W. H., and Cannon, J. P., 1990, Production of dissolved DNA, RNA, and protein by microbial populations in a Florida reservoir, *Appl. Environ. Microbiol.* **56**:2957–2962.

Pedrós-Alió, C., and Newell, S. Y., 1989, Microautoradiographic study of thymidine uptake in brackish waters around Sapelo Island, Georgia, USA, *Mar. Ecol. Prog. Ser.* **55**:83–94.

Pollard, P. C., 1987, Dialysis: A simple method of separating labelled bacterial DNA and tritiated thymidine from aquatic sediments, *J. Microbiol. Methods* **7**:91–101.

Pollard, P. C., and Kogure, K., 1993, Bacterial decomposition of detritus in a tropical seagrass (*Syringodium isoetifolium*) ecosystem, measured with [methyl-^{3}H]thymidine, *Aust. J. Mar. Freshwater Res.* **44**:155–172.

Pollard, P. C., and Moriarty, D. J. W., 1984, Validity of the tritiated thymidine method for estimating bacterial growth rates: Measurement of isotope dilution during DNA synthesis, *Appl. Environ. Microbiol.* **48**:1076–1083.

Psenner, R., 1990, From image analysis to chemical analysis of bacteria: A long-term study? *Limnol. Oceanogr.* **35**:234–237.

Ramsay, A. J., 1974, The use of autoradiography to determine the proportion of bacteria metabolizing in an aquatic environment, *J. Gen. Microbiol.* **80**:363–373.

Riemann, B., 1984, Determining growth rates of natural assemblages of freshwater bacteria by means of ^{3}H-thymidine incorporation into DNA: Comments on methodology, *Arch. Hydrobiol. Beih.* **19**:67–80.

Riemann, B., and Bell, R. T., 1990, Advances in estimating bacterial biomass and growth in aquatic systems, *Arch. Hydrobiol.* **118**:385–402.

Riemann, B., and Lingaard-Jørgensen, P., 1990, Effects of toxic substances on natural bacterial assemblages determined by means of [^{3}H]thymidine incorporation, *Appl. Environ. Microbiol.* **56**:75–80.

Riemann, B., Fuhrman, J., and Azam, F., 1982, Bacterial secondary production in freshwater bacteria by means of ^{3}H-thymidine incorporation method, *Microb. Ecol.* **8**:101–114.

Riemann, B., Bjørnsen, P. K., Newell, S. Y., and Fallon, R., 1987, Calculation of cell production of coastal marine bacteria based on measured incorporation of [^{3}H]-thymidine, *Limnol. Oceanogr.* **32**:471–476.

Rivkin, R. B., 1986, Incorporation of tritiated thymidine by eucaryotic microalgae, *J. Phycol.* **22**:193–198.

Rivkin, R. B., and Voytek, M. A., 1986, Cell division rates of eucaryotic algae measured by tritiated thymidine incorporation into DNA: Coincident measurements of photosynthesis and cell division of individual species of phytoplankton isolated from natural populations, *J. Phycol.* **22**:199–205.

Robarts, R. D., 1986, Decomposition in freshwater ecosystems, *J. Limnol. Soc. S. Afr.* **12**:72–89.

Robarts, R. D., and Wicks, R. J., 1989, [Methyl-³H]thymidine macromolecular incorporation and lipid labeling: Their significance to DNA labeling during measurements of aquatic bacterial growth rate, *Limnol. Oceanogr.* **34**:213–222.

Robarts, R. D., and Wicks, R. J., 1990, Heterotrophic bacterial production and its dependence on autotrophic production in a hypertrophic African reservoir, *Can. J. Fish. Aquat. Sci.* **47**:1027–1037.

Robarts, R. D., Wicks, R. J., and Sephton, L. M., 1986, Spatial and temporal variations in bacterial macromolecule labeling with [*methyl*-³H]thymidine in a hypertrophic lake, *Appl. Environ. Microbiol.* **52**:1368–1373.

Roberts, R. B., Abelson, P. H., Cowrie, D. B., Bolton, E. T., and Britten, R. J., 1963, Studies of biosynthesis in *Escherichia coli,* Carnegie Institute, Washington, D.C.

Roodyn, D. B., and Mandel, H. G., 1960, A simple membrane fractionation method for determining the distribution of radioactivity in chemical fractions of *Bacillus cereus, Biochim. Biophys. Acta* **41**:80–88.

Rosenbaum-Oliver, D., and Zamenhof, S., 1972, Degree of participation of exogenous thymidine in the overall deoxyribonucleic acid synthesis in *Escherichia coli, J. Bacteriol.* **110**:585–591.

Saito, H., Tomioka, H., and Ohkido, S., 1985, Further studies on thymidine kinase: Distribution pattern of the enzyme in bacteria, *J. Gen. Microbiol.* **131**:3091–3098.

Sanders, R. W., and Porter, K. G., 1986, Use of metabolic inhibitors to estimate protozooplankton grazing and bacterial production in a monomictic eutrophic lake with an anaerobic hypolimnion, *Appl. Environ. Microbiol.* **52**:101–107.

Schmidt, G., and Thannhauser, S. J., 1945, A method for the determination of deoxyribonucleic acid, ribonucleic acid, and phosphoproteins in animal tissues, *J. Biol. Chem.* **161**:83–89.

Schneider, W. C., 1945, Phosphorus compounds in animal tissues: Extraction and estimation of deoxypentose nucleic acid and of pentose nucleic acid, *J. Biol. Chem.* **161**:293–303.

Servais, P., Billen, G., and Vives-Rego, J., 1985, Rate of bacterial mortality in aquatic environments, *Appl. Environ. Microbiol.* **49**:1448–1454.

Servais, P., Martinez, J., Billen, G., and Vives-Rego, J., 1987, Determining [³H]thymidine incorporation into bacterioplankton DNA: Improvement of the method by DNase treatment, *Appl. Environ. Microbiol.* **53**:1977–1979.

Simon, M., and Azam, F., 1989, Protein content and protein synthesis rates of planktonic marine bacteria, *Mar. Ecol. Prog. Ser.* **51**:201–213.

Smits, J. D., and Riemann, B., 1988, Calculation of cell production from [³H]thymidine incorporation with freshwater bacteria, *Appl. Environ. Microbiol.* **54**:2213–2219.

Staley, J. T., and Konopka, A., 1985, Measurement of in situ activities of nonphotosynthetic microorganisms in aquatic and terrestrial habitats, *Annu. Rev. Microbiol.* **39**:321–346.

Stock, M. S., and Ward, A. K., 1989, Establishment of a bedrock epilithic community in a small stream: Microbial (algal and bacterial) metabolism and physical structure, *Can. J. Fish. Aquat. Sci.* **46**:1874–1883.

Thomas, D. R., Richardson, J. A., and Dicker, R. J., 1974, The incorporation of tritiated thymidine into DNA as a measure of the activity of soil micro-organisms, *Soil Biol. Biochem.* **6**:293–296.

Thorn, P. M., and Ventullo, R. M., 1988, Measurement of bacterial growth rates in subsurface sediments using the incorporation of tritiated thymidine into DNA, *Microb. Ecol.* **16**:3–16.

Tibbles, B. J., Davis, C. L., Harris, J. M., and Lucas, M. I., 1992, Estimates of bacterial productivity in marine sediments and water from a temperature saltmarsh lagoon, *Microb. Ecol.* **23:**195–209.

Tobin, R. S., and Anthony, D. H. J., 1978, Tritiated thymidine incorporation as a measure of microbial activity in lake sediments, *Limnol. Oceanogr.* **23:**161–165.

Torréton, J. P., and Bouvy, M., 1991, Estimating bacterial DNA synthesis from [³H]thymidine incorporation: Discrepancies among macromolecular extraction procedures, *Limnol. Oceanogr.* **36:**299–306.

Van Es, F. B., and Meyer-Reil, L.-A., 1982, Biomass and metabolic activity of heterotrophic marine bacteria, *Adv. Microb. Ecol.* **6:**111–170.

Vincent, W. F., and Howard-Williams, C., 1989, Microbial communities in southern Victoria Land streams (Antarctica). II. The effects of low temperature, *Hydrobiologia* **172:**39–49.

Vogels, G. D., and van der Drift, C., 1976, Degradation of purines and pyrimidines by microorganisms, *Bacteriol. Rev.* **40:**403–468.

Wetzel, R. G., and Likens, G. E., 1991, *Limnological Analyses*, 2nd ed., Springer-Verlag, Berlin.

Wicks, R. J., and Robarts, R. D., 1987, The extraction and purification of DNA labelled with [methyl-³H]thymidine in aquatic bacterial production studies, *J. Plankton Res.* **9:**1159–1166.

Winding, A., 1992, [³H]thymidine incorporation to estimate growth rates of anaerobic bacterial strains, *Appl. Environ. Microbiol.* **58:**2660–2662.

Witzel, K.-P., and Graf, G., 1984, On the use of different nucleic acid precursors for the measurement of microbial nucleic acid turnover, *Arch. Hydrobiol. Beih.* **19:**59–65.

Wright, R. T., and Hobbie, J. E., 1965, The uptake of organic solutes in lake water, *Limnol. Oceanogr.* **10:**22–28.

Zehr, J. P., Harvey, R. W., Oremland, R. S., Cloern, J. E., and George, L. H., 1987, Big Soda Lake (Nevada). 1. Pelagic bacterial heterotrophy and biomass, *Limnol. Oceanogr.* **32:**781–793.

Zohary, T., and Robarts, R. D., 1992, Bacterial numbers, bacterial production, and heterotrophic nanoplankton abundance in a warm core eddy in the Eastern Mediterranean, *Mar. Ecol. Prog. Ser.* **84:**133–137.

Index